ENZYMES IN NUCLEIC ACID RESEARCH

CHEMISTRY OF NATURAL PRODUCTS

Edited by

EDGAR LEDERER

FACULTÉ DES SCIENCES DE PARIS-ORSAY
AND INSTITUT DE CHIMIE DES SUBSTANCES NATURELLES, GIF-SUR-YVETTE

English Series

French Series

MICHEL PRIVAT DE GARILHE
DOCTEUR ÈS SCIENCES

Enzymes
in
Nucleic Acid Research

Preface by Professor M. Laskowski

HERMANN
Publishers in Arts & Science
115, Boulevard Saint-Germain Paris VI, France

HOLDEN-DAY, INC., PUBLISHERS
500, Sansome Street, San Francisco, California, U.S.A.

Library of Congress catalog Card Number : 68-17 157

This is a revised edition of the original French book " Les nucléases " published by Hermann, Paris, 1964.

Printed in France.

CONTENTS

CHAPTER I. NOMENCLATURE

CHAPTER II. NUCLEIC ACIDS — BASIC CONCEPTS

CHAPTER III. SYNTHESIS, BIOSYNTHESIS AND ISOLATION
FROM TISSUE OF THE NUCLEIC ACIDS

CHAPTER IV. ANALYTICAL METHODS

CHAPTER V. ENZYMES IN NUCLEIC ACID RESEARCH

CHAPTER VI. ENDONUCLEASES

PART I : NON PENTOSE-SPECIFIC ENDONUCLEASES

PART II : RIBONUCLEASES

CHAPTER VII. " NON-SPECIFIC " AND SPECIFIC PHOSPHODIESTERASES (EXONUCLEASES — PHOSPHODIESTERASES)

CHAPTER VIII. PHOSPHATASES AND NUCLEOTIDASES

CHAPTER IX. FINAL REMARKS ON ENZYMES IN NUCLEIC ACID CHEMISTRY

PREFACE

Nucleic acids now represent the most rapidly growing branch of biochemistry. This is not surprising, because for many years nucleic acids, while not entirely neglected, were at least pushed to the periphery of the biochemical domain. The impetus to their fast development was given in 1944 when Avery and his colleagues described the transforming factor. From then on the role of nucleic acids as transmitters of genetic information was no longer only a sensible hypothesis. The interest which was created resulted in rapid progress both in the strictly cheminal and in the genetic aspects of the problem and led to the present concept in which the transmission of genetic information requires a series of steps defined by specific enzymes and equally specific nucleic acids.

From the point of view of a writer this is a very inappropriate moment. In so rapidly moving a field it is almost impossible to keep the book up to date. From the point of view of a reader the situation is diametrically opposite. The harder it is to keep up with the literature, the more desirable the monograph becomes. Even an experienced worker finds it difficult to keep up to date on all aspect of this domain. For a newcomer to the field, for a graduate student, a monograph offers a starting point for information. To my knowledge there is no modern monograph on nucleases and their use in the study of the structure of nucleic acids. Dr. Privat de Garilhe has decided to remedy this situation. Since the book is of medium size, and has no English equivalent, it seems likely that it will reach far beyond the borders of France.

The book has several "spécialité de la maison" qualities. It contains descriptions of numerous techniques and methods in sufficient detail to permit their direct use in the laboratory. In this book the emphasis is placed on nucleolytic enzymes. This is not surprising.

for its author has been actively engaged in this field and has contributed significantly to its growth. The author believes, and I cannot help but agree with him, that the time is ripe for a concentrated attack on elucidation of sequences in nucleic acids. To this end nucleolytic enzymes are certain to become increasingly important tools.

M. Laskowski, Sr.
Roswell, Park
Memorial Institute
Buffalo, N.Y. U.S.A.

INTRODUCTION

The problems raised by the structure and functioning of the nuclei acids are still among the most important to be found in the whole field of contemporary biochemistry. Our knowledge of the role played by nucleic acids will only make definite progress when the structure of these exceptionnally complex macromolecules has been elucidated.

Every time biochemists have tackled the structural determination of macromolecules, such as polysaccharides, polypeptides, proteins, nucleic acids etc., they have had to resort to an initial fragmentation into simpler molecules whose structures were more easily accessible; this fragmentation has been obtainable either by chemical means, often detrimental to the material under study, or by biochemical catalysts, the enzymes, which provide more controlled methods of fragmentation, and are, generally speaking, more compatible with the maintenance of the fundamental structures, since they are themselves of biological origin.

In the particular case we shall be considering, the various enzymes participating in the metabolism of nucleic acids have already supplied important information about the structure of these acids, and will surely continue to do so.

Examination of the reactions that are catalyzed by nucleolytic enzymes affords not only vital information about the structure of the nucleic acids, but also some insight into the mechanism of enzymic reactions in general. Among the enzymes of which the mechanisms of action are the best known are ribonuclease A, deoxyribonuclease I, alkaline phosphatase, etc., and the main characteristics of these could well serve as a model of " well defined enzymes ".

This book, which is a revised edition of the previous french monograph entitled " Les Nucléases " (Hermann 1964), is not an attempt to review all articles or consider all enzymes concerned with the metabolism of nucleic acids, and will not answer all questions remaining in the field of applications of enzymes to the elucidation of nucleic acid structure; it is but an attempt to focus the attention of the reader on some areas of special interest in this field

The first section (chapters I, II and III) contains a brief description of the fundamental properties of nucleic acids, the second section (chapter IV) lists the methods used in the structural study of nucleic acids in connection with the enzymes of their metabolism, and the third section (chapters V, VI, VII, VIII and IX) describes the principal nucleolytic enzymes, the nucleases and phosphatases, and deals with their application to structural problems concerning nucleic acids.

It will be seen that I have described in some detail certain techniques, such as the first nucleoside and nucleotide syntheses, the isolation of transforming DNA, crystallization of the first nucleolytic enzymes, etc., all of which have an interest that is mainly historic; I feel, however, that the merit of these descriptions is in showing to the non-specialist reader, and, more particularly, to younger readers, what extremes of patience, ingenuity and skill were brought into play for us to acquire ideas that seem now to be obvious, this being done with techniques that were often of doubtful precision. There is no question of trying to belittle contemporary contributions, which are immense, but it should not be forgotten that biochemistry did not start with these, and that many of the methods being published now as " original" contain only minor modifications of older methods that are still quite valid.

Indeed, " age " is a strictly relative term when applied to the fundamental research on the nucleic acids, for if we take the date of ribonuclease crystallization (Kunitz, 1940) as the approximate starting point of the bibliography listed in this book, we realize that the whole of the literature quoted has been published in the last 25 years. This fact demonstrates how explosive the development of knowledge about the structure of the nucleic acids has been, as well as how much remains to be accomplished in this field which, fortunately, is in full expansion.

ACKNOWLEDGEMENTS

I should like to express my thanks to Professor E. Lederer for his constant interest in our work and in this book, and to Professor M. Laskowski Sr. (Milwaukee, and Buffalo) for his hospitality during the three years I worked in his laboratory, and for having introduced me to nucleic acid and nuclease biochemistry.

The following authors are thanked for giving permission for the reproduction of figures, tables or large portions of text :

K. Adachi, C.B. Anfinsen. G. Berger, G. Bernardi, E.M. Bradbury, C. Breedis, C.E. Carter, E. Chargaff, F.H.C. Crick, J.N. Davidson R. Delaney, P. Doty, A.L. Dounce, F. Egami, E. Fredericq, R.H. Hall, G. Hamoir, L.A. Heppel, C.H.W. Hirs, M.B. Hoagland, R.H. Holley, H.G. Khorana, K.S. Kirby, A. Kornberg, M. Laskowski, I.R. Lehman, J.Y. Le Talaer, M.V. Lindberg, S. Mandeles, G. Marbaix, R. Markham, S. Moore, R. Nilsson, M. Nirenberg, S. Ochoa, G.B. Petersen, B.R. Rabin, K. Randerath, P. Reichard, H.A. Saroff, E.E. Schreir, D. Shugar, R.L. Sinsheimer, N. Sueoka, W. Szer, K. Takahashi, E. Volkin, P.R. Whitfeld.

Finally, I am grateful to the editors of the following books and journals for permission to quote these extracts :

Acta Biochimica Polonica, Acta Chemica Scandinavica ; Annals of the New York Academy of Sciences ; Biochemical and Biophysical Research Communications ; Biochemical Journal ; Biochemistry ; Biochimica & Biophysica Acta (Elsevier) ; Bulletin de la Société de Chimie Biologique ; Ciba Lectures in Biochemistry (John Wiley & Sons) ; Clinica Chimica Acta (Elsevier) ; Comptes Rendus de l'Académie des Sciences, Experientia ; Journal of Biological Chemistry ; Journal of Chromatography (Elsevier) ; Journal of American Chemical Society ; Journal of Molecular Biology, Journal of Physical Chemistry ; Journal of Theoretical Biology ; Methods in Enzymology (Academic Press); Nature ; The nucleic Acids (Academic Press) ; Proceedings of the National Academy of Sciences (U.S.) ; Progress in Nucleic Acid Research (Academic Press); Science; Virology.

            M. PRIVAT DE GARILHE

ABBREVIATIONS

Aminoacids :

Ala	=	alanine
Arg	=	arginine
Asp	=	aspartic acid
Asp.NH$_2$	=	asparagine
Glu	=	glutamic acid
Glu.NH$_2$	=	glutamine
Gly	=	glycine
His	=	histidine
Ileu	=	isoleucine
Leu	=	leucine
Lys	=	lysine
Met	=	methionine
Phe	=	phenylalanine
Pro	=	proline
Ser	=	serine
Thr	=	threonine
Try	=	tryptophan
Tyr	=	tyrosine
Val	=	valine

Isotopes :

^{14}C, ^{32}P, ^{35}S ... radioactive isotopes of carbon, phosphorus, sulfur, ... used as tracers in biology

Nucleic acids and derivatives :

Nucleosides :

A	=	adenosine
C	=	cytidine
G	=	guanosine
T	=	thymidine
U	=	uridine
Pu	=	purine nucleoside
Py	=	pyrimidine nucleoside
X, Y, X	=	unspecified nucleoside

Mononucleotides :

pA, pC, pG, ..., etc...   = adenosine-5′-phosphate,
                                     cytidine-5′-phosphate,
                                     guanosine-5′-phosphate, etc...
d-pA, d-pC, d-pG, ..., etc...   = deoxyadenosine-5′-phosphate, etc...
Ap, Cp, Gp, ..., etc...   = adenosine-3′-phosphate, etc...
d-Ap, d-Cp, d-Gp, ..., etc...   = deoxyadenosine-3′-phosphate, etc...
ATP, GTP, ...   = adenosine triphosphate,
                                     guanosine triphosphate, ...

Mononucleotides (cyclic) :

Ap!, Cp!, Gp!, etc...   = adenosine-2′-3′-cyclic-phosphate, etc...

Oligonucleotides :

pApCpG   = 5′-adenylyl (3′ → 5′) cytidylyl (3′ → 5′) guanosine
d-pApCpG   = corresponding deoxyribonucleotide

Polynucleotides :

DNA   = deoxyribonucleic acid
RNA   = ribonucleic acid
t-RNA   = transfer-ribonucleic acid
m-RNA   = messenger-ribonucleic acid

Nucleolytic enzymes:

DNase = deoxyribonuclease
RNase = ribonuclease

Reagents:

CMC   = Carboxymethyl cellulose
DCC   = Dicyclohexylcarbodiimide
DEAE-cellulose   = Diethylaminoethyl cellulose
DEAE-Sephadex   = Diethylaminoethyl Sephadex
ECTEOLA-cellulose = Adsorbent obtained by reaction of cellulose with epichlorhydrine
                          and triethylamine
EDTA   = Ethylene Diamine Tetra Acetic acid.
Tris (buffer)   = Tris-hydroxymethylamino-methane

Viruses:

TMV = Tobacco Mosaic Virus
TYMV = Turnip Yellow Mosaic Virus

CHAPTER I

Nomenclature

Nucleic acids are formed by successive linking of simple units or nucleotides, each of these incorporating a purine or pyrimidine base, a pentose and a phosphoryl group. The pentose may be ribose (in the case of ribonucleic acids or RNA) or deoxyribose (in the case of deoxyribonucleic acids or DNA). The distinction between ribonucleic acids and deoxyribonucleic acids lies mainly in the nature of the pentose involved in their constitution, but there is also a difference in the nature of the bases, ribonucleic acids mostly containing the four bases — adenine, guanine, cytosine and uracil — while deoxyribonucleic acids contain the four bases — adenine, guanine, cytosine and thymine.

The first chapter is devoted to an explanation of the detail of the nomenclature used in the different compounds entering into the constitution of the nucleic acids, i.e. purine and pyrimidine bases, nucleosides and nucleotides.

I. PYRIMIDINE AND PURINE BASES

A. PYRIMIDINE BASES

These bases are derived from a common skeleton, pyrimidine, which is numbered as follows :

pyrimidine

The principal naturally occurring pyrimidines are :

NH₂ ... reacting in the ketoform, like the other pyrimidines ... NH₂

Cytosine or 2-hydroxy-6-aminopyrimidine

Uracil or 2,6-dihydroxypyrimidine   Thymine or 5-methyluracil

5-Methylcytosine   5-Hydroxymethylcytosine

5-Hydroxymethylcytosine was discovered only a few years ago in the DNA of the bacteriophage T even of *Escherichia coli*, but not in *E. coli* itself (Wyatt and Cohen, 1953).

The thymine in the *E. coli* may be replaced artificially by 5-bromouracil, thereby introducing unnatural bases within the DNA of the organism, and provoking profound and lasting modifications, which the author of this work, Zamenhof, does not consider to be mutations (Zamenhof, de Giovanni and Rich, 1956).

The experiments of Zamenhof and his co-workers having demonstrated the relative ease with which unnatural pyrimidines can be introduced into deoxyribonucleic acids, the possibility of using pyrimidine (and purine) analogs as anti-metabolites was considered. A large number of uracil and cytosine analogs was then synthesized, such as 5-fluoro-, 5-bromo-, 5-iodo- and 5-chlorouracils, the formulas of which are given below, 4-azauracil and 4-azathymine having a nitrogen atom in place of the CH in the 4-position, and 5-amino-, 5-mercapto- and 5-hydroxy-pyrimidines.

5-Bromouracil, 5-chlorouracil, 5-iodouracil

Many experiments have been carried out with these substances, and it has been shown that several of them have indeed a definite cytostatic action. Their anti-viral or anti-cancer therapeutic application has often been limited, however, on account of the toxicity associated with them (Handschumacher and Welch, 1960).

B. PURINE BASES

The two types of nucleic acid contain the same purine bases : adenine and guanine. These bases are derived from the purine skeleton, common to both.

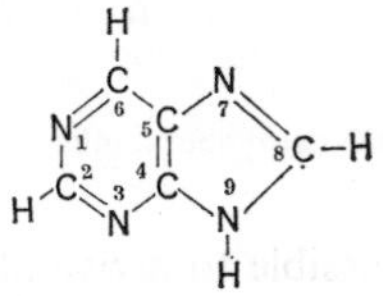

Purine

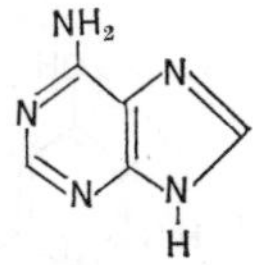

Adenine or 6-aminopurine 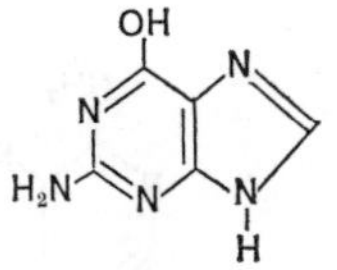   Guanine or 2-amino-6-hydroxypurine.

Besides these two main purine bases, the existence of a purine, 6-methylaminopurine, that has been found in 15T- strains of *E. coli*, should be mentioned (Dunn and Smith, 1955, 1958).

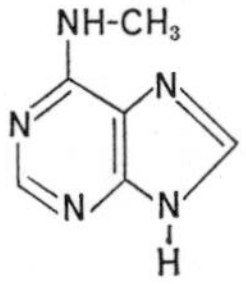

6-Methylaminopurine

In addition to the main purine and pyrimidine bases there are all those involved in the constitution of the transfer ribonucleic acids, and which are described below (p. 24) in the table of " minor" nucleosides from transfer RNA.

So far as synthetic purine and pyrimidine bases are concerned, one need only look at the catalogs of " fine biochemicals " suppliers to have an idea of the enormous number existing.

II. NUCLEOSIDES

Following classical nomenclature, nucleosides result from the combination of a pyrimidine or purine base with a sugar that is either β-D-ribofuranose or β-D-2-deoxyribofuranose.

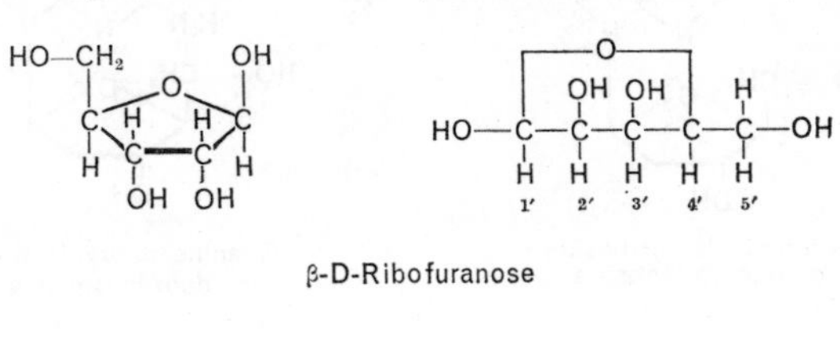

β-D-Ribofuranose

Nucleosides are therefore respectively β-D-ribofuranosides or β-D-2-deoxyribofuranosides.

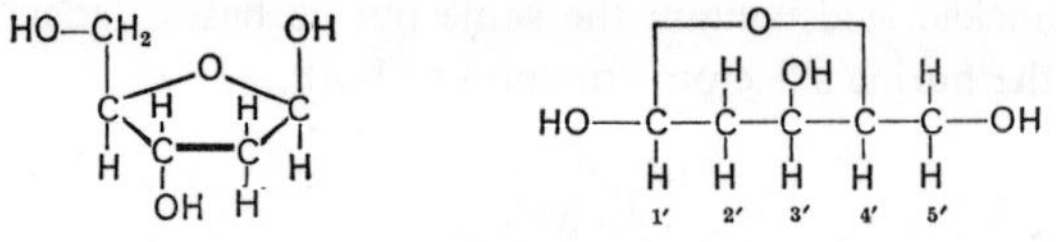

β-D-2-deoxyribofuranose

Starting from ribonucleic acids it is possible to arrive at the following principal nucleosides by joining ribose with one of the four following bases : adenine, guanine, cytosine or uracil.

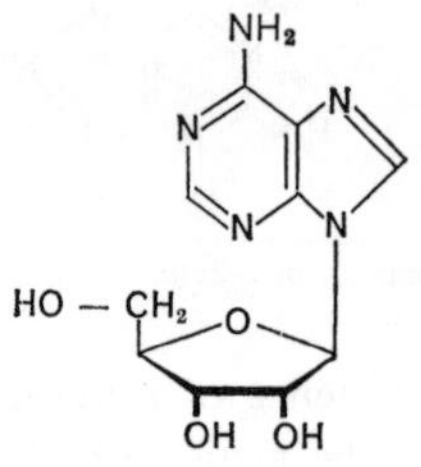

Adenosine

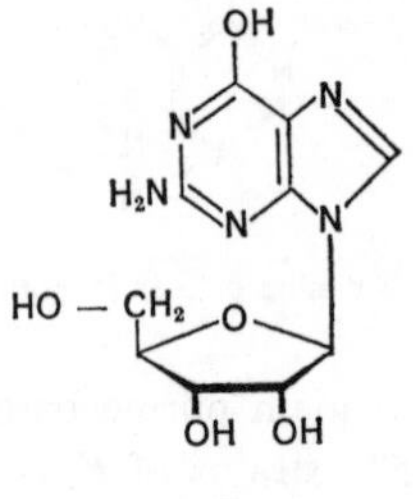

Guanosine

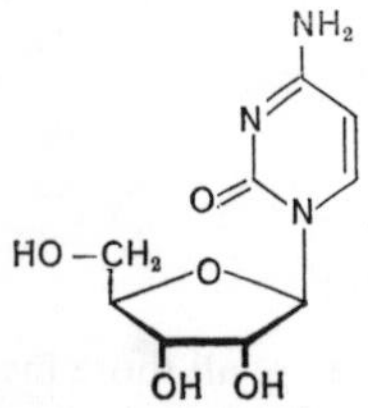

Cytidine

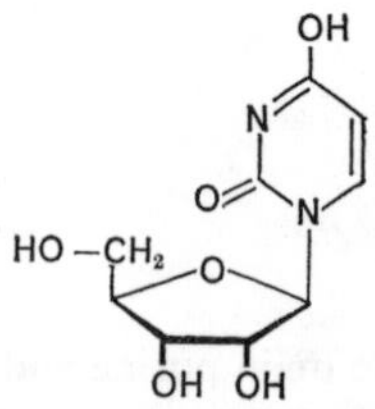

Uridine

Starting from deoxyribonucleic acids, the following main nucleosides will be obtained, these arising by joining deoxyribose with one of the following four main bases : adenine, guanine, cytosine and thymine :

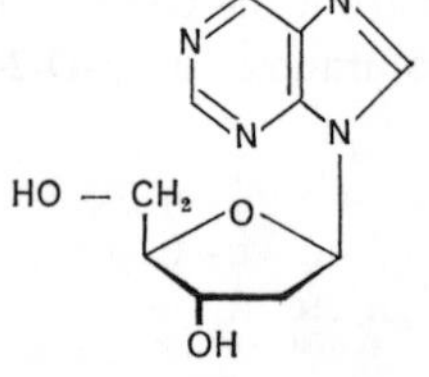

Adenine deoxyriboside
or deoxyadenosine

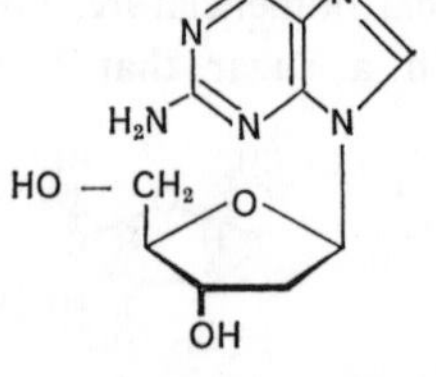

Guanine deoxyriboside
or deoxyguanosine

Cytosine deoxyriboside
or deoxycytidine

Thymine deoxyriboside
or deoxythymidine

Methylcytosine deoxyriboside
or deoxymethylcytidine

The base-pentose linkage is usually considered to occur between the nitrogen at the 3-position in the pyrimidines (or the 9-position of the purines) and the C-1′ carbon of the pentose. One exception must, however, be made in the case of a particular nucleoside found in yeast RNA by Cohn and Volkin, and which they called " pseudouridine " (Ψ-uridine) (Cohn W. E., 1959, 1960). This compound involves a carbon-carbon bond in place of the customary nitrogen-carbon bond, and is called 5-ribosyluracil.

Some most important work carried out over the last few years on transfer RNA has led to the discovery of a large number of minor nucleosides (and nucleotides) differing not only in the nature of the bases involved in their constitution, but also in the nature of the base-pentose link. An article by Hall (1965) illustrates the situation very well; in it are described the isolation and properties of 18 minor nucleosides (Table 1).

NUCLEOSIDE ANALOGS

The recognition of remarkable antagonistic properties of many purine and pyrimidine analogs has led to the synthesis and application of nucleoside analogs. These nucleoside analogs can be constituted in one of the following ways.

1. Analog of the base plus normal pentose. Examples of this type are the halogenated nucleoside derivatives, e.g. 5-fluoro-, 5-bromo-, 5-chloro-, 5-iodouridine, 5-fluoro-, 5-bromo, 5-chloro-5-iododeoxyuridine, 5-fluoro-, 5-bromo, 5-chloro, 5-iodocytidine, 5-fluoro-, 5-bromo-, 5-chloro-5-iododeoxycytidine (Prusoff et al., 1959; Prusoff, 1960; Chang and Welch, 1961a, b; Cramer et al., 1961; Prusoff et al., 1961; Kuemmerle and Preziosi, 1964, etc.).

2. Normal base plus analog of ribose or deoxyribose, when the very interesting series of arabinosides, xylosides, lyxosides, etc. are obtained.

Ribose an I deoxyribose analogs are innumerable, but in view of their biological applications, the following five are among the most thoroughly examined (See p. 24)

Table I. Minor Nucleosides Isolated from Yeast s-RNA* (Hall, 1965)

Nucleoside	Total Amount Obtained from 11.5 g of Mixed Nucleoside in the Digest of s-RNA (mg)	Moles/10000 Moles of Total Nucleosides in the Digest	Previous Reference
N^6-Methyladenosine	48.7	3.9	Littlefield and Dunn (1958)
2′(3′)-O-Ribosyladenosine (adenosine-R)	2.4	0.13	
N^6-(Aminoacyl)-adenosines	5.7	0.34	Hall (1964a)
1-Methylguanosine	12.0	0.90	Smith and Dunn (1959a)
N^2-Methylguanosine	1.9	0.14	Smith and Dunn (1959a)
N^2, N^2-Dimethylguanosine	32.9	2.36	Smith and Dunn (1959a)
3-Methylcytidine	2.0	0.18	Hall (1963a)
5-Methylcytidine	9.6	0.84	Dunn (1960)
3-Methyluridine	1.1	0.1	Hall (1963a)
5-Methyluridine	78	6.9	Littlefield and Dunn (1958)
Pseudouridine	488	45.0	Cohn (1960)
Inosine	26.0	2.2	Hall (1963b)
1-Methylinosine	5.1	0.4	Hall (1963b)
2′-O-Methyladenosine	3.4	0.28	Hall (1964b) Smith and Dunn (1959b)
2′-O-Methyluridine	3.4	0.29	Hall (1964b)
2′-O-Methylguanosine	40.2	3.1	Hall (1964b)
2′-O-Methylcytidine	13.0	1.1	Hall (1964b)
2′-O-Methylpseudouridine	0.1	0.009	Hall (1964b)

* Several additional compounds not detected in this work have been isolated from the hydrolysates of RNA of yeast and/or other tissues : N^6, N^6-dimethyladenine and 2-methyladenine (Littlefield and Dunn, 1958), 1,5-diribosyl uracil (Lis and Lis, 1962), 7-methyguanine (Dunn, 1963), N^2-ribosylguanine (Hemmens, 1964 ; Shapiro and and Gordon, 1964), 4,5-dihydrouridine (Madison and Holley, 1965), 4-thirouridine (Lipsett 1965).

N^4-methyl — 2′-O-methyl cytidine and other methyl substituted nucleosides in *E. coli.* ribosomal and t-RNA (Nichols and Lane, 1966), N^6- isopentyl adenosine (Hall 1966). N^6-(γ. γ-dimethyl allyl) adenosine (Biemann et al 1966), guanosine propionic acid (Ballio et al. 1966), 5-hydroxyuridine (Lis and Passarge, 1966).

β-D-arabinofuranose   α-D-arabinofuranose

β-D-xylofuranose   β-D-lyxofuranose   β-D-2-deoxyxylofuranose

Pride of place among these analogs must be given to the arabinosides, the anti-cancer and anti-viral properties of which have made them the subject of a great deal of work. (See for instance a recent review by De Rudder and Privat de Garilhe, 1966).

These compounds first attracted notice when an article by Bergmann and Feeney (1951) appeared describing a new nucleoside isolated from the sponge *Cryptotethia crypta*, and provisionally called " spongothymidine ", since the authors were not certain of the exact nature of the pentose. Subsequently Bergmann and his associates showed "spongothymidine" to have, in fact, the structure of 3-β-D-arabinofuranosylthymine, and found the sponges to contain another arabinoside similar to the first but derived from uracil. This they called "spongouridine" or 3-β-D-arabinofuranosyluracil (Bergmann and Burke, 1955*a*, *b*).

The first arabinoside synthesis realised in the laboratory was that of uracil arabinoside achieved by Todd and his associates (Brown et al., 1956), after which followed those of thymine arabinoside (Fox et al., 1957), cytosine arabinoside (Hunter, 1963), adenine arabinoside (Lee et al., 1960; Reist et al., 1962; Glaudemans and Fletcher, 1963) and guanine arabinoside (Reist and Goodmann, 1964).

The properties of the arabinosides have been the subject of a certain amount of work, generally emphasizing the possible application of the compounds in antiviral and anti-cancer chemotherapy. Evans et al. (1961) have shown that cytosine arabinoside is a powerful inhibitor of cancerous cell-growth in cell cultures and that it causes a distinct regression of certain mouse tumors.

Recently, Jean Bernard *et al.* (1966) showed the interesting applications of cytosine arabinoside either alone or associated with other antimetabolites, to the treatment of human acute leukemia.

A mechanism for the action of this substance has been proposed by Chu and Fischer (1962), who suggested that it inhibits the conversion of cytidylic acid to deoxycytidylic acid. The action of cytosine arabinoside on vaccinia and herpes viruses in cellular culture as well as in animals and clinically has been examined by Renis and Johnson (1962) and by Underwood (1962, 1964).

Hubert-Habart and Cohen (1962) have demonstrated that adenine arabinoside inhibits the synthesis of DNA by an *Escherichia coli* strain that requires purine. The same authors suggested that the adenine arabinoside becomes localized at the terminal nucleotide of the *t*-RNA, a position that would be expected to exert considerable influence on protein synthesis. Brink and Le Page (1963) have also published data showing that adenine arabinoside inhibits the growth of a certain number of tumors, while Privat de Garilhe and De Rudder (1964) have shown that it has an inhibiting action, as do other arabinosides, on the multiplication of herpes and vaccinia viruses in cell culture.

III. NUCLEOTIDES

Nucleotides result from phosphorylation of nucleosides. Depending on the position of the phosphoryl group on the sugar, it is clear that a single base and a single sugar will furnish two different isomeric nucleotides in the case of deoxyribose, according to whether the phosphoryl group is attached to C-3' or C-5', and three isomeric nucleotides in the case of ribose, according to whether the phosphoryl group is attached to C-2', C-3' or C-5'.

These isomeric mononucleotides have all been obtained by chemical synthesis or by enzymatic hydrolysis of nucleic acids, or they have been found in the free state in nature. A list follows, showing some of the mononucleotides that have been obtained by nucleic acid hydrolysis or that have been isolated from animal or vegetable tissue.

A. THE VARIOUS NUCLEOTIDES DERIVED FROM ADENINE

1. Adenosine phosphate esters

Adenoside-3'-phosphate, obtained in this form after alkaline hydrolysis of yeast RNA or after the action of ribonucleases on yeast RNA.

Adenosine-2'-phosphate

Adenosine-2' : 3'-phosphate, a transition step during the hydrolysis of yeast RNA by RNase (A = adenine)

Adenosine-5'-monophosphate
or muscle adenylic acid : AMP

$$HO-\underset{\underset{O}{\overset{\text{OH}}{|}}}{\overset{}{P}}-O-\underset{\underset{O}{\overset{\text{OH}}{|}}}{\overset{}{P}}-O-CH_2 \quad A$$

Adenosine-5′-diphosphate : ADP

$$HO-\overset{\text{OH}}{\underset{O}{P}}-O-\overset{\text{OH}}{\underset{O}{P}}-O-\overset{\text{OH}}{\underset{O}{P}}-O-CH_2 \quad A$$

Adenosine-5′-triphosphate : ATP

2. Phosphate esters of deoxyadenosine

$$HO - CH_2 \quad A$$
$$O\ PO_3H_2$$

Deoxyadenosine-3′-monophosphate, obtained by the action of DNase II and Staphylococcus nuclease on thymus DNA

$$H_2O_3\ P-O-CH_2 \quad A$$
$$OH$$

Deoxyadenosine-5′-monophosphate, abtained by the action of DNAase I on thymus DNA

B. NUCLEOTIDES DERIVED FROM GUANINE

The main nucleotides derived from adenine have been listed; for the other bases the examples will be limited to a single one of riboside phosphate and another one of deoxyribose phosphate, it being understood that all the other possible combinations exist in the same way as they do in the adenine case. So far as guanine and cytosine derivatives are concerned, the formula of the most common ribose phosphate, i.e. the 3′-phosphate ester, will be given. Still concerning guanine and cytosine, enzymatic hydrolysis of DNA has yielded mononucleotides that were sometimes deoxyriboside-5′-phosphates and sometimes deoxyriboside-3′-phosphates. The only one given here is deoxyriboside-5′-phosphate; this is the oldest, having been obtained some years ago by the action of DNase I on thymus DNA (Hurst and Butler 1951; Hurst, Marko and Butler 1953; Smith and Markham 1952; Sinsheimer and Koerner 1952a, 1952b).

In the case of uracil, which is only found in RNAs, clearly only the riboside-3′-phosphate will be listed, while thymine, mostly found in DNAs, only appears as the corresponding deoxyriboside-5′-phosphate.

It is evident that transfert RNAs include not only the four main nucleotides described below, but also all the nucleotides corresponding to the "minor" nucleosides listed in the table on p. 24

Guanosine-3'-phosphate
or guanylic acid

Deoxyguanosine-3'-monophosphate
or deoxyguanylic acid

C. NUCLEOTIDES DERIVED FROM CYTOSINE

Cytidine-3'-monophosphate
or cytidylic acid

Deoxycytidine-5'-monophosphate
or 5'-deoxycytidylic acid

D. NUCLEOTIDE DERIVED FROM URACIL

Uracil is not involved in the composition of DNAs — at least it has not so far been found in significant amounts — so no deoxyuridylic acid is known in the natural state. The only derivative to be listed is the refore, the following :

Uridine-3'-monophosphate
or uridylic acid

E. Nucleotide derived from thymine

Thymidine-5′-monophosphate
or 5′-thymidylic acid

IV. OLIGONUCLEOTIDES

This rather vague name is used to describe the linking together of a small number of mononucleotides. Somewhat more specifically, one can say that the term oligonucleotides can be applied when the chain considered does not comprise more than ten or so mononucleotides, and one then refers to dinucleotides, trinucleotides, tetranucleotides, etc.

V. POLYNUCLEOTIDES

This term is used to describe chains involving more than ten nucleotides, and can be applied to macromolecules the molecular weight of which is above several millions. All the nucleic acids isolated from animal and plant tissues are macromolecular and belong in this category.

VI. RIBONUCLEIC ACIDS (RNA)

Ribonucleic acids are polynucleotides like those that were defined at the beginning of this chapter, and are formed by the linking together of a large number of nucleotides, each containing :

BASE — RIBOSE — PHOSPHATE

At present three fundamental classes of ribonucleic acids are distinguished by their molecular weight and their function.

A. Transfer ribonucleic acids (t-RNA)

These are chains of 76 to 80 nucleotides, and therefore have a molecular weight of about 25,000. Their designation arises from the fact that they serve to transport activated aminoacids during protein synthesis. There appears to be at least one t-RNA that is specific for the transfer of each aminoacid. It is also possible that each species produces variations in the composition of its t-RNA, so that they exhibit considerable variety.

B. "Messenger" ribonucleic acids (m-RNA)

The attention was focused on these substances by Jacob and Monod (1961), who named them in this way because they are the vectors of the genetic information code utilised in protein synthesis, in other words they carry a "message", namely the one permitting the synthesis of specific proteins. The molecular weight of these messenger RNAs appears to be very variable according to the nature of the proteins they have to synthesize; they are usually unstable, since as soon as they have delivered their message, they should disappear (cf. Function of nucleic acids in chapter II).

C. Macromolecular ribonucleic acids

Under this heading are grouped all the RNAs not belonging to the two previous categories, but which have been known for about fifty years, having been isolated from yeast. Their molecular weight is apparently over 500,000, and they seem to be localized within the cell in cellular subfractions called ribosomes. The ribosomes are themselves only ribonucleoproteins with a molecular weight of 2 to 4.10^6, containing from 40 to 60 % RNA.

VII. DEOXYRIBONUCLEIC ACIDS (DNA)

These are polynucleotides consisting of a chain of a large number of mononucleotides of the type:

$$\text{BASE} - \text{DEOXYRIBOSE} - \text{PHOSPHATE}$$

A high molecular weight DNA may easily be extracted from calf thymus; on account of the source, this particular DNA has for a long time been called thymonucleic acid. The molecular weight of the DNA isolated from a number of sources both animal and vegetable, such as thymus, wheat germ, bacteria, bacteriophages, etc., lies between 6 and several hundred million avograms.

VIII. NUCLEOPROTEINS

Conjugated proteins resulting from the combination of a nucleic acid with a protein are called nucleoproteins. A ribonucleoprotein or a deoxyribonucleoprotein will be formed according to whether the nucleic acid is a RNA or a DNA. Chargaff has said "beneath the simple textbook definition of a nucleoprotein — a combination between a protein and a nucleic acid — there lies an ocean of uncertainties" (1955). There has been for a long time question as to whether the nucleoproteins were definite chemical entities that really existed and had some significance as such, or whether they were artefacts of the preparations, fortuitous compounds forming during tissue disintegration by precipitation of a polycationic high polymer (nucleic acid) at the same time as polycationic molecules (protamines and histones).

We feel, nevertheless, that Chargaff's comment is somewhat over-pessimistic, and that the definite existence of nucleoproteins must be accepted in many cases, particulary those of the viruses and bacteriophages. Viruses have been isolated in crystalline form, and are found to possess a fixed nucleic acid content with respect to protein, the proportion being about 6 % in the case of the tobacco mosaic virus; furthermore, the aminoacid composition of the protein part is strictly the same in any one virus, and is characteristic of that virus. In the case of the nucleohistones and nucleoprotamines, there is generally a very high regularity observed in the aminoacid composition of the histones and protamines, in spite of variations in the method of precipitation.

Briefly, the physico-chemical data that have been accumulating over the past twenty years inevitably lead to the following facts tending to prove the genuine existence of nucleoproteins and refute the idea that they are only fortuitous associations.

a. The extensive work carried out on nucleoprotamines by Felix and his associates (1952, 1958) has shown them to possess a constant aminoacid composition, even when various species of fish have been considered; in every case polypeptides of molecular weight between 6,000 and 7,000 have been found, containing about 50 % arginine together with some other aminoacids; there is a striking analogy between the fish protamines : iridine, truttine, fontidine, clupeine, sturine, etc.

b. Examination of the histones shows a similar analogy to exist between histones extracted from tissues that are very different, e.g. rat liver, calf thymus, rat sarcoma etc., the molecular weight being in every case of the order of 15,000, and the aminoacid compositions being quite similar.

c. Finally, it has been found that the activity of certain viruses containing RNA is restored by recombination of the nucleic part with the protein part; the activity with the RNA alone is very weak, showing that both parts are necessary for biological activity, and that they act together.

Although the significance of certain nucleoproteins is still in some doubt, most authorities nevertheless agree about their genuine existence in tissue, and generally speaking, the only arguments are about the following point : should a particular preparation be considered as an "original" nucleoprotein, i.e. really existing in its original state in the tissue before any precipitation takes place, or should it be considered as a denatured nucleoprotein, i.e. one that, during the precipitation, has had added to the original nucleoprotein other proteins termed "additional proteins" that existed independantly in the tissue before the precipitation?

In fact it is more and more evident that histones and protamines play an important role in modulating and directing the function of DNA *in vivo*.

IX. NUCLEOPROTEIN NOMENCLATURE

A. DEOXYRIBONUCLEOPROTEINS

1. Nucleohistones

The protein part is called histone, and is associated in some glandular tissues, such as the pancreas and the thymus, with nucleic acids.

2. Nucleoprotamines

In addition to the nucleic acid moiety, these substances contain a protein moiety, or protamine. These protamines are polypeptides with a molecular weight varying between 2,000 and 5,000, and contain a high proportion of arginine.

3. Genuine deoxyribonucleoproteins

The DNA is linked in these nucleoproteins, so far as can be ascertained, by secondary valence bonds to a protein that does not have the basic properties of the protamines and histones. A protein of this type has been isolated, for instance, from avian tuberculosis bacilli (Chargaff and Seidel, 1949).

B. RIBONUCLEOPROTEINS

These nucleoproteins consist of a RNA and a protein of no particular characteristics, and are extractable from tissue and from micro-organisms, for example, nucleotropomyosin from carp muscle (Hamoir, 1951) or yeast nucleoproteins (Khouvine and de Robichon-Szulmajster, 1951).

Ribosomes clearly belong in this category (Hoagland, 1960).

C. ANIMAL AND PLANT VIRUSES, BACTERIOPHAGES

In the crystalline state in which they are obtained from organisms attacked by "viral infections", a virus consists mainly of a nucleic acid and proteins ; tobacco mosaic virus contains a RNA and a protein whose structure has been completely elucidated; the polyhedral viruses of insect diseases contain a DNA and a protein; bacteriophages, which are bacterial viruses, consist exclusively of nucleic acids and proteins ; DNA + proteins in the case of DNA bacteriophages, RNA + proteins in the case of RNA bacteriophages.

X. NUCLEOLYTIC ENZYME NOMENCLATURE

This will be discussed at the beginning of chapter V when these enzymes will be dealt with in general.

CHAPTER II

Nucleic Acids — Basic Concepts

I. GENERAL REMARKS

In the introduction it has been shown how a fundamental distinction is made between ribonucleic and deoxyribonucleic acids according to the pentose involved in their constitution. Both acids are found side by side in animal and plant cells. They are, like proteins, giant molecules, and for this reason it is possible to envisage an infinite number of different nucleic acids, differing from one another in the nucleotides that make them up and the order in which these nucleotides are joined together. Preliminary analyses of the purine and pyrimidine bases in them led Levene and others at the same time to recognize the presence of four bases in approximately the same amounts, and this discovery gave rise to the renowned "tetranucleotide" theory, according to which nucleic acids were tetranucleotides containing one molecule of each of four bases : adenine, guanine, cytosine and uracil in the case of RNA, and adenine, guanine, cytosine and thymine in the case of DNA. This theory enabled Levene in the 1930s to believe that everything about the constitution of the nucleic acids was known; more than thirty years later, we have to admit that there is, in fact, still very little information about their structures.

The first attacks on this theory came with the ability to analyse the purine and pyrimidine bases more precisely, this occurring especially with the advent of chromatography. The laboratories of Chargaff and those of Carter analysed the purine and pyrimidine bases in the nucleic acids of a very large number of animal and plant tissues, and they soon realized that these bases were only very approximately present in equimolar ratio. Sometimes there are very large differences, for example RNA from calf pancreas (Volkin and Carter, 1951) gives the following proportions, based on adenylic acid as 10 : guanylic acid 34.5, cytidylic acid 16.8, uridylic acid 9.5. Instead of a 1 : 1 : 1 : 1 molar ratio, it would be nearer 1 : 3 : 2 : 1 (cf. p. 36 for examples of nucleotide composition of some RNAs and p. 62 for compositions of some DNAs).

The discovery of new purine and pyrimidine bases was also incompatible with the tetranucleotide theory. Indeed, as early as 1925 Johnson and Coghill had reported the existence of 5-methylcytosine, a homolog of cytosine. Later, Wyatt and Cohen found 5-hydroxymethylcytosine (Wyatt and Cohen, 1952), Dunn and Smith found 6-methylaminopurine (Dunn and Smith, 1955), and all the recent work on transfer RNA has shown the plurality of the nucleotides that form it (cf. p. 24).

Much work carried out by Burton et al. (Burton and Petersen 1957, 1960; Burton 1960), Cohn and Volkin (1957), Spencer and Chargaff (1961), etc., and confirmed elsewhere has suggested that DNA is formed by alternation of small pyrimidine groups and small purine groups that can contain the same base up to five or six times running.

It is, in fact, possible to effect preliminary fission of the purine bases from DNA by controlled hydrolysis, thereby obtaining an "apurinic" DNA of the type shown in the following diagram :

$$(\text{ (Original purine)}$$
$$... \text{ pTpTpTp.p.p.p.pCpCpTpTp.p.p.pCpCpTp.p.}$$

the dots representing the positions originally occupied by the purines.

In a second stage, more vigorous acid hydrolysis of the apurine DNA liberates the pyrimidine oligonucleotides in the form :

$$(Py.p)_n.p \quad \text{or} \quad Py_np_{(n+1)}$$

In this way it is possible to obtain nucleotides of the type p_4T_5 and even p_6T_5 consisting of an unbroken chain of 5 thymidyl nucleotides. According to Watson and Crick's theory (1953), it is evident that these thymidyl oligonucleotides will have adenylic oligonucleotide counterparts with the same structure. The determination by Holley and his associates (1965) of the full sequence of the 77 nucleotides of alanyl-t-RNA in yeast illustrates the fact that this sequence exhibits no tendency to any particular pattern in the constituent components.

All we can say at present is that nucleic acids — whether RNA or DNA — are formed from nucleotide chains, the internucleotide link being a phosphodiester joining carbon-3' of one to carbon-5' of the next, and so on. Although this 3'-5' linkage is a certainty of long standing in the DNA case where only the 3' and 5' positions in the hydrocarbon chain are available, the others being esterified with phosphoric acid, there remained some doubt in the case of RNA for a long time, since the linkage could be 2'-5' or 3'-5', or sometimes one and sometimes the other. It is in fact the nucleases that have shown that this linkage is 3'-5'.

II. PROPERTIES OF THE RIBONUCLEIC ACIDS

A. NUCLEOTIDE CONSTITUTION, SPATIAL CONFIGURATION

Table II lists the figures concerning the relative proportions of purine and pyrimidine bases (or nucleotides) found in certain RNAs.

The older figures mostly apply to total ribonucleic acids not having any special characteristics, and it is unlikely that much information can be extracted from them, since they are probably associated with mixtures of large numbers of different molecules — with the exception of the viral ribonucleic acids that as a rule correspond to unique molecules having a single chain. Generally speaking, no exact rule of composition can be detected for the examples quoted, unlike the rule established in the DNA case (cf. p. 64, and after), where A — T and G — C correlations were soon noticed, as well as the constancy of the A + T/G + C ratio in a single species. It was these considerations that led Watson and Crick (1953) to formulate their renowned double helical model for the DNA configuration. It would therefore appear that RNA exhibits a lesser tendency to form double-stranded structures.

Although it is possible to arrive at a crystal structure for a product isolated by controlled degradation of ribosomes, it is clear that the "helices" previously attributed to transfer RNA (Spencer et al. 1962), actually belong to structured fragments of ribosomal RNA rather than to transfer RNA. There is less known now about the spatial configuration of transfer RNA than was thought to be known in 1962, in spite of the fact that the primary structure of alanyl-RNA has now been elucidated (Holley et al. 1965). It would be unwise to go further than saying that RNA certainly possesses double-stranded fragments as does DNA, and that the structure of particles rich in RNA like the ribosomes is determined by its RNA which is folded in a particular way during ribosome synthesis in a manner determined by the sequence of the bases, before being "enveloped in proteins". Similarly, the structure of a RNA virus like the tobacco mosaic virus is determined by the helical coiling of the RNA molecule on which the protein units are to be attached (Klug and Caspar 1960; Tsugita and Frankel-Conrat 1963).

The difficulties encountered in the study of the secondary structure of the RNA molecule arise largely because of its instability — a fundamental characteristic associated with it.

Nevertheless, when sufficient precautions are taken to ensure the stability of the ribonucleic fabric, the double-stranded structure may appear quite clearly. For example, Kirby (1965) has extracted ribosomal RNA from rat liver, and, ensuring that the material was not degraded by nucleolytic enzymes, showed that it could be subdivided into two fractions having sedimentation constants respectively of 28S and 18S. These two fractions had purine and pyrimidine base ratios in accord with that expected for double-stranded structures :

	G	A	C	U
RNA 28S :	33.0	17.8	32.2	17.0
RNA 18S :	32.4	19.8	29.8	18.0

Similar observations can be made on RNA isolated from viruses, in particular tobacco mosaic virus grown on tobacco and turnip yellow mosaic virus grown on *Brassica pekinensis* (Ralph et al. 1965). In both cases, the nucleic acids prepared contained a RNase-resistant RNA fraction. This fraction was isolated by sucrose-gradient sedimentation, or by chromatography on columns of kieselguhr coated with methylated albumin. The following facts support the hypothesis of a double-stranded structure :

1. It is found only on virus-infected leaves.
2. Its RNase resistance is lost by heating in salt solution, i.e. by denaturation of the molecule and loss of the helical structure.
3. The material forms a band in Cs_2SO_4 at density greater than 1.6 g/ml.
4. Alkaline hydrolysis yields 3'-ribonucleotides.
5. When the infected leaves are placed in contact with ^{32}P for a few days, the bases are found to be in ratios approaching those expected for a double-stranded structure containing a viral RNA strand paired to a complementary RNA strand. The base ratios found after labeling for short times suggest that the viral RNA is replicated by an asymmetric semiconservative process.

The same kind of work has been carried out by Weissmann et al. (1965) working in Ochoa's group. They have isolated the double-stranded replicative form of viral RNA from tobacco mosaic

Table II. Examples of nucleotide composition of some RNAs.

Source	A	G	C	U	Methods	Literature
I Animal tissues						
Calf liver	10	17.9	14.9	8.4	Alkaline hydrolysis of RNA then separation of mononucleotides on Dowex I	Volkin and Carter (1951)
Calf pancreas	10	34.5	16.8	9.5		Volkin and Carter (1951)
Rat liver (ribosomes), fract. 28 S	10	18.5	18.0	9.5	Acid hydrolysis then paper chromatography	Kirby (1965)
fract. 18 S	10	16.4	15.0	9.1		
Human liver	10	38.6	27.5	11.0	Alkaline hydrolysis of RNA then paper chromatography	Chargaff et al. (1950)
Carp muscle	10	21.0	19.0	11.0	HCl hydrolysis of RNA then separation of bases by paper chromatography	Hamoir (1952)
Sea urchin eggs	10	13.3	12.3	9.3	Alkaline hydrolysis of RNA then paper chromatography	Elson, Gustafson and Chargaff (1954)
II Microorganisms						
Bakers'yeast a) total	10	11.4	7.5	9.0	HCl hydrolysis of RNA then separation of bases on paper.	Khouvine and de Robichon-Szulmaijster (1952a, b)
b) seryl-t-RNA	10	13.8	13.3	10.8*	RNase T$_2$ hydrolysis and paper chromatography	Rushizky and Sober (1965)
Brewers'yeast	10	10.4	9.2	9.6	Alkaline hydrolysis of RNA then paper chromatography	—
E. coli	10	10.2	8.5	8.3		Elson and Chargaff (1954)
Clostridium perfringens	10	11.6	9.4	7.4		Parsons (1953)
Streptomyces fradiae (t-RNA)	10	18.0	13.7	9.5	Alkaline hydrolysis then electrophoresis	Trentalance and Amaldi (1965)
III Plant viruses						
Tobacco mosaic	10	8.5	6.2	8.8	HCl hydrolysis of RNA then separation of bases on paper	Knight (1952)
TMV** (replicative form)	10	7.8	8.0	10.0	Alkaline hydrolysis then electrophoresis	Weissmann et al. (1965)
Cucumber	10	9.9	7.1	11.9		—
Tomato	10	10.0	7.4	8.9		Dorner and Knight (1953)
Turnip, TYMV**	10	7.6	16.8	9.8		Markam and Smith (1951)
TYMV (replicative form)	10	12.2	12.2	10.0	Calculation	Ralph et al. (1965)
IV Animal viruses						
Influenza, infective particle A PR 8	10	8.7	10.3	14.2		Schafer (1959)
Polio virus	10	8.4	6.3	8.1		Schafer (1959)
Rous sarcoma virus	10	11.3	9.6	8.9	Alkaline hydrolysis then electrophoresis	Robinson et al. (1965)

* Uridylic + pseudouridylic acids.
** TMV = Tobacco mosaic virus. — TYMV = Turnip yellow mosaic virus.

virus by RNase T1 hydrolysis of the total RNA of the virus, a treatment that resulted in complete hydrolysis of the single-stranded RNA, leaving the double-stranded RNA intact. The replicative form of TMV RNA labeled with ^{32}P that is obtained by this method has the following nucleotide ratios :

C	22.3 ± 0.2
A	27.8 ± 0.15
G	21.8 ± 0.1
U	28.0 ± 0.3

These ratios are in good agreement with the values calculated for a double-stranded RNA formed by one strand of the viral RNA type ("plus" strand) and its complement ("minus" strand). It is also noticeable that the values found for C and G are similar, as are those for A and U. The ratio G + A/U + C = 0,99. These examples demonstrate that the replicative forms of viral RNA consist of double-stranded RNA.

B. RIBONUCLEIC ACID CLASSIFICATION; MOLECULAR WEIGHT

Rather differing values for the molecular weights of ribonucleic acids have been proposed, the variations arising from the fact that it is difficult to prepare a particular RNA (e.g. yeast RNA) in an undegraded state. This is a fundamental property of RNA : its instability coupled with a rapid renewal rate is opposed to DNA which is a fixed cell component. RNA may be classified into four main groups :

1. Free nucleotides or acid-soluble nucleotides which are present in all cells and which can be obtained by acid extraction of the cells.

2. The so-called "transfer"' RNAs which play a fundamental part in aminoacid activation, and therefore in protein and peptide synthesis. These soluble RNAs are those remaining in solution when a cell extract undergoes centrifugation at 105,000 g for two hours in a medium buffered at pH 7.5. These transfer RNAs are reported to have a molecular weight of about 25,000, i.e. to consist of 76 to 80 nucleotides. They precipitate at the same time as the "pH 5 enzymes", i.e. when the supernatant medium is brought to pH 5.2.

3. Messenger RNA. This ribonucleic fraction is transiently linked to the ribosomes, and is the one that effects the transport of genetic information from the nucleus to the regions of protein synthesis. Considering the diversity of proteins, and supposing three nucleotides to be "used up" for each aminoacid, it is obvious that these messenger RNAs must have widely differing molecular weights, depending on the length of the polypeptide chain whose synthesis they are controlling (Monier et al. 1962).

4. Finally, the macromolecular RNA forming an integral part of the ribosomal nucleoproteins after centrifuging for 2 hours at 105,000 g. It is usually these RNAs that are referred to when one speaks of "yeast RNA" or "calf liver RNA", always supposing that they have escaped spontaneous degradation, or degradation by nucleolytic enzymes, which would alter all the results.

Coming back to the molecular weight of macromolecular RNA, a chronological review of results obtained by different groups will now be given.

Measurements made as long ago as 1939 by Loring (1939a) led to the following conclusions: molecular weights of 37,000 and 17,000 were found respectively for viral nucleic acid and yeast nucleic acid. In this case, a molecule of viral RNA with molecular weight 37,000 would contain

116 mononucleotides, while the yeast RNA with its molecular weight about 17,000 would contain 56 to 88 mononucleotides.

We have given Loring's values in table III, together with those found by a number of other authors. It is difficult to draw any conclusions from this table as a whole; one can only say that the molecular weights of RNAs isolated so far by the mildest methods vary between 5,000 and 300,000, always bearing in mind the possibility that the samples examined were only degraded molecules. Cohen and Stanley (1942) believe that freshly isolated tobacco mosaic virus RNA exists in the form of particles with an average molecular weight of 300,000, these particles undergoing spontaneous decomposition to yield smaller particles with a molecular weight of around 61,000. The highest values obtained from freshly isolated RNA would, therefore, be the most correct, since this supposes that the RNA has escaped the action of the nucleolytic enzymes.

The only reason we have included the older results was for comparison, and to show how ideas about the molecular weight of RNA have evolved. At the present time, for instance, it is known that tobacco mosaic virus RNA, like most other simple viral RNAs has a molecular weight of about 2 million, corresponding to an unbranched chain of 6,400 nucleotides (Tsugita and Frankel-Conrat 1963).

The instability of RNA from ascites cells has been the subject of systematic study by Huppert and Pelmont (1962), and the results these authors obtained can be extended to RNAs from other sources. Huppert and Pelmont showed by analytical ultracentrifugation that there is a progressive evolution during degradation of the components having sedimentation constants of 28, 18 and 3-5 S. The most sensitive component, 28 S, diminishes much quicker than the 18 S component, so that their relative proportions change with the age of the RNA sample.

Table III. Molecular weights of certain ribonucleic acids.

Source of RNA		M.W. $\times$ 10^{-4}	Method	Authors
Yeast				
alanyl-t-RNA		2.66 (Na salt)	Analysis : sum of constituents	Holley et al. (1965)
RNA (unspecified)			Diffusion	Lornig (1939a)
Yeast	1)	1.7		
	2)	1.7-3.5	Diffusion	Watanabe and Ito (1950a,b,c)
Malt		23.45-6.97	Diffusion and sedimentation	Delcambe and Desreux (1950)
Rat liver		6.4	Sedimentation	Grinnan and Mosher (1951)
Beef pancreas		1.15	Diffusion and sedimentation	Delcambe and Desreux (1950)
E. coli		1.75	Diffusion and sedimentation	Delcambe and Desreux (1950)
m-RNA (Gramicidine)		1.14	Osmotic pressure, light scattering, end-group analysis	Sedat and Hall (1965)
Viral RNA :				
Tobacco mosaic virus 1		3.7	Diffusion	Loring (1939a)
2		30.0	Diffusion and sedimentation	Cohen and Stanley (1942)
3		220	Calculation*	Schuster (1960)
Turnip mosaic Virus		230 $\pm$ 15	Sedimentation and viscosity	Haselkorn (1962)
Polio Virus		200	Calculation*	Schuster (1960)

* By supposing that the RNA contained in a viral particle corresponds to a single RNA molecule.

Analogous results to the spontaneous degradation with time have been observed with degradation under the influence of RNase, proving that the so-called "spontaneous" degradation of RNA is more likely to be due to infinitesimal traces of incompletely removed RNase during the phenol extraction (see p. 112).

The values obtained for viral RNAs, both by direct measurement and by reasoning, are very high — at any rate the most recent values are. Indeed, a preliminary series of figures can be obtained by applying classical molecular weight methods to these RNAs. A further method is to count the number of viral particles in the electron microscope, and consequently the number of RNA molecules (assuming that there is only a single molecule per particle) in a given weight of virus. A colorimetric determination of the % RNA in the virus is made, when simple arithmetic allows the molecular weight of the viral RNA to be estimated (Schuster 1960).

C. NATURE OF THE INTERNUCLEOTIDE LINKING

The nature of the internucleotide link has been the subject of considerable discussion over the past ten years (Brown and Todd 1955), mainly as to whether the linkage was between carbons 2' and 5' or between carbons 3' and 5'.

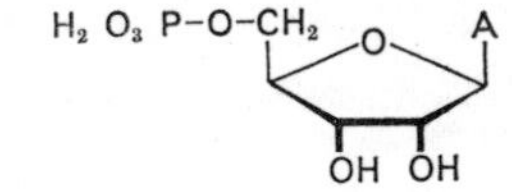

$H_2 O_3 P-O-CH_2$ A

OH   OH

5'-Adenylic acid or adenosine 5'-phosphate
or muscle adenylic acid (I)

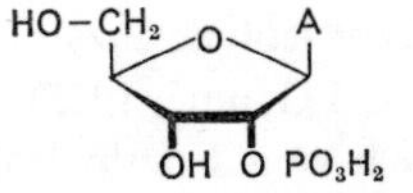

$HO-CH_2$ A

OH   O PO_3H_2

2'-Adenylic acid or
adenosine 2'-monophosphate
or adenylic acid a (II)

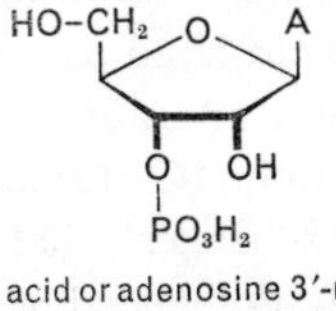

$HO-CH_2$ A

O   OH
|
PO_3H_2

3'-Adenylic acid or adenosine 3'-monophosphate
or adenylic acid b (III)

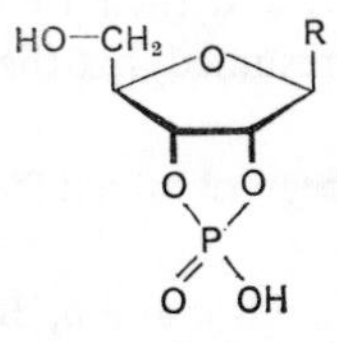

$HO-CH_2$ R

O   O
P
O   OH

Nucleoside 2'   3'-cyclic phosphate (IV)

3′, 5′-Phosphodiester link (V)

2′, 5′-Phosphodiester link (VI)

It has been known for a long time that the internucleotide link was much weaker in the case of the ribonucleic acids than in the case of the deoxyribonucleic acids. This sensitivity can be explained by postulating a ready migration of the phosphoryl group from one carbon to another in the course of both dilute alkaline and nucleolytic enzymic hydrolysis, analogous to the behavior of phosphoric esters of glycerol (Bailly and Gaumé, 1935). There would then be formed a nucleoside 2′ : 3′ cyclic -phosphate (IV), which would be hydrolyzed under more vigorous conditions to a mixture of 2′-phosphate and 3′-phosphate. This hypothesis is strongly supported by the following facts :

1. The intermediate 2′ : 3′-cyclic -phosphates have been synthesized in Todd's group (Brown, Magrath and Todd, 1952), and these esters were shown to have the properties expected of them, i.e. that they were unstable, being rapidly hydrolyzed to a mixture of nucleoside 2′-and 3′-phosphates. The two isomers produced are stable and not interconverted in alkaline solution.

2. As early as 1949-1950, Carter and Cohn (Carter and Cohn, 1949; Cohn, 1950a, b) found, by the use of chromatography on anion exchangers, that alkaline hydrolysates from ribonucleic acid gave two adenylic acids, provisionally designated a and b. These two acids were different from muscle adenylic acid or adenosine 5′-monophosphate (1); yet they contained only one phosphoryl group per molecule of adenine, and their total degradation by concentrated hydrochloric acid yielded only adenine. It was presumed that they were 2′-adenylic acid (II) and 3′-adenylic acid (III).

Isomers of the a and b type have also been obtained for guanylic acids and for the pyrimidine nucleotides, cytidylic and uridylic acids.

In a study of the structure of adenylic acids a and b, Brown et al. (1953) made a direct X-ray structural determination of adenylic acid b. Figure 1 shows quite clearly the position the phosphoryl group occupies on the ribose, confirming that adenylic acid *b* is adenosine 3'-monophosphate while adenylic acid *a* is adenosine 2'-monophosphate.

3. Brown and Todd's hypothesis about the nature of the internucleotide linkage and the migration of phosphoryl groups is further supported by the fact that Markham and Smith (1952*a*) have isolated experimentally all the 2' : 3'-cyclic nucleotides. The cyclic nucleotides corresponding to the pyrimidine bases cytosine and uracil are in greater quantities than the cyclic nucleotides corresponding to the purine bases, adenine and guanine.

4. One of the first successful uses of the nucleases was in confirming the position of the internucleotide link. A fundamental criterion of nuclease specificity, in fact, is that the products formed by their action are either nucleoside 3'-phosphates or nucleoside 5'-phosphates, i.e. the fission occurs on either side of the phosphoryl group, showing the original link to have been 3'-, 5'-phosphate.

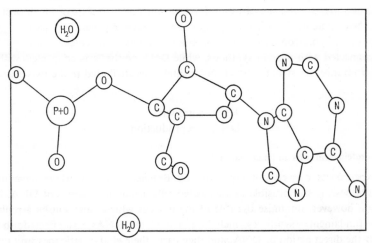

Figure 1. Spatial configuration of adenylic acid *b* by Brown et al. (1953)

III. RIBONUCLEIC ACID FUNCTION : PROTEIN SYNTHESIS, THE CODE

A. GENERAL REMARKS

The fundamental role played by RNA was long suspected to be one involved in protein synthesis, as was shown in 1947 by Caspersson. This role, according to Brachet (1955-58) and others, is illustrated by three fundamental observations :

1) The fact that all the plant viruses examined so far are composed of ribonucleoproteins and that RNA is necessary for their reproduction. What is more, Fraenkel-Conrat as well as Schramm have shown that RNA alone, isolated in the pure state, retains sufficient activity to ensure multiplication of the virus. This viral RNA must therefore function as a messenger RNA in the synthesis of its own protein.

2) The discovery that ribonucleoproteins, probably in the form of microsomes, play an important part in embryonic development.

3) The presence of large amounts of RNA in all the cells where a great deal of protein synthesis occurs, such as embryo cells, regenerating tissue, bacterial cultures in exponential growing phase, tumors etc.

We shall now discuss some particularly significant experiments concerning the part played by the ribonucleic acids in protein synthesis, starting with the most complex systems (whole organisms) and finishing with the simplest systems (acellular systems).

1. RNA and protein synthesis in whole organisms

All those who have studied the distribution of RNA in different tissues in the course of development (this is mainly the work of Mandel and co-workers and of Davidson and co-workers) are agreed that tissues that are the site of rapid development and therefore of much protein synthesis have a high RNA content. This is the case in embryo tissue, regenerating tissue or tissue undergoing compensating hypertrophy, etc. During the development of chicken embryo brain, RNA synthesis is connected with protein synthesis, while DNA synthesis is connected with cell reproduction, and from this fact stem the two fundamental roles attributed to the two classes of nucleic acids :

RNA : growth
DNA : reproduction.

2. RNA and protein synthesis in anuclear cells

Many experiments carried out especially by Brachet and co-workers have demonstrated that protein synthesis is still possible in anucleated cells, i.e. in the absence of DNA. These experiments do not, however, minimise the role of the nucleus which must still be a replacement site where all the fundamental syntheses, including that of the RNAs, are effected; the RNAs are synthesised by the direct action of DNA, and then carry their vital genetic message, passing subsequently into the cytoplasm where they follow their normal function in protein synthesis. It has been found that anucleated fragments of monocellular organisms are capable of surviving for a certain time (as a rule only as long as their supply of RNA messengers is not exhausted), but that this survival is limited.

Brachet et al. (1955) reported that anucleated fragments of the giant monocellular alga *Acetabularia mediterranea* are not only capable of survival over a very long period, but can still cause the formation of the " hat " which is characteristic of reproduction of the alga. The study of the protein and RNA evolution in these anucleated fragments showed that these substances were continuing to be synthesized as in the anucleated fragments, and even that the syntheses initially could be more rapid, though they subsequently slowed down. *Acetabularia* clearly represents a most favorable case for studying the possible survival of anucleated fragments, since these fragments are still capable of feeding themselves like nucleated fragments.

The situation is much less encouraging with other monocellular organisms, such as reticulocytes, sea urchin eggs and amebas.

In order to work out how much protein synthesis was effected by nucleated or anucleated fragments of ameba, Mazia and Prescott (1955) examined the percentage incorporation of methionine-^{35}S by these fragments. Methionine incorporation is a way of measuring protein synthesis, and it is 2.5 times lower in the anucleated fragments, measured immediately after cell fragmentation. The percent incorporation then remains constant in both fragments for three days following the excision. These observations show the important part played by the nucleus in the metabolism necessary for protein synthesis; they show that protein synthesis can take place in the cytoplasm in the absence of the nucleus, but only for a limited length of time.

3. Protein synthesis in disintegrated cells and in non-cellular systems

a. *Disintegrated cells*

Gale and Folkes (1958*a*, *b*) have studied the reactions of disintegrated staphylococci; they no longer breathe or reproduce, but they continue to incorporate aminoacids into their proteins as long as ATP and hexose diphosphate are present in the medium. Removal of the nucleic acids by the nucleases lowers the incorporation, while addition of nucleic acid fragments restores the ability to synthesize proteins.

b. *Bacillus megaterium protoplasts.*

The work of Spiegelman et al. (1957) has shown that the synthesis of a specific enzyme, β-galactosidase, was still possible in a system containing protoplasts that had suffered extensive lysis from the action of osmotic shocks. The idea of these shocks was suggested to the authors in the course of research they were carrying out to find the best stability conditions for isolated protoplasts, with a view to enzyme synthesis. Although the osmotic shocks resulted in considerable lysis, they furnished "pellets" that retained a remarkable capacity for enzyme synthesis.

c. *Microsomes*

α Microsomal reticulocyte fractions : according to Rabinovitz and Olson (1957), a reticulocyte suspension is first labeled with ^{14}C-aminoacids. Subsequently the microsomal fraction of these cells is isolated and incubated with fresh cell fluid. Under these conditions, liberation of a radioactive protein having the color of hemoglobin is observed.

β Guinea-pig liver microsomes : Askonas et al. (1958) have demonstrated that in a completely cell-free system of guinea-pig liver microsomes, ^{14}C-aminoacids are incorporated into the proteins of the microsomal fraction at varying rates.

All these experiments show that many acellular systems without a nucleus and which in principle, therefore, have no DNA, remain capable of effecting limited protein synthesis. The essential condition for protein synthesis to occur is that the systems should be rich in RNA.

B. Aminoacid activation, Properties and function of transfer RNA

It would seem now to be proved that RNAs are required for protein synthesis, but it still remains to show by what mechanism the consecutive aminoacids of the proteins are attached to one another, and what system determines the order of attachment of the aminoacids. We shall see that the aminoacids first undergo an "activation" by the intervention of transfer RNA, and that they are subsequently linked to one another following a code transmitted by the messenger RNA.

Polypeptide syntheses cannot take place by simple reversal of the action of the proteolytic enzymes for the following reasons. First, the thermodynamic argument requires that sufficient energy be supplied to the system for the peptide bonds to be formed. Secondly, the metabolic argument states that all systems effecting protein synthesis must have an exterior energy supply; thus when oxygenation is interrupted by metabolic poisons (e.g. dinitrophenol) the synthesis is halted.

These facts have been recognized for some time, notably by Linderström-Lang and Lipmann in 1940-1941. This is why a pre-activation of the aminoacids, analogous to the fatty acid activation, has had to be postulated before polypeptide linkage.

The fact that the presence of ATP is required in all systems synthesizing proteins leads to consideration of the important position this substance occupies in such syntheses, and to the question of the possibility of mixed anhydride formation between the aminoacids and ATP. Mixed anhydrides have been synthesised, but they cannot function as precursors of the peptide bond without the intervention of an enzyme system; moreover the energy liberated by ATP hydrolysis is well above what is needed to form a peptide bond. Lipmann has suggested that this excess energy might be used for increasing the specificity of the reaction. In any case, the formation of aminoacyl adenylates during the incorporation of aminoacids into liver microsomes is proved.

Up to the present time, the simplest particles found to be still necessary for protein synthesis are the microsomal sub-fractions that could be considered as being ribonucleoprotein particles. Hoagland has pointed out that these experiments have real significance only if the incorporation observed really does represent what happens during *in vivo* protein synthesis.

The various components required to set up a system for incorporating rat liver and ascites tumor cell aminoacids are the following : 1) ^{14}C-aminoacid; 2) adenosine triphosphate (ATP); 3) soluble enzymes of the "pH 5 enzyme" type, which are enzymes activating aminoacids together with other soluble enzymes needed for the process; 4) "soluble" ribonucleic acids; these RNAs form part of the "pH 5 enzymes"; 5) microsomal ribonucleoprotein particles; 6) guanosine triphosphate.

The ribonucleoprotein particles of the microsomes seem to be the actual sites of polypeptide chain formation; the soluble enzymes and ATP effect the initial activation of the aminoacids. Hoagland et al. (1958) have shown that the intermediate stages between activation of the aminoacids and final incorporation into the proteins are effected by a temporary RNA-aminoacid association. This "soluble" RNA fraction becomes labeled by ^{14}C-aminoacids in the presence of ATP and aminoacid-activating enzymes; aminoacid-labeled RNA is subsequently able to transfer the aminoacids it is carrying to the microsomal proteins if in the presence of guanosine triphosphate.

Experimentally, the method is as follows. Cell fractions (microsomes and *p*H 5 enzymes) from rat liver and Erlich ascites tumor are prepared by the methods described by Hoagland, Zamecnik et al. (see particularly Keller and Zamecnik, 1956; Littlefield and Keller, 1957). The microsomes are generally sedimented for 90-120 minutes at 105,000 g, instead of for the 60 minutes previously recommended, in order to be quite sure that all the microsomal particles are completely sedimented. The pH 5 enzymes are precipitated from the supernatant fraction by bringing it to pH 5.2. The pH 5 enzyme fraction is labeled by incubation with ^{14}C-leucine and ATP, and the system is reprecipitated again after labeling by adjusting the *p*H to 5.2.

Finally a RNA carrying ^{14}C-leucine can be isolated using Gierer and Schramm's method (1956) as applied to the whole of the pH 5 enzymes. This extraction allows 30-50 % of the RNA initially present in the incubation mixture to be isolated.

The overall result of the reactions just described may be summarized in the following equations :

$$ATP + Leu\text{-}^{14}C + E = E\ (AMP)\ Leu\text{-}^{14}C + PP$$
$$E\ (AMP)\ Leu\text{-}^{14}C + RNA = RNA\text{-}Leu\text{-}^{14}C + E + (AMP)$$

The RNA-^{14}C-leucine complex can be immediately adsorbed on Dowex 1 and on charcoal at neutral pH. It cannot be dialysed against distilled water, 10 % NaCl or 8M urea. There is no protein precipitable by acid in the phenol-extracted RNA. The leucine appears to be attached by covalent bonds, indeed, ninhydrin treatment of RNA-^{14}C-leucine indicates the absence of free leucine, although leucine is slowly liberated from the RNA during the reaction with ninhydrin.

It has now been clearly shown that the function of transfer RNA is to "accept" an aminoacid at the extremity of its chain, resulting in the formation of an aminoacyl-t-RNA, and to transfer this aminoacid to a polypeptide chain under the control of a messenger RNA, which, in turn, is carried on polyribosomes. These two functions of t-RNA appear to be carried out in different parts of the molecule, for the two can be differentiated. t-RNA can be changed enzymically by the action of RNase from *B. subtilis* or of RNAse T_1 in the presence of Mg^{++} ions in such a way that under the same conditions as described, the acceptor activity for certain aminoacids is retained but the transfer activity is lost (Nishimura and Novelli, 1965).

The particular example quoted above concerned activation and incorporation of leucine, but it is clear that the process is the same for all aminoacids.

Many experiments have been carried out on the isolation, purification and properties of t-RNA. In chapter III details for the preparation of rat liver t-RNA are given, following the work of Zamecnik et al. Since that time, yeast t-RNA has been prepared (Monier et al. 1960-1962) by applying Kirby's phenol method (1956). The total t-RNA fraction thereby obtained from yeast had a sedimentation constant of 4S and contained a complete set of the various t-RNAs corresponding to the different aminoacids. The attempts being made to isolate each t-RNA in the pure state show great promise of with success in the near future.

Because large amounts of t-RNA were needed for structural work, a simplified, large-scale preparation of yeast total t-RNA was required (Holley, 1963). A critical examination of the different preparative methods of yeast t-RNA had been made by Klee and Staehlin (1962). In particular, they had shown that phenol or dodecyl sulfate extraction resulted in highly active t-RNA preparations, while the samples obtained with salt extraction were partially degraded.

Subsequently, to obtain the series of RNAs specific for the incorporation of each aminoacid, starting from total t-RNA, a variety of purifications have been tested, particularly chromatography on hydroxyapatite (Hartmann and Coy, 1961a, b, c), chromatography on DEAE-cellulose (Stephenson and Zamecnik, 1961; Baguley et al., 1965), chromatography on aminoethylcellulose (Zubay, 1962), chromatography on Sephadex (Röschenthaler and Fromageot 1965), chromatography on kieselguhr coated with methylated albumin (Melchers and Zachau, 1965), a combination DEAE-cellulose and DEAE-Sephadex (Cherayil and Bock, 1965), and, above all, countercurrent distribution, which would appear to be the method of choice for this type of separation.

The first counter-current distribution experiments were already of proven value (Doctor et al., 1961; Holley and Lazar, 1961; Apgar et al., 1962), since by 1962 Apgar et al. were able to isolate three transfer-RNAs in the pure state that were specific for, respectively, alanine, tyrosine and valine. Further, by 1962, Apgar and Holley noticed differences between yeast t-RNA and rat liver t-RNA in the course of counter-current distribution.

The extensive work carried out in different laboratories on the counter-current distribution of transfer-RNA has demonstrated how complex the mixtures to be separated, could be, but the isolation of unique molecular species in a state that was sufficiently pure for structural work was finally achieved. Goldstein et al., working in Craig's laboratory (1964), fractionated the total t-RNA from *Escherichia coli* in a system containing phosphate buffer, formamide and isopropanol. In this way, 29 specific RNAs could be characterized.

Also in connection with *coli* t-RNA, Apgar and Holley (1964) observed that the leucine acceptor RNA could be separated into two different peaks, designated Leu I and Leu II, using conditions described by Weisblum et al. (1962). Further fractionation in a different system (1,200 transfers) finally resulted in the resolution of the leucine-accepting activity into 5 different fractions.

Starting from yeast total transfer-RNA, Doctor et al (1963) succeeded in purifying the alanine and tyrosine-accepting RNAs. Karau and Zachau (1964) have also described the isolation of 350 mg of serine-t-RNA from 32 grams of total t-RNA after several counter-current distributions; Rushizky and Sober (1965) obtained 3 fractions having serine-acceptor activity from bakers' yeast, and Melchers and Zachau (1965) have also noted the subdivision of cysteinyl-t-RNA into three distinct peaks. Also from yeast, Hoskinson and Khorana (1965) obtained a phenylalanyl-t-RNA that they estimated to be 80 % pure.

This list is far from complete, since the number of specific t-RNAs isolated in the pure states increases, fortunately, every month, but it indicates the progress made over the past few year in the purification of specific RNAs. The logical step further in this work was naturally the determination of the sequences, using enzymes causing specific degradations.

The preliminary work of Doctor et al. (1965) resulted in their being able to set forth a partial structure of alanine and tyrosine-acceptor RNAs. These two RNAs were broken up by RNase A and the fragments thus obtained analysed in a two-dimensional system; the first dimension was paper electrophoresis in ammonium formate (0.02M) at pH 2.7 for 17 hr. at room temperature with 6 volts/cm; the second dimension was paper chromatography in the system butyl alcohol/-ammonium formate. The numerous oligonucleotides isolated in this way showed significant differences between the sequences present in the two RNAs.

Enzymic hydrolysis and characterization of the nucleotides obtained has also been carried out by Staehelin et al. (1965) and by Doctor and McCormick (1965) on purified fractions isolated from yeast t-RNA.

Penswick and Holley (1965) have reported a way of fission for a specific RNA, the alanine acceptor, into a very limited number of fragments. Brief treatment of this RNA with RNase T_1 cleaves it into only two fragments; the treatment must be carried out for 4 minutes at 0° and the reaction stopped by addition of phenol. The two fragments can then be separated by chromatography on DEAE-cellulose, and the sum of the analysis of fragments I and II corresponding to the analysis of the starting RNA confirms that, under these conditions, the molecule was indeed only split into two fragments.

When the same controlled hydrolytic treatment by RNase T_1 is carried out for 1 hr at 0° (Apgar et al., 1965), a series of four large oligonucleotides is obtained, the sequences of which have been determined :

$$p - G - G - G - C - G - U - G - U - MeG - G - C -$$

C — DiMeG — C (C,C,U) C — U — U — I — G — C —
C — MeI — Ψ — G — G — G — A — G — A — G — U —
A — C — U — C — G — U — C — C — A — C — C — A.

These four sequences already represent a considerable section (47 nucleotides) of the total sequence of alanyl-t-RNA. Zamir et al. (1965), working in the group of Holley, have noticed the presence of a common sequence occurring in all the yeast t-RNA :

— Gp Tp Ψ p CpGp..., and also occurring in the t-RNA from *E. coli* and rat liver.

Preliminary work of the same nature has been carried out on the sequence of transfer RNA by Zachau and his team using seryl-t-RNA isolated in pure form from brewers' yeast. Two such seryl-t-RNAs were isolated (Karau and Zachau, 1964). In the first step, the t-RNA serine acceptor is subjected to hydrolysis by pancreatic RNase, and from this hydrolysate, several oligonucleotides were isolated by chromatography on DEAE-cellulose in a buffer with an ammonium carbonate gradient. The sequence of all the dinucleotides and trinucleotides is known (Melchers and Zachau, 1964). The fraction corresponding to the seryl-t-RNA is then treated with RNase T_1, the oligonucleotides separated and identified by chromatography (Dütting and Zachau, 1964), to such an extent that a large part of the seryl-t-RNA molecule is already known (Dütting et al., 1965). *

Bergquist and Robertson (1965), carrying out comparable work to that of Zachau's team, have succeeded in characterising up to five different species of serine-accepting ribonucleic molecules from brewers' yeast. These samples differ from one another in certain nucleotide sequences obtained after hydrolysis by pancreatic RNase of the various RNAs.

Hydrolysis of the five seryl-t-TNA from brewers' yeast by RNase T_2 after fixing each molecule with serine-[14]C (Bergquist, 1965) has led to the conclusion that all the molecules have the same terminal sequence, accepting the serine :

... Gp (Ap Cp) Cp Cp A — serine

This sequence is different from that identified by Cantoni et al. (1963) in seryl-t-RNA from bakers' yeast :

... Gp Cp Ap Ap Cp Cp A

Bakers' yeast seryl-t-RNAs have been among the most examined so far; Cantoni et al., believing in 1963 that they had a homogeneous preparation of this compound, carried out partial enzymic hydrolyses, and by a great deal of cross-checking set out a possible preliminary structure, this corresponding to a hairpin-like molecule, almost entirely double-stranded.

Since that time, Rushizky and Sober (1965) have fractionated serine-accepting t-RNA by multiple counter-current distribution into 3 distinct fractions : serine I, serine II and serine III RNA. Serine I was present in too small a proportion to be examined at present, but serine II and serine III have been highly purified, the final purity being of the order of 81 %.

Serine II and serine III were subsequently "mapped" after hydrolysis with pancreatic RNase and RNase T_2. The results indicated little variation between the two seryl-t-RNA; in particular, there was no difference in the overall nucleotide ratios, the two RNA containing Cp 27.7; Ap 20.8; pseudo-Up 3.3; Up 19.2 and Gp 28.7 % . It is not impossible that a large part of this RNA is double-stranded, since there are noticeable similarities, Cp/Gp and Ap/Up, ΨUp. On the other hand, the two seryl-t-RNAs are very close in the amounts of the principal mono-, di- and trinucleotides in the hydrolysate from pancreatic RNase.

---

* The complete sequences of two serine-specific transfer RNAS have recently been established by Zachau et al. (1966).

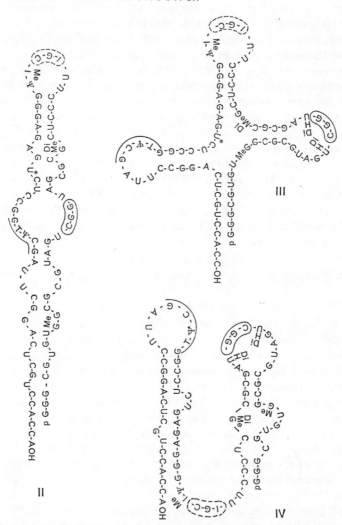

Di   Di

Me   H   H   I

p G-G-G-C-G-U-G-U-G-C-G-C-G-U-A-G-U-(C-G-G)-U-A-G-C-G-C-
Di
Me   Me
-G-C-U-C-C-C-U-U-(I-G-C)-I-Ψ-G-G-G-AA-G-A-G-U-C-U-C-C-G-G-T-Ψ-C-G-A-

U-U-C-C-G-G-A-C-U-C-G-U-C-C-A-C-C-A-OH

Figure 2. Primary structure of alanyl-t-RNA after Holley et al. (1965a).
I — linear sequence; the pentanucleotide common to all t-RNAs is underlined; the two trinucleotides representing the two possible anticodons are surrounded by a full and a dotted line respectively. II, III and IV — three possible conformations of alanyl-t-RNA having short double-stranded regions.

The finest work in this field must, however, be that of Holley and his co-workers (Holley et al., 1964; Holley et al., 1965a, b, c) whose efforts, after several years of research, led to the complete elucidation of the primary structure of a ribonucleic acid, alanyl-t-RNA from yeast. This result is comparable in importance with Sanger's discovery of the total structure of insulin, and marks a milestone in nucleic acid history, at the same time providing a brilliant example of the use of nucleases in nucleic acid research.

For the moment we do not propose to go into the details of the work that led to the elucidation of the structure of alanyl-t-RNA, because this description will be given in the final chapter (application of the nucleases, p. 302), but since we are briefly discussing the part played by t-RNA in connection with its spatial configuration, fig. 2 reproduces the three possible schemes presented by Holley's team (1965a) where the chain has been folded in such a way as to form short double-stranded regions. It can also be seen that the distribution of minor nucleotides does not show any special peculiarity, and that it is impossible to find a scheme fitting an entirely double-stranded structure.

The sequence of five nucleotides (pentanucleotide), in principle common to all transfer RNA (Zamir et al., 1965), G — T — Ψ — C — G, is situated at about 20 nucleotides from the accepting extremity. It is believed that this sequence would be found in the same position for the other t-RNAs. If the whole sequence is examined, it can also be seen that there are several trinucleotides able to function as the coding triplet, or "anticodon", corresponding to alanine transfer (Bernfield and Nirenberg, 1965; Nirenberg et al., 1965). If it is assumed that this triplet contains 2G and 1C, two interesting possibilities emerge; anticodon is situated between two dihydrouridyl residues in the sequence DiHU — C — G — G — DiHU, in which case the two DiHU acids would be present to isolate the right sequence. Another possibility is that the coding triplet I — G — C is placed at about the middle of the sequence.

Examination of the primary structure of alanyl-t-RNA shows, therefore, that it consists of a nucleotide sequence of 77 units having a molecular weight of 26,000, calculated for the sodium salt, the accepting part of the molecule having been known for some time as the terminal three nucleotides pC pC pA. The last nucleotide is an adenosine residue having its 2'- and 3'-hydroxyl groups both free. It is the 3'-hydroxyl group which is esterified by the transfered aminoacid in the course of aminoacid transfer.

Hoagland has proposed the following scheme for activation and transport of aminoacids. (figure 3.)

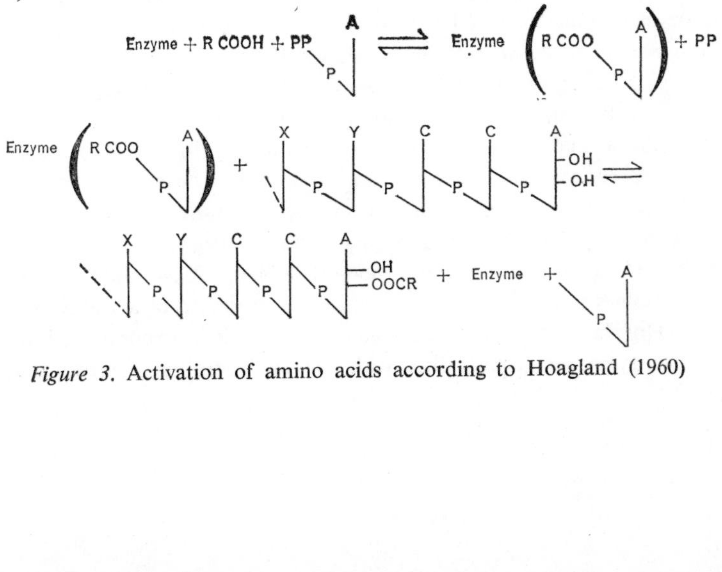

$$\text{Enzyme} + \text{R COOH} + \text{PP} \rightleftharpoons \text{Enzyme} \left(\text{R COO} \right) + \text{PP}$$

Figure 3. Activation of amino acids according to Hoagland (1960)

The aminoacid R. COOH is activated by its (specific) enzyme forming an enzyme-amino-acid-adenylate complex. This complex reacts with a specific t-RNA with esterification of the aminoacid on the 3'-hydroxyl group of the terminal adenosine of the t-RNA.

The question now arises as to how far the specificity of t-RNA and activation enzymes (aminoacyl-t-RNA synthetases) in a species is absolutely adhered to. Several groups have examined this point, and Rendi and Ochoa (1962) have found that aminoacyl-t-RNA synthetases from *E. coli* cannot incorporate leucine into yeast or rat liver t-RNA , or vice-versa. Benzer and Weisblum (1961) have also found striking differences of specificity. Doctor and Mudd (1963) have made a systematic study of the acceptor activity of t-RNA isolated from rat liver, yeast and *E. coli*, these activities being measured in the presence of aminoacyl-t-RNA synthetases isolated from rat liver, yeast and *E. coli*. Their results show that in each case there is at least a slight incorporation of aminoacid, even in a heterogenous system. The specificity is, however, sometimes considerable, and preferential incorporation is generally observed in a homogenous system. Nevertheless, in the case of alanine, complete homology was observed between t-RNA of rat liver, yeast and *E. coli* and their respective enzymes. Doctor and Mudd advise the greatest caution in interpreting their results, because the variables introduced, knowingly or unknowingly, in the experimental conditions can alter the rate of incorporation of the aminoacids into the various t-RNAs.

During the subsequent protein synthesis, the aminoacid carried by its specific t-RNA is incorporated even if it has undergone an artificial modification. Cysteine attached to its specific t-RNA can be reduced by Raney nickel to alanine, when it will be the alanine that is incorporated by the t-RNA specific for cysteine (Chapeville et al., 1962).

The same thing happens if tyrosyl-t-RNA is oxidized to dihydroxyphenylalanyl-t-RNA (DOPA-t-RNA). The experiments carried out in this direction by Chapeville et al. (1963) show that in a system synthesizing a protein, when an unexpected aminoacid like DOPA is introduced combined with the tyrosine-specific RNA, it is incorporated into the protein, and found in the peptide sequence normally containing tyrosine. Altumina et al. (1965) have found that an aminoacyl-t-RNA could be converted *in situ* to dipeptidyl-t-RNA with water-soluble carbodiimide.

Hervé and Chappeville (1963), have also studied the specificity of activating enzymes in the case of the inverse reaction to the formation of aminoacyl-t-RNA. To do this, they used aminoacyl-t-RNA in which the aminoacid had undergone a modification *in situ*, e.g. Cys-SH-t-RNA where the cysteine had been converted to alanine by Raney nickel reduction, or oxidized to cysteic acid with periodate, or methionine oxidized to methionine disulfoxide, etc. The experiment showed that fission of the ester bond between the modified aminoacid and the t-RNA does not occur in the presence of the activating enzymes; for example, in the case of Ala esterified by the t-RNA specific for cysteine, neither the cysteine-activating enzyme nor the alanine one are active. These results are valid for the normal reaction of formation of aminoacyl-t-RNA, so the work of Chapeville and his co-workers shows that it is the activating enzymes that exert the most rigorous control at the moment of loading the aminoacid on its respective t-RNA.

The question of how the RNA-aminoacid system is integrated into particular structures has next to be decided. Incubation of aminoacid-^{14}C-RNA (isolated and purified by the phenol method) with microsomes and GTP results in rapid incorporation of about 20 % of the amino-acid into proteins (Hoagland et al., 1958). In the course of this incorporation, it is supposed that the soluble RNA-carrying aminoacids fuse with the nucleoprotein microsomes. This may be realized by labeling soluble RNA with labeled aminoacids or by labeling the RNA itself on its pyrimidine bases. After incubation of either of these RNA with microsomes and GTP, microsomal particles that have themselves become labeled can be isolated by centrifugation. There must, therefore, really have been a fusion of the RNA- carrying aminoacids and the microsomes.

This phenomenon has been confirmed again by the recent experiments of Marcot-Queiroz et al. (1965), who have been able to demonstrate both in yeast and *E. coli* a small amount of RNA behaving chromatographically like transfer-RNA besides a large amount (95 %) of ribosomal RNA. The presence of transfer RNA results from its participation in protein synthesis at the ribosome level.

C. MESSENGER RNA (m-RNA)

We have now arrived at the crucial point of protein synthesis, in other words, we now have the activated aminoacids carried by the transfer RNA side by side on the ribosomes. In order for the synthesis of a specific protein to take place, these activated aminoacids must organize themselves into a particular order given by the "genetic message" which corresponds to the synthesis of this specific protein. Since this synthesis takes place in the cytoplasm, it can only be assumed that the chromosomes, i.e. DNA, are able to give the genetic information indirectly. In an article on the genetic control mechanism in protein synthesis, Jacob and Monod (1961) introduced a clear definition of *messenger RNA* functioning as a liaison between the genetic information carried by the DNA and the actual site of protein synthesis. If this is so, the ribosomes will not be specific for any particular synthesis, but will function only as a support or site where synthesis can occur; the messenger RNA, carrying certain information perhaps better described as a genetic *code*, is, therefore, only temporarily with the ribosomes.

Jacob and Monod have also said that this messenger RNA (m-RNA) must obey the following conditions :

1) It must be a polynucleotide.

2) So far as the molecular weight is concerned, it must be a very heterogeneous fraction, and this property will depend on the length of the polypeptide chain to be synthesised. If we take it that a nucleotide triplet is needed to code one aminoacid, the molecular weight cannot be less than 500,000 (corresponding to 1,500 — 1,600 nucleotides which, in turn, correspond to 500 aminoacids or a protein of molecular weight 50,000). The larger proteins, therefore, must be coded by messenger RNA with a molecular weight of over 1 million, unless the same protein can be coded by several messenger RNA molecules strung together.

3) It must have a base composition that reproduces that of the DNA.

4) It must at least be temporarily in association with the ribosomes, because there is good reason to believe these to be the area where protein synthesis occurs. The role of the ribosomes in protein synthesis has been increasingly stressed over the past 10 years. In this respect there exists an important review by Hoagland (1960) and work by Decken and Campbell (1962).

5) It must have a rapid renewal rate.

The idea of messenger RNA is not just an ingeneous theory, it is a practical reality supported by a number of experiments carried out in different laboratories. Ribonucleic fractions have, in fact, been found fitting the five criteria set out above in the bacteriophage infecting *E. coli* by Volkin and Astrachan (1957), and in normal yeast by Yčas and Vincent (1960). Both the groups of Gros et al. (1961) and Brenner et al. (1961) have provided convincing evidence to support the existence of messenger RNA. Using a method called " pulse labeling", Gros and co-workers have demonstrated the existence of a metabolically unstable RNA that is (transiently) associated with the ribosomes in *E. coli*.

E. coli is exposed to brief pulsations (10-20 sec.) at 25° (the generating time being 90 min.) from radioactive RNA precursors such as ^{32}P-phosphate or ^{14}C-uracil. The cells are then rapidly cooled with crushed ice and M/100 nitride, a cell-free extract is prepared by powdering with alumina, 5 μg per ml DNase is added and the newly-formed RNA is examined using fractionation by ultracentrifugation in a sucrose gradient (see "Methods" chapter, p. 149).

These experiments show that normal bacterial cells from *E. coli* contain a RNA with a rapid renewal rate associated with active ribosomes of sedimentation constant 70S, which are the sites of protein synthesis. It is both tempting and logical to suppose that these unstable molecules, different both from ribosomal RNA and transfer RNA are a *messenger RNA*.

Brenner, Jacob and Meselson (1961) have independently produced evidence for the existence of an unstable intermediate carrying information for protein synthesis from the genes to the ribosomes. Theses experiments also tend to prove that the ribosomes are non-specialized structures receiving genetic information from the gene (DNA) in the form of an unstable intermediate or "messenger".

The work of Brenner and his colleagues has introduced a further factor, when they examined the behavior of RNA synthesised by *E. coli* infected by its phage. Introduction of the phage into the bacteria amounts to the same thing as adding an extra gene to them, the new gene setting up its own protein synthesis. The following results are obtained :

1) After infection by the phage, no new ribosomes can be detected, everything happens as though the phage were using its host's ribosomes for synthesising its own particular proteins.

2) The synthesis of a new RNA having a rapid renewal rate is observed. This RNA has a base ratio corresponding to that of the phage, adding itself to the ribosomes already existing, from which it can be detached in a CsCl gradient so lowering the Mg^{++} ion concentration.

3) The major part of the protein synthesis, if not all of it, takes place in the ribosomes already in existence.

These conclusions naturally lead to the idea that the phage DNA gives information to a "metabolically unstable" RNA which then enters into association with the ribosomes already existing in the host cell, and these then synthesize proteins following the information they have received from the metabolically unstable RNA. Protein synthesis will occur by the same mechanism in the uninfected cells.

The experiments of Brenner's team have been confirmed by those of Bautz and Hall (1962), who isolated a specific messenger RNA from the bacteriophage T_4, using a DNA-cellulose column. This T_4 specific RNA was quantitatively separated from *E. coli* RNA by chromatography on a column of T_4 DNA bound to cellulose. Fractionation and retention of the T_4 RNA is due to the specific formation of hydrogen bonds between the DNA of the column and the corresponding RNA having a complementary sequence of purine and pyrimidine bases.

Risebrough and co-workers (1962) have shown that in the course of protein synthesis by cell-free systems, the m-RNA attachment only occurs with "heavy" ribosomes of molecular weight 100S or 70S which sediment more rapidly than free ribosomes; these authors believe that many, if not all of these heavy ribosomes are "active", i.e. functioning as sites for protein synthesis, but that these active ribosomes only constitute a small fraction (5-10 %) of the total ribosomes present.

Fresh arguments in favor of the existence of m-RNA have been brought by Otaka et al. (1962) who studied the RNA synthesized in a cell-free system of *E. coli*, and showed that it had all the characteristics of a messenger RNA. Sibatani and co-workers (1962) have isolated a "nuclear" ribonucleic fraction, i.e. a RNA from the nucleus having a high rate of synthesis and a base ratio resembling that of thymus DNA. They suppose this fraction to be a "nuclear messenger RNA".

Originally it was believed that one of the fundamental characteristics of messenger RNA was that of being a metabolically unstable substance with a rapid turnover. It would appear that this notion must be revised — partly so, at any rate — since experiments, such as those of Dure and Waters (1965) have demonstrated the existence of long-lived messenger RNA. The evidence for the existence of this type of m-RNA was found by examining the RNA synthesis during the germination of cotton seeds (*Gossypium hirsutum* var. Coker 100). This synthesis was followed by measuring the incorporation of ^{32}P into the polysomal and ribosomal RNAs of the germinating seeds, when the following observations were made :

1) A substantial incorporation of ^{32}P into the ribosomes was observed.

2) Actinomycin D causes a significant inhibition of ^{32}P incorporation into the RNA.

3) This inhibition, however, does not induce any lowering of the total ribosome population, nor does it diminish protein synthesis.

The maintenance of polysomal structures and protein synthesis in the absence of RNA synthesis thus suggests that in the ripe seeds there exists a relatively stable messenger RNA that is not rapidly degraded.

Although the existence of m-RNA appears to have been established by the brilliant series of experiments we have just described, we must nevertheless point out that there is very little information available about its structure and properties. What is called m-RNA as a whole, is certainly a mixture of various m-RNAs corresponding to each specific protein, and each corresponding to a DNA segment with a complementary sequence of bases. Even though the sum of the DNAs in a cell is complementary to the sum of its m-RNAs, it does not by itself mean that each of the two categories corresponds to homogenous molecular species. For this reason it is necessary to try and purify the m-RNAs.

Attempts in this direction made by Monier et al. (1962) did show the heterogeneity of m-RNA extracted from *E. coli* that had been submitted to pulse labeling.

These authors managed to isolate the rapidly labeled RNA from *E. coli* using extraction procedures that lessen the effects of hydrolytic enzymes as far as possible. m-RNA fractionation was carried out either by preparative sedimentation in a sucrose gradient or by chromatography on a column of kieselguhr coated with methylated albumin following the technique of Mandell and Hershey (1960).

Using column chromatography, the m-RNA was fractionated into 4 principal components : the first component was eluted in the position that transfer-RNA should occupy (sedimentation constant 4S), a second component between the t-RNA and the ribosomal sub-units (16S, component α), a third between the ribosomal sub-units 16S and 23 S (component β) and finally a fourth component was eluted after fraction 23S (component γ).

These various m-RNA categories represent subsidiary fractions of *E. coli* m-RNA, since all these fractions are capable of promoting aminoacid-^{14}C incorporation into cell-free systems.

The high molecular weight of some of these fractions shows that *E. coli* m-RNA is of sufficient size to code large proteins.

Following the same sort of idea, Tsugita and co-workers (1962) showed that the RNA from tobacco mosaic virus could function as a m-RNA in a cell-free *E. coli* system and induce the synthesis of a protein that was in some respects similar to that from the tobacco mosaic virus. This evidence constitutes *initial* evidence favoring the universality of the code.

Similarly, Szafranski et al. (1963, 1964*a*, *b*) have examined the information that can be obtained from the synthesis of silk, a specific protein, by the silk worm, *Bombyx mori*.

The silk worm gland produces a single protein with a specific aminoacid composition, a fact that suggests the possibility of isolating an RNA responsible for the sequence in a well-defined polypeptide chain.

The RNA was, in fact, isolated from the silk glands by phenol extraction and fractionation on ECTEOLA-cellulose. In this way three fractions were obtained from the posterior glands and two from the middle glands.

The RNA isolated from the middle glands stimulates the incorporation of the specific silk aminoacids.

More recently, a specific m-RNA that codes the synthesis of a well-defined polypeptide, gramicidine S, has been isolated and characterized (Hall et al., 1965; Sedat and Hall, 1965). Gramicidine S is the well-known characteristic cyclic decapeptide of *Bacillus brevis*, the biosynthesis of which can occur in a cell-free system, as Berg et al. (1965) have shown. Synthesis of this peptide also occurs when a supernatant at pH 4.8 of ruptured cells of this strain (9999) is incubated with ribosomes and the precipitate at pH 4.8 of the 8185 (Dubos) strain, a variety not normally producing gramicidine (Hall et al., 1965). The factor responsible for directing the gramicidine S synthesis can be extracted with phenol from the supernatant pH 4.8 of the 9999 strain; this factor is sensitive to the action of RNase, so it must be a RNA, which is presumably the messenger RNA directing the gramicidine S synthesis.

The homogeneity of the active fraction obtained by chromatography on DEAE-Sephadex was demonstrated by a second chromatogram on Sephadex G-75, when all points on the RNA peak were found to have the same specific activity (messenger activity in the gramicidine S synthesis).

Subsequently, other physical and chemical properties of this RNA were determined: the molecular weight is 11,400, corresponding to a chain length of 36 ± 2 nucleotides. This poly-

Table IV. Base ratios of messenger RNA and ribosomal RNA of reticulocytes
(Burny and Marbaix, 1965*b*)

	1 RNA ribosomal	2 RNA messenger	3 RNA messenger
C	29.5	27.5	24.0
A	19.5	28.0	28.3
G	35.3	26.3	27.4
U	15.6	18.2	20.3
$\dfrac{G + C}{A + U}$	1.84	1.16	1.06

1. Mean value for 8 determinations.
2, 3. These two determinations were made on m-RNA originating from two different rabbits.

nucleotide does not seem to have a free phosphoryl group, and the two extremities are occupied by adenosine. The molecule is reported to form a random coil with a high G-C content.

Another example that can be quoted of a well-defined messenger RNA is the one responsible for the hemoglobin synthesis, isolated by Burny and Marbaix (1965a, b) from rabbit reticulocytes. In principle, this RNA is the strand linking the ribosomes in the reticulocyte polyribosomes of rabbit, and was purified by sedimentation in a sucrose gradient, by which means 250 µg of the RNA may be isolated per animal. This RNA has a sedimentation constant of 9.5, fitting a molecular weight of about 150,000, a dimension predicted for a monocistronic hemoglobin chain.

The composition of the purine and pyrimidine bases is notably different from that of the ribosome RNA (table IV), as is he ratio G + C/A + U.

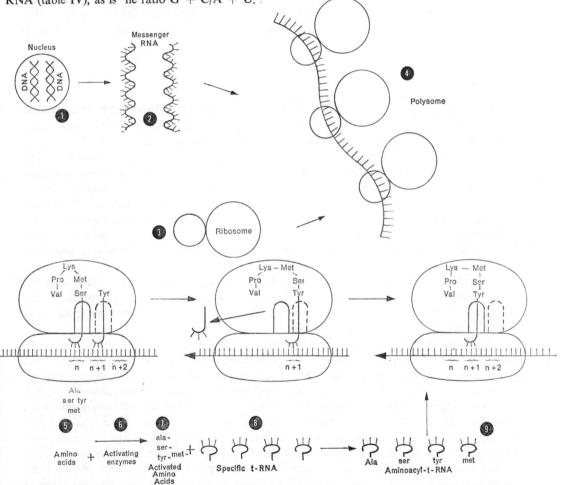

Figure 4. Diagram of the role of nucleic acids in protein synthesis. The messenger RNA receives its information from the DNA in the chromosomes by a mechanism as yet unknown. In all probability the messenger is complementary to the DNA that has given rise to it. This messenger constitutes a metabolically unstable chain, i.e. having a brief life span, and which is fixed on the non-specific ribosomes (3) forming (transiently) a polysome that is specific for synthesis of a protein (4).

In addition, the aminoacids may be seen as an undifferentiated "pool" (5) becoming activated in (7) under the action of the pH 5 enzymes (6). These activated aminoacids are collected by transfer RNA (8), each aminoacid being fixed on its own transfer RNA (9). The crucial point in the synthesis is stage (10) where the aminoacid-t-RNA may be seen aligning itself in a precise order imposed by the messenger RNA through the code it is carrying. The aminoacids are now placed so that they join together to give the protein.

The synthesis of messenger RNA generally takes place through "replicases" under the control of DNA (figure 4 and p. 79). The case of RNA viruses, however, in which the ribonucleic chain holds all the genetic information, sets a special problem; recently, in fact, an RNA-dependent RNA-polymerase or "replicase" from E. coli infected with the RNA bacteriophage MS-2 was reported by Spiegelman and his co-workers (Haruna et al., 1963; Haruna and Spiegelman, 1965). This enzyme requires the presence of RNA and, moreover, exhibits a unique preference for its homologous RNA.

These experiments show that an enzyme such as this replicase is capable of discriminating between all the RNAs in its environment, choosing the sole RNA that will serve it as a template for the synthesis of viral RNA. From coli Haruna and Spiegelman purified two RNA-replicases induced in the same host by two unrelated RNA bacteriophages. They demonstrated that under optimun ionic conditions, one or other of these replicases is inactive with the heterogenetic RNA as template. Neither of the two replicases can function with the RNA of the other, each one recognizing its own RNA.

D. THE CODE

Coordination between the different participants in protein synthesis takes place both *in vitro* and *in vivo* by a process that has not yet been completely elucidated, so that for the present one can only arrive at hypothetical schemes of the type shown in figure 4.

In the course of experiments on protein synthesis, several workers have observed (Warner et al. 1963; Gierer, 1963; Gilbert, 1963; Rich et al., 1963; Ochoa, 1964a, b) ribosome aggregates (polyribosomes or polysomes) apparently joined to one another by an RNA strand, since they can be dissociated by RNase; it is presumed that several ribosomes are simultaneously engaged in synthesizing the same protein chain, the ribosomes either moving along the messenger strand or the messenger moving over the surface of the ribosomes. The role of the messenger is paramount, since in the last analysis it is this that "dictates" the code by which the aminoacids are joined together.

Decyphering the code will therefore require the introduction into a cell-free system like that obtained from E. coli, of a polynucleotide of known sequence, to function as an artificial messenger directing the synthesis of a known polypeptide, or the preferential incorporation of a known aminoacid into a polypeptide.

This was the idea at the start of Nirenberg and Matthaei's experiment (1961), and of the theory of the code, which has proved to be a considerable step forward in nucleic acid history, arousing the excitement not only of scientific circles, but even international public opinion.

Many genetic and enzymatic experiments, as well as theoretical biological considerations, have shown that at least three nucleotides are required for joining on each aminoacid (Yčas, 1960-1961; Woese, 1961-1962). The most convincing reason favoring the existence of these triplets is the following : taking it that about twenty aminoacids exist, there must be at least 3 nucleotides to make up more than 20 different combinations; from four different nucleotides arranged two by two only $4^2 = 16$ different combinations can be obtained, and this is insufficient. From 4 different nucleotides arranged 3 by 3, there are $4^3 = 64$ different combinations. If we accept the existence of 5 nucleotides, including methylcyticylic acid, $5^3 = 125$ different combinations can be arrived at, an amply sufficient number for the determination of the sequence of all the known aminoacids.

The code is thus apparently formed by a succession of triplets or *codons*, each of which determines the incorporation of an aminoacid.

Let us now consider a succession of identical triplets, such as a biosynthetic polynucleotide might be (poly U, cf. p. 98). If such a polymer were capable of functioning as a messenger RNA, it should produce the formation of a polypeptide comprising an in indefinite repetition of the same aminoacid. The fundamental experiment of Nirenberg and Matthaei (1961) did indeed show that poly U was able to function as a messenger RNA, and lead to the synthesis of polyphenylalanine; the molecular weight of the poly U used was 30,000 to 50,000 (Nirenberg et al., 1962) :

	triplet			
... pU	pU pU pU	pU pU pU	pU pU pU	pU ...
....	... Phe ...	... Phe ...	... Phe ...	....

This experiment was the point of departure for many spectacular studies in which biosynthetic polymers of known total composition were used as artificial messenger RNAs in cell-free systems; preferential incorporation of particular individual labeled aminoacids into material of a protein nature has been observed in such cases, the peptide being precipitated in acid medium.

The cell-free systems utilized generally involve *E. coli* ribosomes together with a high-speed supernatant from disintegrated *coli* in order to supply a transfer RNA system, the aminoacyl-t-RNA synthetases and the enzymes being involved in the later stages of protein synthesis. This cell-free medium is then supplemented with the aminoacids, ATP, GTP, salts and t-RNA. In order to observe the effect of synthetic polynucleotides (artificial m-RNA) on the incorporation into proteins of a given aminoacid, the aminoacid in question is labeled with ^{14}C and is present in the medium together the 19 other unlabeled aminoacids. The incorporation into protein of the labeled aminoacid is measured by acid precipitation of the proteins, washing and counting the radioactivity of the precipitate.

The only biosynthetic polymers in which the sequence was unambiguously known at that time were homopolymers involving only one type of nucleotide. Experiments with these homopolymers have successively shown that poly U controls the incorporation of phenylalanine (Nirenberg and Matthaei, 1961) and, to a lesser extent, leucine, poly A controls the incorporation of lysine (Gardner et al., 1962), poly C controls the incorporation of proline and poly G controls the incorporation of glycine (Nirenberg et al., 1965).

The situation becomes more complicated with mixed polymers involving 2, 3 or 4 types of different nucleotides, where one only knows by analysis the exact ratio of the constituent bases, for example A/U = 2/1 or U/C = 3/2, etc.

The activity of these mixed polymers must be determined with statistical assistance. Let us suppose that a copolymer contains U and C in the ratio 2/1. Statistically it may be likened to letters mixed at random in a hat in the proportion of 2 U for every one C. If we now draw three letters from the hat to form a triplet, there are two chances in three of drawing one U, and one chance in three of drawing a C. The chances of forming the triplet UUC are therefore.

$$\frac{2}{3} \times \frac{2}{3} \times \frac{1}{3} = \frac{4}{27}$$

The frequency of the triplet UUC in the chain will therefore be $\frac{4}{27}$, as will be the frequency of the two other triplets having two Us and a C. The distribution of possible frequencies for the eight different triplets corresponding to U/C = 2/1 is the following :

$$2\ U\ 1\ C \quad \begin{cases} U\ U\ C \\ U\ C\ U \\ C\ U\ U \end{cases} \quad 3\left[\frac{2}{3} \times \frac{2}{3} \times \frac{1}{3}\right] = \frac{4}{27} \times 3 = \frac{12}{27}$$

$$3\ U \qquad\quad U\ U\ U \qquad\quad \frac{2}{3} \times \frac{2}{3} \times \frac{2}{3} = \frac{8}{27} \times 1 = \frac{8}{27}$$

$$2\ C\ 1\ U \quad \begin{cases} C\ C\ U \\ C\ U\ C \\ U\ C\ C \end{cases} \quad 3\left[\frac{1}{3} \times \frac{1}{3} \times \frac{2}{3}\right] = \frac{2}{27} \times 3 = \frac{6}{27}$$

$$3\ C \qquad\quad C\ C\ C \qquad\quad \frac{1}{3} \times \frac{1}{3} \times \frac{1}{3} = \frac{1}{27} \times 1 = \frac{1}{27}$$

It can be seen that the 2U 1C polymer has a high chance of stimulating leucine incorporation (2U 1C) and phenylalanine (3U), but very small chance of stimulating proline incorporation (3C).

The correlation between the relative abundance of the triplets forming various biosynthetic polynucleotides and the aminoacid incorporation stimulated by these nucleotides (see table V), has allowed some preliminary decoding of the genetic code to be made by several groups of workers:

Table V. Correlation of relative triplet abundance
with the incorporation of aminoacids promoted by some polynucleotides (Ochoa, 1964)

Polynucleotide	Triplets	Rel. abundance of each triplet	Rel. aminoacid incorporation
Poly UG (5 : 1)	UUU	100	Phe, 100
	UUG, UGU, GUU	20	Cys, 20; val, 20
	UGG, GUG, GGU	4	Gly, 4; try, 5
	GGG	0.8	
Poly AC (5 : 1)	AAA	100	Lys, 100
	AAC, ACA, CAA	20	Asn, 30; thr, 23; glu, 44
	ACC, CAC, CCA	4	Pro, 5
	CCC	0.8	
Poly CG (5 : 1)	CCC	100	Pro, 100
	CCG, CGC, GCC	20	Ala, 22; arg, 19
	CGG, GCG, GGC	4	Gly, 5
	GGG	0.8	

Nirenberg and co-workers (Nirenberg and Matthaei, 1961; Nirenberg et al., 1962; Martin et al., 1962; Nirenberg et al., 1963), Ochoa and co-workers (Speyer et al., 1962a, b; Lengyel et al., 1962a, b; Gardner et al., 1962; Wahba et al., 1962; 1963; Ochoa, 1964a, b; etc.), Bretscher and Grunberg-Manago (1962), Crick (1962a, b), etc.

The code developed as a result of this work gave the overall composition of the triplets fitting each aminoacid without consideration of the interior sequence within the triplets. All the first codons discovered contained uracil, which did not at first seem entirely logical, and caused many criticisms (Chargaff, 1962; Reichmann et al., 1962); it rapidly became apparent that there were more codons possible than there were aminoacids available. The discovery of these additional codons obliged all the protagonists of the code theory to consider the genetic code as "degenerate", since the same message can apparently be transmitted by several different codes. Even now, the problem of the code degeneracy has not yet found a satisfactory solution.

So far as the nucleotide sequence within the triplets is concerned, only the use of nucleotides of known sequence can provide the complete answer to the structure of the different codons.

A preliminary series of experiments in this direction was carried out by Wahba et al. (1962) using as artificial m-RNA polynucleotides beginning with the sequences :

$$ApUpUpUpU \ldots \ldots \rightarrow (Tyr - phe - phe - phe...)$$
$$GpUpUpUpU \ldots \ldots \rightarrow (Cys - phe - phe - phe...)$$

These polynucleotides were obtained by the action of the polynucleotide phosphorylase in the presence of a primer that starts with the same sequence.

The first nucleotide just mentioned was believed to stimulate the incorporation of tyrosine as well as phenylalanine, and the second a small amount of cysteine as well as phenylalanine, from which the authors concluded that the tyrosine code was AUU and the cysteine code was GUU. Later experiments did not confirm this hypothesis (see table VI).

The use of short-sequence oligonucleotides finally led to the elucidation of many codon sequences.

J. D. Smith (1964) was able to show that peptide synthesis in a cell-free system could be realized by using as genetic information that which was supplied by short chain-length oligonucleotides. The oligonucleotides used in J. D. Smith's experiments were obtained by controlled alkaline hydrolysis of poly A, removal of the 3' - and 5'-phosphate groups with *E. coli* phosphomonoesterase and chromatography on a column of DEAE-cellulose eluting with a triethylamine carbonate gradient (pH 7.8) containing urea (7 M).

Polynucleotides containing 7, 8 or 9 adenine residues promoted the incorporation of small amounts of ^{14}C-lysine into the following polypeptides : di-, tri- and tetralysine; even smaller amounts of dilysine were synthesized in the presence of hexaadenylic acid, while the pentanucleotide was inactive. In the course of one experiment using octaadenylic acid, a small amount of ^{14}C-pentalysine could be observed. It was suggested that the explanation of the fact that such short oligonucleotides can function as messenger RNA is that an isolated ribosome would be able to fit more than one short polymer and "read" them consecutively; alternatively, it could be that each triplet in the homopolymers, where each base belongs to the same triplet, can slide over the surface and be read several times.

Following this idea, Nirenberg and Leder (1964) prepared uridyl oligonucleotides of variable chain-length, and showed that these favor the linking of phenylalanyl-t-RNA on the ribosomes. For example, the effect of the trinucleotide pUpUpU on the ^{14}C-Phe-t-RNA to ribosome link was examined at 0°, 24° and 37°, and it was found that the trinucleotide promoted the fixation of ^{14}-C-Phe-t-RNA on the ribosomes, although the reaction was optimal at 24°, over 20-30 minutes. The fixation of ^{14}C-Phe, ^{14}CLys and ^{14}C-Pro was induced apparently specifically by pUpUpU ApApA and pCpCpC respectively. In the course of blank experiments, Nirenberg and Leder, noted that the same trinucleotides are without effect on the linkages between ribosomes and 15 other aminoacyl-t-RNA preparations, each one carrying a different ^{14}C-aminoacid. It would therefore seem that the specificity of each trinucleotide in promoting the fixation of a t-RNA on the ribosomes is high, and corresponds to that of the derived polynucleotide.

These results show that a simple trinucleotide can direct the fixing of an aminoacyl-t-RNA on the ribosomes specifically, and suggests a general method of great simplicity for the precise determination of the genetic role played by each trinucleotide sequence. Logically, all that should be necessary is the isolation in the pure state of all the trinucleotides of known sequence, and the examination of their influence on the fixation of various aminoacyl-t-RNA on the ribosomes. Triplets with a 5′-phosphate group (pUpUpU) are more active than the triplets without a terminal phosphoryl group (UpUpU). Triplets with a phosphate group in the 3′-position (UpUpUp) or bearing a 2′ : 3′ cyclic terminal phosphate are distinctly less active.

Table VI. Nucleotide Sequences of RNA Codons (Nirenberg et al. 1965)

UpUpU	Phe	UpCpU	Ser	UpGpU	Cys	UpApU	Tyr
UpUpC		UpCpC		UpGpC		UpApC	
UpUpA	Leu	UpCpA	Ser	UpGpA	Nonsense*	UpApA	Nonsense †
UpUpG		UpCpG		UpGpG	or Trypt	UpApG	
CpUpU	Leu or	CpCpU	Pro	CpGpU	Arg	CpApU	His
CpUpC	Nonsense*	CpCpC		CpGpC		CpApC	
CpUpA	Leu	CpCpA	Pro	CpGpA	Arg	CpApA	Glu-NH₂
CpUpG		CpCpG		CpGpG		CpApG	
ApUpU	Ileu	ApCpU	Thr	ApGpU	Ser	ApApU	Asp-NH₂
ApUpC		ApCpC		ApGpC		ApApC	
ApUpA	Met	ApCpA	Thr	ApGpA	Arg. or	ApApA	Lys
ApUpG		ApCpG		ApGpG	Nonsense*	ApApG	
GpUpU	Val	GpCpU	Ala	GpGpU	Gly	GpApU	Asp
GpUpC		GpCpC		GpGpC		GpApC	
GpUpA	Val	GpCpA	Ala	GpGpA	Gly	GpApA	Glu
GpUpG		GpCpG		GpGpG		GpApG	

* It is possible that these sequences are readable internal-, but nonreadable terminal-, codons.
† UpApA and UpApG may correspond to Terminator-, or Ser-codons in different strains of *E. coli*.

   Summary and predictions : The template activities of trinucleotides in *ITALICS* have been studied experimentally in this system. Other sequences are predicted. Although trinucleotides are arranged in pairs, one member of a pair may have greater template activity than the other. Estimates of relative template efficiencies are not indicated.

Aminoacid replacement data used for these predictions were obtained with *E. coli* by Yanofsky, (1963) or were induced by HNO₂ in TMV by Wittmann and Wittman-Liebold (1963) or Tsugita (cf. Nirenberg et al. 1965).

The systematic study of the influence of the various triplets on the fixation of aminoacyl-t-RNA to ribosomes (Leder and Nirenberg, 1964; Bernfield and Nirenberg, 1965; Nirenberg et al., 1965) is considered as evidence for the genetic function of these triplets, and has been supported by the data obtained by replacement of the aminoacids of *coli* and TMV mutants; this has enabled Nirenberg and his colleagues to assign a genetic function to 45 of the 64 possible triplets (see table VI). At the present time, not only is the overall composition of the codons known, but also their sequence, and if we add to that the fact that the code is read from the 3′-hydroxyl end to the 5′-hydroxyl end (Eikenberry and Rich, 1965), we can see that the decyphering of the genetic code is advancing at a rapid pace, thanks to the patient work undertaken by outstanding scientific teams.

Nonetheless, some ambiguities remain, and a more exact control of the pH conditions and the t-RNA concentration in the incubation medium might go a long way to remove them (Grunberg-Manago and Dondon, 1965).

On the other hand, it is not illogical to find more than one codon corresponding to a single aminoacid, since we have seen that several different t-RNAs can correspond to the same aminoacid. It is not impossible that these various t-RNAs, although they correspond to the same aminoacid, carry different anticodons. Experiments carried out by Weisblum et al. (1965) have tended to prove this; these authors isolated the different t-RNA corresponding to leucine incorporation by counter-current distribution, then doubly labeled the t-RNAs thus obtained. ³H-Leucine was attached to "peak 1 t-RNA" and ¹⁴C-leucine was attached to "peak 11B t-RNA" .These two fractions were mixed and transfered in hemoglobine *in vitro*. The authors subsequently showed that the two fractions distributed leucine in different places along the hemoglobin chain synthesized, by analyzing the aminoacid composition of the peptides obtained by trypsin hydrolysis of the chain. This result confirms the fact that there are at least two different leucine codons.

Further recent work by Grunberg-Manago, Michelson and their co-workers (Grunberg-Manago and Michelson, 1964; Pochon et al., 1964; Grunberg-Manago and Michelson, 1964; Michelson and Grunberg-Manago, 1964) concerning the genetic information supplied by polynucleotide analogs has brought to light some fresh aspects of the genetic code. Grunberg-Manago, Michelson et al. have shown that various synthetic polymers, such as polybromouridylic acid (poly BrU), polyiodouridylic acid (poly IU), polychlorouridylic acid (poly ClU) were all active in phenylalanine incorporation *in vitro* in the same system as was used for poly U (defined on p. 57). It was also found that poly BrU is not only active in phenylalanine incorporation, but also in Leu and Ileu incorporation, and to a lesser extent, Ser.

Polybromocytidylic acid (poly-5-BrC) promotes proline incorporation more efficiently than poly C.

In the course of the same work, polypseudouridylic acid (poly ΨU) and copolymers poly ΨU -poly U were synthesised. It was found that the homopolymer poly ΨU does not promote Phe incorporation, but that ΨU/U, 1 : 2.5 is active. Contrary to the other halogenated polymers, polyfluorouridylic acid (poly FU) promotes but Phe incorporation to the exclusion of other aminoacids.

Work on the code is at present in full spate, and it continues to raise considerable interest in the scientific world, from pure chemists to geneticists. Many points must still be cleared up, especially those concerning the mechanism of the enzymic reactions which control a process whose complexity we are now able to realize.

Table VII. Purine and pyrimidine ratios of some DNAs

DNA source	A	G	C	T	M*	$\dfrac{A+T}{C+G(+M)}$	Methods**	Authors
Human { thymus	10	6.4	6.3	9.4		1.53	a	Chargaff and Lipshitz (1953)
Human { spleen	10	7.2	7.0	10.1		1.41	b	Hurst, Marko and Butler (1953)
Bovine { thymus 1	10	7.3	7.3	9.8		1.35	a	Chargaff and Lipshitz (1953)
thymus 2	10	7.6	7.2	9.5	0.6	1.27	b	Sinsheimer and Koerner (1952b)
thymus 3	10	8.7	8.2	10.4		1.21	b	Hurst, Marko and Butler (1953)
liver	10	7.2	7.2	10.1		1.39	a	Chargaff and Lipshitz (1953)
pancreas	10	7.7	7.9	10.2		1.31	b	Husrt, Marko and Butler (1953)
spleen	10	7.5	7.4	10.0	0.5	1.30	a	Wyatt (1951)
testes	10	8.5	8.2	10.3		1.24	b	Hurst, Marko and Butler (1953)
sperm	10	7.7	7.3	9.5	0.5	1.26	a	Wyatt (1951)
Ovidae { thymus	10	7.3	7.2	9.7		1.36	a	Chargaff and Lipshitz (1953)
liver	10	7.1	7.1	10.0		1.45	a	—
sperm	10	7.6	7.2	9.5	0.3	1.28	a	Wyatt (1951)
Pig { thymus	10	6.8	6.9	9.6		1.43	a	Chargaff and Lipshitz (1953)
liver	10	7.0	7.0	10.1		1.44	a	—
Rat, medulla	10	7.5	7.1	10.0	0.4	1.33	a	Wyatt (1951)
Hen, blood	10	7.8	7.6	10.2		1.32	b	Hurst, Marko and Butler (1953)
Herring, sperm	10	7.7	7.2	9.6	0.6	1.26	a	Wyatt (1951)
Locusta migratoria (whole)	10	7.0	7.1	10.0		1.42	a	—
Arbacia lixula sperm	10	6.1	6.1	9.8		1.62	a	Chargaff, Lipshitz and Green (1952)
Arbacia punctulata sperm	10	7.0	6.4	10.1		1.40	a	Marshak and Vogel (1951)
Asterias forbesii sperm	10	6.9	6.2	9.1		1.46	a	—
Echinocardium cordatum sperm	10	5.2	5.5	9.8		1.85	a	Chargaff, Lipshitz and Green (1952)
Echinus esculentus sperm	10	6.3	6.0	9.5	0.5	1.52	a	Wyatt (1951)

								Reference
Paracentrotus lividus sperm	10	5.4	5.4	9.7		1.82	a	Chargaff, Lipshitz and Green (1952)
Psammechinus miliaris sperm	10	5.5	5.5	9.8		1.80	a	—
Wheat germ	10	8.9	6.5	10.2	2.2	1.16	a	Wyatt (1951)
Yeast	10	6.5	4.6	9.8		1.78	a	Vischer, Zamenhof and Chargaff (1949)
Mycobacterium } var. *hominis*	10	15.8	18.6	10.5		0.60	a	Smith and Wyatt (1951)
tuberculosis } var. *bovis*	10	16.6	19.0	10.7		0.58	a	
Mycobacterium avium	10	25.8	17.5	8.2		0.42	a	Vischer, Zamenhof and Chargaff (1949)
Bacillus Schatz	10	14.6	16.2	9.4		0.63	a	Zamenhof, Brawerman and Chargaff (1952)
Escherichia coli { B/r	10	10.9	11.4	12.1		0.99	a	Smith and Wyatt (1951)
K 12	10	9.5	8.7	9.2		1.00	a	Gandelman, Zamenhof and Chargaff (1952)
U Q	10	9.7	10.0	9.3		0.98	a	—
Thymineless	10	9.5	10.1	9.7		1.00	a	—
Hemophilus influenzae type C	10	5.7	6.1	9.5		1.65	a	Zamenhof, Brawerman and Chargaff (1952)
Serratia marcescens	10	13.2	15.4	9.7		0.69	a	—
E. coli { T 5	10	6.4	6.4	10.1		1.57	a	Wyatt and Cohen (1953)
bacteriophages { T 2 r+	10	5.6		10.0	*5.1	1.87	a	—
T 2 r	10	5.6		10.0	*5.2	1.85	a	—
T 6 r+	10	5.6		10.0	*5.1	1.87	a	—

* M indicates methylcytosine; when the value is preceded by an asterisk read 'hydroxymethylcytosine' instead of 'methylcytosine'.

** The purine and pyrimidine bases were analysed by two main methods that may be summarized briefly as follows:

1) Acid hydrolysis of DNA and separation of bases by paper chromatography. This method was described by Chargaff and his co-workers, and widely used by them and others (Vischer and Chargaff, 1947, 1948a, b; Chargaff Vischer, Doniger, Green and Misani, 1949; Chargaff, Lipshitz, Green and Hodes, 1951). Roughly, the method is to liberate the purines by N H_2SO_4 (1 hr. at 100°) and chromatograph them in a solvent system consisting of *n*-butanol, diethyleneglycol and water in an ammonia atmosphere; the pyrimidines are liberated with concentrated formic acid (2 hr. at 175°) after having removed the purines as hydrochlorides by treatment with methanolic HCl, then chromatographed in aqueous butanol. Wyatt et al. (Wyatt, 1951; Smith and Wyatt, 1951; Wyatt and Cohen, 1953) used a similar method: formic or perchloric acid hydrolysis of DNA and separation of the purine and pyrimidine bases by a single paper chromatography.

2) Enzymatic DNA hydrolysis by pancreatic DNase and phosphodiesterase (the latter being free of phosphomonoesterase), separation of the mononucleotides thereby obtained by chromatography on Dowex 1, and analysis of mononucleotides by spectrophotometry (Sinsheimer and Koerner, 1951, 1952b; Hurst, Marko and Butler, 1953). The separation of the four mononucleotides can also be effected by paper electrophoresis and elution of the corresponding zones

IV. PROPERTIES OF DEOXYRIBONUCLEIC ACIDS

A. NUCLEOTIDE CONSTITUTION AND SPATIAL ARRANGEMENT

Deoxyribonucleic acids (DNA), isolated from such differing sources as thymus, wheat germ, bacteria, bacteriophages and spermatozoa, always have the aspect of fibrous white masses. These fibres dissolve slowly in distilled water to give very viscous solutions.

Herskovits et al. (1961) have reported that it is possible to obtain partial alcohol solution of DNA by dialysis of aqueous DNA solutions against aqueous alcoholic solutions of increasing alcohol concentration. Furthermore, in the form of the quaternary ammonium salt, DNA becomes soluble in a large number of organic solvents. This quite remarkable property has been examined by Aubel-Sadron et al. (Aubel-Sadron et al., 1960; Hirth et al., 1960; Aubel-Sadron et al., 1961) who showed that in the first stage it is possible to precipitate the deoxy- and ribonucleic acids by a certain number of quaternary ammonium salts and then to dissolve the quaternary ammonium nucleates obtained in many polar organic solvents. The sodium salts of the nucleic acids may then be regenerated by addition of sodium chloride to the organic solutions.

In the dry state, DNA behaves like a semi-conductor (Mesnard and Vasilescu, 1963).

Festy et al. (1965) have obseved that DNA is able to form beryllium complexes that are able considerably to raise the molecular weight of DNA. The DNA that is complexed with beryllium becomes resistent to the action of DNase.

The relative amounts of different nucleotides present in a DNA are usually expressed in the form of purine and pyrimidine bases, or as the ratio $\dfrac{A + T}{G + C}$ and have been studied by many workers; table VII gives the values obtained over the past twenty years. In view of the precision of modern methods (paper chromatography of the bases after acid hydrolysis of the DNA or ion exchange chromatography of the nucleotides obtained by enzymic hydrolysis of DNA), these results can be considered quite valid, and it is esthetically satisfying to note the near identity of the figures obtained in different laboratories, as it is to see the constancy of the $\dfrac{A + T}{G + C}$ ratio throughout almost the whole of the animal kingdom. We shall shortly see the importance this ratio bears in relation to the DNA spatial configuration.

The spatial configuration of DNA has been studied by many authors and has been the source of many theories. Pauling and Corey (1953a, b) proposed the first scheme whereby the DNA was postulated to consist of nucleotide chains linked together by 3', 5'-phosphodiester bonds to form a helix in space turning in a right-handed screw direction. The phosphorylated groups were arranged together about the molecular axis and surrounded by the pentose residues, the purine and pyrimidine bases being projected radially so that their molecular planes were approximately perpendicular to the screw axis of the DNA molecule. In order to progress from one residue to the next along the molecular chain, a rotation of 105° and a translation of 3.4 Å had to be effected.

Watson and Crick (1953a, b) criticized the Pauling and Corey hypothesis and proposed an alternative scheme for the DNA spatial configuration that has met with great success (Fig. 5).

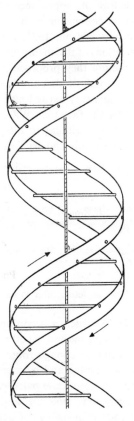

Figure 5. Watson and Crick's helices. The two ribbons represent the two phosphate-pentose chains and the horizontal bars the pairs of bases holding the chains together. The vertical line represents the axis of the strand (after Watson and Crick, 1953a, b)

This structure involves two helical chains wound round the same axis, and assumes the 3′, 5′-phosphodiester bond in accord with currently accepted chemical data. The novelty of this structure lies in the way the two chains are held together by the purine and pyrimidine bases which are joined in pairs, a base of the first chain being hydrogen-bonded to a base in the second chain. In order for these bonds to exist, the pair must be formed from a purine on one side and a pyrimidine on the other. The hydrogen bonds are made from the purine-1 position to the pyrimidine-1 position, and purine-6 to pyrimidine-6. The pairs are then : adenine (purine) coupled with thymine (pyrimidine) on one hand, and guanine coupled with cytosine on the other. The base-pairing concept is in full agreement with many observations, particularly from Chargaff's laboratory (Chargaff, 1950; Chargaff and Lipshitz, 1953), showing that the ratio of the adenine and thymine amounts, as well as the ratio of guanine and cytosine, is about unity. Experiments undertaken in Kornberg's (Josse et al., 1961) and Chargaff's laboratories (Chargaff et al., 1965) have demonstrated that the two strands forming the double helix are antiparallel.

The X-ray diagrams published before the appearance of the Watson and Crick theory were not sufficient to explain the theory in a convincing manner, but later experiments are generally compatible with it (Wilkins, Stokes and Wilson, 1953, Franklin and Gosling, 1953; Wilkins and Randall, 1953). The genetic implications of this theory were discussed by the authors themselves (Watson and Crick, 1953b). The structure they proposed is compatible with auto-reproduction of the molecule. It was first necessary to show that the fibers obtained in the course of DNA isolation corresponded to structures that really existed and not to artefacts of the preparation. The latter possibility was eliminated by the fact that Wilkins et al. obtained X-ray pictures of DNA isolated by chemical means that were similar to those made with DNA in certain intact biological materials such as spermatozoa heads and bacteriophages.

$$
\begin{array}{cc}
\text{Sugar—Base . . . Base—Sugar} \\
\diagup \qquad\qquad \diagdown \\
\text{Phosphate} \qquad\qquad \text{Phosphate} \\
\diagdown \qquad\qquad \diagup \\
\text{Sugar—Base . . . Base—Sugar} \\
\diagup \qquad\qquad \diagdown \\
\text{Phosphate} \qquad\qquad \text{Phosphate} \\
\diagdown \qquad\qquad \diagup \\
\text{Sugar—Base . . . Base—Sugar} \\
\diagup \qquad\qquad \diagdown \\
\text{Phosphate} \qquad\qquad \text{Phosphate}
\end{array}
$$

Figure 6. Detail of the DNA structure after Watson and Crick (1953a, b).

Figure 6 shows a detail of the DNA structure according to Watson and Crick. It may be seen that one member of the pair must be a purine and the other a pyrimidine, since if both members of the pair were purines, there would not be enough room for them. The pairing always takes place between adenine and thymine or guanine and cytosine. The phosphate-sugar skeleton of the model shown is regular, but any sequence of base pairs will fit this structure; as a result, very many permutations are possible in a very long molecule, and it would therefore seem likely that the precise sequence of bases is the code responsible for genetic information. It can indeed be imagined that if one knew the order of the bases in one chain, one could immediately deduce the corresponding order on the other chain from which one might arrive at the possibility of duplicating the molecule and the " template " concept, which has been for a long time already under serious consideration. Duplication of the molecule presupposes that the two strands can separate, i.e. can uncoil and then coil up again. The problem of uncoiling of the chains, like that of the uncoiling and coiling of the chromosomes — the latter reproducing on a microscopic scale what happens on the molecular scale with the nucleic acids — has not yet found a satisfactory solution. In any case, the " genetic message " is transmitted from parent to progeny by means of these polynucleotide chains that remain intact through generations.

The series of short communications published in 1953 by Watson, Crick and Wilkins contained an exact account of the double-stranded DNA structure; this discovery is the most brilliant single scientific contribution of the 20th century (Edsall, 1962) and has resulted in a just reward for its authors in the shape of the Nobel Prize for Medicine-Physiology in 1962. The vast amount of work published since Watson and Crick's theory has confirmed the structural scheme they proposed, and directed other workers in the field of chemical mechanisms of transmission of heredity and in the field of molecules with genetic continuity towards the nucleic acids, instead of the proteins which had been wrongly considered for some time to be the molecules with auto-duplicative properties.

Watson and Crick's theory also focussed attention on the importance of helical structures in biology. In the compass of this book it is impossible to describe all the work carried out on the DNA structure that has appeared since the theory, but mention must be made of the initial observations of Wilkins (1961) on the molecular configuration of DNA by means of X-ray analysis.

The DNA structure has also been examined by small-angle X-ray diffraction by Luzzati et al. (Luzzati and Nicolaieff, 1959, Luzzati, 1961, Luzzati et al., 1961, Luzzati et al., 1962). They showed that DNA existed in the form of long rigid rods whose linear mass is the same in dilute solution as in concentrated gel. The whole of the DNA (at least 90 %) adopts the rod structure in solution, the dimensions being the same as those of Watson and Crick's model. Ion distribution in the solution is strongly perturbed in the vicinity of the DNA molecules; this has resulted in the conclusion that there is a layer of water around each molecule that is impenetrable to ions.

Bradbury et al. (1961) have examined the infra-red spectrum of DNA, all the molecules being oriented in the same direction by spreading a gel on a plate. The spectra obtained vary with the amount of moisture in the preparation; this fact is compatible with a greater or lesser angle between the plane of the purine and pyrimidine bases and their normal angle subtended with the helical axis (see p. 131).

DNA autoreproduction has been elegantly demonstrated in *Escherichia coli* by Meselson and Stahl (1958) by means of experiments using ^{15}N. They initially labeled the bacterial DNA uniformly with nitrogen-^{15}N, and then allowed the labeled bacteria to grow in a medium that now only contained nitrogen-^{14}N. Sedimentation in a CsCl gradient made it possible for Meselson and Stahl to isolate DNA molecules of different densities as the cell multiplication progressed. The results obtained clearly showed that the DNA nitrogen divided equally into two sub-units that were physically continuous. At the next duplication, each daughter-molecule receives one of the sub-units, the sub-units being preserved through many duplications, but at each dupli-cation, the amount of nitrogen-^{15}N is divided by two with respect to the total DNA nitrogen.

The action of heat on macromolecular DNA in solution results in its reversible inactivation the by uncoiling the double helix with passage of the DNA from the doubly stranded to the single-stranded state. This phenomenon corresponds to the "denaturation" of DNA, and accom-panies marked changes in several fundamental properties of DNA such as viscosity, extinction cœfficient, light scattering and optical rotation. The phenomenon the most frequently examined is the variation of extinction cœfficient with temperature, since it is relatively simple to measure the optical density of a DNA solution in a buffer at pH 7.0 in a uniformly increasing or decreasing temperature gradient. The observed changes, signaled by a rise in the optical density (read, for example, at constant wave-length of 260 mμ) correspond to the transition of the molecule from the double helical stage to that of a random coil. When the starting material is entirely in the double-stranded form, the transition occurs over a narrow range of temperature and may be characterized by an inflection on the Tm (melting temperature) curve. Many experiments of this kind have been carried out by Marmur, Doty and co-workers (Marmur and Doty, 1959, 1961; Marmur et al., 1961), where they have plotted a curve such as the one shown in fig. 7 of relative absorbance of DNA solutions versus temperature; it is apparent that the least stable constructions with a low Tm are the richest in A-T, the constructions rich in GC being the most stable, to such an extent that there is a linear rise observed in the denaturation temperature with respect to the GC content (Marmur and Doty, 1959, figure 8), and that this property may be used to determine the GC content of a DNA if its denaturation point is known. This was the method used by Russel and Crawford for determining that herpetic virus DNA contained 67-68 % G + C, knowing that its Tm was 97° (Russel and Crawford, 1963).

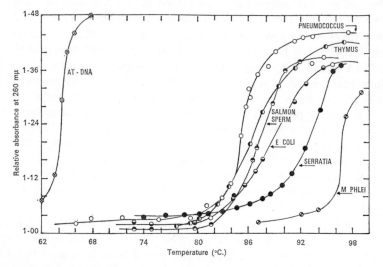

Figure 7. Variation in absorbance (260 mμ) as a function of the temperature of the deoxyribonucleic acid solution. The result for bacteriophage T^4r deoxyribonucleic acid is not plotted because of serious overlap with *D. pneumoniae*. It was sharper and had *Tm* equal to 84°. In all cases the solvent was 0.15 *M* sodium citrate. The samples of bacterial deoxyribonucleic acid were deproteinized by successive mild shaking with chloroform and isoamyl alcohol. The samples of animal deoxyribonucleic aeid were prepared by the Simmons technique using detergents. The bacteriophage T^4r deoxyribonucleic acid was a gift from Mr. J. Fleichman (Marmur and Doty, 1959).

The phenomenon of reversible thermal denaturation of DNA is particularly apparent when DNA with transforming properties (see below, p. 75) is used, since this enables the biological activity of the DNA to be measured at any time. Rownd et al. (1961) observed that the double-stranded to single-stranded transition did not result in total inactivation, but to molecules with only a low level of activity, of the order of 1/10 to a few percent of the initial activity. The same authors have also shown that by slow cooling the denaturation process can be reversed and the DNA " renatured ". In the course of this renaturation, the DNA recovers its helical structure and its biological activity. The restoring of the transforming activity of the DNA increases linearly with the percentage re-winding of the helices.

The reconstitution of the initial configuration of the DNA depends on its origin (Marmur and Doty, 1961). DNA from mammals derived from DNA-rich cells is weakly renatured, whilst bacterial DNA from cells with a low DNA content is considerably renatured. In the case of the small bacteria and bacteriophages, having the lowest DNA content of all, their DNA renaturation is found to be almost total.

These phenomena of uncoiling and recombination of the DNA in its double helix are further illustrated by experiments on the formation of the DNA hydrid from a so-called "heavy" chain containing nitrogen-^{15}N and deuterium, and a light chain arising from normal DNA. Formation of a hybrid is only possible if the bases participating in the constitution of the artificially paired chains are distributed in analogous proportions. Only genetically similar microorganisms, therefore, possess a DNA that is capable *in vitro* of forming a hybrid by thermal denaturation and subsequent recombination.

If all these required conditions are fulfilled, a mixture of a bacterial DNA labeled with heavy isotopes and a normal DNA is submitted to a cycle of heating (DNA "fusion") and recombination, treated with *E. coli* phosphodiesterase (Lehman, 1960) to selectively eliminate the residual unpaired single-stranded DNA, and finally examined by ultracentrifugation in a cesium chloride gradient (cf. p. 149); 3 fractions are obtained in this manner, forming three distinct bands corresponding respectively to the three renatured DNAs, heavy, hybrid and light. In accord with reasonable expectation, the amount of hybrid is twice that of the other two categories.

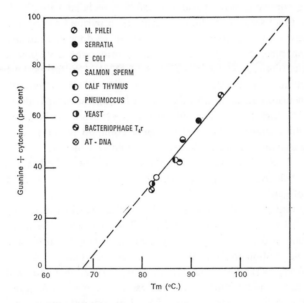

Figure 8. Dependence of the denaturation temperature, *Tm*, on the guanine-cytosine content of various samples of deoxyribonucleic acid (Marmur and Doty, 1959).

The problem of the nucleotide sequence within the DNA chain remains one of the most important of present-day biochemistry, and it may well remain an question unanswered for a long time, considering that there are nearly 20,000 nucleotides in a DNA molecule with a molecular weight of 6 million.

The large amount of work on the controlled degradation of DNA and the formation of purine-free and pyrimidine-free acids (cf. p. 119) undertaken by Chargaff and his co-workers has resulted in the isolation of pyrimidine and purine polynucleotides where the same nucleotide comes in a continuous succession, such as polythymidyl groups like thymidyl hexa- or even heptanucleotides. These polythymidylic acids naturally have their polyadenylic opposite number in the paired antiparallel chain, just as the poly C groups have their opposite poly G. The study of pyrimidine sequences from ΦX 174 DNA that Hall and Sinsheimer (1963) obtained after controlled acid degradation, isolation and characterization of the "isopliths"* chromatographically, showed that the experimentally observed distribution is little different from what would be calculated for random distribution.

The corollary to this study of pyrimidine nucleotide isopliths from ΦX was undertaken on the purine nucleotide isopliths by Sedat and Sinsheimer (1964) obtained from the same bacteriophage. DNA specifically labeled on the purines was prepared, and this DNA was mixed with thymus carrier-DNA and degraded to the stage of purine nucleotide groups by hydrazinolysis followed by alkaline hydrolysis. The oligonucleotides were then separated by chromatography on DEAE-Sephadex at 55° in a 7 M urea solution buffered with 0.005 M tris-Cl using a linear NaCl gradient 0.01 M $\rightarrow$ 0.48 M. In this way nucleotide isopliths involving up to 12 units were collected, separation into the isoplithic groups being quite remarkable. This experiment shows that the complementary nature generally associated with DNA does not apply to that from ΦX, where there seem to be longer purine than pyrimidine groups.

Surveying all the work Chargaff and his co-workers have done on the distribution of nucleotide isopliths in DNA (Shapiro, et al., 1965), leads to consider the deviation from random distribution of the isopliths observed in various classes of DNA. So far as the bacterial DNAs are concerned, the pyrimidine nucleotide isoplith distribution is not significantly different from a random one, this conclusion agreeing with that of Hall and Sinsheimer concerning ΦX 174 DNA; the difference in DNA extracted from mammalian tissue is more marked. In addition, the work of Chargaff's laboratory suggests the existence of a common factor in all the bacterial DNA preparations examined, namely a high similarity in isoplith frequency.

It is clear that the conclusions are cautious and of somewhat limited extent, but this is because information about the distribution of nucleotide isopliths in various DNAs is not yet adequate for the formulation of general rules.

It is quite likely that physical methods of observation will in future provide valuable help in determining the nucleotide sequences of DNA. The time when the molecule can be photographed sufficiently enlarged will go a long way towards solving the problem.

An important contribution to this type of work has been made by Beer and his co-workers. They have shown (Beer, 1961; Beer and Moudrianakis, 1962) that the DNA structure can be examined with the electron microscope, and have described a method for the transport of natural DNA from its solution to the supporting film without breaking the molecules. Use of a reagent specific for guanine groups — 8-amino-1, 3, 6-naphthalenetrisulfonic acid, itself able to form a uranium salt in turn — has made it possible to label selectively all the guanine nucleotides along the chain. After the action of this label on the DNA and transfer of the marked molecule to the electron microscope, the particular triangular marks corresponding to the reagent selectively attached to the guanyl residues can be seen along the chain (Moudrianakis and Beer, 1964, 1965a, b).

Some natural DNA with a particular composition, like the crab satellite " poly-d-AT " DNA, lends itself more readily to sequence study. Pochon et al. (1965) have in this way found

---

* The terms "isoplith" (Hall and Sinsheimer, 1963) or "isostich" (Shapiro and Chargaff, 1964) have been proposed to designate oligonucleotides of the same length, independent of the interior sequence of these oligonucleotides. For reasons of precedence and euphony, we prefer the term "isoplith".

that this "poly-d-AT" extracted from *Cancer pagurus* mostly consisted of alternating units ... — T — A — T — A — T — A ... with occasionally some G — C units, this satellite DNA from crab having only 1.5 % guanine. The ... T — A — T — A — T — A... alternation was shown by the the fact that the "apurinic DNA" prepared from the total DNA only contained the mononucleotide pTp.

In the crab *Cancer borealis*, Cheng and Sueoka (1964) have been able to show the presence of *d*-AT polymers in various tissues, especially the muscles, liver and eggs, in the same proportion as in the testes where it was originally observed. This particular DNA is, therefore, present both in the female and in the male.

B. MOLECULAR WEIGHT OF THE DEOXYRIBONUCLEIC ACIDS

The problems involved in the determination of DNA molecular weight have given rise to a considerable amount of work, as is apparent from the series of recent reviews such as those published by Schmuaker et al. (1965), Crothers and Zimm (1965), Aten and Cohen (1965), Eigner and Doty (1965) or Josse and Eigner (1966). The literature survey of sedimentation-viscosity data for native DNA alone (Eigner and Doty, 1965) consists of a table listing 126 values, solely for these two types of measurement. In spite of this large amount of work, the results obtained seem to be definite only for a rather limited number of DNAs, namely those of viral origin where it was possible actually to make the molecules visible using an electron microscope, thereby ensuring that their integrity had been maintained during the isolation. Measurements carried out on DNA from higher organisms are still fraught with uncertainties, because it is particularly difficult to isolate intact molecules of DNA from these organisms, partly because of hydrolysis by the nucleolytic enzymes, and partly because of the molecules breakings up under the influence of the mechanical means used in the extraction (*shear forces*). The main methods have been used for the determination of DNA molecular weights have been : *diffusion, light scattering, viscosity, sedimentation* and *length measurement*. Whereas the first four methods are standard classical methods having been used many times not only for nucleic acids but for all other macromolecules, the method employing actual measurement of the molecular length and its use in the computation of the molecular weigth is of recent date, and would seem to have been limited to the nucleic acids. The method has already given rise to a number of important discoveries concerning the conformation and the dimensions of the molecules. The first observations of this type were made by Kleinschmidt and Zahn (1959) on bacteriophage T_2 DNA. Subsequently other DNAs were submitted to similar observations (cf. tables VIII and IX), the molecular length being effected on adequately enlarged photomicrographs. Assuming that the mass per unit length of DNA strands is 1.92×10^6 avograms per mµ, the total molecular weight can be established by a simple calculation. The results that have been recently obtained about DNA molecular weights has necessitated some modifications in ideas that have had almost dogmatic status for a number of years. Classical observations from many different laboratories (e.g. those mentioned in the review by Sadron, 1961) tended to show that the various DNA particles extracted from nucleoproteins of different origins seem ed to be built up from rod-like "sub-units" of equal length (3,000 Å). These rods had the double helical structure of Watson and Crick, and their molecular weight was of the order of 0.5×10^6. These rod elements could then associate to give aggregates, the molecular weight of which could attain almost infinite values. It seemed, however, that the very high molecular weight aggregates were the mostly result of accidental agglomeration through weak protein links

Table VIII. Molecular weights of DNA from higher organisms

Origin	Methods		Molecular weight in million avograms	Authors	Observations
	Preparation of DNA	Determination of molecular weight			
Calf thymus	Generally extraction with salts or detergent, alcohol precipitation	Light scattering Sedimentation Viscosity,.... etc.	6.0	Doty & Bunce (1962); Reichmann et al. (1954); Brown et al. (1955), etc. see. ref. in Eigner & Doty (1965)	This value was considered as truc for many years and corresponds to a degraded but particularly stable form of this DNA
	Saline extraction and alcohol precipitation	Light scattering	16.5	Pouyet et al. (1965)	
	Extraction with detergent and alcohol precipitation	Sedimentation	17.3–63 (mean 50)	Aten & Cohen(1965)	
Boar sperm	Ext. of DNA and elim. of proteins by pronase. No precipitation of DNA	Sedimentation	1-33	Hotta & Bassel (1965)	Samples of pig DNA contain circles of various dimensions; 190 of these circles were measured and the lengths ranged from 0.5 to 9.7 μ, i.e. from 1 to 19. 10^6 avograms. The largest circle measured 16.8 μ corresponding to 33.10^6 avograms
Mammalian tumour	Extraction with SDS and phenol at pH 8.0, precipitation with 2-ethoxy-ethanol	Viscosity	130	Tikhonenho et al. (1963)	The DNA obtained had a specific viscosity of about 320 dc/g.
Chicken erythrocytes	Saline extraction then alcohol precipitation	Light scattering	11.6	Pouyet et al. (1956)	
			6.0	Pouyet et al. (1956)	
Trout sperm	Saline extraction then alcohol precipitation DNA isolated under low hydrodynamic shear	Light scattering Sedimentation	60-200	Davison (1960)	The samples prepared under low hydrodynamic shear had a sedimentation constant around 50 S
Honey bee embryonic cells		Examination under electronic microscope		Du Praw (1965)	Chromosomal fibers are single DNA molecules each enclosed in a proteinaceous sheath
Sea urchin (Strongylocentrotus purpuratus) sperm	Isolation of DNA without any mechanical procedure	Length measurement of DNA under electron miscroscope	172	Solari (1965)	Assuming that the state of the DNA in solution was equivalent to the B crystallographic form, DNA units could not be shorter than 90 μ
Wheat nuclei	Extraction of DNA and elimination of proteins by pronase; no precipitation of DNA	Length measurement under electron microscope	61.54	Hotta & Bassel (1965)	One of the molecules of wheat DNA measured 31.4 μ corresponding to the cited molecular weight

Table IX. Molecular weights of DNA from lower organisms : Bacteria and viruses

Origins	Methods — Preparation of DNA	Methods — Molecular weight determination	Molecular weight in million avograms	Authors	Observations
Bacillus subtilis	Careful shear-free isolation	Sedimentation	230	Hanawalt & Ray (1964)	
Escherichia coli chromosomes		Length measurement of DNA	2800	Cairns (1963)	This value was obtained by autoradiography of *E. coli* chromosomes labelled with ^{3}H-thymidine. The DNA of this bacterium is organized as a long duplex molecule. There should exist only one molecule of this type per chromosome.
Hemophilus influenzae, chromosomes	Detergent and phenol	Length measurement of DNA under electron microscope	1500-1600	McHattie et al. (1965)	
PPLO strain H—39		Length measurement	400	Bode & Horowitz (1965) quoted by Josse & Eigner (1966)	Conformation of this DNA : linear, double helical
Bacteriophages of *E. coli* — *E. coli* phage T_2-T_4	Generally : phenol extraction Osmotic shock and spread on a water surface	Viscosity, Sedimentation, Length measurement, Examination under electron microscope	130	Crothers & Zimm (1965); Ris & Chandler (1963); Thomas & McHattie (1964)	
E. coli phage λ			33 for wild λ 27 for λ cb_2	Hershey et al. (1963) Caro (1965)	The DNA of phage λ undergoes reversible transition from linear to characteristically folded molecule. Conformation of this DNA : circular single stranded
E. coli phage Φ X174		Examination under electron microscope	1.6 ± 0.1	Freifelder et al. (1964); Sinsheimer (1959); Eigner et al. (1963)	
Adenovirus type 2	Detergent and phenol	Sedimentation	22.6	Green & Pina (1964)	The value quoted appears to be too large since it leads to unreasonnably high molecular weight for the virus particle
Papilloviridae — *Shope papilloma virus* SPV	Phenol extraction spread in mono layers	Length measurement	5	Kleinschmidt et al. (1965)	The mean length of 261 cyclic molecules of DNA was 2.32 ± 0.14 μ. A ring with a contour length of about 2.5 μ would have a molecular weight of about 5.10^6
Human papilloma virus	Phenol-detergent	Sedimentation	5.3	Crawford (1965)	Conformation of this DNA : circular double helical
Polyoma virus	Detergent-phenol	Sedimentation	3.5	Winocour (1963); Stoeckenius (1965) Crawford (1964); Vinograd et al. (1965)	Circular duplex polyoma virus may be converted to a less compact circular duplex by introducing a single strand scission
Herpes virus — *Herpes virus hominis*	Detergent-phenol	Sedimentation	68	Russell & Crawford (1964)	
H. pseudorabiae	Detergent-phenol	Sedimentation	66	Russell & Crawford (1964)	
H. equi	Detergent-phenol	Sedimentation	84	Russell & Crawford (1964)	
H. rhinotracheitis	Detergent-phenol	Sedimentation	56	Russell & Crawford (1964)	

between particles of unusual stability : the molecular weight of these laying between 6 and 8×10^6. These particles of molecular weight 6 to 8×10^6 were called polytactic and were formed by a succession of about twelve or so units joined together.

According to Cavalieri and co-workers (1961), methods exist of preparing DNA that is neither degraded nor aggregated, and of which the molecular weight is fairly low, of the order of 1.2 — 2.4×10^6. He suggested that the high values often found quoted in the literature are due to the aggregation of several DNA chains by proteins and/or contamination by a bivalent metal. Contamination of DNA by small amounts of protein is, indeed, an old observation (Butler et al., 1957, Hermans, 1958). These conclusions agreed with those of Sponar et al. (1964), who were able to fractionate thymus DNA into a series of relatively homogeneous fractions so far as their molecular parameters were concerned.

It seemed possible that the molecules of astronomical mass that were described in several articles were aggregates of a large number of sub-units, although other authors considered that organisms like the bacteriophages contain only a single enormous molecule of molecular weight 120×10^6 (Thomas and Berns, 1961; Berns and Thomas, 1961) Cairns reported (1962) that the minimum length of E. Coli DNA measured by an auto-radiographic method would imply a molecular weight of at least 10^9. The latest work, however, would appear to support the idea that it is the highest values which are nearest the truth, and even the measurements carried out on DNA from higher organisms show that its molecular weight is generally well above 6×10^6.

In the case of viral particles, on which the most exact determinations can be made (since the DNA can be extracted with the minimum of nucleolytic enzyme attack), each particle only contains a single nucleic acid molecule, the result applying to RNA as well as DNA. By analogy, we should expect that bacterial chromosomes, and by extension also those of higher organisms, will contain only one molecule of DNA per chromosome. The truth of these conclusions is amply illustrated in tables VIII and IX, and it is evident that the older established values corresponded probably to degraded samples, and that even the sacrosanct values of 6 and 12×10^6 for thymus DNA are very doubtful, the currently quoted figures being above 50×10^6, with there being no certainty that they are a maximum. So far as the author is aware, the record is held by the chromosome DNA from the bacterium *Escherichia coli*, for which a value of $2,800 \times 10^6$ has been suggested Cairns (1963).

In contrast to these astronomical figures, it is both comforting and instructive to find that the phage ΦX 174 carries all its genetic information concentrated in a circular single stranded DNA of molecular weight only 1.6×10^6.

C. Function of the Deoxyribonucleic Acids

1. DNA as the Basis of Heredity

The role of DNA in the transmission of heredity has been demonstrated in four series of experiments.

a. *The normal process of cell reproduction*

Every biology student now carries out the classical observation following the fundamental work of T. Morgan fifty years ago; in the course of cell-multiplication it is possible to see under the microscope DNA-rich chromosomes undergo their autoduplication in such a way that the daughter cells possess the same characteristics as the parent cells.   The fact that the chromosomes consist primarily of DNA naturally led to attributing it with a preponderant role in character transmission.   Some excellent reproductions of the phenomena accompanying cell-multiplication can be found in the textbook of Brachet and Mirsky : " The Cell " (1959-1964) as well as in the publications of Ris and Chandler (1963), Cairns (1963), Sueoka and Yoshikawa (1963), etc.

b. *Mutations*

It rapidly became apparent that the so-called "mutagenic" agents, i.e. agents inducing mutations, such as those which can be readily observed on the giant chromosomes of *Drosophila melanogaster*, were all physical or chemical agents inducing an alteration in the DNA structure.   The best known mutagenic agents are :

X-rays. It is known that irradiation of the intact rat thymus or of nucleated erythrocytes results in the depolymerization of DNA in the tissues and cells.

Ultraviolet radiation. The fact that nucleic acids absorb ultraviolet radiation is a proof that the energy supplied by the radiation is used for molecular transformations, and it is in fact found that the most efficient mutagenic rays are those with a wavelength corresponding to the nucleic acid absorption maximum.

Chemical substances.   Mention must be made of acridine and other bases that can form complexes with nucleic acids, and of the substances that are incorrectly called "mustards".   As examples of these substances, two "mustard gases ", a nitrogen mustard and a sulfur mustard, are shown below; they are β-chloroalkylamines or β-chloroalkylsulfides :

$$R_2N - CH_2 - CH_2Cl$$
$$RS - CH_2 - CH_2Cl$$

Mustard derivatives with only one active halogen induce both mutations and depolymerizations of DNA.

The mustards modify the DNA structures because they are alkylating agents reacting mainly with guanine.   This fact was demonstrated particularly by the experiments of Brookes and Lawley (1961), who were able to isolate the alkylated bases after the action of mustards on DNA (and on RNA).   The alkylation occurs on the nitrogen in the 7-position of the guanine, monofunctional alkylating agents resulting in the formation of 7-alkylguanines and bifunctional agents in di-(guanine-7-yl)-derivatives.

Nitrous acid also induces mutations by deaminating the purine and pyrimidine bases.

These examples are sufficient to show clearly that every time the integrity of DNA molecules in a germinal cell is disturbed, serious trouble, or at least considerable changes, are induced in the descendents of this cell.   Evidently, then, DNA are gene-carriers, if not actually the genes themselves.

c. *Transforming agents*

α. Definition and description of bacterial transformations.

In order to prove that DNA was really the gene-carrier, it was necessary to demonstrate that a DNA isolated from cell A was capable of communicating the characters of this A cell to a cell B. Since the classic work of Griffith in 1928, the existence of "transforming factors" in pneumococcal cultures has been known. In brief, Griffith's experiments involved the use of two strains of pneumococcus, one being the "rough" strain (R), and one being a rare mutant leading to an encapsulated strain ("smooth" or S). Bacteria of the S type, after being killed by heat treatment, are still able to induce the appearance of the smooth S type in the R culture. Lacking a more precise explanation, it was postulated that the dead S bacteria had conserved a "transforming factor" capable of acting on the R strain.

Naturally attempts were made to purify this factor, and Avery and his co-workers made a decisive step in genetics history in 1944 when they demonstrated that DNA isolated from pneumococcus strains possessed the characteristics of the transforming agents described by Griffith. The work of Avery et al. may be summarized in figure 9.

Clearly in the course of these experiments, the DNA extracted from an encapsulated pneumococcal strain has transformed the non-encapsulated into an encapsulated strain. Hotchkiss (1955) has pointed out three fundamental aspects of this experiment :

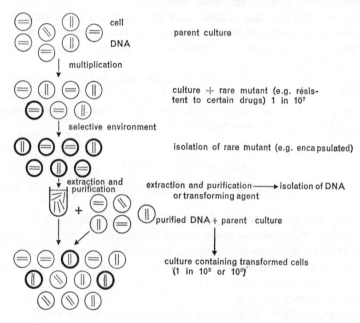

Figure 9. Schematic representation of bacterial transformation

1) The capsule of the new strain consists of the same polysaccharide as the strain from which the DNA was derived.

2) The transformation can be effected on an R strain in which the spontaneous mutation to the S strain has never been observed.

3) The S cells produced go on propagating indefinitely as the encapsulated strain without it ever being necessary to resubmit them to DNA action; they produce unlimited amounts of their own DNA having the same possibilities. The DNA originally isolated from the S strain has, therefore,

accomplished two of the functions attributed to genes; it has induced a specific hereditary characteristic (capsule synthesis), and it has initiated its own reproduction.

Subsequently several authors attempted to show that transforming agents such as those
isolated from pneumococcal strains possessed characteristics of typical DNA (Avery et al., 1944;
Hotchkiss, 1949-1955; Daly et al., 1950; etc.).

β. Identity of DNA and transforming agents.

The transforming factor isolated from pneumococcal strains behaves as a typical DNA;
it contains deoxyribose and no ribose, it contains the four bases adenine, cytosine, guanine and
thymine, and has a phosphorus content comparable to that of other DNA; as impurity it has
only traces of carbohydrate and less than 0.02 % protein.

Much work has been done over the last two decades on the bacterial transformation factors.
In every case, the appearance of a new characteristic in a bacterial strain B is observed under
the influence of DNA isolated from a strain A that already possesses the characteristic. Other
types of capsule have been induced in pneumococci, *E. coli, Hemophilus influenzae* and in *Menin-
gococci*. Drug resistance has been induced in sensitive strains by DNA from resistant strains,
and this has allowed a quantitative study of the cells transformed to be made.

The properties of the transforming agents as DNA have been examined by Zamenhof et
al., and have led to some very interesting conclusions (Zamenhof, 1957). Most of Zamenhof's
work has been done on the *H. influenzae* transforming factor. This factor was purified until
it contained less than 0.4 % of the following impurities : proteins, immunologically active substances and ribonucleic acids.

The action of DNase on transforming factors has provided an additional proof for their
identification : DNase I in crystalline form at concentrations lower than 10^{-4} μg per ml causes a
fall in the activity to the extent of 10 to 1 over 28 minutes.

It could be questioned whether a purified preparation of the transforming factors such as
we have described corresponds to a single DNA or to a mixture of several different DNAs. If
a transformation is effected using a factor carrying several characteristics, it is generally found
that only one new characteristic appears, as if the transforming agent were a mixture of several
different DNA molecules, each carrying a single "marker" per molecule. Among the cells
transformed, those carrying two new characteristics are exceedingly rare, their number being
of the order of the magnitude obtained by working out the probability supposing that one
cell can be reached by two independent markers.

Molecular weight determination of the transforming factor of *Pneumococcus* gives a figure of
6×10^6, which is the same order of magnitude as those found for thymus DNA.

Generally speaking, transforming factors are sensitive to the same physical and chemical
agents as the nucleic acids, in particular they are rapidly inactivated by mutagenic agents, including
nitrous acid (Stuy, 1962).

The mutations observed by the action of nitrous acid on transforming DNA such as that
from *H. influenzae* are probably due to the transformation of cytosine to uracil (Goodgal and
Postel, 1965).

Marmur et al. (Marmur and Lane, 1960; Doty et al., 1960) have demonstrated the double-
stranded nature of transforming DNA from *Diplococcus pneumoniæ*, and shown that its behavior
on thermal denaturation is identical to that of classical DNA. When this DNA is heated
to temperatures at which all the molecules are denatured, however, it still retains some trans-

forming activity.   This activity is increased by slow cooling of the denatured DNA as well as by increasing the ionic strength and DNA concentration during the cooling.

d. *Infectious DNA*

Many experiments have shown that DNA extracted from viruses was alone sufficient to reproduce the virus entirely when injected into animals or used in *in vitro* cell culture. It is this DNA which is provided with all the genetic information required for the reproduction therefore of the whole virus. The infectious DNA of polyoma virus (Di Majorca et al., 1959; Weil, 1961) is thermostable and can thus retain its infectious power after the infected cells from which it is extracted have been heated to 100° for 30 minutes.   This infectious DNA can therefore be extracted by a phenol method from cells heated at 80° for 30 minutes (Paoletti et al., 1963).   DNA from viruses related to polyoma, e.g. shope papilloma (Ito, 1960), SV 40 (Boiron et al., 1962; Gerber, 1962; Boiron et al., 1965), bovine papilloma (Boiron et al., 1965) all belonging to the group called *papova*, exhibit properties that are comparable to those of polyoma virus DNA.

2. DNA function in growth and metabolism; protein synthesis

In the general scheme of the role of nucleic acids we have set out (p. 55), it was noted that the primary source of information necessary for enzyme synthesis was DNA.   The information is then transported from the nucleus to the site of the enzyme synthesis (ribosomes) by a metabolically unstable RNA complementary to the DNA : the messenger RNA.   Inside the nucleus, no protein synthesis is possible in the absence of DNA, a fact that stands out clearly from the work of Allfrey, Mirsky et al. (1955-1958) and which will now be briefly reviewed.

Isolation of cell nuclei from various tissues, especially from thymus, yields high quality preparations that can be considered as 90 % pure nuclei.   When these nuclei are suspended in a sucrose-containing buffer, there is a rapid and considerable incorporation of labeled aminoacids into the proteins of the nucleus.   Experiments have been conducted with the following aminoacids : alanine-1-^{14}C, glycine-1-^{14}C, lysine-2-^{14}C and methionine-^{35}S.   The incorporation was followed by measuring the radioactivity of the total nucleus protein and the results were expressed as counts per minute per milligram protein.

In order to eliminate the possibility that the incorporation is due to whole cells still remaining with the nuclei, a smear of suspension of nuclei after incorporation of the labeled aminoacids was taken on a photographic plate.   Microscopic examination of the radioautogram thus obtained showed that the whole of the suspension was radioactive.   The incorporation is therefore not due simply to a few isolated cells present in the smear.   The incorporation of the labeled aminoacids is preceded by a latent period that can be completely abolished by preincubation of the nuclei with addition of the isotopic aminoacid, and it is supposed that this period is used for the synthesis of the RNA required for aminoacid incorporation.   This can be verified by a study of 5,6-dichloro-β-D-ribofuranosylbenzimidazole (or DRB) action on the phenomenon.   It is known that, when it is added to nuclei, DRB blocks RNA synthesis at some stage.   If DRB is added before the latent period, no aminoacid incorporation is observed; if, on the other hand, the nuclei are first preincubated and DRB is then added, the addition has only slight effect of further incorporation of the labeled aminoacids.

When isolated nuclei are treated with crystalline pancreatic DNase before the addition of labeled aminoacids, the incorporation of the latter is distintly retarded. The more the DNA is removed, the more the slowing down becomes important. An additional proof of the role plays DNA in protein synthesis is that its addition to nuclei which have been submitted to DNase action restores a large amount, if not all the original activity of these nuclei.

3. DNA — RNA interactions. Information transfer from DNA to RNA

Although it is now certain that DNA carries genetic information, it still remains to show by what mechanism this DNA transmits its information to the messenger RNA. In all probability, the information is transmitted at the moment when the double-stranded DNA uncoils to form two single helices. These single strands then appear to act as a template on which a messenger RNA complementary to the DNA is constructed.

Synthesis of a messenger RNA copied from the DNA could take place by the intervention of an enzyme system similar that described by Chamberlin and Berg (1962), who noticed the *in vitro* RNA synthesis by an *E. coli* polymerase "under the control" of DNA. The RNA synthesized by this system had a base composition that was complementary to that of the controlling DNA. Chamberlin and Berg's polymerase had been purified by the following stages :

1) Extraction of *E. coli* cells.

2) Fractionation using the streptomycin-protamine system.

3) Ammonium sulfate fractionation.

4) Adsorption on and elution from a DEAE-cellulose column.

The enzymic activity rose from 40 units per milligram in the initial extract to 6,100 units per milligram in the peak eluted from the DEAE-cellulose column.

In the presence of the four ribonucleoside triphosphates, a bivalent metal and DNA, this polymerase will synthesize an RNA having a complementary base composition to that of the controlling DNA. If, as template, single-stranded DNA from the ΦX 174 bacteriophage (Sinsheimer, 1960) is employed, an RNA is obtained with a complementary base composition to that of the single strand form. On the other hand, if the double stranded form of ΦX 174 DNA is used as template (which can be synthesized artificially using the Kornberg DNA polymerase, p. 103), the synthesis is directed towards an RNA having a purine and pyrimidine base ratio which is practically the same as that of the double-stranded DNA.

The synthesis of RNA complementary to the single-stranded DNA of ΦX 174 takes place through the transient formation of a DNA-RNA hybrid that can be isolated by ultracentrifugation in a cesium chloride gradient (Chamberlin and Berg, 1963). This hybrid exhibits different characteristics from the double-stranded ΦX DNA artificially prepared with DNA polymerase, as well as differences with double-stranded RNA, these differences being particularly apparent if the thermal denaturation of this hybrid is examined. For example, it can be observed that :

1) the thermal transition zone is wider for the ΦX hybrid than for the double-stranded ΦX DNA;

2) the amplitude of the hyperchromic effect is less with the hybrid;

3) the melting point of the hybrid is higher than that of the double-stranded DNA.

Chamberlin and Berg's observations can be summarized by stating that the *E. coli* polymerase converts single-stranded ΦX 174 DNA into a DNA-RNA complex in which the amount of RNA is equivalent to the amount of DNA. Experiments carried out by Geiduschek and co-workers as well as by Chamberlin et al. (quoted by Chamberlin and Berg, 1963) indicate that it is impossible to obtain DNA-RNA hybrids if a double-stranded DNA is used as starting material, and it is clear that it is necessary to have a single strand of DNA for hybrid formation to occur.

The mechanism of RNA polymerase action under DNA control could be as follows : the enzyme fixes itself to the DNA at some point in the molecule in such a way that the DNA-DNA pairing becomes temporarily interrupted. The transference would then take place along one of the DNA strands with transient formation of a DNA-RNA coupling. This hybrid area must later be dissociated in one way or another with restoration of the initial DNA-DNA configuration.

In any case, during this reaction, the DNA reacts as catalyst since at the end of the reaction it is recovered unchanged in its physico-chemical and biological properties (Hurwitz et al., 1963).

The overall reaction leading to RNA, then protein synthesis, taking place under initial DNA control and therefore requiring a highly polymerized DNA to be present in the natural medium at the outset, can take place *in vitro* using synthetic polymers of the deoxyribonucleic type of relatively low molecular weight, such as the polythymidylic acids prepared by total synthesis following the methods described by Khorana and co-workers (see p. 95).

Leder et al. (1963) have actually shown that the whole reaction of protein synthesis could be effected by starting with polythymidylic acid as the fundamental element.

Since poly A serves as template for the synthesis of polylysine (cf. chapter on the code, p. 57) thymidyl oligonucleotides can be used for initially controlling the poly A synthesis by RNA polymerase and this poly A can then function as code for the polylysine synthesis by the two consecutive reactions :

$$\text{pppA (ATP)} \xrightarrow[\text{RNA polymerase}]{\text{oligo T}} \text{polyA} + \text{pp}$$

$$\text{Lys} \xrightarrow[\text{\textit{E. coli} extract, etc}]{\text{poly A}} \text{poly Lys}$$

Mehrotra and Khorana (1965) have studied the influence of temperature on the activity of synthetic deoxyribonucleic polymers as templates. Recent experiments have shown that *E. coli* polymerase can also use polynucleotides of the ribonucleic type, both natural and synthetic as templates for the synthesis of complementary polyribonucleotides. In addition to the synthetic polyribonucleotides, the reaction requires the presence of complementary ribonucleoside triphosphates, a bivalent cation such as Mn^{++} and the enzyme. Homoribopolynucleotides, heteropolyribonucleotides and double-stranded polyribonucleotides can serve as templates (Niyogi and Stevens, 1965a, b).

RNA polymerases having similar properties to those of Chamberlin and Berg's enzyme have been isolated and characterized from many other sources, e.g. from *Azotobacter vinelandii* (Krakow and Ochoa, 1963; Krakow, 1965), chicken embryo (Furth and Loh, 1963), *Pseudomonas aeruginosa* (Kazir and Kamiyama, 1965), rat liver and ventral prostate (Hancock et al., 1965), rat brain (Baroudes, 1965), bovine lymphosarcoma tissue (Furth and Ho, 1965), etc.

Hybrids like those Chamberlin and Berg obtained artificially have been shown to exist in the natural state in many cases for instance : Spiegelman et al. (1961) have reported the occurrence of natural DNA-RNA complexes in *E. coli* infected with the bacteriophage T_2. They carried out double marking of the nucleic acids of the *E. coli* — phage T$_2$ system, on one hand using ^{32}P to label the DNA of the infecting phage and on the other tritiated uridine (^{3}H-uridine) intended to label selectively the RNA synthesized by the system at the beginning of the infection. The choice of this system was suggested by the fact that RNA synthesis in T$_2$-infected cells is virtually limited to that of the complementary type to the viral DNA. Spiegelman and his colleagues were able to isolate a DNA-RNA hybrid fraction containing the double labeling. This complex loses its RNA by alkaline treatment (disappearance of the ^{3}H label), only retaining its DNA (retention of the ^{32}P label).

Similarly, Schulman and Bonner (1962) have noted that *Neurospora crassa* microsomes contain a certain amount of DNA which remains constant even after repeated washings by suspension and centrifugation. Theoretically, these washings eliminate the possibility of a non-specific DNA absorption on the microsomes, a possibility that can also be discounted by the fact that addition of DNA from various sources, including *N. crassa*, does not alter the DNA content of these microsomes after washing and centrifugation. It must in fact be a complex having a definite function, and considering of its biological origin, its chemical composition, its behavior on chromatography, centrifugation in a CsCl gradient and thermal denaturation, it is clear that this complex fulfils some of the conditions required for an intermediate in the DNA-RNA information transfer.

Schulman and Bonner's results are confirmed to some extent by recent observations made in Nirenberg's laboratory (Byrne et al., 1964; Bladen et al., 1965) on DNA-ribosome complexes formed *in vitro* and which can be seen with the electron microscope.

Tongur et al. (1964) have also worked on DNA-RNA associations, noting that when nucleic acids are extracted from animal tissue by the phenol method, a certain amount of RNA does not pass into the aqueous phase but remains in the intermediate phase with the DNA. The composition of this RNA differs from that of the total RNA of the cell, but approaches that of the DNA. Comparison of the results of ultracentrifugation, melting point determinations and sensitivity to enzyme attack suggests that the RNA not extractable by phenol forms a stable helical complex with the DNA, this complex having an identical structure to that of the DNA.

Following the same idea, Mandel and co-workers (Borkowska et al., 1964; Mandel and Borkowska, 1964) have reported the presence of RNA-DNA complexes with natural hybrid characteristics in chromatin from the cell nuclei of mammals, and in cells of an ascites hepatoma.

Smith (1965) has stated that a RNA-DNA complex can be obtained systematically and reproducibly from *E. coli* by centrifugation in a CsCl gradient. A complex has also been reported in *Chlorella pyrenoidosa* by Richter and Senger (1965).

All this work tends to support the idea of a transient association between DNA and RNA, at the moment when the genetic information is transferred.

CHAPTER III

Synthesis, Biosynthesis
and Isolation from Tissue of the Nucleic Acids

I. TOTAL CHEMICAL SYNTHESIS

Synthetic work on the nucleic acids and their derivatives received tremendous encouragement from the work of Lord Todd and his team who, between 1948 and 1958, published a remarkable set of papers including the synthesis of the main nucleosides and nucleotides as well as adenosine diphosphate (ADP), adenosine triphosphate (ATP) etc. Other synthetic methods were perfected later by G. B. Brown et al., Fletcher et al., Fox et al., Khorana et al., Lee, Goodmann Reist et al., Michelson et al., Shimidate et al., Schramm et al., etc.

Important reviews on the whole of this work have been written by Todd (1948, 1951, 1952), Fox and Wempen (1959), Khorana (1961), Michelson (1963), etc.

A. NUCLEOSIDE SYNTHESIS

1. Ribosides

The fundamental principles of nucleoside and nucleotide synthesis have been given by Todd in his review (1948). As an example, the adenosine synthesis (Davoll, Lythgoe and Todd, 1948a) will illustrate the method. Starting from triacetyltriphenylmethylribofuranose, catalytic hydrogenation over palladium gives triacetylribofuranose, which yields tetraacetylribofuranose by the action of acetic anhydride. Tetraacetylribofuranose saturated with HCl gas in ether at 0° gives, after three days, syrupy acetochlororibofuranose which can be condensed with the silver salt of 2,8-dichloroadenine to give a compound that, after hydrolysis with ammoniacal methanol (deacetylation) and catalytic hydrogenation (dechlorination) yields an adenosine that is identical with the natural product.

The adenosine and cytidine syntheses are reproduced overleaf. (Figures. 10 & 11)

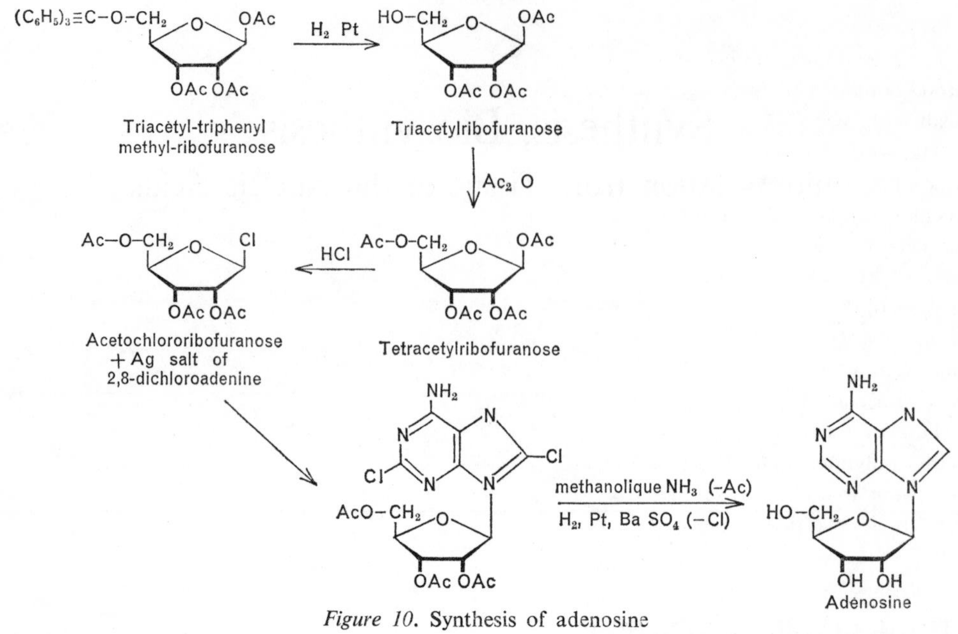

Figure 10. Synthesis of adenosine

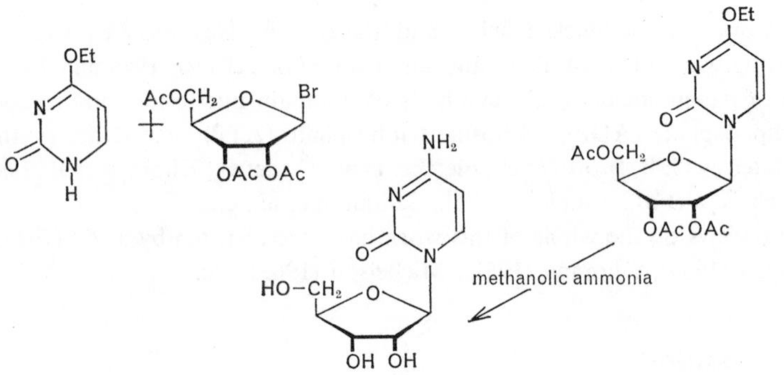

Figure 11. Synthesis of cytidine

Using the method just described, Todd and his co-workers first prepared an unnatural nucleoside, theophylline ribofuranoside (Howard, Lythgoe and Todd, 1947), then cytidine, uridine (Howard, Lythgoe and Todd, 1947), adenosine (Davoll, Lythgoe and Todd, 1948a) and guanosine (Davoll, Lythgoe and Todd, 1948b).

Modifications to the Todd synthesis were subsequently introduced in order to raise the yields or facilitate the reactions. One such modification was that of Fox et al. (1956) who showed that pyrimidine mercurials like dithymyl-mercury were particularly well suited to condensation with the halogenated derivatives of the pentoses such as 1-chloro- (or 1-bromo-) 2, 3, 5-tribenzoyl-β-D-ribofuranose; initially, 2′, 3′, 5′-tribenzoyl-β-D-ribofuranosylthymine is obtained, which yields β-D-ribofuranosylthymine in high yield by treatment with ammoniacal alcohol.

Fox's method is applicable to the synthesis of a wide variety of nucleosides involving various pentoses coupled with various pyrimidines, as we shall see when the synthesis of nucleoside analogs is dealt with (p. 86).

The work of Shimidate et al. (1961) has shown that in certain cases, the nucleoside bond can be obtained by simply melting an acetylated pentose like tetraacetylribose with a base such as 6-chloropurine in the presence of a catalyst that can be p-toluenesulfonic acid or zinc chloride. Treatment of the melted, then cooled, reaction mixture with saturated ammoniacal methanol allows a high yield of adenosine to be obtained which is comparable to the natural product. It would seem, however, that this reaction has not been applied very extensively, and it appears that it only works well with halogenated purines as bases (Michelson, 1964). Furthermore, Pichat et al. (1964) have shown that the synthesis of adenosine by this method results in simultaneous formation of the two anomeric nucleosides α and β.

Direct condensation of bases with pentoses can be realized in certain cases in the presence of ethyl polyphosphate in a solvent such as dimethylformamide. It this way, Schramm et al. (1962) were able to effect the synthesis of adenosine and other adenine nucleosides in fairly high yield. It is nevertheless possible that the α isomer is obtained as well as the natural β isomer.

2. Deoxyribosides

The possibilities of synthesising nucleosides containing deoxyribose using the same stages as for the synthesis of the corresponding ribose derivatives has also been examined (Davoll and Lythgoe, 1949). Acetylation of deoxyribose, halogenation and condensation with the silver salt of the base, e.g. theophylline, gave a poor yield of (3′, 4′-diacetyl-2′-deoxy-D-ribopyranosyl)-theophylline. It thus seems that the synthesis works less well in the case of deoxyribose derivatives than it does in the case of ribose derivatives.

In order to avoid this difficulty, Brown, Parihar, Reese and Todd (1958) proposed a new method for deoxyriboside synthesis that consisted, broadly speaking, in reducing the corresponding ribo-derivatives. The principle is, briefly, as follows.

It had been found that 5′-O-acetyl-2′-O-toluene-p-sulfonyl-uridine (1) reacts instantaneously with sodium iodide in acetonylacetone, and a crystalline iodonucleoside is obtained from the reaction mixture (Brown, Todd and Varadarajan, 1956). This must be a 2′-deoxy-2′-iodo compound, since hydrogenation over a palladium catalyst gives 5′-O-acetyl-2′-deoxyuridine from which deoxyuridine is obtained in high yield, this deoxyuridine being identical with the natural product in every respect*. It is not known whether the intermediate compound is the arabo (III) or the ribo (IV) isomer. A similar process has been successfully applied to the synthesis of thymidine.

---

* "Natural" deoxyuridine, obtained by enzymic hydrolysis of herring sperm DNA (Dekker and Todd, 1950). The appearance of this deoxyuridine is probably due to cytosine deamination, since the deoxyuridine content found is always at the expense of the cytidine content.

3. Nucleoside analogs

Nucleoside analogs including analogs of the bases such as bromo, chloro and iodouridine, chloro and iododeoxyuridine, bromo, chloro and iodocytidine, bromo, chloro and iododeoxy-cytidine, etc. can be prepared by halogenation of the corresponding nucleosides (Prusoff et al., 1959; Prusoff, 1960; Chang and Welch, 1961a, b; Cramer et al., 1961; Prusoff et al., 1961, etc.).

5-Iodo-2′-deoxycytidine (or 5-iodocytosine deoxyriboside; 5-ICDR) may be taken as typical of these preparations. Complete iodination occurs when deoxycytidine is treated with iodine in a mixture of glacial acetic acid, iodic acid, carbon tetrachloride and water. After removal of the acetic acid, ICDR crystallizes in high yield.

Iodination with labelled iodine ^{131}I yields the radioactive nucleoside, as is the case with the other halogens.

Nucleoside analogs resulting from the combination of purine and pyrimidine bases with pentoses other than ribose and deoxyribose are obtained by the conventional methods described for the ribosides, i.e. condensation of a halogenose with a suitably protected base. In this way Fox et al. prepared xylofuranosyl thymine (1956) and lyxofuranosyl thymine (1958). Glaudemans and Fletcher (1963), for the synthesis of arabinofuranosyl adenine, suggested condensation of a particular arabinose derivative with N-benzoyladenine, then elimination of the protecting groups, when adenine arabinoside is obtained in high yield :

p-nitrobenzoyl-2,3,5-tribenzylarabinose ⟶ 1-chloro-2,3,5-tribenzylarabinose + N-benzoy-ladenine ⟶ 2′,3′,5′-tribenzylarabinofuranosyl N-benzoyladenine.

Using the same tribenzylated arabinose, the synthesis of other arabinosides has been accomplished successfully, e.g. cytosine arabinoside and 5-trifluoromethyluracil arabinoside (Shen et al., 1965).

The synthesis of nucleosides resulting from joining adenine with various hexoses, such as allose, altrose, gulose, talose and mannose has been achieved by condensation of the acetylhalogen derivatives of the hexoses with chloromercuri-6-benzamidopurine followed by removal of the protecting groups (Lerner and Kohn, 1964).

A further method for synthesising arabinosides consists in isomerizing a riboside or a xyloside. Such inversions have been successful in the synthesis of uracil arabinoside (Brown et al., 1956), thymine arabinoside (Fox et al., 1956), 5-fluorouracil arabinoside (Yung et al., 1961), cytosine arabinoside (Hunter, 1963), adenine arabinoside (Lee et al., 1960; Reist et al., 1962) and guanine arabinoside (Reist and Goodmann, 1964).

All these syntheses, which are not as simple as might appear at first sight, have been carried out principally with a view to the possible chemotherapeutic application of these nucleosides as anticancer agents.

B. NUCLEOTIDE SYNTHESIS BY NUCLEOSIDE PHOSPHORYLATION

One of the classical phosphorylating reagents is dibenzylchlorophophonate * widely used by Todd and his collaborators :

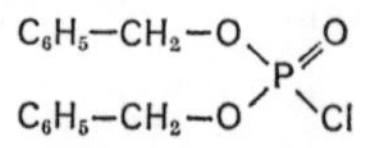

$$C_6H_5-CH_2-O \diagdown \atop C_6H_5-CH_2-O \diagup P \diagup\diagup{O} \atop \diagdown Cl$$

Dibenzylchlorophosphonate

---

* This is the name used by Todd et al. Some other authors prefer dibenzylphospho-chlorhydate or dibenzyl-chlorophosphate.

An example of phosphorylation is the preparation of muscle adenylic acid or adenine-5'-monophosphate (Figure 12) :

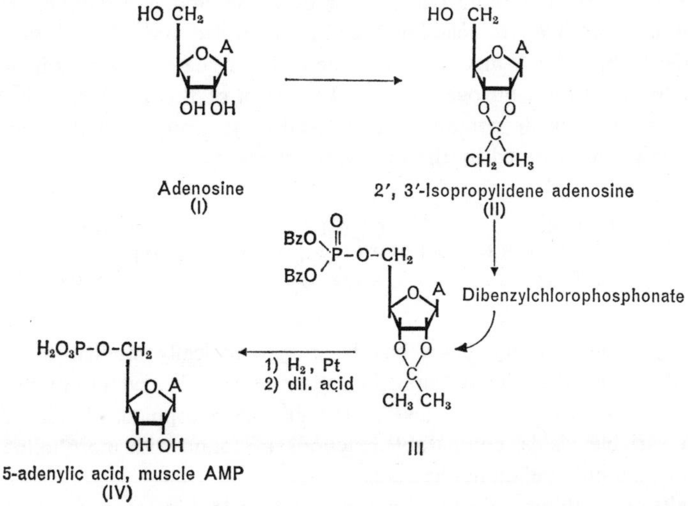

Figure 12. Synthesis of adenylic acid (Todd 1948)

The ADP and ATP syntheses follow the same principle, adenosine diphosphate presenting no special difficulty; it is merely necessary to carry out a second phosphorylation on suitably protected adenosine monophosphate using a second molecule of dibenzylchlorophosphonate as in the following scheme : (Figure 13)

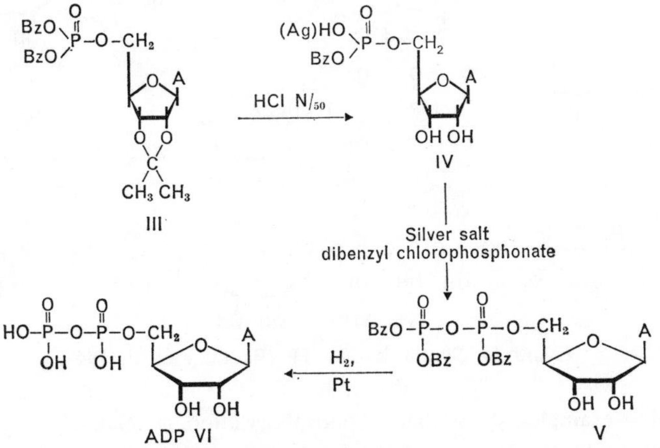

Figure 13. Synthesis of ADP (Todd 1948)

The third phosphorylation to make ATP is more awkward, since compound V (above) must be partially debenzylated to attach a third phosphoryl, furthermore it is not possible to use conditions similar to those employed in the III $\longrightarrow$ IV reaction, even slight acidification causing too extensive a debenzylation. Todd and his co-workers developed an ingenious method, the "quaternization" method, allowing monodebenzylation of compound V (Baddiley, Clark, Michalski and Todd, 1949). This involves reacting the fully esterified phosphates and pyrophosphates wih strong tertiary bases like N-methylmorpholine to form quaternary salts in which the benzyl group is joined to the cationic nitrogen atom. Treatment of this product with dilute acid yields a phosphate or pyrophosphate containing one less benzyl group than the starting compound. This quaternization is represented by the following scheme :

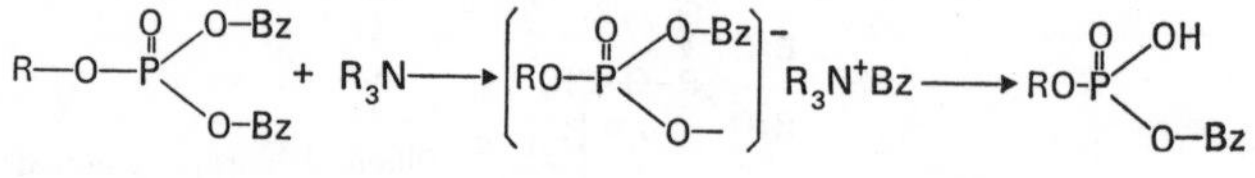

Debenzylation by strong tertiary bases has been systematically studied by Clark and Todd (1950*a*, *b*). They found that the tribenzylphosphate loses a benzyl group in the presence of 4-methylmorpholine to give a 65 % yield of the dibenzylphosphate. Under the same conditions and with variable yields, comparable reactions are found with morpholine, pyridine, quinoline, 2-picoline, 2,6-lutidine, quinaldine etc.

Certains salts, e.g. lithium chloride, lithium acetate, potassium acetate etc., can also induce monodebenzylation of the tribenzylphosphate.

Applying these methods for partial debenzylation, the total synthesis of ATP was realized by Baddily, Michelson and Todd (1948, figure 14) :

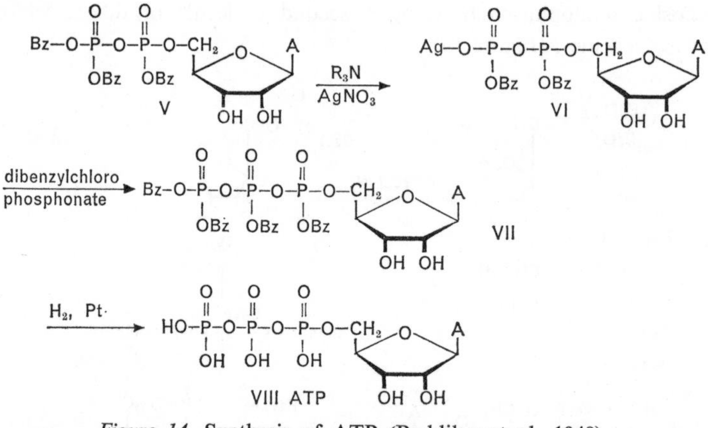

Figure 14. Synthesis of ATP (Baddiley et al. 1948)

The foregoing examples show that 5'-phosphorylation is relatively straightforward since the 2'- and 3'-hydroxyls can be blocked in one step by an isopropylidene or benzylidene group. Michelson and Todd (1949) treated adenosine with benzaldehyde in the presence of $ZnCl_2$ and believed they had obtained 3',5'-benzylideneadenosine, though in fact condensation of adenosine and other nucleosides with benzaldehyde results in formation of the 2',3'-benzylidene nucleoside (Brown, Haynes and Todd, 1950). In order to phosphorylate adenosine in the 2' and 3' positions it is necessary to carry out the following sequence of operations; *a*) block the hydroxyl in the 5′ position with a trityl (triphenylmethyl) group, *b*) phosphorylate the trityladenosine with dibenzylchlorophosphonate, which, after hydrolysis and catalytic hydrogenation leads to a mixture of adenosine-2′- and 3′-phosphates, or adenylic acids (*a* and *b* respectively) (Brown and Todd, 1952).

The 2′ : 3′-cyclic phosphates of adenosine, cytidine and uridine have been obtained as follows (Brown, Magrath and Todd, 1952) : anhydrous adenylic acid is treated overnight at room temperature with trifluoroacetic anhydride; the residue is triturated with ether and the product converted to the ammonium salt with methanol saturated with ammonia, and the ammonium salt heated with barium carbonate on the steam bath to yield the barium salt of adenosine 2′ : 3′-phosphate.

The phosphorylated deoxyribomononucleotides (3′- and 5′-) have been made applying the methods developed for the corresponding ribomononucleotides (Michelson and Todd, 1954; Hayes, Michelson and Todd, 1955).

It can thus be seen that dibenzylchlorophosphonate has made it possible to achieve most of the fundamental syntheses of the classic nucleotides, and in this respect is superior to the older established phosphorylating agents like phosphorus oxychloride or polyphosphoric acid. Nevertheless, it does have the disadvantage that the benzyl groups must be eliminated by catalytic hydrogenation. At a later date, other phosphorylating agents were tried, namely *O*-benzylphosphorous-*O*,*O*-diphenylphosphoric anhydride (Corby et al., 1952), tetra-*p*-nitrophenyl pyrophosphate (Chambers et al., 1957), and especially β-cyanoethyl phosphate (Tener, 1961), the latter remaining the most frequently used phosphorylating agent at the present time :

$$HO - \overset{\displaystyle \overset{O}{\|}}{\underset{\displaystyle OH}{P}} - O - CH_2 - CH_2 - C \equiv N$$

β-cyanoethylphosphate

The synthesis of thymidine-5′-phosphate can be carried out using β-cyanoethylphosphate as phosphorylating agent in the following way : 3′-Acetylthymidine is allowed to react with β-cyanoethylphosphate and dicyclohexylcarbodiimide (DCC) in anhydrous pyridine for two days at room temperature. After this time, the excess DCC is decomposed by the addition of a little water, and the cyanoethyl group removed by carefull alkaline hydrolysis (Tener, 1961). In this way, a series of nucleotides has been prepared, including guanosine-5′-phosphate by phosphorylation of 2′, 3′-isopropylideneguanosine, deoxycytidine-3′-phosphate by phosphorylation of 5′-*O*-trityldeoxycytidine, deoxycytidine-3′, 5′-diphosphate by complete phosphorylation in the 3′ and 5′ positions of deoxycytidine, etc.

Hall and Khorana (1955) have also reported that nucleoside-2′ (3′), 5′-diphosphates could be synthesised in good yield using a mixture of phosphorus pentoxide and phosphoric acid.

The cyclic nucleotides such as uridine-2′ : 3′-cyclic phosphate, cytidine-2′ : 3′-cyclic phosphate, etc., can be prepared by the action of DCC on dimethylformamide solutions of the corresponding nucleoside-3′-phosphates (Shugar and Wierzchowski, 1958).

Nucleotide analogs

Nucleotide analogs (involving analogs of the bases) can be obtained by direct halogenation of the corresponding nucleotides (Frisch and Visser, 1939; Prusoff, 1959; Michelson et al., 1962).

In this way, 5-chlorouridine-5′-phosphate was obtained by allowing a carbon tetrachloride solution of chlorine to react with uridine-5′-phosphate in acetic acid (Michelson et al., 1962).

The synthesis of 4-azauridine-5′-phosphate and its methylated derivative has been effected in an original way by Pryštaš and Šorm (1965) by condensing ribofuranosylphosphate halogenid with salts of protected 4-azauracil :

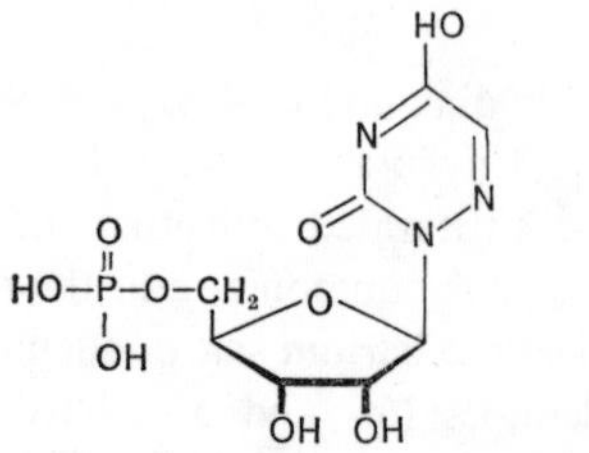

4-azauridine-5′-phosphate

The synthesis of various 5-halogenouridine-5′-pyrophosphates was carried out by anionic displacement of diphenyl phosphate from P¹-halogenouridine-5′-P²-diphenyl pyrophosphate with inorganic orthophosphate, the intermediate anhydride being obtained quantitatively by treatment of the halogenouridine-5′-phosphate with diphenyl phosphorochloridate (Michelson et al. 1962).

The synthesis of nucleotide analogs involving sugars other than ribose and deoxyribose can be achieved by phosphorylation of the corresponding nucleosides following the procedures that have been described for the natural nucleotides. In this manner the synthesis of arabinoside phosphates has been mentioned by Cardeilhac and Cohen (1964).

Bové et al. (1964) have described the preparation of ^{32}P-labeled ribonucleoside — and deoxy-ribonucleoside-5′-monophosphates. These compounds are obtained by specific hydrolysis of whole RNA and DNA from E. coli grown in the presence of inorganic ^{32}P.

C. Polynucleotide synthesis

1. Ribopolynycleotides

The standard methods have been successfully applied to the synthesis of dinucleotides. Todd and his co-workers obtained adenosine-2′-uridine-5′-phosphate in the following way (Michelson, Szabo and Todd, 1956) : 3′, 5′-di-O-acetyladenosine-2′-benzylphosphochloride was condensed with 2′, 3′-di-O-acetyluridine, and the protecting groups subsequently removed. (Figure 15)

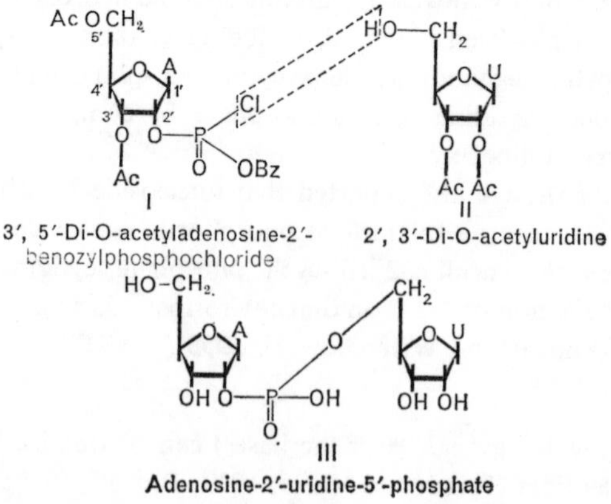

3′, 5′-Di-O-acetyladenosine-2′-   2′, 3′-Di-O-acetyluridine
benozylphosphochloride

Adenosine-2′-uridine-5′-phosphate

Figure 15. Synthesis of a dinucleotide (Michelson et al, 1956)

These methods, however, give only poor yields of dinucleotides, and necessitate the complete protection of all the derivatives undergoing reaction.

The specific synthesis of the 3′-5′-bond in the case of the ribonucleic dinucleotides has been examined systematically by Smyth et al. (1962) using dicyclohexylcarbodiimide as the condensing agent. A publication by these authors reports the specific synthesis of the 3′-5′ bond, using as example of its application, the synthesis of uridylyl-(3′-5′)-uridine (UpU) and uridylyl-(3′-5′)-adenosine (UpA). Condensation of 5′-O-di-p-anisylphenylmethyl-2′-O-tetrahydropyranyluridine-3′-phosphate with 2′, 3′-di-O-acetyluridine in the presence of DCC gives an intermediate compound that is treated directly with ammonia to eliminate the acetyl groups, then with 80 % acetic acid at room temperature to remove the 5′-O-di-p-anisylphenylmethyl and tetrahydropyranyl groups. Comparison of the product thus obtained with UpU made by enzymic synthesis (Heppel et al., 1955) shows that it is necessary to limit the duration of the acid treatment, since after 30 hours at room temperature, the formation of some RNase-resistent product (probably uridylyl-(2′-5′)-uridine was observed. Using 4 hours hydrolysis with 80 % acetic acid, the formation of UpU identical with the product of enzyme synthesis was observed.

Using new nucleoside derivatives, a series of diribonucleoside phosphates such as CpA, CpC, CpG and CpU have been synthesized (Lohrmann and Khorana, 1964).

Concerning the synthesis of ribonucleic polymers, Michelson (1958) has published a rapid and elegant method which has enabled him to obtain polynucleotides containing 2 to 10 nucleotide residues, and which exhibit the properties of natural ribonucleic acids. Some details of this unusually interesting method are given below.

The possibility of polymerizing nucleotides already formed (2′- or 3′-monophosphates) had been examined, and it was realized that, as a first step, cyclic 2′ : 3′-phosphates were readily available from them (Brown, Magrath and Todd, 1952); the cyclic phosphates are quantitatively polymerized in a second step by the action of tetraphenylpyrophosphate at room temperature. A solution of mono tri-n-octylammonium- or mono tri-n-decylammonium nucleotide (I in the figure below) is treated with tetraphenylphosphate or diphenylchlorophosphonate and tri-n-butylamine to give the cyclic phosphate (II) quantitatively. The latter reacts in situ with another tetraphenylpyrophosphate molecule, when a rapid polymerization results with production of heat, in all likelihood through the intermediate formation of an unstable pyrophosphate (III), which reacts either directly or via the dinucleoside pyrophosphate with primary hydroxyl groups to give a polymer mixture (IV). These polymers contain 2′ (3′), 5′-phosphate bonds in the chain and 2′ : 3′-cyclic ends. (Figure 16).

Some such polymers have been synthesized by Michelson, for instance polyadenylic and polyuridylic acids, and polymers containing varying proportions of adenylic and uridylic acids. Using uridine 2′ : 3′-cyclic-5′-phosphate in the presence of an excess of adenosine 2′ : 3′-cyclic phosphate, it was possible to synthesize adenylic acid polymers terminating with uridine-5′-phosphate at the head and adenosine-2′-3′-phosphate at the tail. Using a reaction mixture of four mononucleotides, adenosine-2′ (3′)-phosphate, guanosine-2′ (3′)-phosphate, uridine-2′ (3′)-phosphate and cytidine-2′ (3′)-phosphate, a synthetic "ribonucleic acid" was obtained.

The properties of these polymers are in general those which are associated with the natural oligonucleotides, although, as might be expected, only 50-60 % of the internucleotide links are 3′-5′ bonds, the remainder being 2′-5′ bonds. These polymers are completely degraded by 0.1 N sodium hydroxide at 37° for 24 hours, right to the stage of the corresponding mononucleotide -2′

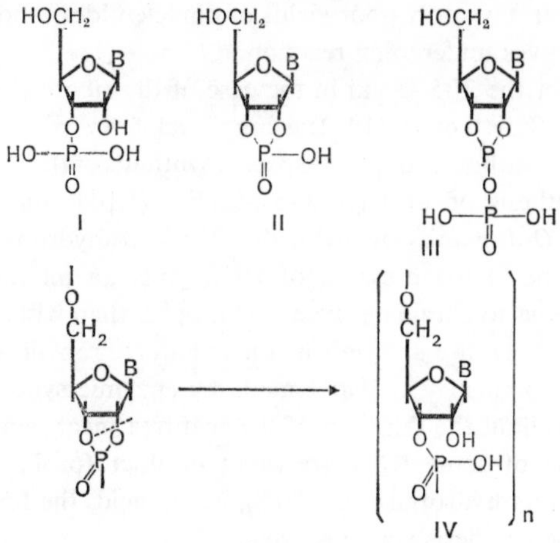

Figure 16. Synthesis of an RNA polymer (Michelson 1958)

(3′)-phosphates. Preliminary work showed that the polymerization conditions just described lead to molecules containing 2 to 10 nucleotides, so that it appears unlikely that it would be possible to synthesize polymers of very high molecular weight such as natural RNA by this method. Concerning the action of ribonuclease A, it is found that polyadenylic acid is resistant to its action, a fact that concords with the properties of the enzyme since we know that only Pyp-Pup or Pyp-Pyp bonds are cleaved by it. Polyuridylic acid, on the other hand, has 50-60 % of its internucleotide bonds cleaved by ribonuclease. These are only approximate figures, since only part of the reaction products appear in the form of uridine-3′-phosphate, the others appearing as di-, tri-and tetranucleotides containing exclusively 2′-5′-phosphate linkages.

Over the past few years, Khorana's team has been occupied in preparing synthetic polymers of the ribonucleic type, and containing exclusively the natural 3′-5′ linkage, with a sequence of different nucleotides in a known order. An example of the reactions developed by Lapidot and Khorana (1963*a, b*) is reproduced below (Figure 17) :

It can be seen that the reaction of (pyridinium)-uridine-3′-phosphate with monomethoxytrityl chloride in pyridine gives after chromatography 5′-*O*-monomethoxytrityluridine. Acetylation of this compound with acetic anhydride in the presence of excess triethylammonium acetate leads to the 2′-*O*-acetyl derivative, condensation of which with excess N, 2′-*O*, 3′-*O*-tribenzoyluridine in the presence of DCC followed by mild acid treatment gives 2′-*O*-acetyluridylyl-(3′-5′)-N,$O^{2'}$, $O^{3'}$-tribenzoyluridine (IV), which is completely resistant to the action of RNase A. Ammonia treatment of IV yields uridylyl-uridine which is now hydrolysed by RNase. Condensation of IV with excess N,2′-*O*,3′-*O*-triacetyladenosine-3′-phosphate, then with 2′,5′-di-*O*-acetyluridine-3′-phosphate in the presence of DCC followed by ammonia treatment gives the tetranucleotide UpApUpU.

A series of ribonucleic oligonucleotides has been made by the same process, and enzyme action has shown that the internucleotide bonds were all of the 3′-5′ variety. It was further found that reaction between *N*-benzoyl-2′-*O*-acetyladenosine-3′-phosphate and *N*,-2′,5′-triacetyladenosine-3′-phosphate in anhydrous pyridine with DCC, followed by several treatments with acetic anhydride in pyridine then and ammonia leads to the series of homologous adenylic oligonucleotides of the ApApAp... type (Lapidot and Khorana, 1963c).

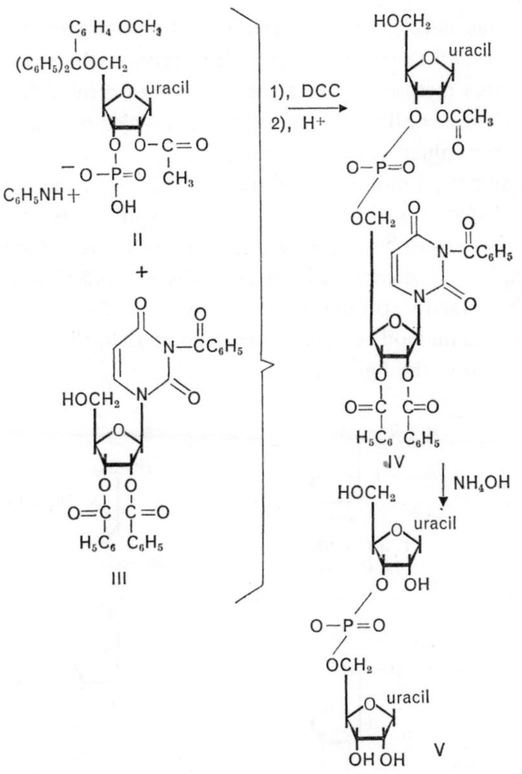

Figure 17. Synthesis of a ribodinucleotide (Lapidot and Khorana 1963)

The efforts of Khorana and his co-workers in the specific synthesis of the $C_{3'}$-$C_{5'}$ interribonu-cleotidic linkages have culminated recently with the synthesis of the 64 possible ribotrinucleotides derived from the 4 major ribomononucleotides, in view of their applications in deciphering the genetic code (Lohrmann et al. 1966, Söll et al. 1965).

Amongst other research focused on the synthesis of ribopolynucleotides, let us mention that of Šmrt and Šorm who have also described methods allowing the stepwise synthesis of uridylic acid polymers, all containing the 3'-5' bond. In particular, these authors have realized the syntheses of tetrauridylic acid and pentauridylic acid (Šmrt, 1964; Šmrt and Šorm, 1964).

Mention might also be made of the synthesis of polyuridylic acid by γ-irradiation of uridylic acid (Aguilera et al., 1965).

Synthesis of ribonucleic polymers can be effected by simple treatment of nucleoside-2'(3')-phosphates with polyphosphoric acid (Schramm et al., 1962), but not only do the polymers obtained have the nucleotides joined in unknown sequence, but it is not at all certain that the internucleotide linkage is of the 3'-5' type; indeed, Kochetkov et al. (1964) have shown that several types of linkages could occur in this case.

2. Deoxyribo-di and polynucleotide synthesis

a. *Dinucleotide synthesis*

A new technique was developed by Khorana and co-workers (Khorana et al., 1957-1959 ; Gilham and Khorana, 1958; Tener et al., 1958) to arrive at the specific synthesis of the inter-nucleotide 5'-3' bond; this method involves the reaction of a suitably protected deoxynucleotide with a second deoxynucleotide or deoxynucleoside which is also protected, by the presence of dicy-clohexylcarbodiimide or *p*-toluenesulfonyl chloride.

In the initial experiments, a molecule of 5'-thymidylic acid in anhydrous pyridine was allowed to react with excess 5'-*O*-tritylthymidine and 1.5 molar equivalents of *p*-toluenesulfonyl chloride. After removal of the trityl group by dilute acid hydrolysis, the reaction products can be separated by paper chromatography. The expected product, thymidyl-(5'-3')-thymidine (IIIa) is obtained in 50 % yield, the other reaction products being polymers of a type to be discussed later on.

It was possible by this method to synthesize in good yield the three dinucleoside monophosphates IIIa, *b* and *c* shown in the figure below :

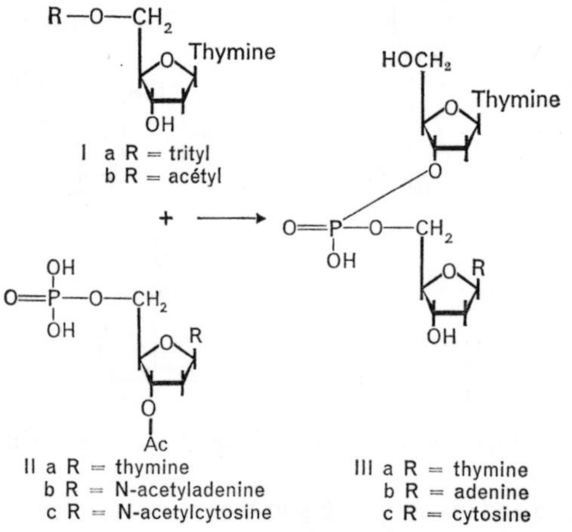

Figure 18. Synthesis of various deoxyribodinucleotides (Khorana et al. 1957-195(6

In a second group of experiments, Khorana et al. attempted to synthesize true dinucleotides containing a 3', 5'-phosphodiester and carrying a terminal monoesterified phosphoryl group. Two methods suitable for general application were developed :

1) Phosphorylation of a suitably protected dinucleoside monophosphate to give a dinucleo-tide terminated by either a 3'- or a 5'-phosphate.

2) Synthesis from two mononucleotides, one of which contains a completely protected phosphoryl group. Reproduced in Figure 19 is the course of this second type of reaction, which the authors claim is more widely applicable than phosphorylation of dinucleoside monophosphates.

The protected nucleotide is allowed to react with 3'-*O*-acetylthymidylic acid and DCC. Removal of the protecting groups and chromatographic purification of the product furnishes thymidylyl-(5'-3')-thymidylic-(5') acid, or pTpT, in 35 — 40 % yield.

The structures of the dinucleotides obtained was confirmed by enzymatic studies.

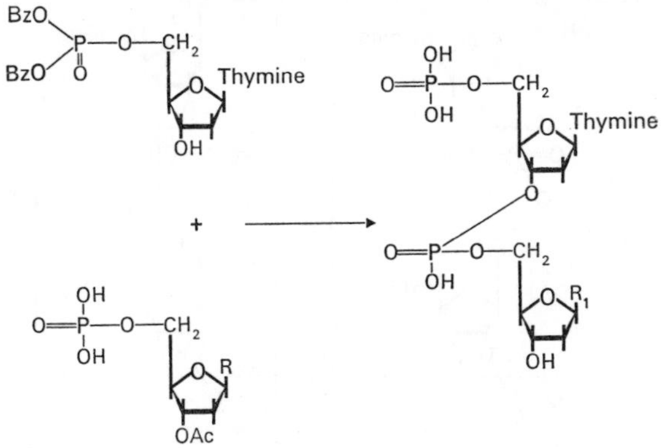

Figure 19. Synthesis of deoxyribodinucleotides (Khorana et al. 1957-1959)

b. *Polynucleotide synthesis*

Reaction of 5'-thymidylic acid or thymidine-5'-monophosphate, pT, in anhydrous pyridine solution with *p*-toluenesulfonyl chloride or DCC at room temperature gives a series of polymers which can be conveniently separated by chromatography on DEAE-cellulose or ECTEOLA-cellulose columns. The latter are prepared with substituted aminoalkyl celluloses obtained by the procedure, now well established, of Peterson and Sober (1956). The chromatographic results obtained indicate the presence of polymers containing up to 11 residues. Two homologous series are formed (I and II) of the following types :

1) Linear oligonucleotides consisting of repeating 5'-3' internucleotide links, and carrying 5'-phosphoryl groups at one end and 3'-phosphoryl groups at the other.

2) Cyclic oligonucleotides in which the linear compounds are cyclized by phosphorylation of the terminal 3'-hydroxyl group by the terminal 5'-phosphoryl group. The proportion these intramolecularly cyclized products constitute falls with increasing chain length until at the penta-nucleotide stage. Only traces of cyclized compounds are found. Above the pentanucleotide, only linear polymers are formed.

Khorana and Vizsolyi (1961) have published an article on the improved synthesis of linear thymidyl polynucleotides and of corresponding compounds joined by deoxycytidyl units.

This method makes use of the polymerization by DCC of a mixture of 3'-*O*-acetylthymidine-5'-phosphate (25%) and thymidine-5'-phosphate (75%), stirring for 6 days in the dark in anhydrous pyridine at room temperature. In this way, polymers consisting of up to 11 nucleotides can be made. Fractionation of these different polymers is carried out by chromatography on DEAE-cellulose (in carbonate form), in a triethylamine bicarbonate gradient, this being better than ammonium bicarbonate since it is more volatile.

Polymerization of a mixture of *N*,3'-*O*-diacetyldeoxycytidine-5'-phosphate (25%) and thymidine-5'-phosphate (78 %) also yields products from which polynucleotides carrying deoxycytidine at one end can be isolated. These compounds have been isolated in the pure state and characterized.

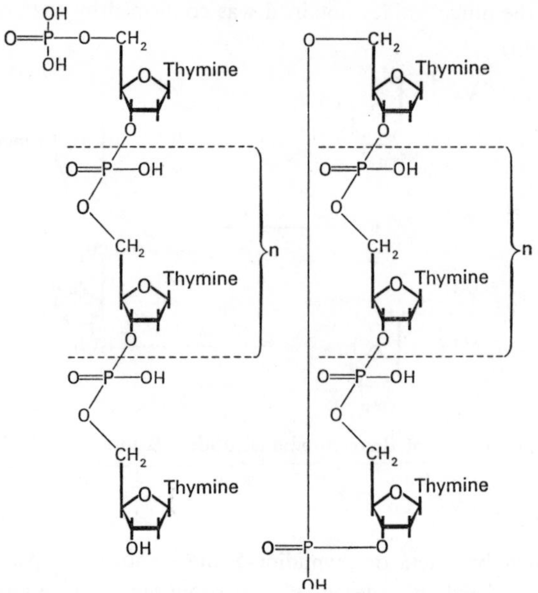

Figure 20. Synthesis of polythymidylic acids (Khorana and Vizsolyi 1961)

Weimann and Khorana (1962) have examined the possibility of preparing thymidyl oligo-nucleotides (di-, tri-, and tetranucleotides) carrying a monoesterified phosphoryl group in the 3'-position, all the earlier ones having been 5'-phosphates (Figure 21).

Phosphorylation of 5'-*O*-tritylthymidine with a mixture of β-cyanoethylphosphate and DCC, followed by alkaline treatment of the product (II), gives 5'-*O*-tritylthymidine-3'-phosphate. Acid treatment of II gives β-cyanoethylthymidine-3'-phosphate (IV).

Condensation of 5'-*O*-tritylthymidine-3'-phosphate (III) with 3'-*O*-acetylthymidine in the presence of DCC gives 5'-*O*-tritylthymidylyl-(3'-5')-thymidine (V). The desired product, 5'-*O*-tritylthymidylyl-(3'-5')-thymidine-3'-phosphate (dinucleotide) is prepared by phosphorylation of V by the β-cyanoethylphosphate-DCC mixture. A further step, condensation of the protected dinucleotide with 3'-*O*-acetylthymidine, gives 5'-*O*-tritylthymidylyl-(3'-5')-thymidylyl-(3'-5')-thymidine.

The trinucleotide TpTpTp is formed by condensation of the protected dinucleotide trityl-TpTp with β-cyanoethylthymidine-3'-phosphate. Condensation of the same trityl-TpTp with thymidylyl-(3'-5')-3'-*O*-acetylthymidine, followed by treatment by alkali results in trityl-TpTpTpT, from which the corresponding tetranucleotide can be obtained by cyanoethylphosphate phos-phorylation.

Khorana, Vizsolyi and Ralph (1962) then carried out many experiments on the polymeri-zation of mononucleotides with a view to comparing the different polymerizing reagents, at the same time studying the improvement in isolation techniques for synthetic oligonucleotides.

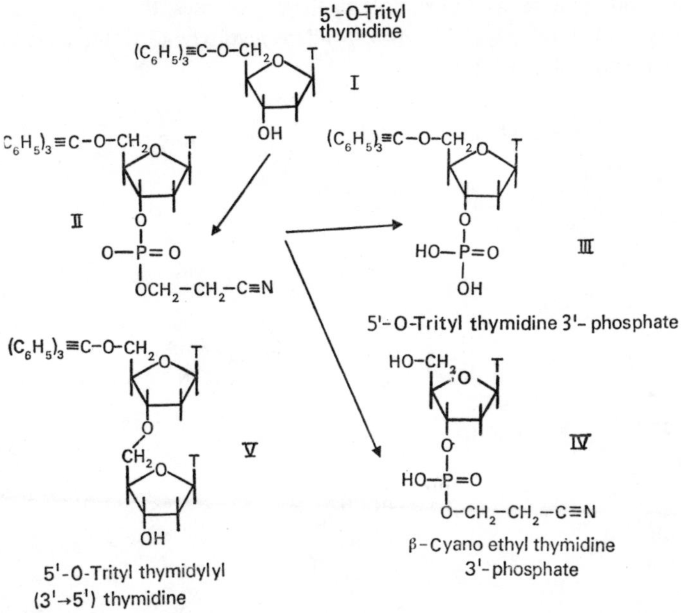

Figure 21. Synthesis of polythymidylic acids bearing terminal 3'-phosphates (Weimann & Khorana 1962).

It have been state that the polymerization reaction of 3'-*O*-acetyl-pT with pT in the presence of DCC in anhydrous pyridine has been mentioned to occur with formation of oligonucleotides; this reaction was examined using the following condensing agents :

Dicyclohexylcarbodiimide (DCC),

Toluene-*p*-sulfonyl chloride,

2,5-dimethylbenzenesulfonyl chloride,

2,4,6-trimethylbenzenesulfonyl chloride,

diphenylchlorophosphonate

diisopropylcarbodiimide.

Out of all these substances, DCC is the most satisfactory. The method used for fractionating the oligonucleotides can be improved by treatment of the mixture of total oligonucleotides with excess acetic anhydride in dry pyridine. This treatment causes fission of the by-products frequently observed, and which arise by the joining of nucleotides to one another by pyrophosphate bonds between their phosphomonoester groups.

The logical sequence of the work carried out by Khorana and his team was to attempt to synthesize deoxyribonucleic polynucleotides that involved the joining of different nucleotides in a known order.

Initially, the special methods used for the protection of the nucleotides involved in the reactions were perfected (Schaller et al., 1963; Schaller and Khorana, 1963a). A variety of oligonucleotides was then prepared, such as thymidylyl-(3'-5')-deoxyadenylyl-(3'-5')-thymidine and polynucleotides including thymidine and deoxyadenosine in alternate sequences (Weimann et al., 1963). Schaller and Khorana (1963b) have also developed the synthesis of oligonucleotides involving guanine and cytidine, as an example of these syntheses, the synthesis of deoxycytidylyl-(3'-5')-deoxyguanylyl-(3'-5')-deoxycytidylyl-(3'-5')-deoxycytidylyl-(3'-5')-deoxycytidine, d-CpGp-Cp-CpC, is shown below (Figure 22) :

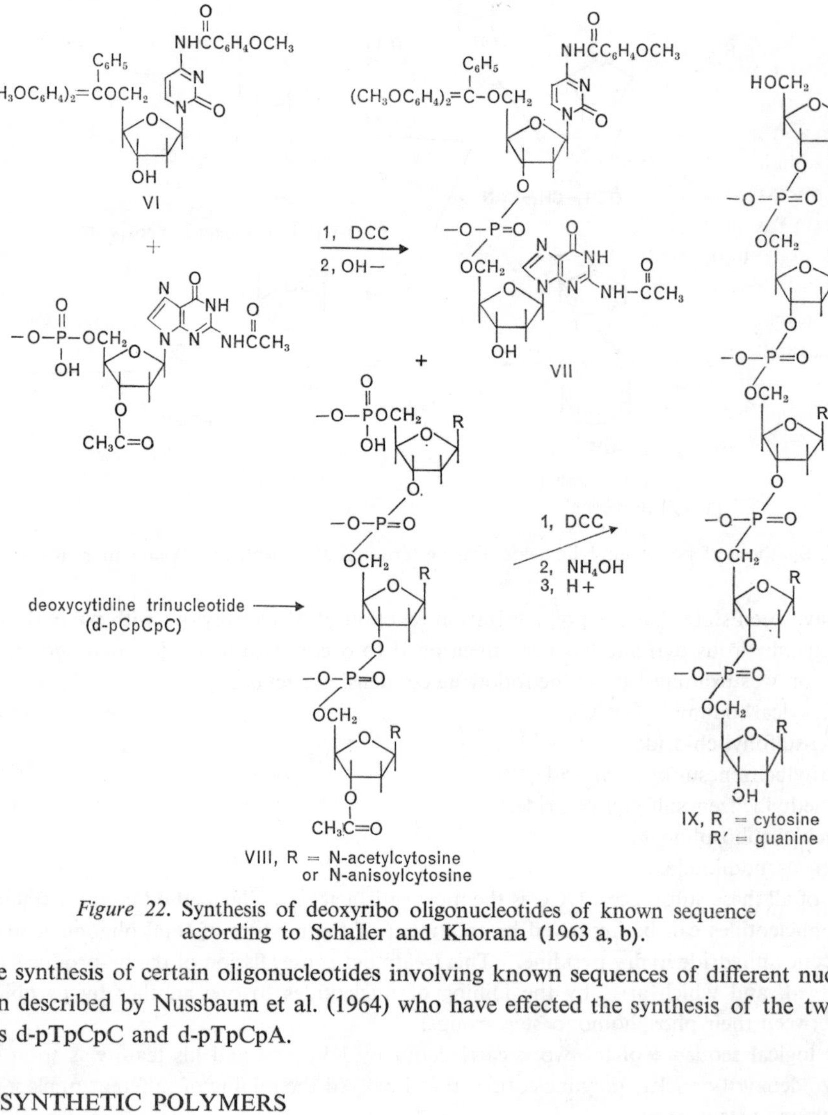

Figure 22. Synthesis of deoxyribo oligonucleotides of known sequence according to Schaller and Khorana (1963 a, b).

The synthesis of certain oligonucleotides involving known sequences of different nucleotides has been described by Nussbaum et al. (1964) who have effected the synthesis of the two trinucleotides d-pTpCpC and d-pTpCpA.

II. BIOSYNTHETIC POLYMERS

Grunberg-Manago, Ochoa and co-workers' studies on the biosynthesis of ribonucleic acids, and Kornberg and co-workers' on the synthesis of the deoxyribonucleic acids have made a great step forward in our knowledge of the biochemistry of the nucleic acids. This work has been reviewed by Grunberg-Manago (1955, 1963), Heppel and Rabinowitz (1958), Khorana (1960), Kornberg (1962), Richardson et al. (1963).

A. SYNTHESIS OF RNA-TYPE POLYNUCLEOTIDES : POLYNUCLEOTIDE PHOSPHORYLASE : POLYRIBONU-
CLEOTIDE, ORTHOPHOSPHATE-NUCLEOTIDYLTRANSFERASE (EC.2.7.7.8).

In the course of their work on biological phosphorylation, Grunberg-Manago and Ochoa
(1955a, 1955b) noticed that extracts of *Azotobacter vinelandii* contained an enzyme that they called
polynucleotide phosphorylase, which was able to catalyse rapid exchange of orthophosphate-^{32}P
with the terminal phosphate in the following nucleotides : ADP, IDP, UDP, CDP and, to
a lesser extent, GDP.   There was no reaction with nucleoside triphosphates, nor with nucleoside
monophosphates.   The exchange is accompanied by the liberation of inorganic phosphate (Pi)
and requires Mg^{++} ions.   Incubation of the purified enzyme with a nucleoside diphosphate such
as IDP (IDP is used in preference to ADP to avoid any complications due to the presence of
traces of myokinase which does not react with IDP, Grunberg-Manago, 1955) in the presence
of Mg^{++}, shows that 50-60 % of the nucleoside diphosphate disappears with the liberation
of a stoichiometric amount of Pi.   The enzyme has thus effected two distinct reactions : a) Exchange
of the terminal phosphoryl group of the nucleoside phosphates with mineral phosphate ^{32} P, and
b) polymerization of the nucleoside diphosphates with liberation of the stoichiometric amount
of inorganic phosphate.

The enzyme was therefore purified using one or the other of these reactions as an assay method,
in other words by measuring the rate of radioactive orthophosphate incorporation into nucleoside
diphosphates, or "phosphate exchange method", and measuring the rate at which orthophosphate
is liberated from nucleoside diphosphates ADP or IDP, but mostly from the latter (Grunberg-
Manago, Ortiz and Ochoa, 1956).   The polynucleotide phosphorylase was purified 40-fold using
the following steps : *Azotobacter* cells dried in acetone were extracted several times by dilute
solutions of KCl; ammonium sulfate precipitation, chromatography on calcium phosphate gel
and a second ammonium sulfate precipitation completed the process.

Ochoa and Mii (1961) went much further in the purification of the phosphorylase from
Azotobacter by using chromatography on hydroxyapatite as the final stage in the purification.
During this chromatography, was found to the peak corresponding to the enzymic activity
coincides exactly with the protein peak, this being a good criterion for the homogeneity of the
fraction.

If all that is wanted is the preparation of ribonucleic polynucleotides of high molecular weight,
there is no need to use highly purified enzyme from *A. vinelandii*; Shiobara and Itagaki (1965)
have shown that a partially purified enzyme preparation suffices, on condition that the polymers
are protected from enzymic degradation by urea.

1, Properties of the various polynucleotide-phosphorylases

Enzymic preparations from *A. vinelandii* remain active for periods of up to a year provided
that they are kept at -18°.   They are nevertheless deactivated by a series of successive freezings
and thawings.   Heating at 50° for 5 minutes at pH 5.8 destroys 50 % of the enzymic activity.
The enzyme is completely destroyed by heating for 5 minutes at 60° and pH 5.6, or for one minute
at 100° and pH 7.4.   The optimum pH for activity is 8.1.

Incubation of the purified enzyme with nucleoside diphosphates results in the disappearance
of the latter with the liberation of the stoichiometric amount of inorganic phosphate.   The nucleotide in question is replaced by a water-soluble product which is not dialysable but is precipitated

by trichloracetic acid and alcohol. A polymer obtained, for example, from IDP yields IMP on mild alkaline hydrolysis, and thus appears as a poly-IMP. Inosine-3'-phosphate and inosine-2'-phosphate have been identified among the products of basic hydrolysis of the polymer. These results suggest that the polymers are chains of nucleotides, the units being linked together by 3'-5'-phosphodiester bonds as in the natural nucleic acids.

The reaction catalyzed by polynucleotide phosphorylase is reversible. In the presence of the enzyme and Mg^{++}, the IMP polynucleotide suffers phosphorolysis to the IDP stage. The enzyme-catalyzed reaction can therefore be schematically represented by the equation :

$$nX - R - P - P \rightleftharpoons (X - R - P)_n + nPi$$

The synthesis of poly G by polynucleotide phosphorylase catalysis is recognized to be difficult by a majority of workers. It is, nevertheless, made possible by the use of high concentrations of the enzyme and low concentrations of GDP. Under these conditions, single stranded polymers with a degree of polymerization of at least 100 have been synthesized (Fresco and Su, 1962).

Similarly, Thang et al. (1965) have noted that, using the polynucleotide phosphorylase from E. coli, guanylyl polymers of high molecular weight (sedimentation constant 8S) can be obtained, provided a high temperature is maintained, and Mg^{++} ions are present. Polymers obtained in this way react rapidly with polyC to form a stable stoichiometric complex (1 : 1) (Pochon and Michelson, 1965).

Various analogs of nucleoside diphosphates can act as polynucleotide phosphorylase substrates. Szer and Shugar (1961) have shown, for instance, that methyluridine diphosphate is polymerized by the action of the enzyme, forming polymethyluridylate.

In the same way Grunberg-Manago and Michelson (1964) have shown that halonucleoside pyrophosphates such as 5-chloro- (bromo- or iodo-) uridine-5'-pyrophosphates can act as substrate to the Azotobacter vinelandii polynucleotide phosphorylase, both in polymerization and phosphorolysis. The same is true for pseudouridine phosphate, which can be used as the starting point for poly-pseudouridylic acid synthesis (Pochon et al., 1964). The polynucleotide analogs thus obtained have some interesting applications since they are provided with genetic information in the same way as the "normal" ribonucleic polymers (cf. p. 61).

Polynucleotide phosphorylases comparable to the one discovered in Azotobacter vinelandii (or Azotobacter agilis) are very widely distributed enzymes. Among the more closely examined polynucleotide phosphorylases, mention might be made of :

1) Escherichia coli polynucleotide phosphorylase, isolated by Littauer and Kornberg (1957). The enzyme was localized in the ribosomes of E. coli by Andoh et al. (1963), and they attributed to it the principal property of participating in the degradation of messenger RNA by phosphorolysis. This enzyme has in fact been highly purified to the extent of about 600 times (Williams and Grunberg-Manago, 1964; Lucas and Grunberg-Manago, 1964), and has been obtained free from all contamination by related enzymes such as nucleases, phosphatases and kinases. It does not require a primer to polymerize the four standard nucleoside diphosphates. Incubated alone, E. coli polynucleotide phosphorylase begins to lose its activity at 55°, while the optimal temperature for ADP and GDP polymerization and for poly A and C phosphorolysis is 60°. These results suggest that the enzyme is protected against thermal deactivation by the nucleoside diphosphates and or the polymer. It is generally accepted that Mg^{++} is a necessary cation for reactions catalysed by this enzyme, though and bivalent cations except Ca^{++} can replace Mg^{++} in phosphor-

olysis. The behavior of the different cations in the polymerization is variable, and in addition, the enzyme behaves differently in phosphorolysis and polymerization in the presence of each cation (Grunberg-Manago, 1963; Babinet et al., 1965).

2) *Micrococcus lysodeikticus* polynucleotide phosphorylase, an enzyme originally described by Beers (1957) and by Olmsted (1957, 1959a, b). The purification and some of the properties of the enzyme have been studied by Singer and O'Brien (Singer and O'Brien, 1963; Singer, 1963) who brought evidence for a new fundamental property of polynucleotide phosphorylase, namely, the *arsenolysis* of polynucleotides under its influence. This reaction occurs in accordance with the following scheme :

$$(\text{Nucleoside-P})n \xrightarrow[\text{Na}_2\text{HAsO}_4]{\text{Mg}^{++}} n \text{ Nucleoside-P}$$

In other words, the polynucleotides are hydrolyzed to the corresponding mononucleotide stage, the arsenate acting as catalyst. Arsenolysis has been found to occur with polyA, polyC and polyU. With poly G, no evidence of arsenolysis has been found, either before or after treatment of the polymer at 100°. Yeast RNA is very slowly arsenolyzed, while t-RNA is arsenolyzed to a barely significant degree. RNA arsenolysis results in the formation of nucleoside monophosphates. The reaction depends on the presence of polynucleotides, indeed, it is accelerated between 10 to 100 times by the addition of oligonucleotides with a free C-3' hydroxyl group.

Thach and Doty (1965a, b) have shown that *M. lysodeikticus* polynucleotide phosphorylase is able to catalyze the formation of relatively low molecular weight oligonucleotides by the addition of only a few nucleotides at the end of a polynucleotide used as a primer in this way. They were able to synthesize such polymers as :

$$U_{14}^{-} C_6^{-*}, \quad U_{14}^{-} A_5^{-}, \quad U_7^{-} I_3^{-}, \text{ etc.}$$

3) *Clostridium perfringens* polynucleotide phosphorylase, an enzyme isolated from the anaerobic bacteria by Dolin (1962), working in Grunberg-Manago's laboratory, has a somewhat different behavior from that of *Azotobacter*. As its purification progresses, the enzyme becomes more and more specific for ADP, no longer catalyzing CDP and UDP polymerization, while the well-known *Azotobacter* enzyme exhibits the same activity with each of the three substrates whatever its state of purification.

The enzyme from *C. perfringens* is associated with another peculiarity, in that it becomes, when highly purified, completely inactive as a polymerase in the absence of a basic polymer of high molecular weight such as polylysine, polyornithine, etc. The most efficient activators are the poly-α-aminoacids, although polyvinylamine also possesses significant activity.

The fact that several of its activities disappear from the enzyme during its purification tends to show that the crude extract from *C. perfringens* contains at least two enzymes each associated with a different activity (Knight et al., 1963).

4) The polynucleotide phosphorylase from *Streptomyces faecalis* was observed by Abrams and McNamara (1962) in isolated bacterial cell membranes.

The *S. faecalis* cell membranes catalyze a clear synthesis of polyribonucleotides from nucle-

---

* The horizontal line above the figures indicates a polynucleotide consisting of 14 consecutive uridylate residue, then 6 consecutive cytidylate residues.

oside diphosphates, as well as an ADP-^{32}P$_1$ exchange, thereby showing the characteristic properties of a polynucleotide phosphorylase. The membranes are prepared by [metabolic lysis of the protoplasts, a mild process that leaves the membranes in the form of cell ghosts, morphologically recognizable.

2. Properties of the polymers

Polymers containing AMP ,IMP, GMP, UMP or CMP as the unique base have been obtained by incubation of polynucleotide phosphorylase with the corresponding nucleoside-5′-diphosphates. Provided heat and acidity are avoided during the isolation of these polymers, the average molecular weight can attain very high values. Figures of 570,000 and 800,000 have been obtained by light-scattering techniques on the AMP and IMP polymers respectively. Mixed polymers containing adenine and uracil (AU polymers) and the four bases, adenine, guanine, uracil and cytosine in the proportions 1 : 0. 5 : 1 (AGUC polymer) have been synthesised by the same procedure (Grunberg-Manago, Ortiz and Ochoa, 1955; Grunberg-Manago, 1955; Grunberg-Manago, Ortiz and Ochoa, 1956).

The structure of these polymers has been elucidated by employing specific phosphodiesterases (Heppel, Ortiz and Ochoa, 1957a, 1957b). The action of snake venom phosphodiesterase yields nucleotides terminating in 5′-phosphate groups (cf. p. 262), while spleen phosphodiesterase (Heppel, Markham and Hilmoe, 1953; Heppel and Whitfeld, 1955) gives nucleotides terminating in 3′-phosphate groups. Complete digestion of the UMP polymer with crystalline pancreatic ribonuclease gives uridine-5′-monophosphate, while uridine cyclic-2′ : 3′-monophosphate is obtained using dilute ribonuclease.

The sum of these results, obtained with a variety of enzymes, and coupled with the results from X-ray analysis of the polymers, tends to prove that there is a close analogy between these biosynthetic polymers and natural ribonucleic acids.

The structure of poly A fibers at acid pH has been examined by Rich et al. (1961), who propose a model consisting of two parallel helical twin chains, each with a pitch of 3.8 Å and an angle of 45º.

Warner (1957) has demonstrated that poly-A and poly-U which have been enzymically synthe sized, react spontaneously in dilute saline solution with each other to form a stable aggregate- of high molecular weight and of lower extinction coefficient than either of the constituents. The aggregate migrates electrophoretically as a single compound having a mobility intermediate between that of its two components. It is also possible to obtain mixed complexes between oligonucleotides and polymers (Lipsett et al., 1961).

Concerning the resistance various ribonucleotides show towards phosphorolysis by polynucleotide phosphorylase from A. vinelandii, Ochoa (1957) has pointed out that ribonucleotides can be classified into three groups according to their susceptibility to this enzyme :

a. those which are rapidly phosphorolysed : poly-A, poly-U, and in general the polymers of the same nucleotide;

b. those which are slowly phosphorolysed : synthetic poly-AGUC, yeast and bacterial RNA, and poly-(A + U) aggregates;

c. those which are phosphorolysed at an intermediate rate : tobacco mosaic virus RNA.

The slower phosphorolysis of the polynucleotides in group b) could be due to the fact that, unlike those of group a), they consist largely of multiple strands rather than simple strands. Similarly, the medium speed of phosphorolysis of tobacco mosaic virus RNA is explicable by the slight tendency its components have of adopting a multiple strand structure.

Singer et al. (Singer, Heppel and Hilmoe, 1957) noticed that with highly purified preparations of polynucleotide phosphorylases isolated from *A. vinelandii*, the formation of polymers from nucleotide diphosphates occurs only after an initial latent period. This latent period can be completely suppressed by the presence of pApApA. The same "priming" effect can be achieved with the dinucleotide pApA and the tetranucleotide pApApApA. Similar observations have been made of the phosphorylase from *Micrococcus lysodeikticus* (Singer and Guss, 1962).

B. SYNTHESIS OF DNA-TYPE POLYNUCLEOTIDES : DEOXYNUCLEOSIDE TRIPHOSPHATE : DNA DEOXY- NUCLEOTIDYL TRANSFERASE (EC 2.7.7.7)

The preliminary studies of Kornberg and his co-workers (Kornberg, Lehman and Simms, 1956; Kornberg, Lehman, Bessman and Simms, 1956) had resulted in the discovery of an enzyme system contained in *E. coli* extracts that was able to effect the incorporation of deoxyribonucleotides into DNA. Two publications by the same authors (Lehman, Bessman, Simms and Kornberg, 1958; Bessman, Lehman, Simms and ¡Kornberg, 1958) described the experiments they carried out in their systematic work on the enzyme. Purification of the enzyme led to the discovery that the four natural deoxyribonucleotides as their triphosphates were necessary, as well as the presence of highly polymerised DNA and Mg^{++} ions. Deoxyribonucleoside diphosphates are inert. The DNA synthesis is accompanied by the liberation of inorganic phosphate. These findings led to representing the reaction by the equation :

$$
n \begin{cases} \text{d-ppp*T} \\ \text{d-ppp*G} \\ \text{d-ppp*C} \\ \text{d-ppp*A} \end{cases} + \text{DNA} \rightleftharpoons \text{DNA} - \begin{vmatrix} \text{dp*T} \\ \text{dp*G} \\ \text{dp*C} \\ \text{dp*A} \end{vmatrix} + 4 \text{ (n) pp}
$$

The enzyme responsible for the incorporation of deoxyribonucleotides to form a high molecular weight deoxyribonucleic polymer was originally called DNA polymerase by Kornberg et al., the name being later given officially as DNA Deoxynucleoside triphosphate : deoxynucleoti- dyltransferase was abbreviated to DNA nucleotidyl transferase (E.C.2.7.7.7) by the enzyme nomenclature commision (1965).

The need for working with labeled substrates led Kornberg to prepare nucleoside triphos- phate ^{32}P labeled on the first phosphate. This was done by growing *E. coli* on a medium containing orthophosphate ^{32}P. The DNA was then isolated from the bacteria by a known method and hydrolyzed to the mononucleotide stage by treatment with first, crystalline pancreatic DNase, then with phosphodiesterase free from 5'-nucleotidase. The labeled and unlabeled mononu- cleotides which are actually nucleoside-5'-monophosphates are converted to nucleoside triphos- phates by the action of a "deoxynucleotide kinase", also extracted from *E. coli*, in the presence of ATP. The excess ATP can be selectively destroyed, even in the presence of deoxyribonu- cleotide, by periodate and alkali treatment. The nucleoside triphosphates are finally isolated by chromatography on Dowex 1.

The polymerase subsequently serving to incorporate nucleotides into DNA was purified more than 2,000-fold by precipitation with streptomycin, treatment with DNase, adsorption on and elution from Cγ alumina, and fractionation on DEAE-cellulose.

Maximal incorporation of labeled deoxyribonucleotide into DNA depends on the presence of highly polymerized DNA, Mg^{++} and deoxyribonucleoside triphosphates of thymine, cytosine, guanine and adenine.

A comparison based on the incorporation of labeled thymidine triphosphate, d-pppT, shows that the incorporation is the same as when d-pppA, d-pppC or thymidine triphosphate ^{14}C are used as substrate. Omitting any one of these triphosphates reduces the rate of incorporation to 0.5 % of its maximum value, while leaving out the DNA suppresses all synthesis practically completely (less than 0.05 %).

Under optimal conditions, "new" DNA is synthesized in amounts of up to 10 times the quantity of "primer" DNA added, and analysis of the dinucleotides obtained by hydrolysis of the "new" DNA with pancreatic DNase shows that these nucleotides contain the 3'-5'-phosphodiester linkages characteristic of DNA isolated from natural sources. Taking all these results together, they prove that a close analogy exists between the natural deoxyribonucleic acids and deoxyribonucleic acids synthesised by *E. coli* polymerase.

Davidson and co-workers (Smellie, McArdle, Keir and Davidson, 1958; Davidson, Smellie, Keir and McArdle, 1958) have shown that "non-particulate" cell extracts of mammals were able to effect the synthesis of deoxyribonucleic acid *in vitro*. Bollum (1960) has similarly shown the presence of polymerase in thymus, and Main and Cole (1965) the presence of DNA polymerase in the nuclear thymus fractions isolated in the presence of Ca^{++}.

The spatial configuration of these biosynthetic polymers of the deoxyribonucleic type has also been examined, and it has been accepted that it is helical in the same way as natural DNA. Whilst the AT polymer is formed by two complementary strands in which A and T alternate within the chains (1), polymer GC consists of a C chain a G chain, without there being an alternation within the chain (II) (Radding, Josse and Kornberg, 1962).

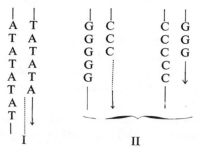

The unprimed synthesis of a GC polymer from the corresponding triphosphates can take place in the absence of the priming polymer only after a long latent period. The GC polymer isolated from the reaction will prime the enzymic synthesis of an identical polymer. The kinetics of the primed and unprimed reactions have been studied by Radding and Kornberg (1962). Using 5-bromodeoxycytidine triphosphate as substrate in place of deoxycytidine triphosphate, Rading et al. (1962) have synthesized polyguanylic-polybromocytidylic acid, that is remarkably stable.

Mixed synthetic polymers of the DNA-RNA type can be obtained by artificially combining polydeoxyguanylic and polycytidylic acids (Schildkraut et al., 1961). This complex has a similar helical structure to DNA, but is much more stable than the one in which the two strands are of the deoxyribose type as in DNA. This result suggests that in nature, complementary DNA and RNA strands should, in appropriate circumstances, combine preferentially. Subsequently, the RNA carrying genetic information by virtue of its base sequence, can be distinguished from the other RNA by its ability to combine with the DNA of the same cell.

The analogy between the synthetic polymers obtained by Kornberg and co-workers and natural DNA has been reinforced by Sueoka and Cheng's work (1962a, b). They discovered polymers such as poly (deoxyadenylate-thymidylate) of natural origin, during examination of various DNA samples coming from several animal species, when they found that the DNA distribution in a centrifugal gradient is generally unimodal, but that there are exceptions. In particular, the DNA isolated from marine crabs (*Cancer borealis* and *Cancer irroratus*) possesses an additional band of lower density than the principal DNA band. The relative "light DNA" content is 30 % in *C. borealis* and 10 % in *C. irroratus*. This light DNA contains 97 % deoxyadenylate and thymidylate in which alternating sequences predominate.

C. MIXED DNA-RNA POLYMERS

Mixed DNA-RNA polymers have been obtained by Lee Huang and Cavalieri (1964) using an *E. coli* enzyme. The polymers obtained under these conditions are homopolymeric DNA-RNA hybrids. The products synthesized by Lee Huang and Cavalieri's enzyme are ordered structures of high molecular weight. Polymers such as poly (dG + C) and poly (dC + G) obtained when poly (C + I) is used as primer, have a sedimentation constant of 12 S.

III. NUCLEOPROTEINS AND TISSUE NUCLEIC ACIDS

A. PREPARATION OF NUCLEOPROTEINS

1. Ribonucleoproteins

As an example we will briefly describe here the isolation of nucleotropomyosin from carp muscle by Hamoir's method (1951).

The preparation is carried out throughout in the cold and all separations are done by centrifugation. Carp muscles cut with a freezing microtome into slices 40μ thick (Dubuisson, 1947) are extracted for 20 min. with 3 vol. of a KCl-phosphate solution (0.15 M-KCl and 0.1 M-KH$_2$PO$_4$ brought to pH 5). This extract is diluted with 3.5 vol. of cold water; the precipitate is dicarded and the supernatant (1) kept.

The residue from this first extraction is re-extracted for 10 min. with 3 vol. of 0.5 M-phosphate solution of pH 5.5 containing 0.3 % sodium adenosine triphosphate. The residue is discarded and the extract (II) is diluted with 7 vol. of water. A precipitate of myosins and nucleotropomyosin forms which is washed twice with water and redissolved in 0.5 M-KCl at neutral pH. The supernatant (II) and the supernatant (I) are mixed and brought to pH 4.6. The precipitate containing tropomyosin is washed twice with water and redissolved in 0.5 M-KCl at neutral pH.

Both solutions are now centrifuged for 30 min. at 14,000 rev./min. to remove some turbid material and are purified by a second precipitation by dilution with 8 vol. of water at neutral pH (nucleotropomyosin) or at pH 4.6 (tropomyosin). The precipitates are washed twice with water and redissolved in 0.5 M-KCl at neutral pH.

Both tropomyosins are isolated from these two solutions by $(NH_4)_2SO_4$ fractionation at neutral pH : the major part of the total protein content of the solutions precipitates between 30 and 50 % saturation, whilst the tropomyosins precipitate between 50 and 66 % saturation. The precipitate can be redissolved very quickly by a slight dilution with water, giving a water-clear solution.

Although these methods of preparation are very reproducible, some variations are observed in the yields obtained, which are usually about 0.07 % of the wet weight for nucleotropomyosin and 0.03 % for tropomyosin. A better yield, amounting to 0.5 % of the fresh muscle weight, has been obtained after organic solvent treatment (Bailey, 1948). This discrepancy is not due to loss during the isolation. The quantity of tropomyosins and myosins extracted from fresh muscles under the conditions described amounts to 1 % of the wet weight and the tropomyosin content of the solution varies from 10 to 20 %. Fractionation by $(NH_4)_2SO_4$ is very effective : no precipitation of tropomyosin occurs before 40 % saturation while the major part of the myosins has already been removed. The denaturation of the myosins by organic solvent treatment probably increases the differences in extractability of the myosins and tropomyosins and allows a more complete removal of the tropomyosins.

Crystallization. The undiluted salted-out precipitates are used for crystallization. This is carried out using the conditions previously described for tropomyosin (Bailey, 1948), i.e. by dialysing an approx. 1.5 % solution against a solution containing 16 g. $(NH_4)_2SO_4/l.$ and 0.01 M-acetate buffer of pH 5.4. Nucleotropomyosin crystallizes in elongated prisms, tropomyosin in quadrangular plates.

2. Deoxyribonucleoproteins

Various methods have been described in the past 20 years for the preparation of deoxyribonucleoproteins, e.g. by Mirsky and Pollister (1952, 1943a, b, 1946a, b), Pollister and Mirsky (1946, quoted with comments by Frick 1949), Crampton et al. (1954), Busch (1965)... etc. Here we shall only give two examples of such preparations :

1) Preparation of calf thymus nucleohistone (thymonucleohistone or thymonucleoprotein) according to Crampton, Lipshitz and Chargaff (1954).

Trimmed calf thymus was obtained fresh from the slaughter-house, chilled immediately, and processed without delay. All subsequent operations were performed at 4-6°. Fifty-gram portions of tissue were triturated for 30 seconds in a high-speed mixer equipped with cutting blades with 50 ml. of an ice-cold mixture of aqueous 0.1 M NaCl and 0.05 M sodium citrate (previously adjusted to pH 7). The supernatant fluid obtained from centrifugation at 2000 × g for 30 minutes was discarded and the suspension of the sediment in 100 ml. of saline-citrate once more centrifuged. The sediment was washed three times by thorough resuspension and centrifugation, each time with 50 ml. of distilled water (previously adjusted to pH 7 by being made about 0.0004 M with respect to $NaHCO_3$), in order to remove electrolytes. During the final washing the sediment swelled, but yielded less than 0.5 % of its total phosphorus to the supernatant fluid. The gelatinous sediment then was blended (15 seconds in the high-speed mixer) with 250 ml. of distilled water (pH 7) and shaken overnight. The extremely viscous mixture was again briefly stirred in the high-speed mixer and centrifuged for 30 minutes at 2000 × *g*. The P contents of the very viscous, opalescent supernatant fluids averaged 430 µg. per ml. (about 90 % of total P in the mixture). The reextraction of the insoluble residue with water or M NaCl yielded negligible amounts of P.

For the precipitation of the nucleohistone the aqueous solution was made 0.15 M with respect to NaCl by the addition of 5.66 vol. of 0.177 M NaCl. The resulting precipitate was collected 30 minutes later by centrifugation and washed on the centrifuge with 0.15 M NaCl and then, very briefly, with a very small amount of distilled water. The weight ratio of protein to P in such preparations was approximately 12.

2) A nucleoprotein preparation : the nucleoprotein from trout sperm (Pollister and Mirsky, 1946).

Before extraction, the trout sperm are washed to free them of the small quantities of intercellular material present. The wash fluid contains in 1000 ml. : 7.8 gm. NaCl, 0.664 gm. KCl, and 0.687 gm. K_2SO_4. After stirring, the sperm suspension is centrifuged at 5000 revolutions per minute for 15 minutes. The supernatant is waterclear.

The washed sperm are extracted with 1 M NaCl, final concentration after mixing. On adding salt solution, the sperm mass immediately becomes sticky and gelatinous, so that it appears at first as if the cells are merely swelling. It is necessary to add a large volume of solution and to stir vigorously in a Waring mixer before it becomes apparent that the cells are breaking up as their contents pass into solution. For a mass of sperm with a dry weight of 900 mg. the volume of the extraction mixture should be about 500 ml. Even so, the mixture is quite viscous. After vigorous stirring the mixture is centrifuged at 12,000 revolutions per minute for 60 minutes. A perfectly clear, viscous supernatant and a scanty residue are obtained. The material extracted from the sperm is precipitated by pouring the supernatant into 6 volumes of water. The precipitate is in the form of long fibrous strands, so fibrous that they can easily be wound around a rod and, if the rod has a crook at its lower end, the fibers can be transferred to another vessel while still clinging to the rod. If the fibers are not twisted around a rod they soon settle and ofter the supernatant is decanted, much fluid can be pressed from the fibrous mass. The fibrous precipitate redissolves in 1 M NaCl. Vigorous stirring shortens the time needed to dissolve the precipitate. The solution is as viscous as it was when the material was initally extracted from the sperm. Any suspended particles are removed by centrifugation and the dissolved material is then reprecipitated by pouring the solution into 6 volumes of water. The precipitate has the same fibrous character as when first formed. The fibrous material is soluble in 1 M NaCl and insoluble in 0.14 M NaCl and, because of these properties can easily be reprecipitated and redissolved any number of times. Dissolved in 1 M NaCl it keeps well without any preservative at 0°.

A fibrous nucleoprotein has also been extracted with 1 M NaCl from the sperm of another fish, the shad. From the sperm of the sea urchin, key-hole limpet, and fresh-water clam no nucleoprotein was extractable with 1 M NaCl. With 2 M NaCl, however, there was no difficulty extracting fibrous nucleoproteins from this sperm. From frog and mouse testes, nucleoproteins were extracted with 1 M NaCl. No nucleoproteins could be extracted from bull sperm (obtained by centrifuging bull semen) with either 1 M or 2 M NaCl. It would be interesting to know the nature of the change that occurs in the maturation of mammalian sperm that prevents extraction of nucleoproteins with concentrated salt solutions.

3. Examples of virus preparations

a. *Tobacco mosaic virus*

This virus has been much studied on account of its high stability, indeed, it will retains its infectious properties for years at room temperature. It can infect large numbers of plants, but it is preferably grown on tobacco and tomato. In the case of the tomato, it is possible to arrive at a virus concentration of the order of 1-2 g per liter cell fluid, but in young plants this concentration can easily be surpassed (Markham and Smith, 1954).

Sap from diseased plants is heated rapidly to 60°, cooled, and centrifuged. Half a volume of saturated $(NH_4)_2SO_4$ is added to the supernatant liquid, and the virus precipitates as fine needles which cause the suspension to show a silky sheen when it is stirred. The needles are centrifuged off, and the supernatant liquid is discarded. The pellet is redissolved in water using about 1/5-1/10 the sap volume, and the solution is centrifuged to remove debris. The virus is then precipitated with salt and resuspended as before, previously. The solution may then be dialyzed against running tap water and then centrifuged to remove any precipitate, or it may be treated with trypsin (0.5 per cent in solution) for a day at 37°. The trypsin is removed in the supernatants when the virus is precipitated a few times with ammonium sulfate.

The purified virus is best stored in water as a 1 per cent solution or as a precipitate under ammonium sulfate. It should *not* be dried under any circumstance, as drying tends to make it insoluble. The process known variously as freeze-drying or lyophilization is particularly to be avoided, nor should the solutions be frozen for the purpose of storage. These remarks apply equally to other plant viruses, which should *always* be kept either as solutions or under strong salt solutions.

Under examination in the electron microscope, the virus appears as rods hexagonal cross-section. This electron microscopic examination has allowed the length of the monomer to be determined, and which is found to be 298 ± 1 mμ (Williams and Steere, 1951). The molecular weight of the virus has been determined by several methods such as sedimentation, diffusion, viscosity (Lauffer, 1944), light scattering (Oster, Doty and Zimm, 1947) and even by an original method due to Williams and co-workers (1951) consisting in counting the number of particles actually observed in the electron microscope in a known dry weight of virus. This molecular weight turns out to be 50×10^6.

Ribonucleic acid constitutes only 6 % of the virus; its purine and pyrimidine base ratio has been given (p. 36), and it is readily separable from the protein part of the virus (Gierer and Schramm, 1956). In a series of brilliant papers (Fraenkel-Conrat et al., 1956, 1957, 1959 etc., and also Schramm and co-workers, e.g. Schramm, 1959) it was demonstrated that the two components, RNA and protein, apparently inactive when used separately, are able to reconstitute the active virus if they are artificially recombined. Indeed, it became rapidly apparent that a small amount of RNA alone was able to initiate infection and cause the complete formation of the virus. This RNA alone has only very weak infecting power, of the order of 0.1 — 0.5 % of the RNA activity of the intact virus. It is likely that this weakening of the activity is due to degradation of the RNA in the course of its extraction by the influence of the various RNases that are known to be present in all vegetable tissues. Gierer (1957) has reported that a molecular weight of at least 2 million is needed for infecting action of this RNA.

b. *Tomato bushy stunt virus*

Markham and Smith (1954) have shown that this nomenclature is doubly unsatisfactory, since in the first place the virus develops on the tomato only with difficulty, and secondly, if it does develop, it rarely leads to the formation of a bushy plant. The *Datura* plant (*tatula* or *stramonium*) constitutes a much more satisfactory host than the tomato.

The sap from *Datura* or tomato plants is best clarified with ethanol (300 ml. to each liter), and the virus is precipitated by the addition of 1/2 vol. of saturated ammonium sulfate. The precipitation is repeated, and a further purification may be carried out by adjusting the solution to pH 4 with acetic acid. The virus is soluble over a wide range of pH values including the iso-electric point, which is pH 4.6. Treatment with trypsin is also possible, but the virus should be kept at low temperatures as much as possible, because it rapidly loses infectivity at temperatures above 20° without any apparent chemical or immunological change taking place.

Crystallization is carried out by a procedure which has been used for several plant viruses (Bawden & Pirie 1938). Bushy stunt virus is precipitated by ammonium sulfate in an amorphous form which has a negative temperature coefficient of solubility. On cooling the syspension to 0-5°, the amorphous material goes into solution, and the salt concentration is then adjusted until the solution is saturated with the amorphous form of the virus. On standing at 0-5° for a few days, the virus deposits in the form of beautiful rhombic dodecahedral crystals. These crystals only dissolve slowly in water, thus can be washed rapidly with water on the centrifuge as a further stage of purification.

This virus has a molecular weight of 10.6×10^6, and an exceptionally high nucleic acid content of 16 %. Contrary to what happens with most viruses, the nucleic acid is so firmly bound to the protein part that it is impossible to dissociate them without profound alteration of the two components. The reasons behind this unusual affinity are still obscure; it is possible that the high proportion of basic aminoacids in the protein is related to the phenomenon.

B. Nucleic acid preparation

1. Ribonucleic acids

Generally speaking, the isolation of ribonucleic acids encounters two main difficulties :

1) Elimination as completely as possible of the protein without damaging the ribonucleic acid.

2) Preventing hydrolysis by the ribonucleases which are now known to be present in all tissues.

General reviews on the preparation of RNA have been written by Magasanik (1955) and F. W. Allen (1962).

a. *Preparation of ribonucleic acids from mammalian tissue by the method of Volkin and Carter* (1951)

The method consists of *a*) removal of the DNA as a DNA-protein complex; *b*) RNA precipitation from a cold solution of 2 M guanidine hydrochloride, during which most of the proteins remain in solution; *c*) further purification of the ribonucleic acid by extraction in chloroform and precipitation with alcohol.

The possibility for nuclease action during the preliminary stages of the preparation can be avoided by homogenizing the tissue directly in the concentrated guanidine hydrochloride solution, this reagent being an efficient protein denaturant. The method to be described below is applicable to a large selection of mammalian tissue, and the experimental details to be followed are as follows :

Fresh or frozen tissue was cut in small pieces and blended for 6 to 8 minutes with 3 volumes per gram tissue of a 0.15 M sodium chloride-0.02 M phosphate buffer, pH 6.8. A few drops of octyl alcohol were added to reduce foaming. The homogenate was then centrifuged at 3,000 g for 30 minutes. Essentially all the desoxyribonucleic acid was removed in the form of an insoluble nucleic acid protein complex as described by Mirsky and Pollister (1946). All operations were carried out between 2 and 5°.

To the supernatant solution enough solid guanidine hydrochloride was added, with rapid stirring, to make the solution 2 molar with respect to guanidine hydrochloride. The solution was placed in a 38° bath and allowed to stand at this temperature for 30 minutes, then chilled at 0° for 1 hour. Under these conditions most of the protein of the tissue extract remained soluble, while a gelatinous precipitate formed which contained ribonucleic acid and a small amount of protein. The precipitate was washed twice with a cold solution of 2 M guanidine hydrochloride in pH 6.8 saline-phosphate buffer. By this process any deoxyribonucleoprotein which remained soluble in the high guanidine concentration was removed by the washing process. To remove the contaminating proteins the precipitate was then suspended in 2 M guanidine hydrochloride (one volume per gram of original tissue) and extracted with chloroform-octyl alcohol 5/1. The suspension of nucleic acid in guanidine hydrochloride was added to an equal volume of the chloroform-octyl alcohol mixture, warmed to 40°, then shaken mechanically for 30 minutes. The mixture was centrifuged and the upper aqueous layer containing the nucleic acid removed. The extraction of the aqueous solution at 40° was repeated twice with fresh chloroform-octyl alcohol. Extractions in the cold, or in saline or water solutions, resulted in incomplete separation of the nucleic acid from protein. Nucleic acid was precipitated in the cold from the guanidine solution by adjusting the acidity to pH 4.2-4.5 with acetic acid and adding two volumes of cold ethanol. The white, flocculent ribonucleic acid precipitate was centrifuged and washed twice with cold 70 % alcohol. The precipitate was then dissolved in water, carefully adjusted to pH 6.8 with dilute sodium hydroxide and any insoluble material (denatured protein) centrifuged off. The ribonucleic acid was purified by adding enough 1 M sodium chloride to bring the final concentration to 0.05 M sodium chloride and precipitating the sodium ribonucleate with 2 volumes of cold ethanol. The product was washed twice with cold 70 % ethanol.

In the second method the tissue was immediately homogenized with 3 volumes per gram tissue of cold 2.5 M guanidine hydrochloride solution. The rest of the procedure followed that of the first method, except that the ribonucleic acid-protein complex was washed at least three times with cold 2 M guanidine hydrochloride to ensure complete removal of any contaminating deoxyribonucleic acid. Excess foaming, which occurred during the blending in the presence of guanidine hydrochloride, was alleviated by adding a few drops of octyl alcohol after the solution had been warmed for a few minutes in the 38° bath.

Duplicate liver ribonucleic acid preparations made by the two methods yielded essentially identical analytical compositions, indicating that in liver little or no enzymatic hydrolysis occurred in the first procedure.

The mammalian ribonucleic acids dissolved readily in water to give clear, colorless solutions. Preparations to be stored were lyophilized from water solutions. Concentrations as high as 20 mg. per ml. failed to give a reaction with diphenylamine reagent, indicating that all the nucleic acid was of the ribose type. Similar concentrations gave negative biuret tests. The yield of ribonucleic acids varied from 20 to 30 % of the total tissue ribonucleic acid.

b. *Improved method for preparation of rat liver RNA (Kirby, 1962, 1965)*

Rats were killed by breaking their necks, the livers were removed quickly and dropped immediately on to solid CO_2. Liver (50 g) was broken down in a high-speed mixer in 0.015 M naphthalene-1,5-disulphonate (400 ml, pH 6.8) and mixed quickly with phenol (400 ml of 90 % containing 0.1 % 8-hydroxyquinoline, Analar). The mixture was stirred for 20 min at 20° and then centrifuged at 700 × g for 40 min at 0°. The supernatant liquid was removed by suction and the interfacial material which was packed tightly at the interface was either washed with a further 50 ml of 0.015 M naphthalene-1,5-disulphonate or withdrawn and centrifuged at 5000 × g for 15 min at 0°. The supernatant fractions were combined and after addition of 2 vol. of ethanol the RNA which precipitated was deposited by centrifugation (700 × g for 10 min at 0°). The sediment was washed once with ethanol-water (3 : 1) and then with 2-methoxyethanol (30 ml). After this washing it was essential to centrifuge the mixture in polyethylene tubes at about 5000 × g for 20 min at 0° to pack the precipitate as tightly as possible, otherwise the separation from glycogen proved difficult. The precipitate dissolved completely in water (20-35 ml, depending upon the glycogen content) and the RNA separated from glycogen by mixing with equal vol. of 2.5 M potassium phosphate (pH 7.5) and 2-methoxyethanol and isolating as described before.

If it was necessary to use larger volumes for the 2-phase separation of RNA from glycogen it was possible to precipitate the RNA from the methoxyethanol phase by adding 1.5 vol. ethanol. The precipitate was centrifuged off, mixed with water (20 ml), dialysed and the RNA recovered in the usual way.

The same volume of dimethyl sulphoxide could be used in place of 2-methoxyethanol to separate RNA from glycogen. RNA was again entirely in the upper phase and in this case a lower centrifugal speed was required to separate the polysaccharides. This solvent system may therefore be of value when separation of RNA from polysaccharides proves difficult.

The yield of RNA was about 750 mg/100 g rat liver.

Analyses of the RNA showed P, 6.45 % and $\varepsilon(P)$ (water) 8650 and the base composition was guanine : adenine : cytosine : uracil = 32.8 : 19.2 : 31.0 : 17.0.

The similarity between G/C and A/U is striking, and this observation tends to support the theory that RNA has a paired strand structure.

Kirby (1965) has also given a method enabling ribosomal RNA to be obtained from rat liver : the total RNA is extracted by a phenol-cresol mixture, and the ribosomal RNA can then be selectively precipitated by *m*-cresol. The yield of ribosomal RNA is about 60 mg from two livers (14 g).

Two main constituents can be separated from this RNA by centrifugation in a sucrose gradient. One constituent at 28S and one at 18S are obtained, the purine and pyrimidine base ratio of which (see p. 36) indicates a double strand structure.

c. *Preparation of wheat germ RNA by the method of Glitz and Dekker* (1963)

Wheat germ RNA is purified by treatment of a de-fatted aqueous extract with phenol by what is now a standard technique. The RNA extracted in this way contains a small proportion of t-RNA and a main macromolecular fraction that can be sub-divided by ultracentrifugation into two components : one 18S component and one 24S component. The high molecular weight of these two components points to a ribosomal origin.

d. *Preparation of yeast ribonucleic acid (macromolecular RNA)*

The preparation was made from freshly ground, defatted baker's yeast (Chargaff et al., 1950). The yeast cells (95 g.) were washed with 0.14 M NaCl, and then with 50, 75, 95, and 100 % ethanol. Their suspension in equal volumes of 0.14 M NaCl and absolute alcohol was passed throughan ice cooled wet crushing mill for bacteria and 2 vol. (240 ml.) of 70% ethanol was added to the mixture. The precipitate mostly of crushed cells was washed repeatedly with 80 and 90 % ethanol, ethano-ether (1 : 1), and ether, and dried *in vacuo*. It was twice extracted with 100-ml. portions of 10 % aqueous sodium chloride at 90° for 1/2 hour, and 2 vol. of ethanol was added to the combined centrifuged extracts. The resulting precipitate, washed with dilute and absolute alcohol and ether and dried, weighed 0.71 g. It was taken up in 35 ml. of water, the mixture was centrifuged, and 0.25 vol. of 20 % barium acetate solution (pH 7) and 1 vol. of ethanol were added to the supernatant. The precipitate resulting from the centrifugation of the chilled mixture was washed with 5 % barium acetate and its aqueous suspension (17 ml.) stirred in a high-speed mixer in the presence of a small excess (150 mg.) of sodium sulfate. The solution, clarified by centrifugation, was freed of protein by being stirred six times in a high-speed mixer with chloroform-octanol (9 : 1) and then was poured into 2 ½ vol. of ice-cold ethanol (50 ml.) that was made 0.05 N with respect to HCl. The mixture was chilled overnight and the precipitate, after being washed with alcohol, was suspended in 20 ml. of water and brought into solution by the cautious addition of dilute ammonia to pH 6. The precipitation with acidified alcohol was repeated and the nucleic acid washed with 80 and 100 % alcohol and ether and dried, when 0.17 g. of an almost white powder was obtained.

An improved technique has been proposed by Crestfield et al. (1955) in which the RNA is rapidly extracted hot in the presence of dodecyl sulfate then precipitated with alcohol and 1 M NaCl.

e. *Preparation of a viral "infectious" RNA from several RNA-containing viruses*

The first infectious RNA from virus was extracted from tobacco mosaic virus following a procedure described by Gierer and Schramm (1956). The originality of this procedure lies in carrying out as rapid an extraction as possible of the RNA in order to avoid any degradation by the nucleolytic enzymes. The technique has since been applied to extraction of all the nucleic acids, RNA as well as DNA.

A 10 % solution of tobacco mosaic virus in 0.02 M phosphate buffer at pH 7.3 is shaken for 8 minutes at 5° with an equal volume of phenol saturated with water. The aqueous phase containing the ribonucleic acid is separated by centrifugation and the phenol extraction procedure repeated at least twice for two minutes. The phenol is then extracted from the aqueous phase with ether. The whole of the extraction is carried out at 5° and must not last longer than 50 minutes and it is immediately followed by an infectivity test.

The RNA thus obtained can be fractionated : 97 % of it can be precipitated by NaCl to give infectious material, the part remaining in solution no longer being infectious. The precipitated material is heterogeneous by ultracentrifugation, although the bulk of it has a sedimentation constant of 35 S in 0.2 M NaCl, corresponding to a whole RNA molecule per viral particle (Miura et al., 1963).

Infectious RNAs have also been isolated and characterized from many other RNA-containing viruses; examples are the infectious RNA from polio virus (Bachrach, 1961; Loddo et al., 1963), the foot and mouth disease virus (Bachrach, 1961), the coxsackie virus (Kiepal-Kochanska and Taytsch, 1963) and the infectious RNA extracted from bacterial viruses (or RNA-containing bacteriophages) (Takito et al., 1965).

f. Transfer RNA

The predominating role played by low molecular weight RNA, or t-RNA in the incorporation of aminoacids into proteins, i.e. in protein synthesis, has been known since the work of Hoagland, Zamecnik and their co-workers (e.g. the review by Hoagland, 1958). This role was briefly recalled in Chapter I, and an example of the preparation of this t-RNA will now be given. Complete structural studies of nucleic acids should start with these because of their relative simplicity (see p. 302).

The t-RNAs form part of the "pH 5 enzymes" fraction, and their preparation takes place in two stages : isolation of the pH 5 enzymes and working up of the t-RNA from the pH 5 enzymes.

Preparation of microsomes and pH 5 *enzymes (Zamecnik and Keller, 1954; Keller and Zamecnik 1956)* Rat liver (18 g) is minced in fractions of 3.5 g with 2.3 volumes of buffered medium. The liver is initially cut up with scissors for 15-20 seconds in 1 ml of the medium (see below for composition) in a glass recepticle surrounded with ice. The chopped up liver is transferred to a tube for blending which is kept in an ice bath at 0°, and is blended for 15-25 seconds in 2.5 times its weight of medium with a pre-cooled glass pestle. Wide variations from these proportions produce less favorable results. The difference between the diameter of the tube and that of the pestle is generally 0.6 mm, and the speed of revolution of the pestle is 600 r.p.m.

The medium used for blending contains : 0.35 M sucrose, 0.035 M $KHCO_3$, 0.004 M $MgCl_2$ and 0.025 M KCl (medium A). The homogenate is centrifuged at 15,000 g for 10 minutes at 0°. The supernatant containing the microsomes and the soluble cell fractions is removed and diluted with 3 volumes of unbuffered medium containing 0.90 M sucrose, 0.004 M $MgCl_2$ and 0.025 M KCl (medium B). The diluted extract is centrifuged at 105.000 g (average R) for 90-120 minutes in a preparative ultracentrifuge ("Spinco") in order to ensure the most complete sedimentation possible of the microsomal particles.

The clear supernatant is removed with a pipette. The pH 5 enzymes are precipitated from this fraction at the same time as the t-RNA by adjusting the pH to 5.2.

The pH 5 enzyme fraction containing the t-RNA can be labeled with ^{14}C in the following way : 10 ml of the fraction (containing 100 — 200 mg protein) dissolved in buffered medium (medium A) are incubated with 4.0 μmoles L-leucine ^{14}C (containing 7.2 × 10^6 cpm) and 200 μmoles ATP to make a final volume of 20 ml, for 10 minutes at 37°. The reaction mixture is cooled to 0°, diluted 3 times with cold water and the enzymes precipitated by the addition of

1.0 M acetic acid to pH 5.2. The precipitate is redissolved in 5 — 10 ml buffered medium, diluted again to 60 ml with water, and the enzymes precipitated at pH 5.2 ¡with acetic acid. The final precipitate is washed with water and dissolved in 5 — 10 ml of cold buffered medium.

Isolation of the t-RNA. This isolation is achieved by minor modifications to the methods of Gierer and Schramm (1956, see, p. 112) and Kirby (1956). The solution of the pH 5 enzymes is shaken mechanically for one hour with an equal volume of 90 % phenol followed by centrifugation at 15,000 *g* for 10 minutes. The aqueous supernatant phase containing the RNA is removed by means of a syringe; water is again added and after shaking energetically, the centrifugation is repeated, with removal of the aqueous phase. The phenol contained in the combined aqueous phases is removed by three ether extractions. Then 0.1 vol. potassium acetate (pH 5) is added and the t-RNA precipitated with 60 % alcohol. The final precipitate is dissolved in a small volume of water and dialyzed against water for 4 hours in the cold.

This method is used on a preparative scale, and yields 50-70 % of the RNA initially present in the pH 5 enzyme preparation.

In the same laboratories (Monier et al., 1960), as well as by Holley et al. (1961), it was shown that low molecular weight RNA which was biologically active could also be obtained from yeast by direct phenol extraction by Kirby's (1956) method. Separation of two soluble RNAs, specific acceptors of valine and tyrosine, was effected by counter-current distribution with only 6 transfers (Holley et al., 1961). This ready separation is due to the fact that these two acceptor RNAs have very different partition coefficients in a system using phosphate buffer at pH 6.0, formamide and isopropanol.

Following this initial observation, Holley's group (Doctor et al., 1961; Holley and Lazar, 1961; Apgar et al., 1962) achieved high purification of the alanine, valine, histidine and tyrosine-accepting RNAs. Adequate precautions must be taken if the fractions obtained are to be stable, in particular, contact with the fingers, which are rich in ribonuclease, must be avoided. The best three fractions of these t-RNAs, the alanine-, valine- and tyrosine acceptors were estimated to be in a sufficiently high state of purity for structural studies to be undertaken. (p. 302)

Other techniques than counter-current distribution have been recommended for the purification of transfer RNA; Stephenson and Zamecnik (1961) suggested the use of reaction of RNA in a first step with a specific dyestuff, followed by chromatography on DEAE-cellulose. In the case of valyl-t-RNA, 65-80 % purification was achieved by this method. The technique can be improved since a purification of about 90 % was achieved during a particularly favorable experiment.

Hartmann and Coy (1961) have used chromatography on hydroxyapatite for the fractionation of specific t-RNAs from yeast, while Zubay (1962) has examined the t-RNA from *Escherichia coli* and the isolation from this material of leucyl-t-RNA. Zubay has shown that t-RNA may be coupled with a single aminoacid, leucine, in a first step. The whole (various free t-RNAs + t-RNA-leucine) is oxidized with periodate, resulting in the appearance of 2′, 3′-dialdehyde groups in the positions where there previously were 2′, 3′ terminal hydroxyls on all the t-RNAs except the leucyl-t-RNA protected by its leucine attached in the 3′-position. The RNA-dialdehyde is separated from the Leu-t-RNA by passage over an aminoethylcellulose column. It is presumed that the dialdehydic t-RNA reacts with the primary amino group to form a Schiff base. This reaction stops the oxidized t-RNA, allowing only the free Leu-t-RNA to pass through the column.

g. *Macromolecular RNA fractionation*

Macromolecular RNA prepared from various sources is often contaminated by a little t-RNA. Harshaw et al. (1962) have shown that it is possible to obtain macromolecular RNA (from mammalian cells) entirely free from t-RNA contamination by means of streptomycin fractionation. Barker and Jones (1964) have used a particular ion exchange system for the fractionation of RNA in which a uracil derivative is attached to cellulose. This is obtained by treating partially acetylated cellulose with 5-hydroxymethyluracil in the presence of dilute acid, then eliminating the acetyl groups by mild alkaline hydrolysis. m-RNA samples from yeast, pig liver and *Serratia marcescens* were fractionated on hydroxymethyluracil-cellulose, and were generally resolved into two or three fractions.

A different system consisting of a column of protamine adsorbed on Hyflo Supercel has also been successfully used in the fractionation of various nucleic acids (Legault-Démare et al., 1964). Interesting results were also obtained using methylated albumin on Celite columns (Koch and Kubinsky, 1964), see also p. 143.

2. Deoxyribonucleic acids

Methods employed in the preparation of DNA generally follow three successive steps : the first step involves rapidly shaking or stirring the disintegrated tissue with a dilute salt solution, in order to dissolve out as many impurities as possible, these including RNA which is soluble in 0.9 % NaCl, DNA remaining insoluble in the form of " chromatin threads". In the second step, the DNA is brought into solution, while a second fraction of impurities is separated, this time by centrifugation. The final stage is the precipitation of DNA from its solution by addition of ethanol. Solubilization of DNA is carried out either by prolonged stirring with salt solution, following the older method of Hammarsten (1924), or in the presence of detergents as in the method of Kay, Simmons and Dounce (1952). These methods have been reviewed and criticized by Chargaff (1955). More recently, phenol extraction has been widely used for DNA as well as for RNA purification.

a. *Preparation of thymus DNA (Kay, Simmons and Dounce, 1952)*

1) Calf thymus is obtained as soon as possible after death of the animal. In order to obtain a product of the highest degree of polymerization, very fresh material must be used. The thymus is transported to the laboratory packed in ice. The tissue is then frozen and if not used immediately after freezing, it can be stored at — 15° for several days but should not be stored at this temperature for longer than one week. For some reason freezing seems to be essential, since the use of fresh unfrozen tissue samples has resulted in a partially depolymerized product.

2) Fifty grams of frozen thymus is chopped into small fragments and homogenized at high speed in a Waring blendor for 3 minutes with 200 ml. of ice-cold 0.9 % NaCl made up in 0.01 M sodium citrate*. The homogenate thus produced is centrifuged at 0° at approximately 2500 r.p.m. for 30 minutes. The supernatant suspension is discarded and the sediment is subjected to homogenization and centrifugation three times exactly as described above for the original 50 g. of frozen thymus. The final sediment consists mainly of chromatin threads contaminated with some fiber.

* See footnote p. 116.

3) The sediment is next homogenized in the Waring blendor for three minutes with 1 liter of ice-cold 0.9 % NaCl made up in distilled water and the material is then placed in a large beaker fitted with a heavy duty stirrer. Ninety ml. of a detergent solution (5 % sodium laurylsulfate or Duponol in 45 % ethauol) is then added slowly, during which time the suspension becomes converted to a fairly stiff gel. This gel is stirred vigorously for three hours at room temperature during which it gradually becomes converted to a very viscous sirupy solution. The concentration of the sodium dodecyl sulfate in this solution is 0.41 %.

4) After this stirring, 55 g. of NaCl is added to bring the NaCl concentration up to 1 M. stirring is continued for 5 or 10 minutes longer to ensure complete solution of the NaCl. Addition of the NaCl causes a noticeable drop in viscosity.

5) The material is then centrifuged at 2500 r.p.m. for 3 hours at 0° or at higher speeds if available. (Higher speeds give a clearer supernatant and shorten the required time of centrifugation and are therefore desirable.)

6) The opalescent supernatant fluid is decanted from the protein sediment and an equal volume of 95 % ethanol is added to the viscous solution with stirring. A highly gelatinous precipitate forms that gradually loses water and develops into a white fibrous mass which can be wound up on the end of a stirring rod*. The entrapped supernatant is pressed out and the precipitate is transferred to another beaker.

7) The precipitate is washed three times with 95 % alcohol and then with acetone until the acetone supernatant is no longer cloudy. The washed material is dried in the air, yielding a crude product which should amount to about 2.0 g. under optimal conditions. A small amount of protein is present as impurity.

8) The crude Na-DNA is dissolved in 700 ml. of distilled water at room temperature. This process requires at least 2 hours with continuous rapid stirring using a heavy duty stirrer. When the material has entirely dissolved, 63 ml. of the detergent solution is added, followed by additional stirring for one hour. Forty-five g. of NaCl is then added to make the NaCl concentration 1 M. The solution is stirred for 5 to 10 minutes to ensure solution of the NaCl and then is centrifuged in a Servall or similar high speed centrifuge at top speed (*ca.* 13,000 r.p.m. for at least 1 hour). The supernatant is decanted from the small amount of precipitate and the Na-DNA is precipitated from the solution with 1 volume of 95 % ethanol as before. The precipitated Na-DNA is washed with alcohol and acetone as before, and is finally dried in the air.

9) The material from step 8 is dissolved in 700 ml. of distilled water at room temperature. This process will again require at least 1 hour of continuous rapid stirring. Six and three-tenths g. of NaCl is then added to make the NaCl concentration 0.9 % (0.14 M) at which concentration any protein remaining will precipitate together with a very small amount of DNA. The solution

---

* Comments on the method of Kay, Simmons and Dounce

Stage 2. The addition of citrate is of doubtful utility; in fact the citrate was intended to inhibit the action of the DNase present in the thymus by analogy with pancreatic DNase that is inhibited by citrate ions (Kunitz, 1950). It is now known that DNases from other sources than pancreas have very different properties (Cunningham and Laskowski, 1953; Cunningham, Catlin and Privat de Garilhe, 1956; Shimomura and Laskowski, 1957; etc.). Apparently, indeed, thymus DNase is not inhibited by citrate ions, but, contrary to pancreatic DNase, it is inhibited by Mg^{++} ions at a concentration at which pancreatic DNase is strongly activated (Maver and Greco, 1949; Webb, 1952; Brown, Jacobs and Laskowski, 1952; Laskowski, Steberl, Akka and Watson, 1954). The addition of citrate, the point of which was to inhibit any depolymerization by thymus DNase, is thus not indispensable.

Stage 5. Utilisation of a high-speed centrifuge allows the centrifugation time to be reduced, thereby obtaining a purer DNA ("new DNA", as opposed to "old DNA").

is centrifuged at room temperature for one hour at 13,000 r.p.m. in the Servall and the supernatant is then decanted from any precipitate in the bottom of the centrifuge tubes.

10) The NaCl concentration is increased to 1 M by adding 35 g. of NaCl and the Na-DNA is then precipitated by slowly adding one volume of 95 % ethanol with stirring. The precipitate is washed with ethanol and acetone, care being taken that the acetone washings are continued until the acetone supernatant is clear. The resulting highly purified product is dried in the air.

The yield of purified product is about 1.3 to 1.4 g. under optimal conditions, or about 8 to 9 % of the weight of thymus (on a dry weight basis).

b. *Wheat germ DNA*

A modification of the method described by Lipshitz and Chargaff (1956) involves plunging the wheat germs into absolute alcohol as soon as they come out of the separating apparatus. The object of this precaution is to avoid degradation which is very fast with all germs. The manipulations to be described are carried out at 4° in a cold room.

1) 300 g wheat germs are minced in a "Turmix" or "Waring" blendor for 8 minutes at maximum speed with 750 ml ethanol. After addition of 750 ml ether, the mixture is shaken gently for 90 minutes to dissolve the lipids.

2) After filtration and air drying, the residue is suspended in 750 ml 0.9 % NaCl solution containing a 0.05 M concentration of sodium citrate. The mixture is rapidly stirred for one hour and centrifuged at 3,600 g for 15 minutes. The sediment (a mixture of bran, starch and nucleic acid) is submitted nine times to the process just described. After these repeated washings, the NaCl solution should be transparent.

3) The final sediment is then minced in the blendor for 2 minutes with a 10 % NaCl solution; the suspension obtained is very viscous on account of the passage of the nucleoproteins into solution. Centrifugation for 15 minutes at 3,600 g removes most of the insoluble material, after which the solution is spun for one hour in a "Spinco" ultracentrifuge at 20,000 r.p.m.

4) The supernatant solution is slowly poured, and stirred, into twice its volume of 95 % ethanol. Part of the fibrous precipitate can be rolled round a stirrer, the remainder of the precipitate being collected by filtration. The whole is washed with alcohol, first 80 %, then 95 %.

5) The nucleoprotein from wheat germ obtained from stage 4 is dissolved in 500 ml distilled water and treated by the method described by Kay et al. (1952, see above, p. 115).

6) The sodium deoxyribonucleate obtained from stage 5 contains nearly 20 % RNA (phloroglucinol reaction of von Euler et al., 1946-1947, see below, p. 153); it is redissolved in the minimum amount of distilled water, and the solution is treated for 30 minutes at 37° and pH 7.0 with a small amount of ribonuclease (Worthington, crystallized) equivalent to 1 % of the dry weight DNA. Dialysis against distilled water removes the RNA fragments that have gone into solution, then the DNA solution is brought to 1 M concentration of NaCl by the addition of crystalline NaCl, and the DNA precipitated by addition of an equal volume of 95 % alcohol. The effect of the RNase treatment is to remove 97 % of the RNA. The final yield is 800 mg DNA per kilogram of wheat germ.

c. *Pneumococcal DNA or "transforming factor", bacterial DNA*

The isolation of pneumococcal DNA or "transforming factor" is quoted as a historic example of the preparation of a bacterial DNA. This preparation makes up part of the now classic work of Avery, MacLeod and McCarty (1944) during which they showed that DNA isolated from one type of cell A was able to communicate the [characteristics of this cell A to a second type of cell B. These experiments formed the starting point for present-day theories on the genetic function of DNA.

1) Preliminary extraction. In order to produce a significant amount of DNA it is necessary to start with 50-70 liters culture. The bacteria are isolated by centrifugation (Sharples), killed by heat and washed 3 times with 0.85 % saline solution. They are then extracted by vigorous shaking for 30-60 minutes in 150 ml saline solution containing sodium deoxycholate at 0.5 % concentration. The cells are removed by centrifugation, and the extraction is repeated 2 or 3 times on the sediment of bacteria until a clear solution is obtained. Three or four volumes of alcohol are added to the combined extracts. The precipitate is removed with a spatula and dissolved in 50 ml of saline solution.

2) Deproteinization and removal of polysaccharide sheath. The solution obtained is deproteinized by the method of Sevag et al. (1938) : 0.25 vol. chloroform and 0.1 vol. amyl alcohol are added to the solution which is then stirred for 15 to 60 minutes and centrifuged.

The formation of two layers is observed, a lower layer of protein gel in chloroform, and an upper layer which is an aqueous DNA solution.

The Sevag process is repeated 2 or 3 times until a completely clear DNA solution is obtained. The DNA is precipitated by adding 3 or 4 volumes alcohol and dissolved in 150 ml saline solution, to which 3-5 mg of a purified enzyme preparation hydrolysing polysaccharides is added. The solution is incubated at 37°, following the destruction of the polysaccharides by serological testing. Polysaccharide destruction is complete after 4 to 6 hours. The DNA is then precipitated from the hydrolysate with 3 or 4 volumes of alcohol, and redissolved in 50 ml saline solution. This is again deproteinized once or twice by the Sevag chloroform method, the process being repeated until there is no longer a film at the interface.

3) Alcoholic fractionation. Alcohol is added drop by drop, with constant stirring, to the DNA solution from the last Sevag process. At a critical concentration, situated between 0.8 and 1 vol. alcohol, the active material separates in fibrous form; these fibers are removed by rolling them round a stirrer, and are washed with 50 % alcohol. Adding alcohol to the mother liquors yields flocculent DNA that is centrifuged, redissolved in the minimum of saline solution and reprecipitated with alcohol, at which point it is obtained as a small amount of fibers that can be added to the material from the first separation.

The operations just described make it possible to obtain an overall yield of about 10-25 mg fibrous material, i.e. highly polymerized, dried, from 75 liters pneumococcal culture.

In the course of time, Avery's method has undergone many modifications. Marmur (1961), for instance, has made a systematic study of the most favorable conditions for obtaining stable microbial DNA that is biologically active, highly polymerized and free of any contamination by RNA and proteins. Lysis of the microorganisms is obtained either with lauryl sulfate or with lysozyme, deproteinization is effected with the chloroform-amyl alcohol system and RNA removed with RNase.

d. *Phenol method for DNA extraction*

The phenol method was initially described for isolating infectious RNA from TMV, but can be successfully applied to DNA purification. Huppert and Rebeyrotte (1960), for instance, have applied it to the purification of a transforming factor from pneumococci.   The bacteria are washed and diluted with a 0,02 M phosphate — 0.01 M ethylenediaminetetraacetate buffer of pH 7.2 to obtain 5×10^8 to 2×10^9 bacteria/ml (the DNA yield falls if the bacterial concentration is higher).   Sodium dodecyl sulfate (20 % solution in 0.2 M phosphate buffer at pH 7.3) is added to give a final concentration of 0.4 %.   After 3 -5 minutes shaking in the Mickle (1948) apparatus an equal volume of phenol (B.D.H. "Anala R" quality) saturated with water is added, and the mixture shaken 5 minutes.   After centrifugation, the aqueous phase is separated, and the same treatment is repeated on it at least twice, sometimes more, depending on the degree of purification desired. The aqueous phase is finally washed with ether (5-6 times). The nucleic acids are precipitated rapidly with 2 vols. cold ethanol in the presence of 2 % sodium acetate.   The precipitate is immediately separated by centrifugation in order to avoid carrying down the SDS (the latter being precipitated by alcohol, but more slowly than the nucleic acids).

An analogous method has enabled a highly polymerized DNA from *Hemophilus influenzae* to be obtained in a sufficiently pure state to give very good electron microscope photographs (Berns and Thomas, 1965; MacHattie et al., 1965).

e. *Apurinic DNA*

The classic experiments of Chargaff and co-workers (Chargaff, 1955) have shown that it is possible to remove the purine bases preferentially from thymus DNA thereby obtaining a "apurinic" DNA of high molecular weight.

Preparation of apurinic DNA (Chargaff, 1955) : To a solution of 105.0 mg of the sodium deoxyribonucleate in 42.5 ml water, a total of [12.5 ml 0.1 N aqueous HCl is added gradually, when a pH of 1.6 is reached.   During the addition a heavy precipitate forms.   The mixture is immediately transferred to a cellophane bag and dialyzed at 37° against 440 ml dilute HCl at pH 1.6 for 26 hours.   No change in pH occurs during this time.   The clear fluid inside the bag is dialyzed against 750 ml 0.2 M borate buffer (pH 7.3) for 22 hours at 4°, against running tap water about 12°) for the same period, against frequent changes of distilled water at 4° for 24 hours and finally lyophilized.   The apurinic acid formed a pure white fluff weighing 76.7 mg and containing 9.7 % moisture.

It can be seen that Chargaff's method yields about 72 mg apurinic DNA from 100 mg DNA. There are no purines in the compound obtained, which contains 10.6 — 10.7 % phosphorus. The molecular weight does not appear to be above 15,000, indicating that the chain has been broken in a number of places besides being depurinated.   The following scheme can be attributed to the purine-free DNA constitution.

$$...p.p.p.pCpCpCpTp.p.p.pTpTpTpCp.p.p...$$

the chain remaining after removal of the purines consisting of alternating pyrimidine polynucleotides and polydeoxyribose phosphate.   Many experiments have shown (Cohn and Volkin, 1957; Shapiro and Chargaff, 1960; Burton and Petersen, 1960; Burton, 1962; Spencer and Chargaff, 1961) that more extensive hydrolysis of apurine DNA results in the isolation of pyrimidine oligonucleotides of the type :

$$pTpTpCp \quad or \quad p_{(n+1)} \, Py_n$$

i.e. pyrimidine oligonucleotides having a phosphoryl group at each end.   The isolation and purification of these oligonucleotides presents a double interest in connection with DNA structure :

1) oligonucleotides of known structure have thereby been obtained from the original DNA;

2) important information concerning the structure of the DNA starting material can be obtained, since with a knowledge of the sequence of the pyrimidine oligonucleotides, the structure of the complementary purine nucleotides can be deduced by making use of Watson and Crick's theory.

Greer and Zamenhof (1962) have made a systematic study of the depurination of DNA by heat, and have shown that the extent of depurination in solution varies inversely with the ionic strength and the pH. Depurination at high temperature in solution appears to be mainly hydrolysis catalyzed by acid media.

If pyrimidine oligonucleotides are desired, there is no need to go through the intermediate isolation of apurinic DNA, and one can proceed immediately to the DNA hydrolysis to the stage of these oligonucleotides either with dilute mineral acids (Cohn and Volkin, 1957; Shapiro and Chargaff, 1960; Privat de Garilhe, 1962, etc.) or with diphenylamine in formic acid (Burton, 1962).

As an example, the degradation of DNA in dilute sulfuric acid and isolation of the pyrimidine oligonucleotides by chromatography on Dowex 1-X2 using a volatile buffer gradient will be given (Privat de Garilhe, 1962).

α. Hydrolysis, ion exchange chromatography, paper chromatography

400 mg Calf thymus DNA are hydrolysed by refluxing for one hour with 20 ml 0.1 N sulfuric acid.

The cooled hydrolysate has total optical density of 8,540 spectrophotometric units at 260 mμ, and is neutralized by 50 % ammonia in the presence of a colored indicator.

The solution obtained is applied to a 10 × 1 cm column of Dowex 1-X2 200-400 mesh, previously equilibrated with a 0.1 M ammonium acetate buffer at pH 4.5.

The column is then eluted with a linear gradient of ammonium acetate, the two mixing flasks containing :

3 liters 0.1 M ammonium acetate buffer at pH 4.5

3 liters 2.0 M ammonium acetate buffer at pH 4.5.

In this way the mixture is fractionated into about twelve peaks, from which the ammonium acetate is removed by sublimation. The paper chromatographically non-homogeneous peaks are purified by preparative paper chromatography on Whatman No. 3 *MM* in the system saturated ammonium sulfate/water/isopropanol (80/18/2; v/v/v). The substances eluted are freed from ammonium sulfate by adsorption on charcoal and elution.

β. Adsorption on and elution from charcoal.

The charcoal used is Norit S × 30 which is partially deactivated by treatment with absolute ethyl alcohol containing 8 % octanol.

A solution of 10 — 20 μmol. of nucleotide dissolved in 20 ml water is adsorbed on about 100 mg charcoal + 100 mg Celite 535 suspended in the nucleotide solution and stirred continu-

Table X. Pyrimidine oligonucleotides obtained by acid hydrolysis of thymus DNA
(Privat de Garilhe, 1962)

Fractions obtained by chromatography		Pyrimidine E 260 total	Pyrimidine Base Composition	p^* Total (μ at)	p^* Terminal (μ at)	$\dfrac{p\ total}{p\ terminal}$	Proposed structure	Oligonucleotides identified by Cohn and Volkin (1957)
Column	Paper							
2	a	14.25	C	2.15	—	—	pC (?)	CpCp pCpCp
	b	30.0	C	4.93	2.64	1.87 (2.0)**	p_4C_3	pCp
3	a	37.5	CT	6.28	3.65	1.72 (1.5)	$p_3(C,T)$	pCpTp pTpCp
	b	61.8	CT	8.48	5.71	1.49 (1.5)	$p_3(C,T)$	pTp
4		8.4	T	1.00	—	—	p_2T_2	
5		45.0	T	6.81	4.40	1.55 (1.5)	p_3T_2	p_3T_2
6	a	11.5	—	1.65	—	—	—	$p_5(C_2,T_2)$
	b	21.85	C_2T	2.19	—	—	$p_4(C_2,T)$	$p_4(C_2,T)$
7	a	35.75	CT_2	5.07	2.61	1.95 (2.0)	$p_4(C,T_2)$	$p_4(C,T_2)$
	b	28.5	C_2T_3	4.72	2.08	2.26	?	
9		31.5	T	5.43	2.44	2.22 (2.0)	p_4T_3	p_4T_3
10		19.25	CT_3	2.93	—	—	$p_5(C,T_3)$	$p_5(C,T_3)$
11	a	34,5	CT_2	5.33	1.76	3.0 (3.0)	$p_6(C_2,T_3)$?	
	b	29.0	T	5.10	1.68	3.0 (3.0)	p_6T_5	
12		42.0	CT_2 or C_2T_4	6.41	2.04	3.14 (3.5)	$p_7(C_2,T_4)$	

* Average of two estimations.
** Theoretical value corresponding to the formula proposed.

ously for 1/4 hour.   At the end of this time the charcoal-Celite mixture is filtered on a Buchner funnel, making sure that all the nucleotide is adsorbed by measuring the optical density of the filtrate at 260 mμ.   The nucleotide is then eluted with 100 ml of a mixture containig alcohol/-concentrated ammonia/water (50/40/10; v/v/v).

It is apparent on measuring the optical density of the eluate that 60 -80 % of the nucleotide fraction is eluted in this fraction; the elution can be completed with a second, and even a third passage of ammoniacal alcohol.   The ammoniacal solution of the nucleotide is immediately evaporated to dryness, taken up in water and lyophilized.

γ. Structural determination of the oligonucleotides

Determination of the structure of oligonucleotides is carried out using the methods described in the chapter immediately following the present one (table X) :

1) Direct spectrophotometry allows easy location of those containing only one type of base; they have the spectrum corresponding to cytidylic or thymidylic acid, in this case.

2) Analysis of the total bases by hydrolysis of the sample for 1 hour at 180° in concentrated formic acid and chromatography under the conditions described by Hotchkiss (p. 134) allows

the ratio of the two pyrimidine bases to be determined in the case of oligonucleotides containing both pyrimidine bases.

3) Finally, the total phosphorus is estimated by applying the method of Fiske and Subbarow on the submicroscopic scale, and the terminal phosphorus (monoesterified) determined after dephosphorylation of an aliquot of nucleotide by *coli* phosphomonoesterase (p. 287).

The total P/ terminal P ratio theoretically allows unambiguous structural determination of the nucleotide. Results of a typical experiment of this nature are listed in table X.

From this table it can be seen that it is possible to isolate in good yield thymidyl oligonucleotides with the same base occurring up to four times, in succession in lower yield, oligothymidylic acids with a polymerization degree of five or six units, an observation implying the existence in the natural state of a complementary strand having 5 or 6 consecutive adenylic acid units.

We shall see that these pyrimidine oligonucleotides isolated by acid hydrolysis of DNA have interesting applications in the study of nuclease specificity.

δ. Comparison of methods for obtaining pyrimidine oligonucleotides by DNA depurination

For the separation of pyrimidine oligonucleotide isopliths, Spencer and Chargaff (1965a, b) have recommended the use of DEAE-cellulose columns, eluting with a lithium salt gradient, and finally paper chromatography.

Two-dimensional paper chromatography allows direct separation of pyrimidine oligonucleotides of chain length from one to six nucleotides. The method is applicable to as little as 2 mg DNA, and its delicacy led to its use in the study of human bile DNA (Shapiro and Chargaff, 1963).

A variety of hydrolytic conditions can be used for the depurination of DNA. In order to compare the results given by the different methods, Shapiro and Chargaff (1964) hydrolysed calf thymus DNA and human bile DNA under the following conditions :

1) DNA degradation by means of dilute sulfuric acid;

2) degradation with the formic acid — diphenylamine system;

3) degradation of the apurinic acid with dilute alkali.

Comparison of the isopliths obtained by these three methods indicated that the concordance of the results was not always what might be desired.

Petersen (1963) has used a combination of paper chromatography and paper electrophoresis to separate the pyrimidine oligonucleotides obtained by the action of diphenylamine in acid solution and by phosphomonoesterase on DNA. In this way he identified 34 components by means of their pyrimidine composition and their chain length. These various components were determined for thymus DNA and herring testes DNA, and it was found that many sequences were present in significantly different amounts from what would be expected for random distribution. No common tendency, however, was noted for one or the other DNA. Table XI, reproduced from Petersen (1963), is a demonstration of the enormous amount of work these analyses represent. In the hope of obtaining cytidyl sequences of as high a molecular weight as possible, Petersen and Burton (1964) have developed new conditions. Action of formic acid containing 2 % diphenylamine is followed by adsorption of the reaction mixture on a Dowex I-X 8 column (formate form). The free purines are removed with 0.005 M formic acid, and the cytidyl oligonucleotides eluted as a single peak by 0.9 M formic acid. The cytidyl peak is freed from its formic acid by repeated evaporations and then fractionated on DEAE-Sephadex with a linear

Table XI. Amounts of various pyrimidine oligonucleotides isolated from deoxyribonucleic acid, compared with the amounts expected from a randomly arranged polymer of the same base composition (Petersen 1963).
Values are expressed as moles of pyrimidine/100 g atoms of DNA phosphorus $\pm$ s.e.m. with the number of estimations given in parentheses. Values for T_6p_5 and T_7p_6 of calf thymus were obtained from another sample of DNA, more heavily loaded paper chromatograms (approx. 18.5 µg. atoms of DNA phosphorus/paper) being used

	Calf-thymus DNA			Herring-testis DNA		
Sequence	Found	Random	% of random	Found	Random	% of random
C	3.92 ± 0.06 (8)	5.35	73	6.02 ± 0.05 (9)	5.20	116
T	6.23 ± 0.04 (6)	7.08	88	7.76 ± 0.1 (8)	7.30	106
C_2p	1.99 ± 0.01 (8)	2.29	87	2.07 ± 0.01 (8)	2.16	96
CpT	2.96 ± 0.06 (7)	3.03	98	3.14 ± 0.01 (9)	3.04	103
TpC	2.23 ± 0.04 (7)	3.03	77	2.00 ± 0.04 (8)	3.04	66
T_2p	2.62 ± 0.02 (8)	4.01	65	3.02 ± 0.03 (9)	4.26	71
C_3p_2	0.76 ± 0.02 (7)	0.74	103	0.63 ± 0.03 (6)	0.68	93
$(C_2T)p_2$	2.73 ± 0.05 (7)	2.92	94	2.48 ± 0.02 (9)	2.84	87
$(CT_2)p_2$	2.64 ± 0.03 (8)	3.86	68	2.81 ± 0.05 (9)	3.99	70
T_3p_2	1.28 ± 0.03 (8)	1.70	75	1.71 ± 0.02 (8)	1.87	91
C_4p_3	0.31 ± 0.02 (8)	0.21	148	0.11 ± 0.01 (5)	0.19	58
$(C_3T)p_3$	1.39 ± 0.02 (7)	1.11	125	1.03 ± 0.04 (7)	1.05	98
$(C_2T_2)p_3$	1.99 ± 0.04 (8)	2.20	91	1.57 ± 0.05 (6)	2.21	71
$(CT_3)p_3$	1.53 ± 0.04 (7)	1.94	79	1.36 ± 0.04 (9)	2.07	66
T_4p_3	0.55 ± 0.03 (8)	0.64	86	0.61 ± 0.01 (9)	0.73	84
$(C_4T)p_4$	0.39, 0.39 (2)	0.37	105	0.35 ± 0.03 (4)	0.34	103
$(C_3T_2)p_4$	1.06 ± 0.04 (8)	0.98	108	0.84 ± 0.01 (7)	0.96	88
$(C_2T_3)p_4$	1.27 ± 0.03 (7)	1.30	98	0.94 ± 0.03 (6)	1.35	70
$(C_4T)p_4$	0.82 ± 0.02 (7)	0.86	95	0.59 ± 0.02 (6)	0.94	63
T_5p_4	0.19 ± 0.01 (7)	0.23	83	0.19 ± 0.02 (7)	0.27	70
$(C_4T_2)p_5$	0.40 ± 0.02 (5)	0.38	105	0.25, 0.21 (2)	0.36	64
$(C_3T_3)p_5$	0.85 ± 0.02 (8)	0.67	128	0.51 ± 0.03 (7)	0.67	76
$(C_2T_4)p_5$	0.79 ± 0.02 (7)	0.66	120	0.41 ± 0.02 (7)	0.71	58
$(CT_5)p_5$	0.42 ± 0.01 (6)	0.35	120	0.14 ± 0.03 (6)	0.40	35
T_6p_5	0.083±0.003 (9)	0.077	107	0.04, 0.04 (2)	0.09	43
$(C_4T_3)p_6$	0.41 ± 0.01 (7)	0.29	141	0.23 ± 0.01 (7)	0.29	122
$(C_3T_4)p_6$	0.39 ± 0.01 (6)	0.38	103	0.26 ± 0.02 (7)	0.40	65
$(C_2T_5)p_6$	0.29 ± 0.01 (7)	0.31	94	0.15 ± 0.01 (6)	0.34	44
$(CT_6)p_6$	0.11 ± 0.01 (6)	0.13	85	0.07 (1)	0.16	(44)
T_7p_6	0.034±0.002 (5)	0.025	136	—	—	—
$(C_4T_4)p_7$	0.26 ± 0.01 (7)	0.19	137	0.13 ± 0.01 (7)	0.19	68
$(C_3T_5)p_7$	0.22 ± 0.01 (7)	0.20	110	0.08 ± 0.01 (6)	0.21	38
$(C_2T_6)p_7$	0.13 ± 0.02 (7)	0.13	100	0.04 (1)	0.15	(27)
$(C_4T_5)p_8$	0.10 ± 0.01 (5)	0.11	91	0.05 ± 0.02 (4)	0.11	46
$(C_3T_6)p_8$	0.08 ± 0.01 (5)	0.10	79	—	—	—

gradient of ammonium bicarbonate buffer. In this way five clearly separated peaks are obtained, representing cytidyl oligonucleotides containing up to 5 nucleotides in a single sequence.

f. *Apyrimidinic DNA, oxidized DNA*

Chargaff and his co-workers have shown that treatment of DNA with anhydrous hydrazine hydrate for 4 hours at 60°, followed by treatment with benzaldehyde results in the formation of apyrimidinic DNA by selective loss of the thymine and cytosine residues (Chargaff et al., 1963; Temperli et al., 1964).   When these apyrimidinic DNA preparations are hydrolysed with potassium hydroxide (0.3 N KOH at 37° for 22 hours), a series of purine polynucleotides is obtained that can subsequently be separated by chromatography on DEAE-cellulose.   Habermann and Maidlova (1963) have also proposed a method for DNA degradation to the stage of purine oligonucleotides that is comparable to Chargaff's.

Sedat and Sinsheimer (1964) have recorded the separation of isoplithic purine nucleotides from controlled degradation of DNA by chromatography on DEAE-Sephadex at 55° in a molar KCl-7 M urea gradient.

According to Jones et al. (Jones et al., 1964; Jones and Walker, 1964 a, b; Jones and Truman, 1964), treatment of DNA with potassium permanganate at pH 8 and 37° for 19 hours oxidizes the C, T and G groups to ureide residues.

The oxidized DNA (ODNA) remaining can be slowly hydrolysed with N KOH at 37° to give urea and oligonucleotides containing adenine and the ureide groups, whilst treatment at 100° for one hour liberates all the urea and gives adenine, deoxyadenosine, d-ApA, d-pAp and adenylic oligonucleotides. This technique has been applied to the determination of the distribution of the adenine residues in DNA from various species, in particular bovine thymus, *B. subtilis*, *Alkaligenes faecalis* and *Mycobacterium phlei*.

CHAPTER IV

Analytical Methods

1. SPECTROPHOTOMETRY

A. DIRECT OBSERVATION OF NUCLEIC ACIDS IN THE ULTRAVIOLET

Conventional ultraviolet lamps, fitted with the appropriate filters, are commercially available and in use in all laboratories. If a drop of a nucleic acid compound is now placed on a filter paper and this filter paper examined in a dark room by the aid of an ultraviolet lamp, the paper becomes fluorescent, appearing white in the darkness, except in the place where the nucleic acids are. We can therefore localize the position of the nucleic acids by means of a dark spot on a bright background. This property has found many applications in electrophoresis and paper chromatography of nucleic acids.

In the same way, the displacement of nucleic acids during column chromatography can be followed in the ultraviolet provided the adsorbent does not itself absorb too much, and provided this adsorbent is contained in a transparent silica column.

B. SPECTROPHOTOMETRY IN SOLUTION

The purine and pyrimidine bases possess quite characteristic ultraviolet absorption spectra in the region from 220-300 mμ. The nucleosides and mononucleotides possess practically the same spectrum as their constituent base, the pentose and the phosphate residues having only slight influence on the absorption spectra. Neither is there any significant difference between the absorption of the ribonucleic acids and the deoxyribonucleic acids. On the other hand, ionization causes considerable changes in spectra that are measured at different pH for the same compound, so that it is important to state at what pH any particular substance was measured. This fact is clearly illustrated in the examples of absorption spectra given below (Figures 23 and 24).

The absorption spectra of nucleic acid derivatives have been the subject of a large number of publications; in particular, Beaven, Holiday and Johnson (1955) have collected a large number

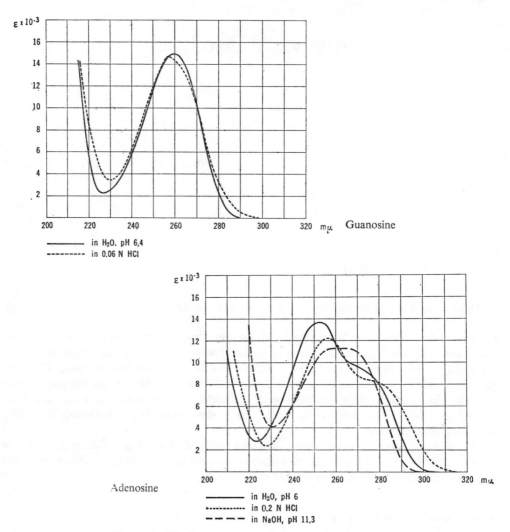

Figure 23. UV-absorption spectra of two nucleosides

of data together in the form of tables (optical densities related to wave lengths) and graphs. In this review can be found graphs of the absorption spectra of the following compounds :

Bases : adenine, cytosine, 5-methylcytosine, guanine, thymine, uracil, xanthine.

Nucleosides : adenosine, cytidine, cytosine deoxyriboside, guanosine, inosine, thymidine, uridine, xanthosine.

Nucleotides : deoxy-5-methylcytidylic acid, guanylic acid (mainly 3′).

Figures for the optical densities at different pH and wavelengths are given for the following nucleotides :

Ribomononucleotides : 2′-adenylic, 3′-adenylic, 5′-adenylic acids, 2′-cytidylic, 3′-cytidylic, 5′-

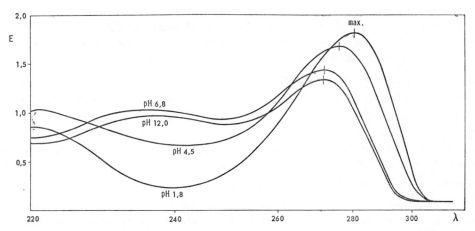

Figure 24. Deoxycytidylic acid (deoxycytidine-5'-monophosphate) : UV absorption spectra automatically recorded with the "Lérès" apparatus (Privat de Garilhe, 1958)

cytidylic acids, cytidine diphosphate, 2'- guanylic, 3'-guanylic and 5'-guanylic acids, 2'-uridylic, 3'-uridylic, 5'-uridylic acids, uridine diphosphate, 5-methylcytidylic acid.

Deoxyribomononucleotides : deoxycytidylic acid, thymidylic acid, thymidine diphosphate.

Absorption spectra of the deoxyribomononucleotides have been determined by Sinsheimer (1954) on nucleotides isolated by chromatography. The optical density was calculated according to the phosphorus content of solutions considered to be homogeneous by chromatographic analysis. Table XII given below reproduces the values given by Sinsheimer.

In addition, spectral data concerning the nucleic acids and their derivatives, as well as other organic compounds are supplied and revised anually by the well known index "Organic Electronic Spectral Data" (Interscience Publishers, New York), or the "Sadtler Alphabetical Index" (Sadtler Research Laboratories, Inc., 3314-20 Spring Garden St., Philadelphia, Penna 19104, U.S.A.).

Table XII. Ultraviolet absorption spectra
of deoxyribonucleotides expressed as ε P.10^{-3} vs. λ (Sinsheimer, 1954)

Deoxyribonucleotides		*Wavelength mμ*							
	pH	240	250	253	260	270	280	290	300
5-Methylcytidylic acid	4.3	3.47	2.89	3.08	4.25	7.37	10.1	9.49	5.27
	5.5-7.0	6.84	5.24	5.00	5.45	7.74	8.55	5.64	1.39
Cytidylic	4.3	4.14	4.48	5.06	7.30	11.0	11.5	6.90	1.59
	5.5-7.0	7.38	6.54	6.68	8.10	10.1	7.95	2.42	0.20
Thymidylic	4.3-7.0	3.06	6.00	7.07	9.13	10.0	6.60	1.99	0.16
Adenylic	4.3	5.98	12.1	13.7	15.3	10.5	2.48	0.18	0
	5.5-7.0	6.61	12.5	14.1	15.7	10.4	2.21	0.11	0
Guanylic	4.3-7.0	10.1	14.5	14.9	12.8	10.4	8.55	3.45	0.36

9

We do not intend to go into the details of nucleic acid spectrophotometry, which has become a standard technique since the advent of precise and easily manipulated UV-spectrometers throughout the world, but we should like to mention a few practical tricks that enable one to draw the maximum possible information from the measurements. Examination of table XII shows that the ratio $\frac{E260}{E280}$ has very different values characteristic of the different mononucleotides. The ratio at pH 4.3 is 0.42 for d-pM, 0.63 for d-pC, 1.38 for d-pT, 6.16 for d-pA and 1.49 for d-pG.

Let us suppose that the fractionation of a DNA hydrolysate, arising from the action of pancreatic DNase, is being carried out on a Dowex 1 column — a method which will be described later. If the optical density as a function of the volume of liquid eluted is measured at one wavelength of, say, 260 mμ, a symmetrical peak will be obtained at the exit of a pure nucleotide. If, now, the ratio $\frac{E260}{E280}$ or the ratio $\frac{E270}{E290}$ is plotted on the same curve, a series of equal ratios is obtained for a pure nucleotide so long as the same substance is coming out. The fact of obtaining a constant ratio is an excellent criterion of purity for the substance being observed, besides being a very good identification method (cf. figure 25).

Conversely, obtaining a ratio that is not constant is an indication that one is dealing with a mixture of compounds. It is, of course, clear that all the compounds containing the same purine or pyrimidine base will have close $\frac{E260}{E280}$ ratios, such as, for example, cytosine, cytidine deoxycytidine, cytidine-2'-phosphate, cytidine-3'-phosphate, cytidine-5'-phosphate, cytidine

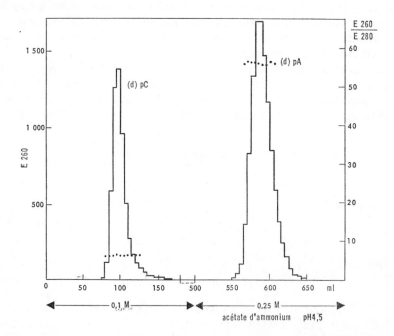

Figure 25. Chromatography of a mononucleotide mixture : 5μ mol. of d-pC + 5μ mol. of d-pA. Column : Dowex-1-X2, 1 M 10 cm, equilibrated with 0.1 M ammonium acetate buffer of pH 4.5. The column is then eluted with the buffers indicated (Privat de Garilhe, 1958)

diphosphate, deoxycytidine monophosphate, deoxycytidine diphosphate, besides the polynucleotides of the type d-pCpC and d-pCpCpC, etc. These various compounds then have to be identified by the nature of the pentose, the phosphorus content, their position in the elution sequence at the exit of the column, the fact that they are dephosphorylated or not by 3'- or 5'-nucleotidase, their behavior on paper chromatography or on electrophoresis etc. (cf. detailed analysis of a DNA hydrolysate, p. 138).

Dinucleotides involving two different bases, for instance such as d-pCpT, d-pCpA, d-pMpG, usually have a characteristic spectrum that is the average of the spectra of the two constituent bases.

It is obvious that the ratio will be constant, whatever the order of the nucleotides within the dinucleotide, and it would be quite conceivable that one peak with a constant $\dfrac{E260}{E280}$ ratio might still contain a mixture of two nucleotides pXpY and pYpX.

C. MICROSPECTROPHOTOMETRY

The spectroscopy that has just been described is concerned with substances in solution. The method can be reduced in scale to a single cell or a single cell nucleus by employing special techniques termed "quantitative microspectrophotometry"; these are valid in the visible and ultraviolet regions but are somewhat difficult to apply.

For microspectrophotometry in the visible, the preparation under study must first be stained either with Feulgen's reagent or with methyl green. To obtain consistent results, the reaction between the nucleic acid and the dyestuff must be sufficiently reproducible for the amount of dyestuff fixed to be proportional to the amount of the cell constituent being determined. The stained sample is placed under a microscope and illuminated with monochromatic light. The microscope is focussed on a particular point of the cell being examined, and the magnified image of this zone is projected on to a photoelectric cell, which then produces a certain amount of current, q. Secondly, a reading in a transparent zone of the cell is taken, the strength of current produced in this case being Q. If these two values q and Q are known, as well as the dimensions of the sample, the amount of stained material can be determined. Using ultraviolet radiation, a microscope with quartz lenses must be employed, but the principle remains the same.

Visible wavelength microspectrophotometry has mainly been developed by Mirsky, Pollister and their co-workers (Pollister 1950, 1952a, b; Pollister, Himes and Ornstein, 1951; Pollister, Swift and Alfert, 1951; Mirsky and Ris, 1951).

Ultraviolet microspectrophotometric techniques are closely linked with the name of Caspersson, who instigated the techniques about twenty years ago (Caspersson, 1936, 1940, 1947, 1950).

Microspectrophotometric techniques in the visible are as a rule specific for DNA, since only these are stained by Feulgen's reagent or methyl green. The ultraviolet methods, on the other hand, can be used to measure all the compounds, purine and pyrimidine bases, nucleosides, nucleotides, RNA, DNA, all of which include a purine or pyrimidine ring. Fortunately the protein absorption at 260 mμ is quite negligible, and even at its absorption maximum, 280 mμ, a serum albumin solution absorbs 40 times less light than a nucleic acid solution of equal strength does at 260 mμ. It is preferable to combine the two microspectrophotometric methods, visible and UV, to be able to distinguish between what is associated with DNA and what with RNA.

D. DETERMINATION OF NUCLEIC ACID COMPONENTS MIXTURES BY U.V. SPECTROPHOTOMETRY

Various spectrophotometric methods have been proposed for the direct determination of pyrimidine and purine bases arising, for example, from total hydrolysis of nucleic acids.   Chen-Pin et al. (1963) in particular have suggested a system allowing determination of the four bases by using a series of spectrophotometric readings at various wavelengths and pH.   After degradation with $HClO_4$, the RNA hydrolysate is diluted with distilled water to a concentration of 2.0 N with respect to $HClO_4$ and is then centrifuged.   Two samples of known volume of supernatant are taken, and after addition of standard acid or base, optical densities are measured at 249, 262, 274 and 290 mμ for acid solutions and 256, 258, 282 and 290 mμ for basic solutions.   A total content of 60-160 μg of bases per 5.0 ml solution is suitable for optical density measurement. The amount of each of the purine and pyrimidine bases is then calculated using the following equations :

$$U = 0.194. \quad \Delta E_{290_{13}-290_1}. \quad V$$
$$A = 0.108. \quad \Delta E_{262_1-282_{13}}. \quad V - 0.221. \quad U$$
$$G = 0.198. \quad \Delta E_{249_1-258_{13}}. \quad V - 0.542. \quad U$$
$$C = 0.127. \quad \Delta E_{274_1-256_{13}}. \quad V - 0.133. \quad G$$

where A, G, C and U represent the μmole of the bases and V the total volume (in ml) of the solution, and the indices 13 and 1 the pH at which the readings are performed.

For RNA samples digested by 1.0 N HCl, the content of cytidylic acid (or cytosine) can be calculated from the following equation :

$$C = 0.149. \quad \Delta E_{290_1-290_{13}}. \quad V$$

In systems where not all four bases are present, this method can be used for the identification of the principal bases and the determination of their approximate contents.

Guschbauer et al. (1965) have also developed an analytic spectrophotometric method based on the examination of the spectra of mixtures of ribonucleotides before and after UV irradiation. This method requires the samples to be present as mononucleotides, so that polynucleotides or RNA must first be totally hydrolysed by alkali.   The values found are generally in agreement with those given in the literature.

U. V. spectrophotometry may also be applied to the base determination in DNA solutions, without it being necessary to perform a complete hydrolysis of the sample. For example, Frédéricq et al. (1961), showed that the spectrum of denatured thymus DNA at pH 3.0 in 0.1 N acetic acid was almost identical to the calculated spectrum of its constituent nucleotides and this appears to be a convenient way for a rapid determination of the base composition and concentration.   In the same order of ideas, Hirschman and Felsenfeld (1966), described a slightly different method for the determination of base composition and concentration of unknown DNA samples, using the spectra of native or denatured material : measurements are required at only 4 wavelengths and the base compositions are accurate within $\pm$ 0.03 mole fraction A-T.   It is clamed that the length of time necessary for the calculations does noe exceed 5 minutes.   However this direct spectrophotometry on DNA solutions requires highly purified material and extremely precise optical density measurements.

E. INFRA-RED SPECTROPHOTOMETRY

The infra-red spectrometry of many constituents of the nucleic acids such as purine and pyrimidine bases, pentose nucleosides, nucleotides, etc., has been the subject of much very important work, and the spectra obtained for all these substances may be found in the standard reference indexes such as the "Sadtler alphabetical Index" (published by Sadtler Research Laboratories, Inc., 3314-20, Spring Garden St., Philadelphia, Penna 19104, U.S.A). These indexes are brought up to date every year, and constitute a valuable tool for the analyst. So far as IR. spectrophotometry of macromolecular nucleic acids are concerned, little information is available so far, although the method would appear assured of future success. The possibilities offered by the technique in the structural investigation of nucleic acids have been well illustrated by the experiments of Bradbury and co-workers (see the history of the method and description of experiments concerned with infrared structural analysis of DNA in Bradbury, Price and Wilkinson, 1961).

These authors have given a detailed description of the experimental techniques employed in the infrared study of biological polymer *films*, the configuration of which depends on the water content of the samples.

Oriented films of sodium or lithium deoxyribonucleate are made by spreading highly polymerised aqueous solutions on a support in one direction by means of a horn spatula that has been carefully polished. The spreading is continued until the film is dry, and the film support is made of silver chloride or beryllium fluoride plates.

The polarized infrared absorption spectrum of these films is then recorded in an atmosphere where the relative humidity varies from 0 to 94 % (figure 26).

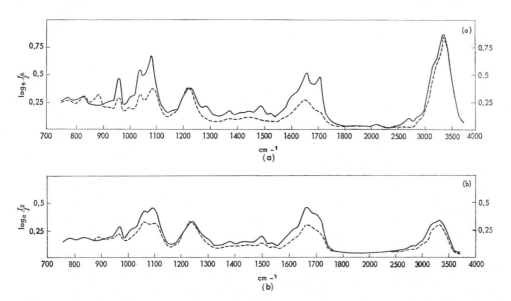

Figure 26. Infrared spectra of Li-DNA *a*) at 80 % relative humidity; *b*) at 25 % relative humidity. The full line is E measured perpendicular to the fiber axis, the dotted line is the vector E parallel to the fiber axis (Bradbury et al., 1962)

Bradbury et al. (1961) have been able to show that the Li-DNA spectrum is similar to that of Na-DNA, and that in both cases three regions of strong absorption are observed : (1) between 3,500 and 2,500 cm-¹, (2) between 1,750 and 1,550 cm-¹ and (3) between 1,300 and 900 cm-¹.

It has been possible to discriminate between two forms of Na-DNate, one at relative humidities over 90 % in which the bases are perpendicular to the helical axis (form B) and one at relative humidities between 70 and 80 %, in which the bases are inclined at an angle of about 13º from normal to the helical axis (form A). In the case of Li-DNate, the B form exists for relative humidities above 60 %, and there exists a second form which is different from the Na-DNate A form, that exists between 47 and 56 % relative humidity, in which the bases are inclined at 4º to the perpendicular (form C).

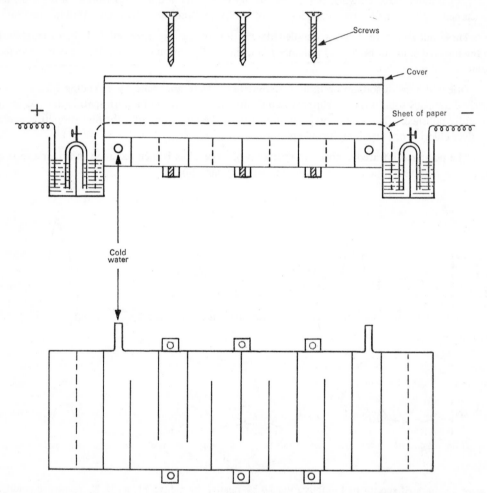

Figure 27. Scheme for an electrophoresis apparatus made of "Plexiglass". Cooled by constant water circulation

II. ELECTROPHORESIS

The method giving the most satisfactory result is that described by Markham and Smith (Markham and Smith, 1952a; Smith, 1955), together with its numerous modifications. This method is an application of the well-known paper electrophoretic technique. The originality lies in the fact that it is run for short periods at very high voltages (figure 27). All electrophoretic apparatus gives good results an condition that high voltages for short periods are used.

The paper (a strip of Whatman no. 1 or no. 3, 47 × 19 cm) is dipped in ammonium acetate or formate buffer, usually 0.1 M ammonium acetate buffer pH 3.5, and blotted between two sheets of filter paper to remove the excess liquid. The mixture to be analysed is usually placed 12 cm from the negative end on a line that is perpendicular to the longer axis of the paper : 0.01 — 0.02 ml solution is used. A variation of the method consists in placing the solution on the dry paper and then impregnating the paper carefully. This way has the advantage that if a very dilute solution is being used, several drops can be placed at the same point, drying between each drop. On the other hand, the spots obtained after the electrophoresis are a little less well-defined than when the solution is dropped onto the wetted paper.

The strip, prepared in either way, is placed on the apparatus, and a potential of 1,000 to 1,500 volts is applied to the extremities of the paper. Suitable energy generators, such as those schematically represented by Markham and Smith, are now sufficiently well distributed from commercial sources for there no longer to be any need to build them oneself. Carbon electrodes tend to deteriorate rapidly, especially the anode, but they may be replaced advantageously with platinum electrodes. The apparatus should always be manipulated with the greatest care in view of the high voltage. The average duration of an experiment is two hours; when working in a phosphate buffer it is convenient to lower the potential to 700 volts to avoid overheating.

Location of spots.

After the electrophoresis, the paper is dried between two sheets of filter paper and the spots located with a low wavelength ultraviolet lamp. The spots can be observed during the electrophoresis using the technique of Holiday and Johnson (1949) which consists in interrupting the electrophoresis, removing the strip, examining it rapidly in ultraviolet light, then replacing it in the tank and continuing the electrophoresis, apparently without ill effect on the course of the experiment.

After the electrophoresis, once the spots have been located, they can be cut out, and the substances eluted and identified by their ultraviolet spectra. These substances can also be determined spectrophotometrically. It is advisable to cut out a band from a blank electrophoretic paper that is eluted exactly like the one under examination, the liquid from this serving as blank in spectrophotometric determination.

Thin layer electrophoresis

Thin layer electrophoretic separation of the four ribonucleic mononucleotides can be achieved on thin layers of cellulose in a sodium formate buffer, 0.1 M at pH 3.4 (De Filippes, 1964).

Microelectrophoresis

Special and delicate techniques of "Microextraction and microelectrophoresis" have been devised by Edström (1964), permitting an acurate determination of nucleic acid components in isolated cellular units.

III. PAPER CHROMATOGRAPHY

A. GENERAL PRINCIPLES

The classic method of paper chromatography as it was described by Consden, Gordon and Martin (1944) was first applied to nucleic acid derivatives (purine bases arising from a nucleic acid hydrolysis) by Vischer and Chargaff (1947). In order to detect the purine bases, they were obliged to convert these bases to their mercury salts in the first place, by spraying the paper with a mercuric nitrate solution, and then to convert the mercury complexes of the bases to mercuric sulfide by impregnating with ammonium sulfide. The positions originally occupied by the bases appeared as black spots. The original developing solvent used by Vischer and Chargaff was a 3/1 mixture of quinoline-collidine, saturated with water by shaking with $1\frac{1}{2}$ parts water, but this can no longer be used if the chromatogram is to be examined in UV light, since even after washing with ether, enough quinoline-collidine remains to cause the whole of the sheet to appear black, without being able to distinguish the bases. Subsequently, Vischer and Chargaff (1948a, b) as well as Hotchkiss (1948), Wyatt (1951), Markham and Smith (1952a) etc., proposed a whole series of solvents, some of which will be quoted later. Most of the solvents do not absorb in the ultraviolet and allow ready examination of the chromatograms.

Various systems have been proposed for locating the spots corresponding to the nucleic derivatives on paper; the first was the chemical method of Vischer and Chargaff (1947), then the photographic method of Markham and Smith (1949). This consisted in laying the chromatogram on a photographic plate in the dark, then exposing the whole to UV irradiation for $1\frac{1}{2}$ minutes. Since the UV was intercepted by the spots of the nucleic derivatives, these appeared after development as white spots on a dark background. At the present time, almost the only method in use is direct examination in ultraviolet light.

B. SEPARATION OF PURINE AND PYRIMIDINE BASES AND NUCLEOSIDES

1) Hotchkiss's method (1948) uses for chromatography (descending) amount of substance of the order of a microgram, this being spotted on to Whatman no. 1 or Whatman no. 3 paper. The bottom of the chromatography tank contains equal quantities of n-butanol and an aqueous phase of 2.5 % gaseous ammonia in water. The trough contains n-butanol saturated with water at room temperature without the addition of ammonia.

The system of Hotchkiss can also be used for the separation of isomeric dinucleoside monophosphates of the type XpY + YpX (Privat de Garilhe, Cunningham, Laurila and Laskowski, 1957). These dinucleoside monophosphates move very slowly in the Hotchkiss system, so that resolution of the pair d-CpT + d-TpC was only achieved after 6 days of chromatography, and resolution of the pair d-GpA + d-ApG after 14 days. It is possible to examine the chromatograms in the ultraviolet during the chromatography by removing them from the tank, then quickly replacing them, without any appreciable disruption to the experiment.

2) Many other systems can be used for the separation of bases and nucleosides such as :
a) butanol saturated with water (in the absence of ammonia),
b) butanol/acetic acid/water (40 : 10 : 10),
c) isopropanol/concentrated HCl/H_2O (170 : 40 : 40) at 20-23°, etc.

C. Nucleotide separation

1. Ascending chromatographic method (Carter, 1950)

The following systems have been used :

1) butanol saturated a 10 % aqueous urea solution, 2) 5 % monopotassium phosphate or 5 % disodium phosphate, 3) citric acid adjusted to the required pH with a concentrated ammonia solution.

The butanol-urea solution is used in an atmosphere saturated with water vapor, and the salt solutions with isoamyl alcohol as a non-aqueous supernatant phase. The latter system, which differs somewhat from classical paper chromatography, consists in saturating the salt solution with isoamyl alcohol, allowing the two layers to separate and then using a sufficiently large receptacle for both phases to be present in the form of a thin layer (1 cm for the aqueous phase and 0.5 cm for the organic phase). The paper is introduced into the solution in such a way that it passes through both layers. The chromatograms are developed in cylindrical jars 45 cm high. The paper sheets are suspended from the top and dip into dishes placed at the bottom of the jars. It is also possible to roll the papers into cylinders and rest them on the bottom of the jar which is itself used as the solvent container.

In table XIII, reprinted from Carter, are given the R_f values of different nucleic acid derivatives in the systems that have just been described.

Table XIII. Solvents for paper chromatography of certain nucleic acid derivatives, and R_f values (Carter, 1950)

	1	2	3	4	5	6
Adenine	0.69	0.37	0.53	0.44	0.42	0.41
Guanine	0.50	0.37	0	0.02	0.02	0.05
Hypoxanthine	0.63	0.49	0.52	0.57	0.59	0.29
Xanthine	0.52	0.45	0.56	0.49	0.42	0.12
Uracil	0.72	0.72	0.78	0.73	0.74	0.35
Cytosine	0.83	0.72	0.79	0.73	0.74	0.29
Thymine	0.72	0.72	0.77	0.73	0.74	0.52
Adenosine	0.68	0.52	0.58	0.54	0.53	0.28
Guanosine	0.66	0.59	0.68	0.62	0.64	0.17
Uridine	0.80	0.80	0.88	0.79	0.80	0.23
Cytidine	0.86	0.77	0.88	0.76	0.80	0.17
Adenylic acid *a*	0.74	0.65	0.72	0.74	0.74	0
Adenylic acid *b*	0.74	0.60	0.81	0.67	0.63	0
Guanylic acid	0.80	0.73	0.87	0.79	0.78	0
Cytidylic acid	0.89	0.82	0.93	0.85	0.86	0
Uridylic acid	0.89	0.82	0.93	0.85	0.86	0

1. ammonium citrate 5 % pH 3.6 + isoamyl alcohol
2. ammonium citrate 5 % pH 8.6 + isoamyl alcohol
3. KH_2PO_4 5 % + isoamyl alcohol
4. Na_2HPO_4 5 % + isoamyl alcohol
5. phosphates 5 % pH 7.0 + isoamyl alcohol
6. urea-butanol

2. Descending chromatographic method (Markham and Smith, 1952a)

Solvent no. 1: saturated aqueous ammonium sulfate, 80 parts, sodium acetate 0.5 M, 18 parts, isopropanol, 2 parts (v/v/v).

Solvent no. 2: isopropanol, 70 parts, water, 30 parts (v/v).

Solvent no. 3: the same as solvent no. 2 with, in addition, 0.35 ml ammonia (d = 0.880) per liter gas space in the tank, into the bottom of which it is poured.

Solvent no. 4: sec-butanol saturated with water, 98 parts, glacial acetic acid, 2 parts (v/v).

This method enabled Markham and Smith to resolve enzymatic RNA hydrolysates into a large number of distinct bands. The cyclic pyrimidine nucleotides are those which are displaced the fastest. Generally speaking, all guanylic compounds move slower than do similar compounds from other bases, and cyclic compounds move faster than the corresponding linear compounds. The mononucleotides move quicker than the dinucleotides, which, in turn move quicker than the trinucleotides, etc. The spots or bands obtained after chromatography can easily be located in the ultraviolet. These bands or spots can be eluted, and can serve as starting material for another chromatogram or electrophoresis. Preparative chromatography has been successfully applied to nucleic derivatives; a hydrolysate corresponding to 100 mg nucleic acid, for instance, can easily be fractionated on a strip of Whatman no. 3 paper, 20 cm wide.

3. Separation of the various nucleoside phosphoric esters

Quantitative separation of adenosine and inosine phosphoric esters can be achieved using solvent systems described by Krebs and Hems (1953).

Solvent no. 1: 90 ml diisopropyl ether/60 ml 90 % formic acid (v/v),

Solvent no. 2: 100 ml isobutyric acid, 60 ml N ammonia and 1.6 ml M ethylenediamine-tetraacetic acid (EDTA).

IV. COLUMN CHROMATOGRAPHY

A. ION EXCHANGE RESINS

1. Substituted polystyrene resins (Dowex)

Chromatography of nucleotides, nucleosides and bases on columns of ion exchange resins has mostly been studied by Carter, Cohn and their co-workers in the case of the ribonucleic acid derivatives (Carter and Cohn, 1949, Cohn, 1950a, b, 1951; Volkin and Cohn, 1953), by the same laboratory and by Sinsheimer and co-workers in the case of deoxyribonucleic acids (Volkin, Khym and Cohn, 1951; Sinsheimer and Koerner, 1951; Sinsheimer, 1954). All these methods have been the subject of detailed reviews by Cohn (1955, 1957).

The chromatography of nucleotides on anion exchangers utilize resins such as Dowex 1 and Dowex 2 having different amounts of cross-linking, X2 = 2 %, X8 = 8 %. These resins, used in the form of a fine powder "200-400 mesh" prepared for chromatography, can be purchased from the Fisher Scientific Corporation, Greenwich and Morton Streets, New York 14, N.Y.

In theory, the net negative charge per molecule of nucleotide rises in the following order for the ribonucleotides : cytidylic, adenylic, guanylic and uridylic acids; and in the following order for the deoxyribonucleotides : cytidylic, thymidylic, adenylic and guanylic acids. Cytidylic and adenylic acids show a net positive charge, and are therefore cations at pHs above 1.5, while uridylic acid remains an anion down to pH 0.

If all four are adsorbed on a resin like Dowex 1 at a pH higher than 2.5, the nucleotides can then be desorbed by using eluents of lower and lower pH, each nucleotide desorbing theoretically at the point when it becomes cationic, i.e. the nucleotides ought to desorb in the inverse order of their negative charges, and the successive elution of cytidylic (the least adsorbed), adenylic guanylic and uridylic (the most adsorbed) should be observed. Experimentally, it is indeed found that the purine nucleotides tend to be more strongly adsorbed than the pyrimidine nucleotides so that the order of elution by, for instance, 0.003 N HCl, of the four ribonucleotides is the following : cytidylic, adenylic, uridylic and guanylic acids.

Elution of the nucleotides by dilute HCl can present some inconvenience partly because of the instability of the nucleotides in acid solution, and partly because Cl⁻ ions must be added in the form of NaCl to the eluent solutions if the elution is to be completed in a reasonably short time. This is the reason that solutions containing other ions than Cl⁻ and of relatively high pH have been used. Examples of these are the solutions of ammonium formate and acetate which are readily removed afterwards by sublimation (Cohn, 1950a).

Elution of nucleotides at high pH (between 4.5 and 7.0) results in modifying the elution order. Cohn has found (1955), for instance, that at pHs approaching neutral the purine nucleotides appear together (adenylic at the same time as guanylic), as do the pyrimidine nucleotides (uridylic or thymidylic with cytidylic). The separation of each pair at lower pHs in the order cytidylic,

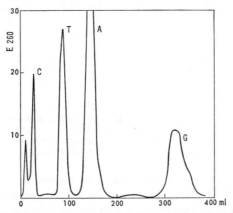

Figure 28. Elution diagram of a mixture of deoxyribomononucleotides (30 mg) obtained by the action of phosphodiesterase on a mixture of polynucleotides. Column : Dowex 1-X2, 0.8 x6 cm, equilibrated with a 0.1 M ammonium formate buffer and then washed with the same buffer (Privat de Garilhe and Laskowski, 1955a)

adenylic, uridylic or thymidylic and guanylic is due to the development of a cationic group that causes the appearance of adenylic before guanylic (pK 3.7 against 2.3) and cytidylic before uridylic (pK 4.2 against 0). The relative positions of cytidylic and adenylic are retained at all pH values, but those of uridylic and guanylic invert at low pH.

To summarize the results of Cohn (1955): at pH 2-3 (dilute HCl), the mononucleotides appear in the order cytidylic, adenylic, uridylic or thymidylic and guanylic acid; at pH 4.5 (ammonium acetate), they appear in the order cytidylic, uridylic or thymidylic, adenylic, guanylic acid.

Figure 28 represents the elution of deoxyribomononucleotides adsorbed on a column of Dowex 1-X2 by a solution of ammonium formate at pH 4.5.

Elution of polynucleotides that are more strongly adsorbed on Dowex 1 can be effected by gradually increasing the ionic strength of the ammonium formate or acetate solutions without changing the pH.

Sinsheimer and co-workers (Sinsheimer and Koerner, 1951; Sinsheimer, 1954) have suggested that Dowex 1-X2 might be used for rapid fractionation of oligonucleotide mixtures such as those arising from enzymic hydrolysis of DNA. The separation into several large groups (mono-, di-, tri-, tetranucleotides, etc.) would then be followed by a more refined separation of the mono-, di- and trinucleotides, possibly by rechromatographing each fraction on Dowex 1-X8. The improved resolution in the oligonucleotide separation by employing resins with greater cross-linking is analogous to the behavior of aminoacids and peptides.

In the study of certain metabolic processes, it sometimes happens that one come across a complex mixture containing nucleotides, nucleosides and free bases all together.

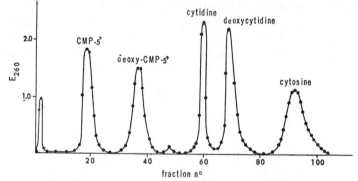

Figure 29. Separation of 4-5 μmol. of each of the following compounds : cytidine-5′-phosphate, cytidine, deoxycytidine and cytosine on Dowex 50 (H⁺ form, length 10 cm, diam. 0.9 cm). Fraction size 4-5 ml every 30 minutes; the chromatogram was first developed with 0.2 N acetic acid; after the exit of the nucleotides elution is continued with N HCl. The first peak represents compounds containing uracil, present as impurity in the commercial samples (reproduced from Reichard, 1958)

Reichard (1958) has examined the fractionation of various compounds containing cytosine and has shown that by chromatographing a mixture of such compounds on the cation exchanger, Dowex 50, it is possible to achieve a very well-resolved separation of such closely related compounds as cytidine-5′-monophosphate, deoxycytidine-5′-monophosphate, cytidine, deoxycytidine and cytosine (fig. 29).

Chromatography of enzymic hydrolysates of nucleic acids

The separation of the ribonuclease hydrolysis products from calf liver RNA has been described by Volkin and Cohn (1953), and it will be the subject of some discussion in the chapter on ribonuclease (see p. 204). The eluents used by these authors were mixtures of hydrochloric acid and sodium chloride, these having the disadvantage that elimination of the salts after chromatography is difficult.

Sinsheimer (1954) has encouraged the general use of volatile buffers, and in his method, a hydrolysate corresponding to 200 mg DNA can be chromatographed on a 0.8 × 10 cm column of Dowex 1-X2, pre-washed with several cycles of 1 N NaOH and HCl N acetic acid until the optical density of the filtrate is below 0.010 at 260 mμ, when the resin is equilibrated with 0.1 M ammonium acetate or formate buffer at pH 4.5. About 20 ml filtrate is collected per hour, to do which, it may be necessary to apply a hydrostatic pressure of 3 or 4 meters to the column. With the 0.1 M buffer, all the mononucleotides are removed, together with some dinucleotides : d-pCpC, d-pCpT, d-pCpA. The buffer concentration is then raised to 0.25 M, and the other dinucleotides come off. Raising the buffer concentration stepwise to 0.5 M, 1 M and 2 M, oligonucleotides of increasing molecular weight are desorbed, and the whole of the hydrolysate can be recovered with buffers of molar concentration lower than, or equal, to 2 M. The dinucleotides, which are incompletely separated during the first chromatography, can be rechromatographed after subliming the buffer; for this second chromatogram, it is advantageous to use a 0.8 × 10 cm column of Dowex 1-X8, the resolving power of which is higher than Dowex 1-X2.

Identification of the dinucleotides can be carried out in the following way. Let us suppose that a homogeneous fraction has been obtained, and that it is believed to be a dinucleotide. From the UV absorption, E, at known wavelength, λ, it is possible to conclude that a mononucleotide is not present, but it is difficult to say what the constituents of the dinucleotide are. To find out what mononucleotides form the dinucleotide, one method is to hydrolyze with concentrated formic acid in a sealed tube for 40 minutes (Lipshitz and Chargaff, 1956) and identify the purine and pyrimidine bases paper chromatographically (Vischer and Chargaff, 1948a, b; Hotchkiss, 1948). The other method consists in hydrolyzing by incubation at 37° with phosphodiesterase, an enzyme specific for diester bonds, which hydrolyzes all oligonucleotides to yield mononucleotide. Paper or column chromatography or paper electrophoresis will then enable the mononucleotides formed to be identified.

This does not give any information about the order in which the two mononucleotides are joined together. Supposing a dinucleotide contains pC and pA, in order to determine the sequence, two enzyme systems would be required, first, a phosphomonoesterase to remove a phosphoric acid by the reaction

$$pCpA \longrightarrow p + CpA$$

followed by a phosphodiesterase to hydrolyze the dinucleoside monophosphate CpA, producing C + pA. It is indeed known that snake venom phosphodiesterase cleaves deoxyribonucleotides at the 3′-position, thus always liberating nucleotides ending with a 5′-phosphate. After action of phosphodiesterase, therefore, there remain in solution a nucleotide, pA, and a nucleoside C, which can readily be identified by one of the usual methods.

There is a further difficulty that may arise, namely the presence of two isomers of the type pCpA and pApC in the same chromatographic fraction. It is inevitable that isomers of this type will have very closely related properties — the ratio E_{260}/E_{280}, in particular, is the same. It is therefore legitimate to wonder whether a homogeneous peak containing only the two mono-nucleotides pC andpA is not a mixture of pCpA + pApC. In order to answer this question, the system is dephosphorylated :

$$p : CpA$$
$$p : ApC$$

then the phosphatase is destroyed by heat or removed by column chromatography, and the system is hydrolyzed by phosphodiesterase. If the original system were a mixture of two isomers, the constituents remaining after this hydrolysis should be identifiable as

$$C + pA \quad \text{and} \quad A + pC.$$

The amount of C must be stoichiometrically equal to that of pA, and the amount of A stoichiometrically equal to that of pC. Such combinations have been found in the following cases (Privat de Garilhe, Cunningham, Laurila and Laskowski, 1957) :

$$\begin{cases} \text{d-pCpT} & 75 \% \\ \text{d-pTpC} & 25 \% \end{cases} \qquad \begin{cases} \text{d-pTpG} & 95 \% \\ \text{d-pGpT} & 5 \% \end{cases} \qquad \begin{cases} \text{d-pGpA} & 60 \% \\ \text{d-pApG} & 40 \% \end{cases}$$

On the other hand, the dinucleotides d-pCpA, d-pMpG and d-pTpA were shown to be free of contamination.

2. Substituted celluloses

It has been known since the work of Peterson, Sober and co-workers (Peterson and Sober, 1956; Sober et al., 1956) that it is possible to attach various groups to cellulose that render it an exceedingly good ion-exchange system. Reaction of cellulose that monochloracetic acid under controlled conditions, for instance, results in the formation of carboxymethylcellulose (CM-cellulose), which is a cation exchanger used extensively in the fractionation of proteins and peptides.

In order to obtain anion exchangers, cellulose is made to react with diethylaminoethyl chloride, thus fixing diethylaminoethyl groups on the cellulose chain, resulting in formation of Di-Ethyl-Amino-Ethyl-Cellulose, or DEAE-cellulose.

In the same way, reaction between epichlorhydrin, triethanolamine and cellulose results in a compound called ECTEOLA-cellulose.

These anion exchangers have been utilized very extensively in fractionating nucleic acids, and they are now widely available commercially, so that there is no longer any need to prepare them in the laboratory (e.g. Serva-celluloses).

a. *Nucleotide fractionation on DEAE-cellulose*

Chromatography on DEAE-cellulose was suggested by Khorana and his co-workers, who used it successfully in the fractionation of synthetic polypyrimidine acids (Tener et al., 1958; Khorana, 1959; Khorana and Vizsolyi, 1961; Khorana et al., 1962; Weimann and Khorana, 1962). Since then, the method has been extended to other separations, among which we might mention chromatography of the homologous series of polyadenylic acids (Staehelin et al., 1959; Stevens and Hilmoe, 1960), chromatography of yeast transfer RNA (Monier et al., 1960), influenza virus (Portocala et al., 1964), etc.

In practise, the column is prepared in the following manner. The solution, corresponding to 1 mmol nucleotide (of the p_nT_n type, for instance, see p. 95) is adjusted to pH 8-9 with ammonia and applied to the top of a column of DEAE-cellulose (200-400 mesh, dry) in carbonate form. The column is prepared by suspending the DEAE-cellulose in distilled water, then pouring the suspension into a column 30 × 4 cm under a hydrostatic pressure of about 1½ meters. If the chromatogram is to be carried out in ammonium bicarbonate buffer at pH 8.6, the column is converted to the bicarbonate form by passing through it about 1 liter of 1/100 molar ammonium bicarbonate buffer until the liquid coming out of the column is at pH 8.6.

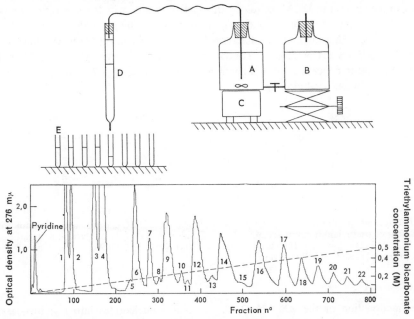

Figure 30. Chromatography of synthetic polynucleotides obtained by Khorana and Vizsolyi (1961). The experiment followed the description given in the text, using the apparatus shown above, where A represents the less concentrated buffer, B the concentrated buffer, C a magnetic stirrer, D the column and E a fraction collector.

1. N-pyridinium nucleotide compound.
2. Thymidine-3', 5'-cyclic phosphate.
3. pT
4. Cyclic dinucleotide
6. pTpT
7. Cyclic trinucleotide
9. pTpTpT
10. Cyclic tetranucleotide
12. pTpTpTpT

13. Cyclic pentanucleotide
14. p_5T_5
16. p_6T_6
17. p_7T_7
18. p_8T_8
19. p_9T_9
20. $p_{10}T_{10}$
21. $p_{11}T_{11}$
22. $p_{12}T_{12}$

Once the nucleotide solution has been sorbed on the column, the latter is carefully washed with 300 ml distilled water. Elution is then carried out using a linear gradient of buffer concentration, which can either be ammonium bicarbonate or triethylammonium bicarbonate which is more volatile (fig. 30).

b. *Nucleotide fractionation on ECTEOLA-cellulose*

This adsorbent was successfully used for separating macromolecular deoxyribonucleic acids (Bendich et al., 1955, 1958), for the fractionation of oligonucleotides, and for the fractionation of mononucleotides (Tener et al., 1958; Michelson, 1959; Nilsson and Sjunnesson, 1961).

The separation of nucleoside polyphosphates has been achieved in a very satisfactory way by Nilsson and Sjunnesson (figure 31).

Tomlinson and Tener (1962, 1963) have demonstrated that it is possible to resolve ribonucleic oligonucleotides (e.g. those arising from pancreatic RNase hydrolysis of t-RNA) in the presence of 7 M urea on a column of DEAE-cellulose, this system resulting in the separation of the oligonucleotides according to their degree of polymerization (or net charge), independent of the composition of the bases. This method was later used by Bartos et al. (1963) in the chromatography of RNase T_1 hydrolysates of RNA. The latter authors used yeast RNA and TMV RNA as substrates, and linear concentration gradients of sodium acetate (+ 7 M urea) and ammonium carbonate (+ 7 M urea) as eluting systems.

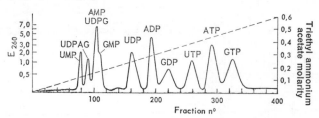

Figure 31. Chromatography of nucleoside polyphosphates on ECTEOLA-cellulose. Column : 25 x 1 cm linear gradient of triethylammonium acetate, pH 6. Total optical density of starting material $E_{260} = 825$. Yield 98 %. Abbreviation as p. 18, except UDPG = UDP glucose, UDPAG = UDP acetylglucosamine (reproduced from Nilsson and Sjunnesson, 1961)

3. DEAE-Sephadex

The fractionation of the ϕX 174 DNA pyrimidine nucleotides into isopliths was effected by Hall and Sinsheimer (1963) on columns of DEAE-Sephadex (A 25-medium) under comparable conditions to those utilized for chromatography on DEAE-cellulose (figure 30). The eluting agent was a linear gradient of triethylammonium bicarbonate.

The separation of isoplithic purine oligonucleotides resulting from the degradation of pyrimidine-free DNA from ϕX was also possible on DEAE-Sephadex, but in the presence of 7 M urea, and on a column thermostated at 55°. In this case, the eluent was KCl of linearly increasing molarity (Sedat and Sinsheimer, 1964).

Rushizky et al. (1964) have also developed a method for fractionating oligonucleotides resulting from the partial RNase hydrolysis of RNA, this time on DEAE-Sephadex columns in the presence of 7 M urea.

B. CHROMATOGRAPHY ON CALCIUM PHOSPHATE COLUMNS

In the course of their work on protein chromatography, Tiselius and co-workers developed a technique using gels of calcium phosphate, which is applicable not only to proteins, but also to other macromolecules (Tiselius, Hjerten and Levin, 1956). A mixture of equal parts of calcium chloride (0.5 M) and disodium phosphate (0.5 M) precipitates at room temperature, giving microcrystals consisting mainly of *brushite* ($CaHPO_4 \cdot 2H_2O$). The brushite columns are not completely stable at pH higher than 7, when they gradually change to another crystalline form, *hydroxyapatite*, $Ca_5(P_4O)_3OH$. At lower pH than 7, either crystalline form may be used advantageously, but at pH higher than 7, hydroxyapatite ought to be used since it is more stable. Hydroxyapatite can be prepared from brushite by boiling in alkali (Tiselius et al., 1956).

A typical experiment described by these authors is the chromatography of bovine serum albumin, for which the column (130 × 10 mm) is initially prepared by saturating hydroxyapatite for 12½ hours with 0.02 M phosphate buffer at pH 6.8 at room temperature (21°). To this column is added 1 ml of a 1 % bovine plasma albumin ("Armour") dialyzed against 0.02 M phosphate buffer of pH 6.8, after which stepwise elution leads to the observation of three peaks, respectively at 0.07, 0.11 and 0.40 M. Each of these peaks taken individually and rechromatographed is eluted by a buffer of the same concentration as the first time.

Experiments of a similar nature have been carried out on many proteins such as phycoerythrin, phycocyanin, ovalbumin, lysozyme, protamine sulfate, hemocyanin and γ-globulin. It has been found that stepwise elution is more satisfactory than gradient elution which does not lead to the formation of well defined peaks.

In the field of nucleic acids and nucleoproteins, many interesting examples have been reported; among those concerning the nucleic acids, mention may be made of the work of Main and Cole (1957), Semenza (1957), Main, Wilkins and Cole (1959), Bernardi (1961) and Bernardi and Timasheff (1961).

Bernardi's technique uses a DNA sample (25 mg in 50 ml 0.005 M phosphate buffer pH 6.8) sorbed on a 2 × 15 cm column of hydroxyapatite. The column is first washed with the starting buffer, and the DNA can then be eluted with 0.5 M buffer.

The RNA isolated from Erlich ascites cells can be sorbed in 0.05 M buffer and eluted by 0.2 M buffer of pH 6.8.

For purification and concentration of viruses, Taverne, Marshall and Fulton (1958) recommend the use of brushite, and have obtained interesting results inthe purification of the following viruses : vaccinia, encephalomyocarditis, coxsackie and poliomyelitis type III. The same technique was used by Wildy et al. (1960) and by Russell (1962) for purification of the *Herpes* virus.

C. Chromatography on Kieselguhr Coated with Methylated Albumin

This technique was introduced by Lermann (1955) who proposed the use of columns of methylated albumin adsorbed on kieselguhr for the fractionation of DNA. Mandell and Hershey (1960) perfected the method to the extent of being able to separate DNA and RNA. Since then, the method has received many applications; for instance, Sueoka and Cheng (1962) achieved a DNA fractionation according to its composition in purine and pyrimidine bases; Monier et al. (1962) applied the method to the isolation of messenger RNA, and Kubinski to the separation of polio virus RNA and cell RNA (1962).

Sueoka and Cheng believe that the high resolutions observed in the fractionations are due to three main effects:

1) an effect due to hydrogen bonds,

2) an effect due to the base composition ("the guanine-cytosine" effect),

3) an effect due to the molecular dimensions.

In view of the complexity of these phenomena, it is not clear whether chromatography on kieselguhr impregnated with methylated albumin should be classed under the ion exchangers or under the molecular sieves. For this reason they have been given a separate section here.

The chromatography is effected in the following way, by the method of Mandell and Hershey (1960) adapted by Sueoka and Cheng (1962).

Methylated albumin was made by the method originally reported by Fraenkel-Conrat & Olcott (1945) and later described also by Mandell and Hershey (1960). The method of Mandell and Hershey, will be cited here.

"Suspend 5 g albumin in 500 ml. absolute methyl alcohol and add 4.2 ml. of 12 N-HCl. The protein dissolves and eventually precipitates again. Allow the mixture to stand in the dark for 3 days or more with occasional shaking. Collect the precipitate in 250 ml. centrifuge bottles, wash twice with methyl alcohol, and twice with anhydrous ether in the centrifuge. Evaporate most of the ether in air and then *in vacuo* over KOH. Reduce the material to a powder and store it over KOH. Failure to remove promptly the residual acid reduces the basicity of the final product. The material is readily soluble in water and is stable either in solution or in the dry form. Reproducible preparations are easily made. The protein is used in the form of a 1 % solution in water."

The preparation of protein-coated kieselguhr and the description of the chromatographic technique cited below are taken from the publication of Sueoka and Cheng (1962).

Washed, protein-coated kieselguhr, used for the second layer in the column, is prepared as follows: Boil (to expel air) and cool a suspension of 20 g kieselguhr in 100 ml. of 0.1 M-buffered saline. Add 5 ml. of 1 % esterified albumin, stir, and add 20 ml. of additional saline. We designate this suspension of kieselguhr coated with methylated albumin as MAK, and methylated albumin itself as MA.

Buffered saline solutions are 0.05 M-Na phosphate buffer plus various amounts of NaCl. The pH of the buffer is 6.7 and although it becomes lower with the addition of salt, the solutions are not adjusted to 6.7, but are used as such. The buffered saline solutions are stored in the cold.

The chromatographic columns have an inner joint with a sealed-in fritted glass disc on an adapter tube (e.g. Kontes Glass Co.), which can be fastened with a pair of steel springs or rubber bands. The air pressure is controlled by a pressure regulator and the air is filtered through a 500 ml. filtering flask filled with cotton. The pressure is applied directly to the column by using a rubber stopper with a glass tube connected to the air line.

The column is packed directly by pouring a known amount of MAK. The excess buffered saline is driven down just to the level of the packed material by applying air pressure of 2 lb./sq in (140 g/cm²). The packed volume of the column is about half of the volume of the MAK used. The most convenient height of the packed material is between 1 and 2 cm. The scale of the fractionation, therefore, is varied by using different sizes of columns and not by increasing the height. For microscale operation, using less than 2 ml. of MAK, small columns are conveniently made of a 5 or 10 ml. pipette from which the narrow neck (mouthpiece) has been removed and the tip packed with fine glass wool.

The column is washed with 10 volumes of buffered saline to 1 volume of MAK. In general, the concentration of the washing salt solution is 0.4 M-buffered saline, but for smaller DNA or RNA 0.1 M-buffered saline is used. The concentration of the nucleic acid sample is adjusted to about 20 μg/ml. with standard saline citrate, applied to the column with as little as possible disturbance to the surface and passed through the column under an air pressure which gives a flow rate of about 3 ml./min. The effluent of the sample solution was kept for ultraviolet absorption measurement to check the extent of absorption of the sample on to the column.

Elution of the nucleic acid is accomplished by passing stepwise through the column a series of buffered saline solutions of increasing salt concentrations, starting with the same concentration used for equilibrating the column. Each time the buffered saline is driven down to the level of the packed material. The amount of eluting solution per step should be chosen to suit the purpose of the fractionation. Several examples described in the section on experimental results will illustrate this point. It is desirable to keep the DNA concentration as high as possible in order to facilitate further investigation of the main fractions. To minimize tailing of DNA from one step to another, the volume of the last eluate of the step should be increased. For a 10 ml. MAK column, two 5 ml. and one 10 ml. elution for each salt-concentration step are usually satisfactory. The concentration increment of salt for each step should also be selected to suit the purpose. The amount of nucleic acid in each fraction is estimated from ultraviolet absorption at 260 mμ. For convenience, a conversion factor of 0.02 O.D.$_{260}$ for 1 μg/ml. of native DNA and 0.022 O.D.$_{260}$ for 1 μg/ml. of denatured DNA has been used.

After use, the inner joint of the column with a sealed-in fritted glass disc should be immersed in dichromate-sulfuric cleaning solution overnight to remove the column material trapped in the fritted glass disc. This is the main cause for the necessity of applying an unusually high air pressure (more than 10 lb./sq in. i. e. 700 g/cm^2) for the later fractions with higher salt concentrations. The entire operation is carried out at room temperature.

This relatively straightforward method has made it possible to separate a DNA of the polydeoxyadenylic-polythymidylic type from the total DNA of the crab *Cancer borealis*, as well as to separate various classes of RNA (Mandell and Hershey, 1960; Sueoka and Cheng, 1962; Monier et al., 1962).

D. Specific adsorbents

As we have seen earlier, the Watson and Crick's helices are bound together by hydrogen bonds between complementary purine and pyrimidine bases (p. 65). Several authors tried, successfully to use the same complementarity, i. e. hydrogen bonds between two base pairs for, the separation of polynucleotides. For instance Bautz and Hall (1962), prepared a column of cellulose chimically combined with DNA and showed that this column was capable of adsorbing specifically RNA. The same year Adler and Rich (1962) combined acetylated phosphocellulose with various polynucleotides (poly-A, poly-C, poly-I, poly-U, bacteriophage RNA, t-RNA) in the presence of dicyclohexyl carbodiimide; the polynucleotides were fixed on the phosphocellulose and the " specific celluloses " thus obtained had the property of adsorbing the complementary polynucleotides through hydrogen bonds. Gilham (1962, 1964) combined cellulose directly with polynucleotides such as poly-thymidine, poly-deoxyadenosine, poly-deoxycytidine, in the presence of DCC, and showed that a column of poly-T-cellulose could actually separate various deoxyadenosine nucleotides. Edmonds and Abrams (1963), applied the same method to isolate a natural poly-A by chromatography on a poly-T-cellulose column. In the same fashion Gilham and Robinson used specific celluloses for the separation of oligonucleotides obtained after enzymic hydrolysis of nucleic acids (Gilham and Robinson 1964).

V. THIN LAYER CHROMATOGRAPHY

This method consists in spreading on a glass plate a thin layer of adsorbent in the form of an aqueous suspension, generally containing a small amount of plaster of Paris. When the layer has set and dried sufficiently, the substances to be analyzed are placed in the form of small droplets on the plate and the operation is continued as for ascending paper chromatography. The enormous advantage of this technique is its speed, since complete development of the chromatogram is generally obtained in less than few hours. The solvent systems used are those employed in paper chromatography (cf. e.g. Stahl, 1958).

Examples of the application of the technique are innumerable, as is the case for paper chromatography. It has mostly been used for analytical purposes, but Riiter and Mayer (1962) have shown that it is possible to use it for preparative purposes.

The extension of thin layer chromatography to derivatives of nucleic acids is mainly the work of Randerath (1961-1964).

Randerath has shown that it is possible to make thin layers of cellulose or ECTEOLA-cellulose on glass plates, and that these systems possess high resolving power in the case of purine and pyrimidine bases, nucleosides and nucleotides. In the case of nucleotide separation on ECTEOLA-cellulose, for instance, it is possible to obtain well standardized samples of the adsorbent (Serva Entwicklungslabor, Heidelberg, Germany), and on these samples, complete resolution can be obtained of substances as closely related as adenosine diphosphate and adenosine triphosphate in 5-10 minutes. Separation of CTP, ATP, GTP and UTP requires 60 — 100 minutes, which is still very quick compared with paper chromatography.

The layers are prepared in the following manner : a suspension is made by shaking vigorously for 30-45 seconds 10 g of the ion-exchange powder with 60-70 ml distilled water. This suspension is spread over glass plates (10 × 20 or 20 × 29 cm) that have been scrupulously cleaned with a detergent, and allowed to dry at room temperature overnight.

The nucleotide solutions are then applied (usually 10^{-3} to 10^{-1} μmol. of each substance) by means of a 10 μl micropipette along a line 3 cm the edge of the plate. The plates are then dipped into the appropriate solvent, a height of 1-2 cm of which is contained in an open beaker. It is unnecessary to cover the vessel. The chromatography can be followed by means of a UV lamp, and is interrupted when the solvent has traveled a suitable distance. A tracing of the chromatography on a cellophane sheet can be drawn with the aid of the UV lamp.

Randerath has observed that dilute hydrochloric acid is an adequate solvent for effecting a number of separations (table XIV).

Table XIV. R_f values of nucleoside di- and triphosphates (from Randerath, 1962)

	N HCl 0.02	N HCl 0.03	N HCl 0.04
ADP	0.48	0.68	—
ATP	0.11	0.20	0.56
GDP	0.27	0.51	—
GTP	0.07	0.14	0.41
CDP	0.53	—	—
CTP	0.13	0.31	0.64
UDP	0.15	0.25	—
UTP	0.04	0.08	0.18

Continuing their work on thin layer chromatography of nucleic acids and their derivatives, the Randeraths (Randerath, 1963, Randerath and Randerath, 1964a, b; Randerath, 1964) have shown how deoxyribonucleotides and ribonucleotides can be separated by thin layer anion exchange chromatography, the ion exchanger used being poly-(ethyleneimine)-cellulose. The developing solvent is a solution of LiCl in dilute boric acid. The principle of the method depends on the formation of complexes between borate and ribose derivatives, which then move slower than the corresponding deoxyribose compounds. Subsequently, the same authors made a systematic study of the thin layer chromatography on poly-(ethyleneimine)-cellulose of a large number of compounds, and gave the Rf values for 33 different compounds (Randerath and Randerath, 1964a). Finally, they have described the resolution of complex nucleotide mixtures using two-dimensional thin layer chromatography (cf. figure 32).

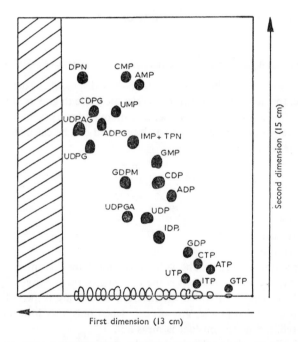

Figure 32. Two-dimensional anion-exchange thin-layer chromatogram of mononucleotides. 0.5 mm thick PEI-cellulose layer. 0.1 ml of a solution containing 23 ribonucleotides (10-15 mμ mol. each) was applied slowly in two 0.05 ml portions with intermediate drying from a micropipette to the layer Elution and detection was carried out as described in the text. The shaded area was removed after the elution in the first dimension (Randerath and Randerath, 1964b)

Grippo et al. (1965) have also described the thin layer chromatography of nucleic acids on two other adsobants, microcrystalline cellulose and DEAE-cellulose using various solvent systems.

VI. SEDIMENTATION, ULTRACENTRIFUGATION

The technique is an application of the general method introduced by Svedberg and co-workers.

The principle of the method is simple, a macromolecular substance as a colloidal solution is submitted to a gravitational field (ultracentrifugation) and, by means of an optical method, the displacement that the substance under study suffers, in the field, is observed.

It is logical to find that the substances with the highest molecular weight are those that sediment the most rapidly.

Without going into details of the mathematics that have led to the full understanding of this phenomenon, we can define the sedimentation constant by the equation :

$$s = \frac{1}{\omega^2 x} \frac{dx}{dt}$$

where :

$\frac{dx}{dt}$ is the displacement of a particle in unit time,

$\omega^2 x$ is the gravitational field in which the particles are displaced. This is usually expressed as a number of g i.e. the number by which the acceleration due to gravity ($1\,g$) must be multiplied. One might talk, for instance, of a colloidal suspension submitted to a gravitational field of 100,000 g.

The molecular weight of the colloidal particles studied can be calculated from the sedimentation constants by the relation :

$$M = \frac{RTs}{D\,(1 - V\rho)}$$

where :

R = gas constant;

T = absolute temperature;

D = diffusion constant;

V = partial specific volume, i.e. the volume occupied by 1 gram protein, nucleic acid or nucleoprotein, etc.; practically speaking, it is the opposite of the density;

ρ = density of the solvent in which the macromolecules are dispersed.

It is not easy to determine D and V, especially when only very little substance is available, so usually only the sedimentation constant is measured.

This constant is directly deduced from optical measurements carried out during the centrifugation, which give the rate of displacement $\frac{dx}{dt}$. Taking a hypothetical example, if a speed of 0.4 mm per hour were observed, i.e. about 10^{-5} cm per second, in a field of 100,000 g,

$$s = \frac{10^{-5}}{10^5 . 980} = \sim 10^{-13} \text{ (seconds)}$$

Because of the inconvenient size of s, it is expressed in Svedberg units, where

$$1 \text{ Svedberg unit} = 10^{-13} \text{ seconds,}$$

in the example just given,

$$s = 1 \text{ Svedberg unit.}$$

For most macromolecules, s falls between 1 and 200 Svedberg units, a low molecular weight protein, e.g. lactalbumin, having a sedimentation constant of 1.9 Svedberg units, while a high molecular weight macromolecule such as tobacco mosaic virus has a sedimentation constant of 193 Svedberg units in water at 20°. Some examples of sedimentation constants are to be found in table XV.

PREPARATIVE ULTRACENTRIFUGATION IN A DENSITY GRADIENT

This method was devised by Meselson, Stahl and Vinograd (1957) and has had many applications in the fractionation of nucleic acids and nucleoproteins.

The method consists in observing the equilibrium distribution of macromolecules in a density gradient which is itself in equilibrium. The density gradient is obtained by sedimentation of a solute of low molecular weight in a solvent under a constant gravitational field. The initial concentration of the solute, the gravitational field and the lenght of the liquid column must be

Table XV. Sedimentation constants and molecular weights *

Macromolecule	Sedimentation constant in Svedbergunits (S)	Molecular weight	Authors
RNA :			
Transfer	4	25,000	in Gros et al. (1961)
Ribosomal	16	5.5×10^5	in Gros et al. (1961)
	23	1.1×10^6	—
Viral (turnip yellow mosaic)	21-8	2.3×10^6	Haselkorn (1962)
Messenger	23-30	—	Monier et al. (1962)
Ribonucleoprotein (rat liver)	80	3.6×10^6	Hamilton et al. (1962)
DNA :			
B. cereus	22.0	7×10^6	Sueoka and Cheng (1962)
B. subtilis	23.9	10×10^6	—
S. marcescens	23.3	10×10^6	—
M. lysodeikticus	24.5	11×10^6	—
E. coli	27.5	14×10^6	—
Virus			
turnip yellow mosaic	106	5×10^6	in Schachman and Williams (1959)
tomato bushy stunt	132	10.6×10^6	—
polio	158	$6.8\text{-}10 \times 10^6$	—
tobacco mosaic	185-198	$31\text{-}45 \times 10^6$	—

* The relation belween S_{20w}^0 (sedimentation coefficient in water at 20° exrapolated to zero concentration) and molecular weight is thoroughly discussed in the article of Eigner & Doty (1965)

chosen in such a way that the scale of densities obtained covers the effective density of the macro-molecule to be analyzed. The gravitational field tends to bring the macromolecules to a point where the sum of forces acting on them is zero.

The first examples described by Meselson et al. concerned the DNA (from bacteriophage T_4, thymus, etc.) equilibrium in a cesium chloride gradient. Later, other systems were proposed, particularly equilibrium in a density gradient of sucrose (McQuillen et al., 1959), but the principle stays the same.

The substances to be fractionated are dissolved in a cesium chloride or sucrose solution so that they form a homogeneous colloidal solution. This solution is then submitted to prolonged ultracentrifugation to create a low molecular weight solute density gradient. When equilibrium is attained, for example after 24 hours, the macromolecules to be separated are found distributed in a certain number of horizontal layers situated in zones where the surrounding solution has the same density. For ultracentrifuging, it is necessary to use a rotor where the tubes become horizontal, angular rotors obviously resulting in deformed layers. Recovery and analysis of the horizontal bands corresponding to different zones can take place by two means :

1) by piercing the bottom of the centrifuge tube and collecting the various fractions drop by drop (Brenner et al., 1961; Gros et al., 1961; Monier et al., 1960; Sinsheimer et al., 1962).

2) by carefully syphoning the layers one after the other from the top of the tube (Breedis et al., 1962).

In order to be able better to visualize the actual procedure, an actual case will be described : the fractionation of the papilloma virus effected by Breedis et al. (1962).

The crude virus preparation is suspended in a 0.0067 M phosphate buffer at $10^{11} - 10^{12}$ particles per milliliter. A mixture containing two parts of this suspension and one part of a saturated cesium chloride solution produces a mixture with an initial density of 1.31. The density gradient resulting from centrifuging this suspension at 35,000 r.p.m. for 24 hours results in sus-pending all the particles of a viral nature.

The virus layers floating at different levels in the density gradient are recovered by syphoning with a polyethylene tube that can be inserted into the tube very carefully using a precision micro-meter system.

The density of CsCl solutions at different levels is determined by taking aliquots of the solution in a blank tube prepared under identical conditions to the actual experiment except that it contains no virus. The samples are taken with the same syphon system at the same depths in the tube. The average density of each region is determined by weighing 0.1 to 0.5 ml solution in Pregl micro-pyknometers.

The amount of virus in each layer is estimated by measuring the optical density at 270 mμ of the layers after dialysis.

The results of this analysis are as follows. The virus is distributed into four bands in the CsCl gradient (figure 33). These bands are localized at levels where the CsCl has densities respec-tively of 1.29, 1.32, 1.33 and 1.34. The densest band (4) is thin and opalescent to Tyndall rays. UV absorption spectra, infectivity tests and examination of particle homogeneity make it likely that the most dense band (4) contains the highest amount of DNA and represents the complete virus.

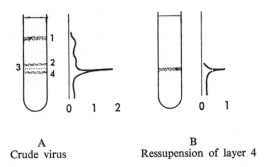

A
Crude virus

B
Ressupension of layer 4

Figure 33. A. Schematic representation of a crude viral preparation after 24 hours' centrifuging in a CsCl gradient. The preparation separates into four recognizable layers, the optical densities of which at 260 mμ are shown on the right of the tube.

B. Appearance of layer 4 after resuspension in the cesium chloride gradient, together with its optical density at 260 mμ (reproduced from Breedis et al., 1962)

VII. CHEMICAL REACTIONS USED IN THE QUALITATIVE AND QUANTITATIVE ANALYSIS OF NUCLEIC ACIDS

It can be useful either to localize the nucleic acids qualitatively within the cells by using histochemical reactions such as the Feulgen reaction or reactions with basic dyestuffs, or to study quantitatively the distribution of nucleic acids in the tissues by selectively determining RNA and DNA by colorimetric methods that are specific (color reactions of ribose and deoxyribose), or by successive extraction of RNA and DNA by various fractionations, subsequently estimating the phosphorus contained in one or the other compound. The various methods in use will now be briefly reviewed.

A. HISTOCHEMICAL METHODS

1. Feulgen's method

The method, described in 1924 by Feulgen and Rossenbeck, makes use of the fact that DNA hydrolysis products restore the color to fuschine reduced by sulfurous acid, or Schiff's reagent. This technique has been used for forty years to color cell nuclei and chromosomes.

Experimental procedure (Swift, 1955).

Feulgen's reagent. 0.5 g Fuschine base, or *p*-rosaniline is added to 100 ml water at room temperature, then 1 g potassium or sodium metabisulfite and 10 ml concentrated HCl. The solution is shaken from time to time until the straw yellow color appears (about 3 hours), when 0.25 — 0.50 g active charcoal is added, the mixture shaken, filtered and stored in a well sealed bottle in the cold room. The reagent must be water-white, if it is still yellowish, active charcoal should be added and filtered.

Rinsing liquid : 10 ml N HCl, 10 ml 5 % K or Na metabisulfite, and 180 ml water.

Experimental procedure. The sections are hydrolyzed in N HCl at 60°. For the majority of tissues fixed in alcohol — acetic acid, the optimal duration of the treatment is 12 minutes, and for tissues fixed in formalin it is 14 minutes. The section is treated with the Feulgen reagent for one hour, followed by 3 rinses of 10 minutes each (longer is required for thicker sections), washing with water for 5 minutes, drying and mounting.

Should the hydrolysis tend to displace the sections from the slide, they can be maintained in place by means of a collodion film. To do this, the sections must be rinsed in absolute alcohol, rapidly dipped in a 0.5 % collodion solution in absolute alcohol—ether (1 : 1), allowed to dry partially in air for 15 — 30 seconds and then placed in water for the hydrolysis.

2. Basic dyestuffs : methylpyronine green (Brachet, 1953; Kurnick, 1962)

There have been numerous procedures recommended. That of Kurnick gives very satisfactory results with most acetic alcohol-fixed tissues. Methyl green loses its specificity for DNA in some tissues after formalin fixation. Methyl green (C.I. 684) or ethyl green (C.I. 685) (0.2 %) may be made up in water or acetate buffer (0.1 M) at pH 4.2. Solutions should be shaken repeatedly with chloroform in a separatory funnel until the chloroform ceases to show traces of color from crystal violet contamination. Kurnick recommends staining for 6 minutes, although longer times are desirable for some tissues. Blot, and differentiate in two changes of n-butyl alcohol (overnight differentiation in tert-butyl alcohol has also been recommended). Counterstain in pyronin B (C.I. 741) in acetone 30 to 90 seconds, clear in xylene, and mount in balsam or plastic media. Kurnick obtained the best differentiation with n-butyl alcohol, which removes pyronin, hence the necessity of separate staining solutions. Many workers have found pyronin unsatisfactory for RNA. Kurnick reports that it "serves primarily as a counterstain and is not found to be a reliable indicator of ribonucleic acid." For this reason Korson (1951) has replaced pyronin with an aqueous solution of the more dependable toluidine blue O (C.I. 925).

B. Chemical reactions used in the determination of nucleic acids

1. Methods involving estimation of sugars

The reaction of pentoses with orcinol (Mejbaum, 1939) is routinely used for the determination of RNA, and the reaction of deoxypentoses with diphenylamine (Dische, 1930) for the determination of DNA. The experimental details as given by Davidson and Waymouth (1944) will be given for both determinations.

a. Preparation of the tissue

The tissue to be examined is first carefully minced and de-fatted; it is minced and dehydrated by successive fractions of ethanol and ether, and dried. The dried material is transferred to a stoppered 50 ml centrifuge tube, and shaken with successive 40 ml fractions of 0.1 N HCl for one hour each time, this procedure being destined to remove the soluble phosphorus, including the simple nucleotides. The residue is washed twice with ethanol, then extracted twice for 2 hours on reflux at 65° with portions of an ethanol-chloroform (3/1) mixture. It is then washed with ether, dried and finely powdered in a mechanical mortar, and passed through a 120 mesh per sq. cm. sieve. The total phosphorus can be determined on this powder before the nucleic acids.

To estimate the sugars, amounts of powder corresponding to 100-200 μg ribonucleic P are taken for the ribose estimation, and 100-300 μg deoxyribonucleic P for the deoxyribose estimation.

b. *Pentose estimation*

Appropriate amounts of powder (generally 20 mg) are weighed into two 10 ml graduated centrifuge tubes. To one of the tubes are added 2 ml water and 2 ml Mejbaum's reagent (100 mg orcinol in 10 ml conc. HCl containing 0.1 % $FeCl_3.6H_2O$), and in the other 2 ml water and 2 ml HCl containing 0.1 % $FeCl_3.6H_2O$, but no orcinol. The two tubes are heated with shaking in a boiling water bath for exactly 10 min., then cooled. The blue-green substance is extracted by successive extractions with 2.2 and 1.5 ml amyl alcohol. The amyl alcohol layers are separated by centrifugation, combined, mixed with 1 ml ethanol, and brought to a total volume of 8 ml with amyl alcohol. Exactly similar extractions are performed on the blank which does not contain orcinol; a reading is then taken at 670 mμ on the photometer. A standard curve is established using yeast RNA; 2 ml aliquots at various concentrations (25 — 200 μg P) are treated as in the determination just described.

If the RNA to be determined is already in solution, the estimation of the pentose (and therefore of the RNA) can be carried out by the orcinol method as originally described by Mejbaum (1939), or by the phloroglucinol method of von Euler and Hahn (1947). In our own experience, the phloroglucinol reagent is much more specific for RNA than the orcinol reagent which also reacts with DNA.

c. *Orcinol reaction*

To one part of the unknown, an equal vol. conc. HCl (sp. g. 1.19) containing 0.1 % $FeCl_3$. $6H_2O$ and 0.1 % orcinol is added and the mixture heated on the boiling water bath for 20 min. (45 min. according to Albaum and Umbreit (1947). A standard RNA solution and a blank are treated simultaneously. A reading at 670 mμ is taken. A standard curve is plotted from a 1 mg/ml RNA solution, taking 0.1, 0.2 and 0.3 ml of this solution for the estimation and making up to 1 ml with distilled water. Finally 1 ml of the Mejbaum reagent is added, etc.

d. *Phloroglucinol reaction*

The sample (1 ml) containing 2 mg RNA is thoroughly mixed with 8 ml 0.1 % $FeCl_3$ in 1 part HCl and 6 parts glacial acetic acid. The mixture is immersed in a boiling water bath for 50 min., then cooled to room temperature, when 1 ml 0.25 % phloroglucinol in a mixture of 1 part conc. HCl, 1 part water and 2 parts acetic acid is added. This mixture is allowed to stand for 20 min. at room temperature then put in a boiling water bath for just 4 min., cooled and kept at room temperature for 4-24 hr. The maximum coloration appears after 10 hours and is read at 680 mμ.

e. *Deoxypentose estimation (whole tissue)* :

A suitable amount of powder (generally 200 mg) is heated in a 10 ml graduated centrifuge tube with 8 ml 0.1 N HCl for 20 min. with frequent shaking. After cooling, the volume is adjusted to 8 ml and the mixture centrifuged. A 3 ml amount of the supernatant is heated for just 6 min. in a boiling water bath with 8 ml of the diphenylamine reagent (1 g diphenylamine recrystallized twice from alcohol, 2 ml conc. H_2SO_4 and 98 ml glacial acetic acid). A blank solution is prepared from a second amount of supernatant and 8 ml acetic acid. The cooled solution is read in the photometer at 595 mμ. A standard curve is prepared from DNA in the following way : 4 ml amounts are hydrolyzed in HCl of final concentration 0.1 N, and 3 ml supernatant are used with 8 ml reagent to develop the color.

If the DNA to be determined is already in solution, the deoxypentose determination as it was originally described by Dische (1930) may be used directly.

f. *Deoxypentose estimation (DNA in solution)* :

A volume of solution containing 50 — 500 γ DNA per ml is mixed with 2 vol. of the Dische reagent. This reagent is prepared by dissolving 1 g diphenylamine (twice recrystallized from 70 % alcohol or petroleum ether) in 100 ml analytical grade acetic acid ; 2.75 ml analytical grade conc. sulfuric acid are added to 100 ml of the diphenylamine solution. The reaction mixture is heated for at least 10 min., a blank containing water instead of DNA is carried out simultaneously. The DNA gives a blue solution that is stable for several hours. The absorption curve, read on a spectrophotometer, exhibits a maximum at 595 mμ.

This method has recently been improved by Giles and Myers (1965) who proceed in the following way. Two ml of a 4 % diphenylamine solution in glacial acetic acid are added to 2 ml of the DNA sample in 10 % perchloric acid, followed by 0.1 ml of an aqueous solution containing 1.6 mg/ml acetaldehyde. After incubation overnight at 30°, the optical density at 595 — 700 mμ is measured.

2. Methods utilizing precipitation of the nucleic acids as lanthanum salts, followed by colorimetric determination of ribose and deoxyribose

The nucleic acids are extracted from powdered tissue with 10 % NaCl and precipitated as La salts. The nucleic acid solution obtained from the lanthanum salt precipitate is then used for determination of the ribose and deoxyribose by the method described above (Davidson and Waymouth, 1944).

For extraction of the nucleic acids, a suitable amount of tissue powder (i.e. about 400 mg) is weighed into a 15 ml conical centrifuge tube, and 4 drops of triacetin (= glycerol triacetate) are added. The NaCl extraction is carried out in several successive steps : *a*) 3 ml overnight at 0°, *b*) 2 ml for 30 min. at 100°, *c*) 2 ml for 30 min. at 100°, *d*) 2 ml. for 2 min. at 100°, *e*) 2 ml for 10 min. at 100°. The combined extracts are brought to 10 ml. From these 10 ml., 0.5 ml are for the total P determination, and 9 ml are pipetted into a 25 ml test-tube to which 1 ml La acetate and 10 ml ethanol are added. After one hour at 0°, the precipitate is centrifuged, then washed twice with 3 ml of 2 % La acetate. The moist precipitate is decomposed by 2 successive

0.5 ml portions of 0.5 M Na$_2$CO$_3$. The La carbonate is removed by centrifugation and the supernatant adjusted to 5 ml.

The extract is treated in the following way : 1) 0.5 ml is removed for the total P estimation; 2) 0.2 — 0.3 ml are pipetted into a tube for the ribose determination by a modification of the Mejbaum (1939) method — the volume is brought to 2 ml with water and 2 ml of the Mejbaum reagent (see above) are added. The tube is heated for 30 min. in a boiling water bath, following the advice of Schlenk (1942) then cooled. Ethanol (2 ml) and water (1 ml) are then added, and the green color is read on the photometer. This is compared with a standard curve of P-RNA that has been established from liver RNA, precipitated with lanthanum and treated like the unknown; 3) 3 ml are removed for the deoxyribose colorimetric determination by the diphenylamine reaction, and measured into a graduated conical centrifuge tube containing 1 ml 0.55 N HCl. The tube is heated in a boiling water bath for 20 min., cooled and made up to 4 ml. To this are added 8 ml of the diphenylamine reagent (see above) and the tube is placed in a boiling water bath for 6 minutes, rapidly cooled, and the blue color read on the photometer, then compared with a standard curve P-DNA established from thymus DNA precipitated by lanthanum.

3. Methods involving the successive isolation of RNA and DNA and determination of them as P-RNA and P-DNA

These methods were developed by Schmidt and Thannhauser (1945), by Schneider (1945) and by Ogur and Rosen (1950). They have been amply reviewed and criticized by Leslie (1955).

According to the methods of Schmidt and Thannhauser and Schneider, the tissue is treated with dilute alkali to cause the RNA to pass into solution in the form of small nucleotides; the DNA, which also dissolves, is not degraded by this treatment. When the solution is acidified by trichloroacetic acid, the DNA precipitates at the same time as the phosphoproteins, the RNA remaining in solution. The phosphorus corresponding to the phosphoproteins most of the time being negligible in respect to the total phosphorus, it can be roughly considered that the phosphorus content of the supernatant corresponds to the RNA, while the phosphorus in the precipitate corresponds to the DNA. In Ogur and Rosen's method, which was originally intended for plant tissues, the tissue, after being defatted and having its acid-soluble parts removed, is treated with N perchloric acid at 4° for 18 hours to take out the RNA, and with 0.5 N perchloric acid at 70° for 20 minutes to take out the DNA. Phosphorus determination on the two perchloric acid extracts gives the P-RNA and P-DNA amounts. The main disadvantage of the Ogur and Rosen method is that part of the DNA passes into the first perchloric acid extract.

The authors of these methods (Schmidt, 1957) are themselves quite aware of their imperfections. Since the methods are differential, one cannot hope to obtain valid results except when the DNA and RNA quantities are of the same order. Another weak point of the method is the existence in some tissue of unidentified phosphorus-containing substances which are not nucleotides and which are neither acid-soluble nor ether-soluble. The phosphorus of these substances (which probably are certain phospholipids) is added to that of the P-RNA. The error arising from this additional phosphorus is particularly serious in the case of nervous tissue.

4. Application: Nucleic acid content of cells and tissue

The nucleic acid content of tissue in normal conditions, during development or in certain pathological conditions, has been studied by many authors using methods comparable to those of Davidson and Waymouth (1944) or Schmidt and Thannhauser (1945, 1957).

Among this important work, special mention must be made of that of Davidson's laboratory (cf. reviews published by Davidson, 1947, 1953a, 1953b; Leslie, 1955) and that undertaken in Mandel's laboratory (Mandel, 1951; Mandel, Jacob and Mandel, 1950, 1954; Bieth and Mandel, 1953; Weill, Mandel and Kayser, 1957; Mandel and Schmidt, 1957; Sigot and Mandel 1957). Table XVI (Davidson, 1953a) lists the P-RNA and P-DNA values of some animal tissue.

Table XVI. Nucleic acid content of certain animal tissues expressed in milligrams P-RNA and milligrams P-DNA per 100 grams fresh tissue (method of Schmidt and Thannhauser), reproduced from Davidson (1953 a)

Tissue	Species	P-RNA	P-DNA	Ratio RNA/DNA
Liver	Rat (200-240 g)	77-110	21-25	4.0
	Rat (60-80g)	106-122	28-37	3.6
	Rat (pregnant female)	110-118	21-23	5.2
	Rat (embryo)	87-134	35-65	2.2
	Rabbit	44-76	16-29	2.7
	Rabbit (pregnant female)	67-138	14-17	6.8
	Rabbit (embryo)	87-105	61-84	1.3
	Cat	72-85	25-43	2.3
	Sheep	55-84	23-33	2.5
	Man	37-74	16-25	3.0
Pancreas	Rabbit	108-130	44-61	2.3
	Cat	130-165	38-49	3.4
	Ox	170-185	21-22	8.1
	Man (one sample)	42	31	1.3
Kidney	Rat	25-47	33-43	0.7
Brain	Rat	20-33	15-19	1.5
Spleen	Rat (200-240 g)	63-86	76-85	0.9
	Rat (60-80 g)	70-82	68-70	1.0
	Rabbit	67-79	81-96	0.3
	Cat	84-151	73-94	1.4
	Man (one sample)	36	77	0.5
Thymus	Rat (200-240 g)	87-116	181-242	0.5
	Rat (60-60 g)	114-135	181-261	0.6
	Rabbit	89-99	181-250	0.4
	Calf	80-100	224-250	0.4

The study of the RNA and DNA content of many tissues, both normal and pathological, as well as in the course of their evolution (embryonic and regenerating tissue, compensating hypertrophy, young tissue, etc.) has allowed a certain number of generalizations to be made (Mandel, Jacob and Mandel, 1949, 1950; Leslie, 1955).

In physiological conditions that are favorable to the growth or multiplication of cells, such as in embryonic or regenerating tissue, neoplastic tissue, bacterial populations dividing rapidly, etc., an increase in the RNA content with respect to the protein content of these tissues and cells is observable. On the other hand, prolonged protein starvation causes the muscular tissue to suffer an RNA fall that can lead to RNA levels of 40 % of the figure under normal conditions. In protein starvation conditions, it is also found that DNA behaves as a stable entity, and the contrast between the stable nature of DNA and the labile nature of RNA leads to an extension of the idea of the stable and unstable elements forming the DNA-RNA pair. During very prolonged protein starvation, this contrast becomes increasingly striking : while the RNA content falls, the DNA content of the liver, kidney and brain in the rat remains constant, and the number of nuclei in the liver also remains constant. It is therefore probable that the number of cells has remained unchanged, so that the constancy of the total DNA amount and the number of cell nuclei leads to the conclusion that the DNA content of the nuclei is fixed during protein starvation.

The problem of the DNA content of cell nuclei has aroused considerable interest in the past twenty years, as Vendrely (1955, 1956) pointed out. The amount of DNA in isolated cell nuclei can be determined microspectrophotometrically by the techniques of either Pollister et al. or Caspersson (cf. p. 129). The methods using visible radiation have the advantage over the others of being in more common use, and of not requiring such expensive apparatus (the expense arising mainly because of the quartz lenses necessary for the ultraviolet methods).

In table XVII reproduced from Vendrely (1956), some values for the absolute DNA content of isolated cell nuclei are given.

Table XVII. DNA content (picograms or 10^{-12} grams) per nucleus of diploid and sperm cells of different animal species

Species	Erythrocytes	Liver	Sperm	References
Bovidae	—	6.4	3.3	Boivin, Vendrely and Vendrely (1948) ; Vendrely (1952).
Gallinaceae	2.34	2.39	1.26	Mirsky and Ris (1949)
Toad	7.33	—	3.70	—
Alosa	1.97	2.01	0.91	—
	3.49	3.33	1.64	—
Carp	3.3	3.0	1.6	Vendrely and Vendrely (1952)
Trout (brown)	5.79	—	2.67	Mirsky and Ris (1949)
Trout (rainbow)	4.9	—	2.45	Vendrely and Vendrely (1952)
Pike	1.7	—	0.85	—
Tench	1.7	—	0.85	—

This table allows the following conclusions to be drawn :

Nuclei from the same tissue have a DNA content varying from one species to another ; but the DNA content of different tissues in the same species is constant, haploid nuclei having half the diploid nucleus content, as pointed out by Boivin et al. (1948). The DNA content is proportional to the number of chromosomes in the nucleus, and Mirsky and Ris (1949) showed, for example, that in rat liver, three types of nuclei exist with DNA ratios of 2/1, 4/1 and 8/1 to the chromosomes, depending on whether the nuclei are di-, tetra- or octaploid. These observations are of paramount importance in demonstrating the genetic rôle of DNA.

CHAPTER V

Enzymes in nucleic acid research

GENERAL REMARKS

Many enzymes belonging to the general group of the hydrolases (E.C.3) and some belonging to the general group of the transferases (E.C.2) attack the nucleic structure resulting in the formation of a greater or lesser number of fragments, depending on the specificity of the enzyme. These "nucleolytic" enzymes can be subdivided into four main categories :

1) Nucleases (generally of the "phosphoric diester hydrolase" type, E.C.3.1.4) catalyzing cleavage of the internucleotide bridges, without liberating inorganic phosphate.

2) Phosphatases (phosphoric monoester hydrolases E.C.3.1.3) causing the formation of free inorganic phosphate by hydrolysis of the nucleotide terminal phosphoryl groups.

3) Nucleosidases (hydrolyzing N-glycosyl compounds E.C.2.3.2) liberating free bases by hydrolyzing the base-pentose bonds. Generally, these enzymes are specific for a single cleavage, e.g. inosine ribohydrolase, uridine ribohydrolase, etc.

4) Nucleodeaminases (enzymes acting on C-N bonds, other than peptide bonds in cyclic amidines E.C.3.5.4) causing the appearance of free ammonia from purine and pyrimidine bases by deamination. Among such enzymes, there have been described : cytosine aminohydrolase, adenine aminohydrolase, guanine aminohydrolase, etc.

Only the first two categories have interesting applications so far as the macromolecular nucleic acid structures are concerned, and these will be described below.

I. THE NUCLEASES

The nucleases are themselves subdivided into two large classes, endonucleases and exonucleases.

A. ENDONUCLEASES

These are enzymes that attack the nucleic chain by rupture of the phosphodiester bond at several points with simultaneous liberation of many mono- and oligonucleotide fragments. These enzymes consist of the following types :

1) Enzymes that are non-specific towards the nature of the pentose; this means that DNA, RNA and various polynucleotides are hydrolyzed with formation of oligonucleotides, the latter being terminated by either 3′-phosphate or 5′-phosphate groups.

Although these enzymes are not specific as to the nature of the pentose, they are specific when it comes to the nature of the purine or pyrimidine linkages, some bonds being preferentially broken with the appearance of oligonucleotides as well as mononucleotides.

2) The ribonucleases (RNases) which hydrolyze only polynucleotides of the ribonucleic type with the formation of mono- and oligonucleotides.

For most of the known RNases, the position of the cleavage is such that the fragments appearing are terminated by 3′-phosphate groups. The only exceptions so far reported appear to be the RNase II from *Escherichia coli* (Spahr, 1964, see p. 226) and the RNase from pig liver nuclei (Lipsett et al., 1961; Singer and Guss, 1962), and in the latter case, the enzyme was not purified enough for it to be certain that it was not simply a non-specific endonuclease that was responsible for the activity.

As in the case of the "non specific" nucleases, the position of bond rupture along the ribonucleic chain is determined by the sequence of the purine and pyrimidine bases.

3) The deoxyribonucleases (DNases). These enzymes hydrolyze only polynucleotides of the deoxyribonucleic type with formation of mono- and oligonucleotides that can be terminated with either 3′-phosphate or 5′-phosphate groups.

The nature of the bonds broken preferentially is determined, as for the other nucleases, by the sequence of purine and pyrimidine bases.

B. EXONUCLEASES

These are enzymes that attack the chain repeatedly, giving a stepwise degradation of a single mononucleotide at a time. They are, in fact, the enzymes that have been known for some time as phosphodiesterases, which hydrolyze oligonucleotides to the mononucleotide stage. The mononucleotides obtained are sometimes 3′-phosphates and sometimes 5′-phosphates, depending on the specificity of the enzyme.

This rather summary classification of nucleases into endonucleases and exonucleases only rests on the exterior appearance of phenomena taking place during the enzymatic degradation of the nucleic acids, being merely a convenient way of cataloging them when it is absolutely essential to make such a classification.

The limits are, indeed, not always as clear cut : it is rare to find an enzyme of strict specificity towards the nature of pentoses or towards the purine and pyrimidine base sequence. Specificity towards the nature of the bonds broken preferentially is mostly a tendency which has not yet been exactly worked out in many cases. Nevertheless, one single absolute criterion for the mode of action of the nucleases must be noted, namely the position of the rupture and the nature of the terminal phosphoryl group in the nucleotides formed. In every case examined, the formation of nucleoside-5′-phosphates or nucleoside-3′-phosphates was observed, but *never both at the same time.*

Attention ought to be drawn, moreover, to the particular case of the "ribonucleases", so called because they provoke RNA depolymerization. It is due to this phenomenon that they were discovered, and it has attracted many applications as a method of estimation. It is the result of migration of the internucleotide phosphoryl group with transient formation of a 2'-3'-cyclic nucleotide. This is the reason that the ribonucleases have been classified by the Enzyme Commission among the transferases, pancreatic ribonuclease being defined as a "ribonucleate pyrimidine-nucleotide-2'-transferase" (cyclizing) E.C.2.7.7.16.

II. PHOSPHATASES (PHOSPHORIC MONOESTER PHOSPHOHYDROLASES)

The phosphatases are subdivided into 19 main categories, only four of which have important applications in the study of nucleic acid structure.

"*Non-specific*" *Phosphomonoesterases*, hydrolyzing all phosphomonoesters, i.e. 3'-phosphates as well as 5'-phosphates. These enzymes also hydrolyze all the natural or synthetic phospho-monoesters not necessarily belonging to the nucleic acid field (glycerophosphate, phenylphosphate, etc.). It is advisable to distinguish between the acid and alkaline phosphatases among these "non-specific" phosphatases.

3'-*Nucleotidases*, hydrolyzing only nucleotides carrying a phosphoryl group in the 3'-position
5'-*Nucleotidases*, hydrolyzing only nucleotides carrying a phosphoryl group in the 5'-position.

A synoptic table, summarizing all the present knowledge concerning the classification of nucleolytic enzymes is given below (cf. table XVIII 162-163).

So far as the position of bond breakage by the nucleolytic enzymes is concerned, the experiments of M. Cohn (1959), carried out with O^{18}-labeled water, showed that the fission occurred between the phosphorus and the oxygen by the scheme :

$$\begin{array}{ccc} OH & & OH \\ | & & | \\ O = P - O - R & \longrightarrow & O = P - {}^{18}OH + HO - R \\ | & & | \\ OH \nwarrow {}^{18}OH_2 & & OH \end{array}$$

In the case of phosphodiesterases and nucleases, the experiments of Hilmoe et al. (1961) indicate that the situation is the same. Using the same technique, Hilmoe et al. demonstrated, in fact, that the P — O cleavage also occurred during hydrolysis of the phosphodiester bond by the following enzymes :

spleen nuclease,
spleen phosphodiesterase,
pancreatic ribonuclease.

It would therefore appear to be a general rule, valid for all nucleolytic enzymes.

In the light of the very extensive work that has been carried out on nucleolytic enzymes, it has become evident that these enzymes have varying specificities, which we have tried to define

Table XVIII. ENZYMES PARTICIPAT
Hydrolases (acting on ester bonds, E.C

NUCLEASES

Hydrolysis of the phosphodiester bond or transfer of
internucleotide linkage leading to depolymerization without liberation of inorganic
phosphate

Non-specific phosphata

Hydrolysis of all phosph
monoesters; includes all
line phosphatases, e.g.
coli E.C.3.1.3.1 and a
phosphatases, e.g. prost
E.C.3.1.3.2

ENDONUCLEASES

Simultaneous hydrolysis of
nucleic chain at several
points

Non pentose-specific nucleases	*Ribonucleases*	*Deoxyribonucleases*
Hydrolysis at multiple points determined by the base sequence, producing 1. Mono- and oligonucleotides terminated by 3′-phosphate (e.g. nuclease from *S. pyogenes*, E.C.3.1.4.7) 2. Mono- and oligonucleotides terminated by 5′-phosphate (e.g. nuclease from *Azotobacter agilis* E.C.3.1.4.9)	Hydrolysis of RNA type molecules: 1. By transfer of nucleotide bond resulting in depolymerization of RNA-type molecules at multiple points, producing mono- and oligonucleotides terminated by 3′-phosphates (e.g. pancreatic RNase, E.C.2.7.7.16). 2. Production of mono- and oligonucleotides terminated by 5′-phosphates (e.g. RNase II from *E. coli*).	Specific hydrolysis of DNA-type molecules at multiple points, producing : 1. Mono- and oligonucleotides terminated by 3′-phosphates (e.g. thymus DNase, E.C.3.1.4.6). 2. Mono- and oligonucleotides terminated by 5′-phosphates (e.g. pancreatic DNase, E.C.3.1.4.5).

NUCLEIC ACID METABOLISM
transferases (nucleotidyl-transferases, E.C.2.7.7)

PHOSPHATASES

Phosphoric monoester hy-
drolases E.C.3.1.4
Hydrolysis of phosphomo-
noester bond liberating free
inorganic phosphate

NUCLEOSIDASES

Hydrolyzing N-glycosy compounds E.C.3.2.2.
Hydrolysis of base-pentose
bond

NUCLEODEAMINASES

Enzymes acting on C-N
bonds, other than peptide
bonds, in cyclic amidines
E.C.3.5.4.
Hydrolysis of free amine
groups of bases, liberating
ammonia.

3'-Nucleosidases
E.C.3.1.3.6.

drolysis of 3'-nucleotides
rming nucleoside + phos-
ate e.g. germ of *Lolium*
ltiflorum

5'-Nucleosidases
E.C.3.1.3.5.

Hydrolysis of 5'-nucleotides
forming nucleoside + phosphate, e.g. snake venom

EXONUCLEASES-
PHOSPHODIESTERASES
E.C.3.1.4.1.

Stepwise hydrolysis, one nucleotide after another, beginning at one end. Can be
specific or not for internu-
cleotidic linkages.

Phosphodiesterases
3'-phosphate-formers

Liberation of mononucle-
otides terminated by a phosphoryl group in position
5'(e.g. phosphodiesterase of
calf spleen).

Phosphodiesterases
5'-phosphate-formers

Liberation of mononucle-
otides terminated by a phosphoryl group in position 3'-
(e.g. phosphodiesterase of
Crotalus adamanteus venom)

as closely as possible in table XVI.   Laskowski (1959) has suggested that in future a new enzyme should be defined in accordance with four essential criteria :

 1) substrate hydrolyzed (RNA, DNA, synthetic polynucleotides, etc.)

 2) type of attack, endonuclease, exonuclease.

 3) products formed during the hydrolysis (mono- and oligonucleotides terminated by a 3'- or 5'-phosphate group).

 4) bonds broken preferentially.   The latter criterion is theoretically only applicable to endonucleases, since the exonucleases (apparently) do not distinguish between the bases.   It is nevertheless possible that if one were to examine the exact way nucleotide liberation was effected by the exonucleases, one might come across some surprising facts such as finding that a particular nucleotide is liberated quicker than the others, as is the case for the exopeptidases.

In many cases it has been possible to determine exactly the nature of the bonds preferentially cleaved by the endonucleases; thus for pancreatic ribonuclease, to quote only one example, it is known that it hydrolyzes only the bonds Pyrimidine-p | Pyrimidine or Pyrimidine-p | Purine, but not the bonds Purine-p | Purine or Purine-p | Pyrimidine.

Considering that there are four different nucleotides within the nucleic acids, it is clear that there must be 16 different types of bond, and there ought to be, in theory, a strictly specific enzyme for each type of bond, only hydrolyzing one out of the 16.   Most known nucleases do not possess such strict specificity, and result in the formation of a mass of shorter fragments.   As we shall see, however, they can still contribute very interesting knowledge about the nucleic acid structure. The nucleases have already been the subject of a number of reviews, both from the point of view of general enzymology and nucleic acid biochemistry, among which we might mention those of McDonald (1955a, b), Shugar (1955), Heppel and Rabinowitz (1958), Roth (1959), Laskowski (1951, 1959, 1961), Khorana (1961), Schmidt and Laskowski (1961), Privat de Garilhe (1961, 1964, 1965), Josefsson and Lagerstedt (1952), Kurnick (1962), Lehman (1963), Lehman et al. (1965), Egami et al., (1964), Burton (1965), Raj Bhandary and Stuart (1966), etc.

In the next part of this book, it will be necessary to make two fundamental subdivisions.

Chapter VI, the endonucleases, which may be defined as enzymes hydrolyzing synthetic or natural polynucleotides, with or without distinction of the nature of the pentose, and attacking at multiple points along the chain.   Everything appears to indicate that endonucleases are not hindered in their action by the double helical structure of molecules like natural DNA.

Chapter VII, the exonucleases, which so far as we are aware only consist of the enzymes now known as phosphodiesterases, hydrolyze polynucleotides by stepwise degradation, beginning their attack at one end of the chain.   These nucleases act with or without discrimination of the nature of the pentose.   Contrary to the endonucleases, the exonucleases seem to be hindered in their action by the double helical structure of intact DNA molecules, and become particularly active when the secondary structure of such molecules has been destroyed by the action of either heat or another enzyme.

A convenient way of distinguishing between the two types of hydrolysis has been recently devised by Birnboim (1966 a) : the use of gel filtration.   It is most evident that in the case of exonucleolytic hydrolysis, a small amount of monocleotides will appear besides the remaining macromolecular core; the latter will be excluded from the gel while the mononucleotides will be retained, thus producing two distinct peaks. In the case of endonucleolytic hydrolysis when various oligonucleotides are produced, only one ill-defined peak will appear.

NOMENCLATURE OF THE COMMISSION ON ENZYMES (1961-1965)

The Commission on Enzymes has published a pamphlet entitled "Report of the Commission on Enzymes of the International Union of Biochemistry" (Pergamon Press, London, 1961). This monograph was later corrected and enlarged, and now constitutes volume 13 of "Comprehensive Biochemistry", edited by Florkin and Stotz (1965). This lists the best known enzymes at the present time in a rational classification. Only a small number of the nucleolytic enzymes are priviledged to appear in this classification together with an identification number. These are :

2.7.7. *Nucleotidyl Transferases*
2.7.7.16. (Polyribonucleotide-2-oligonucleotidotransferase (cyclizing))   Ribonuclease

3.1.3. *Phosphomonoester Hydrolases*   Phosphomonoesterase
3.1.3.1.   Orthophomonoester phosphohydrolase   Alkaline phosphatase
3.1.3.2.   Orthophosphomonoester phosphohydrolase   Acid phosphatase
3.1.3.5.   5'-Ribonucleotide phosphohydrolase   5'-Nucleotidase
3.1.3.6.   3'-Ribonucleotide phosphohydrolase   3'-Nucleotidase

3.1.4. *Phosphodiester Hydrolases*   Phosphodiesterases and Nucleases

3.1.4.1.   Orthophosphodiester phosphohydrolase   Phosphodiesterase
3.1.4.5.   Deoxyribonucleate oligonucleotidohydrolase   Deoxyribonuclease
3.1.4.6.   Deoxyribonucleate-3'-nucleotidohydrolase   Deoxyribonuclease II
3.1.4.7.   Micrococcal nuclease
3.1.4.7.   Ribonucleate 3'-guanylohydrolase   Ribonuclease from *Aspergillus oryzae* (RNase T$_1$)

Endonucleases

Part I

NON PENTOSE-SPECIFIC ENDONUCLEASES

The idea of a non-specific endonuclease, i.e. an enzyme able to hydrolyze certain phospho-diester linkages within a nucleic chain but without discrimination in the nature of the pentose making up the chain is a relatively new one, which was introduced after the discovery of certain enzymes acting against both DNA and RNA, it having been believed for several decades previous to this that there were RNases on one hand, and DNases on the other.

I. ANIMAL ENDONUCLEASES

A. SHEEP BRAIN ENDONUCLEASE

An endonuclease preferentially hydrolyzing thermally denatured DNA was detected by Healy et al. (1963) in lamb brain homogenates. The enzyme was prepared and purified by the following series of operations :

1) Homogenization
2) Acetone fractionation
3) Precipitation with ammonium sulfate
4) Adsorption and elution from a DEAE-cellulose column.

An enrichment of about 180-fold was obtained.

This nuclease is activated by Mn^{++} and Mg^{++}, and the optimum pH lies between 7.0 and 9.0.

The enzyme attacks both DNA and denatured DNA, but with a preference for denatured DNA, to such an extent, in fact, that Healy et al. suggested its use for the characterization of

fragments of single-stranded DNA chains.   DNA hydrolysis results in the formation of relatively
high molecular weight oligonucleotides : these fractions involve an average of from 5 to 14 nucleotides in a chain, all of them apparently being terminated by 5'-phosphate groups.   Although
the authors classified this enzyme with the endonucleases, their study was limited to hydrolysis
of DNA-type chains.

B. ENDONUCLEASE OF *Bothrops atrox* VENOM

Snake venoms have long been known for the large number of nucleolytic enzymes they contain.
Most of the work on these enzymes, however, has been centered on the phosphomonoesterases
and diesterases (see p. 266).   Georgatsos and Laskowski (1962), thinking that the snake venom
nucleases isolated so far and considered to be "contaminants" of phosphodiesterase preparations
merited a more thorough examination, made a special study of the purification and specificity
of a particular nuclease, that of *Bothrops atrox* venom.

The enzyme is purified from the precipitate with 42 % acetone obtained during preparation
of the phosphodiesterase by the method of Williams et al. (1961).   The different purification
stages for this nuclease involve :

1) Heating at 60° for 30 minutes, the object of which is to nearly totally deactivate the
5'-nucleotidase and part of the residual phosphodiesterase.

2) Adsorption on a calcium phosphate gel which eliminates the rest of the 5'-nucleotidase
and a further part of the phosphodiesterase.
The nuclease activity is found in the calcium phosphate supernatant, introduced into the
solution with stirring.

3) Fractionation with ammonium sulfate.

4) An initial chromatography on DEAE-cellulose

5) Chromatography on Amberlite IRC-50

6) A second chromatography on DEAE-cellulose

7) Precipitation with ammonium sulfate.

After the completion of the cycle of operations, the yield is 16 % and the enrichment about
1,000-fold.

B. atrox nuclease exhibits interesting properties, notably optimal activity at pH 5, and a
relatively high specificity of attack, since it would appear that only a small number of fissions
occur.

The enzyme reacts at the same rate with DNA and RNA, and in both cases the nucleotides
produced are terminated with 3'-phosphate groups.

At the beginning of the hydrolysis, d-Gp-Gp is the type of bond that is preferentially broken.
As the hydrolysis proceeds, the specificity with respect to adjacent bases decreases, the chain
length of the substrate becoming an increasingly limiting factor.   Fragments obtained after
exhaustive hydrolysis contain the four different nucleotides in end-positions in random distribution.

II PLANT NUCLEASES

A. *Phaseolus aureus* NUCLEASES

An endonuclease of vegetable origin, which was non-specific towards the pentose was isolated by Sung and Laskowski (1962) from *Phaseolus aureus*, known in the United States as "Mung bean". This enzyme was purified by successive fractionation with ammonium sulfate, adsorption on phosphate gel and elution by Keilin and Hartree's method (1938), fractionation by means of ethyl alcohol and chromatography on DEAE-cellulose. The product obtained at the end of the purification contains 300 units of enzyme per spectrophotometric unit at 280 mμ, compared with only 0.13 in the starting extract, i.e. a 2,500-fold enrichment. An optimum peak of activity was observed at pH 5.0. At this point in the purification, the enzyme shows no specificity concerning the pentose portion of the nucleic acid molecule, hydrolyzing RNA and DNA at the same rate; the fact that the enrichment is over 2,000 times for the RNA as well as the DNA is an argument in favor of there being one and the same enzyme responsible for both activities.

This enzyme must be classed among the endonucleases for the following reasons. 1) The high viscosity of the substrates at the outset disappears with the appearance of acid-soluble fragments (i.e. initial fission at several points in the interior of the chain). 2) Identification of reaction products as fragments having a length of mono- to heptanucleotide excludes a purely exonucleolytic action.

In spite of this, the appearance of a relatively large amount of mononucleotides leads one to suspect that there must be some partial exonuclease action.

As far as the point of cleavage of the phosphodiester bonds is concerned, a marked preference has been observed for the d-pA -pX bond, and in any case, all the liberated nucleotides are terminated by 5'-phosphate groups.

Sung and Laskowski have proposed a possible mechanism for the action of the *P. aureus* nuclease. According to them, the d-pA-pX bonds are preferentially hydrolyzed at first, the d-pT-pX bonds being hydrolyzed at half the rate. Chains of the d-pX-(pY)$_n$pA type predominate among the products from this first phase.

During the second phase, the nearness of the monoesterified phosphate exerts a labilizing effect on the neighboring groups, and the liberation of d-pX and possibly d-pXpY is observed. If X is deoxyadenosine, a pA mononucleotide is immediately freed. If X is deoxyguanosine the fragment is relatively resistent, from whence arises the higher frequency of deoxyguanosine in the terminal 5'-position.

B. POTATO TUBER NUCLEASES

Björk (1965) succeeded in purifying two endonucleases from potato tubers by the following steps : adsorption on phosphate gel and elution, precipitation with ethanol and ammonium sulfate, gel filtration, ion exchange chromatography and column electrophoresis. The two enzymes are freed from any contamination by the following enzymes : phosphomonoesterase, phosphodiesterase and exonuclease.

1) *Nuclease I*, acting on DNA and RNA, has been purified 2,000 times from the acetone powder of crude extract, in a yield of 23 %. This enzyme is inactivated by 10^{-3} M EDTA,

but the activity can be entirely restored with 0.002 M $MgCl_2$. The optimum pH lies between 6.0 and 7.0.

2) *Nuclease II* has been purified 830 times from the acetone powder of the crude extract in 60 % yield. The optimum pH is 5.2-6.1. This enzyme is not influenced by EDTA, contrary to what happens with potato nuclease I.

III MICROBIAL NUCLEASES

A. *Staphylococcus pyogenes* NUCLEASE (E.C.3.1.4.7)

Among all the bacterial nucleases, the most studied is certainly the exocellular nuclease produced by *S. pyogenes*. This nuclease, discovered in 1956 by Cunningham, Catlin and Privat de Garilhe, showed unusual properties compared with known nucleases right from the start. At first it was described as a "deoxyribonuclease" produced exocellularly by *S. pyogenes*, this being at a time then enzymes capable of degrading DNA in a controlled manner and having different specificity from the known DNases (DNase I and thymus DNase or DNase II) were being sought. We shall see shortly how this enzyme also hydrolyzes certain ribonucleic chains, and so has a less strict specificity than was at first believed.

We still feel that it should not be considered as a phosphodiesterase (as Reddi, 1958-1959 suggested) since it is without action on the classical phosphodiesters, as well as being without action on the dinucleotides.

The most recent work has shown that the *S. pyogenes* nuclease functions as an endonuclease in the initial stages of its action since the fall in DNA viscosity resulting from its action is rapid; it then functions as an exonuclease to the point where the fragments obtained are dinucleotides, at which point its action ceases, whatever the concentrations of enzyme and substrate. In every case, the fragments obtained are terminated by 3'-phosphate groups, and the hydrolysis is strongly activated by the presence of Ca^{++} ions. Finally, to complete this introduction, it might be mentioned that the *S. pyogenes* nuclease is remarkably thermostable and has its pH for optimum activity at 8.6 (Cunningham et al., 1956, 1958, 1959; Privat de Garilhe et al., 1957, 1958).

1. Purification of *S. pyogenes* nuclease

The partial purification of *S. pyogenes* nuclease from a culture broth of the bacteria was realized by the following stages (Pochon and Privat de Garilhe, 1960) :

1) Fractional precipitation with ammonium sulfate, the nuclease precipitating between 60 and 80 % saturation of ammonium sulfate. The precipitate is redissolved in water and subjected to exhaustive dialysis against distilled water. The dialyzed solution is the starting point for the chromatography.

2) Chromatography on Amberlite IRC 50-XE-64. Made by this procedure, the best preparations have a specific activity, measured spectrophotometrically, equal to three or four times that of crystalline DNase I. The enrichment compared to the centrifuged culture is 4,500-fold.

Anfinsen et al. (1963), using a different method of purification involving chromatography on CM-cellulose, obtained an enzyme that was essentially homogenous by sedimentation and electrophoresis. The sedimentation constant was 1.7 S and the isoelectric point 7.0 — 7.5. Mukai et al. (1965), working in Laskowski's laboratory, developed a method for purifying the *S. pyogenes* nuclease in eight successive steps, the last of which, chromatography on DEAE-cellulose, yielded preparations having a specific activity of 120 spectrophotometric units per mg (12 times more than Kunitz's crystalline DNase, the specific activity of which, measured by the spectrophotometric method, is of the order of 10). Finally, this enzyme has been obtained in the crystalline state (Cotton et al. 1966, Sulkowski and Laskowski 1966).

2. Properties of *S. pyogenes* nuclease

a. *Pathogenic strains and DNase production.* According to the findings of Weckmann and Catlin (1957), the pathogenic strains of *S. pyogenes* are the ones that produce most nuclease. This fact has been confirmed from a number of other sources, in particular Privat de Garilhe et al. (1958), who measured the DNase production by several *S. pyogenes* strains from the collection in the Institut Pasteur, and one strain (SAB) supplied by Dr. B. W. Catlin. The results of these experiments are illustrated in table XIX. The strains are cultivated for 48 hours at 37° on a meat broth in test-tubes without shaking. The cultures are then sterilized by immersion in a water bath at 90° for 15 minutes, when their DNase activity is determined by the viscometric method of Laskowski and Seidel (see p. 229).

The SAB strain produces 1,040 units par ml when it is grown in test-tubes without shaking, and up to 50,000 units per ml when it is grown with vigorous aeration. By making turbidimetric measurements and DNase determinations at regular time intervals, it is verified that the DNase production runs parallel to the growth. In addition, this production is extracellular, vigorous lysis of the bacteria by 0.8 % pyrophosphate and M glycocol (final concentrations in the medium) by Salmon's technique (1952) does not induce a concomitant liberation of DNase.

Osowiecki and Pakula (1962*a*, *b*, *c*, *d*) have also systematically studied the distribution of DNase formed at the same time as other enzymes by various *staphylococci* strains. Modification

Table XIX. DNase activity produced by different strains of *S. pyogenes* (Privat de Garilhe et al., 1958)

Strain*	Units DNase per ml culture (viscometry)
SAB	1,040
E 4 α	250
616 α	100
1005 α	70
1016 α	65
1010 α	50
1012 α	50
90 β	23
6135 α	0
899 α	0
280 (not pathogenic)	0

* Apart from the SAB strain supplied by Dr. Catlin and which is pathogenic (Weckmann and Catlin, 1957), the strains figuring in this colum are from the collection of the Institut Pasteur ; they are all pathogenic, except strain 280, and produce either an α hemolytic toxin (α-hemolysin) or a β hemolytic toxin (β-hemolysin)

of the culture medium can influence the DNase production; addition of glucose, for instance, inhibits production of the enzyme, while aeration is necessary for its formation.

    b. *Activators and inhibitors.* Table XX shows the activity of purified micrococcal nuclease in the presence of various salt solutions. These are viscometric DNase measurements in 0.01 M borate buffer at pH 8.6.

Table XX. Effect of cations on micrococcal nuclease activity (Cunningham et al., 1956)

Cation, final molarity*	Units DNase
Ca 0.001	7.5
Ca 0.01	24.0
Ca 0.1	4.0
Ca 0.01, Na 0.1	14.0
Mg 0.01	0.0

* These cations are introduced in the form of chlorides. Calcium acetate and calcium chloride are equally active.

    Poggiolini (1962a, b) has examined the action of various inhibitors on staphylococcal DNase; he has shown that this enzyme is inhibited by periodate in the same way as pancreatic DNase; on the other hand, iodoacetic acid, p-chloromercuribenzoic acid and heparin have weak or no action. The latter facts should be considered in the light of the absence of -SH groups in the molecule (table XXI). The various fractions of horse serum, far from inhibiting the action of the enzyme, on the contrary, have a tendency to increase it.

    c. *Constitution of S. pyogenes nuclease*

    The results of the study of aminoacid analysis of the nuclease (table XXI) indicate a molecular weight of 11,000 to 12,000 based on two histidine residues (Anfinsen et al., 1963). On the other hand, preparations that are homogeneous by ultracentrifugation and electrophoresis have a molecular weight of about 20,000 determined by physical methods (Taniuchi et al., 1965) which tends to prove that the molecule can form dimers under certain conditions.

    The aminoacid analysis shows the presence of a single tryptophan residue, and the absence of any free -SH groups. The latter result suggests that the Ca^{++} required for the activity of the enzyme may play some part in the stabilization of the tertiary structure.

    The primary sequence of the nuclease is under examination in Anfinsen's laboratory; it appears that the amino end consists of alanine and the carboxyl end of glutamine (Taniuchi et al., 1965, Taniuchi and Anfisen 1966).

Table XXI. Aminoacid analyses of purified *S. pyogenes* nuclease (Anfinsen et all., 1963)

Aminoacid	20 h. hydrolysate		44 h. hydrolysate		Average	Assumed number of residues
	μmoles	% of total μmoles	μmoles	% of total μmoles	% of total μmoles	
Lysine	0,56	14.8	0.65	13.8	14.3	14
Histidine	0.08	2.1	0.08	1.7	1.9	2
Arginine	0.13	3.4	0.12	2.5	3.0	3
Aspartic acid	0.37	9.8	0.47	9.9	9.9	10
Threonine	0.25	6.6	0.30	6.3	6.5	7
Serine	0.12	3.2	0.14	3.0	3.1	3
Glutamic acid	0.47	12.4	0.60	12.7	12.6	13
Proline	0.17	4.5	0.23	4.9	4.7	5
Glycine	0.27	7.1	0.35	7.4	7.3	7
Alanine	0.35	9.2	0.45	9.5	9.4	9
Half cystine	0		0		0	0
Valine	0.23	6.1	0.27	5.7	5.9	6
Methionine	0.08	2.1	0.06	1.3	(2.1)	(2)*
Isoleucine	0.12	3.2	0.17	3.6	3.4	4
Leucine	0.31	8.2	0.46	9.8	9.0	9
Tyrosine	0.19	5.0	0.25	5.3	5.2	5
Phenylalanine	0.09	2.4	0.11	2.3	2.4	2
Tryptophan						(1)**
Total μmoles	3.79		4.71			
Total residues						102**

* Loss of methionine is presumably due to inadequate evacuation of the hydrolysis tubes.
** Based on the presence of a single Ehrlich-positive peptide on "fingerprints".
*** Assuming 2 moles of histidine/mole.

d. *Specificity, nucleotides produced*

α. *Action of the nuclease on deoxyribonucleic-type polymers.*

The highly purified nuclease has only been produced in small amounts, that were, nevertheless, enough for a systematic study of the nucleotides produced by its action on various substrates such as thymus DNA and wheat germ DNA, yeast RNA, polyadenylic acid and various oligonucleotides of known structure (Pochon and Privat de Garilhe; Privat de Garlihe, 1962). These DNA hydrolyzates were prepared under the same conditions as for DNase I and II, then chromatographed on Dowex 1 columns. The following results were found.

A considerable amount of mononucleotides is produced, which can reach 30 to 40 % (see table XXII below). These nucleotides, which are not dephosphorylated by the action of 5'-nucleotidase from *C. adamantus* venom, therefore carry a monoesterified phosphoryl group in the C-3' position. *S. pyogenes* nuclease has thus made it possible for the first time to isolate deoxyribomononucleotides with a phosphoryl group in C-3'.

Table XXII. Mononucleotides produced by the action of *S. pyogenes* nuclease on thymus DNA, expressed in moles of nucleotide per moles d-Ap. (Cunningham et al., 1956)

Experiment	A		B		C	
	%	mol.	%	mol.	%	mol.
Deoxycytidylic	8.9	1.0	6.8	0.8	6.8	0.88
Thymidylic	9.0	1.0	7.7	0.9	8.2	1.04
Deoxyadenylic	9.35	1.0	8.8	1.0	8.1	1.00
Deoxyguanylic	3.88	0.4	3.7	0.4	3.2	0.38
Total	31.13		27.0		26.3	

The dinucleotides and trinucleotides were all isolated by chromatography on Dowex 1-X2, and if necessary purified by a second chromatography on Dowex 1-X8. Hydrolysis of them by *C. adamanteus* phosphodiesterase allowed their structure to be rapidly determined :

Dinucleotide : $\overset{\downarrow}{X}pYp \to X + pYp$

Trinucleotide : $\overset{\downarrow}{X}p\overset{\downarrow}{Y}pZp \to X + pY + pZp$

Isolation and characterization by column or paper chromatography (see fig. 34) of the reaction products makes reconstitution of the original di- or trinucleotide structure possible in one operation.

Dinucleotides of the XpYp type are particularly resistant to the action of venom phosphodiesterase, so high concentrations of enzyme for unusually long periods are needed for the hydrolysis of these nucleotides.

In table XXIII are listed the results of the complete qualitative and quantitative analysis of the products of thymus DNA hydrolyzed by the nuclease. A similar study has been made with wheat germ DNA as substrate.

The relatively high amounts of the dinucleotides TpCp, TpTp, TpAp and especially TpGp are notable. All these nucleotides include the TpXp sequence, which, like the ApAp and ApCp groups, appear to be particularly resistant to the action of the nuclease.

Comparable results have been obtained in the laboratory of Dekker and his co-workers, who expressed them in the form of an "A-T preference" of the enzyme (Rushizky et al., 1960; Dekker, 1960; Roberts et al., 1962).

More detailed examination of the mechanism of action of the micrococcal nuclease on DNA have been undertaken by Sulkowski and Laskowski (1962*a*, *b*), in the course of which the products appearing at different stages of the hydrolysis were analysed.

The dinucleotides these authors identified are the same as those identified by Pochon and Privat de Garilhe, with, in addition, 7.7 % d-ApCp, 0.5 % d-CpGp, 0.5 % d-GpCp and 1.0 % d-GpGp. Only the first is in relatively high proportion, and confirms the AT preference of the enzyme, the three others being in practically negligible proportions.

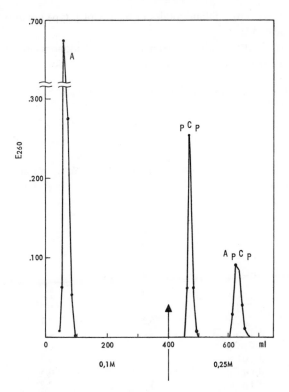

Figure 34. Chromatographic separation of a hydrolysate of d-ApCp ($E_{260} = 8$) by highly purified phosphodiesterase (1.0 unit). Hydrolysis for 48 hrs. at 37° in glycine — 0.3 M NaOH, pH 9.0. Chromatography on Dowex 1-X2 10 × 0.8 cm, elution with ammonium formate buffers of pH 4.5 the ionic strengths indicated. The total phosphorus for the peak marked pCp (from Sinsheimer's (1954) values), calc. 34γ; found 31.5γ (Privat de Garilhe et al., 1957)

Although only present in small amounts, a certain number of trinucleotides have also been identified*.

It is notable that all the trinucleotides begin with either Tp or with Ap.

These combined results led Sulkowski and Laskowski to consider the mechanism of the action of the nuclease on thymus DNA to take place as follows.

The endonucleolytic action is at first directed against the d-Xp-Tp and d-Xp-Ap bonds, resulting in formation of fragments like

$$\text{d-Tp(Yp)}_n\text{Zp} \qquad \text{and} \qquad \text{d-Ap(Yp)}_n\text{Zp}.$$

This process continues until the fragments obtained contain no more than 3 to 9 nucleotides ($1 < n < 7$). At this point, the proximity of the 3′-phosphate group interferes with the endonucleolytic character of the reaction and cleavage of d-Tp and d-Ap occurs if they happen to

---

* These trinucleotides were not looked for systematically by Pochon and Privat de Garilhe. As Dr. Sulkowski (1963 personal communication) has very reasonably pointed out, the very high amount of trinucleotide, ApGpC, that we found both in thymus and wheat germ DNA arises no doubt because of extensive contamination with the dinucleotide Ap Gp, not identified among the dinucleotides.

be in the terminal position (Zp). Dinucleotides of the d-CpCp type are also formed at this stage from tetra- or pentanucleotides.

As the chain shortens, the relative amount of terminal mononucleotide liberated rises, but at no time does the action become predominantly exonucleolytic.

Table XXIII. Oligonucleotides identified and determined analytically after exhaustive action of *S. pyogenes* nuclease on DNA

Nucleotides	Structure	% optical density recovered after chromatography		
		thymus DNA		Wheat germ DNA
		Pochon and Garilhe	Sulkowski and Laskowski	Pochon and Garilhe
Mono	d-Mp	—		2.1
	d-Cp	7.55		7.1
	d-Tp	12.8		16.6
	d-Ap	21.8		24.0
	d-Gp	4.95		10.0
Di	d-CpCp	1.43	1.8	1.4
	d-CpTp	trace	0.2	trace
	d-TpCp	6.5	7.7	6.1
	d-TpMp	—	—	0.8
	d-CpGp		0.5	
	d-TpTp	3.8	4.3	2.9
	d-GpCp		0.5	
	d-TpAp	3.9	2.8	2.5
	d-ApCp	2.5	4.3	3.6
	d-ApAp	5.25	3.8	6.35
	d-TpGp	10.5	10.6	7.1
	d-ApTp	trace	1.9	trace
	d-ApGp		7.7	
	d-GpGp		1.0	
Tri	d-TpCpCp		0.9	
	d-TpGpCp		0.9	
	d-ApGpCp	18.8	0.5	8.0
	d-TpApGp		0.4	
	d-ApApGp		0.8	
	d-TpGpGp		3.8	
	d-ApGpGp		2.9	
	d-ApGpMp			1.3

When the trinucleotide stage is reached, the proximity of the 3′-phosphate group rather than the nature of the bases is a decisive factor, and the only reaction likely to occur is

$$\text{d-XpYpZp} \longrightarrow \text{d-XpYp} + \text{d-Zp}$$

These conclusions are in agreement with independent experiments (Privat de Garilhe, 1962) using the series of pyrimidine oligonucleotides obtained after acid DNA hydrolysis as substrate the following reactions were observed :

$$pTpTpTp \longrightarrow pTpTp + Tp$$
$$pTpCpTp \longrightarrow pTpCp + Tp$$
$$pTpTpTpTp \longrightarrow pTpTp + 2Tp$$

The third of these reactions is particularly interesting, since it demonstrates that the tetranucleotide is hydrolyzed stepwise with liberation of 2Tp.

Laskowski and his co-workers (Ohsaka et al., 1964) have indicated a convenient method for identifying the extremities of homogeneous oligonucleotides of structure $(pX)_n$, since the use of massive doses of *S. pyogenes* nuclease results ultimately in the formation of 1 nucleoside diphosphate, $(n - 2)$ nucleoside monophosphates of structure Xp, and 1 nucleoside. Hydrolysis of a series of well-defined substrates, namely the oligonucleotide series of the pnTn type, using catalytic doses of nuclease has confirmed the stepwise nature of this hydrolysis (de Meuron-Landolt and Privat de Garilhe, 1964); the tri- and tetranucleotides are attacked with liberation of the 3'-terminal T nucleoside in the case of the trinucleotide, liberation of T then Tp is similarly observed in the case of the tetranucleotide, following the scheme

$$pTpTpTpT \rightarrow pTpTp \uparrow Tp \uparrow T$$

These reactions are relatively simple, especially since in the case of the tetranucleotide, only reaction 1) takes place in the first few hours of incubation using catalytic amounts of nuclease. It was therefore easily possible to measure titrimetrically the various parameters of standard enzymic kinetics, using *S. pyogenes* nuclease as enzyme and the oligonucleotides pnTn as substrates.

In practice, the experiments are conducted under the following conditions. Into a beaker maintained at 36° are measured : 2.5 ml $CaCl_2$ ($10^{-2}M$) and 1 ml of an aqueous solution of substrate containing $0.5 - 2$ µmoles of oligonucleotide. The total volume is then brought to 25 ml. The solution is mixed at 36° by means of magnetic stirring. The pH of the solution is brought to 8.64 with a trace of NaOH, then 3.25 milliunits of enzyme in 0.1 ml of aqueous solution containing 5 mg/ml of gelatin, are added to the substrate. This latter volume is considered to be negligible compared to the total volume. The concentration of the enzyme (0.13 milliunit per ml) is that used in most experiments.

The initial velocity of the reaction is expressed as the µl of 0.01 N NaOH added per min. to maintain the pH of the system at 8.64.

In the case of the trinucleotide the calculated constants were :

$$0.0537 < V_m < 0.0540 \quad \mu\text{equivalent/min.}$$
$$1.15 \times 10^{-5} \text{ M} < K_m < 1.20 \times 10^{-5} \text{ M}$$

Using the same substrate and Mg^{++} instead of Ca^{++}, the parameters were :

$$0.115 < V_m < 0.118 \quad \mu\text{equivalent/min.}$$
$$5.75 \times 10^{-5} \text{ M} < K_m < 5.90 \times 10^{-5} \text{ M}$$

Comparison of the values obtained with the two different cations shows that the enzyme-substrate affinity, characterized by K_m, decreases with Mg^{++}, whereas V_m doubles. Mg^{++} at a concentration of 10^{-3} M permits a faster liberation of the hydrolysis products, although it does not favor the formation of the enzyme-substrate complex.

This experiment, which may have interesting applications, is worth confirming.

In the case of the tetranucleotide, only the following reaction was studied within the limits of the experiment :

$$pTpTpTpT \longrightarrow pTpTpTp + T$$
$$0.049 < V_m < 0.051 \text{ } \mu\text{equivalent/min.}$$
$$0.41 \times 10^{-5} \text{ M} < K_m < 0.49 \times 10^{-5} \text{ M}$$

In the case of the pentanucleotide where the reaction is more complex, it was found that

$$0.244 < V_m < 0.247$$
$$14.4 \times 10^{-5} \text{ M} < K_m < 14.7 \times 10^{-5} \text{ M}$$

β Hydrolysis of various deoxyribonucleic acids

Measurements of the initial hydrolysis velocity of various samples of macromolecular DNA by the nuclease of *S. pyogenes* were performed by the spectrophotometric method of Kunitz (1950). The initial velocity of the reaction was expressed as the increase in absorbance at 260 mμ of a DNA solution per unit of time. The concentrations of substrate were expressed either in spectrophotometric units at 260 mμ, or in weight DNA per ml solution. The procedure was as follows. Into a series of calibrated flasks (10 ml), 0.05 — 1.00 ml of a 0.05 % solution of DNA in distilled water was measured in such a way that final DNA concentrations of 2.5 — 50 μg/ml were obtained. Then 1.0 ml of 0.2 M borate buffer (pH 8.6) and 1.0 ml of CaCl₂ (10⁻² M) were added. The volume was then finally adjusted to 10 ml. For spectrophotometric reading in a Jobin and Yvon spectrophotometer at 22 ± 0.5°, 2.5 ml of substrate and 0.05 ml of a purified nuclease solution corresponding to a final dilution of 0.4 μg/ml, or 32 milliunits (spectrophotometric) of nuclease per ml were placed in each cell. The enzyme solution was prepared by dilution of a stock solution of nuclease at 0.05 % in an aqueous 1 % solution of gelatin with distilled water. Readings of the absorbance were taken every two minutes, and V calculated from these data as ΔE_{260}/min. By plotting 1/S against 1/V, a series of graphs was obtained from which V_m and K_m can be calculated. Since we do not know the exact molecular weights of the substrates, K_m was provisionally expressed either in spectrophotometric units at 260 mμ or in μg/ml.

The first fact appearing is the agreement between the values obtained for thymus and wheat-germ DNA, and the difference observed for *S. pyogenes* DNA. This fact is consistent with the high A-T content of the latter DNA and the "A-T preference" of the enzyme.

In table XXIV are gathered the results of the quantitative systematic hydrolysis of various natural and synthetic polynucleotides by micrococcal nuclease. The latter results confirm and complete those found by chromatographic analysis of the same phenomenon.

Another feature of micrococcal nuclease was studied by von Hippel and Felsenfeld (1964) who demonstrated that this enzyme can be used as a test of DNA conformation. Their observations agree with those of Dirksen and Dekker (1960) who showed that denatured DNA is hydrolyzed faster than natural DNA. The site of the initial attack of the enzyme depends on the latters' secondary and tertiary structures, and at 60°, denatured DNA is attacked essentially at random.

Table XXIV V*m* and K*m* Corresponding to the hydrolysis of various synthetic and natural substrates by micrococcal nuclease

Substrate	Cation	Vm (μequiv/min)	Km (mol. substrate/l)
Synthetic polynucleotides			
pTpTpT	CaCl$_2$(10^{-3}M)	0.0537 - 0.0540	1.15 - 1.20 . 10^{-5}M
pTpTpT	MgCl$_2$(10^{-3}M)	0.115 - 0.118	5.75 - 5.90 . 10^{-5}M
pTpTpTpT	CaCl$_2$(10^{-3}M)	0.049 - 0.051	0.41 - 0.49 . 10^{-5}M
pTpTpTpTpT	CaCl$_2$(10^{-3}M)	0.244 - 0.247	14.4 - 14.7 . 10^{-5}M

Natural deoxyribonucleic acids					
Substrate	Cation	Vm (E$_{260}$/min × 10^3)	Km E$_{260}$/ml	Km μg/ml	Km Molar conc. mononucleotide*
Thymus DNA	CaCl$_2$(10^{-3}M)	8.86 ± 0.08	0.56 ± 0.08	36.1 ± 5.8	5.6 . 10^{-5}M
Wheat-germ DNA	CaCl$_2$(10^{-3}M)	8.47 ± 1.36	0.54 ± 0.13	38.3 ± 8.5	5.4 . 10^{-5}M
S. pyogenes DNA	CaCl$_2$(10^{-3}M)	3.95 ± 0.38	0.11 ± 0.02	12.0 ± 2.5	1.1 . 10^{-5}M

* Assuming that the millimolecule of any nucleotide has an average absorbance of 10,000 spectrophotometric units at 260 mμ.

γ. *Action of the nuclease on ribonucleic type polymers*

The enzymatic preparations, originally described as "deoxyribonuclease", which were obtained from *S. pyogenes*, were also found to be active on polymers of the ribonucleic type by several research groups (Cunningham, 1959; Reddi, 1959*a*, *b*; Alexander et al., 1961; Rushizky et al., 1962, etc.). None of these groups, however, was working with enzyme samples of guaranteed purity, so that there is still a question as to whether the effects observed on DNA and on the various ribonucleic polymers are due to the same enzyme. The doubts over the interpretation of the results obtained are increased by the inconsistency of the ratio DNase activity/RNase activity observed during the purification of the enzyme.

In fact, estimation of the two activities by different methods during the purification of the enzyme (Pochon, 1960; Pochon and Privat de Garilhe, 1960) shows a rise in the ratio DNase/RNase as if the two activities were dissociated. The variation of the ratio DNase/RNase was also observed by Alexander, Heppel and Hurwitz (1961) in the course of a purification involving chromatography on DEAE-cellulose.

The main argument in favor of enzymic unity is the similarity of the observed specificities with the two categories of substrate (Rushizky et al., 1962). The results of these investigations show that the enzyme hydrolyzes the ribonucleic chain preferentially (represented in Rushizky and co-workers' experiments by the tobacco mosaic virus) at points adjacent to the adenylic and uridylic nucleotides, i.e. most of the di- and trinucleotides identified began with Ap or Up. The enzyme appeared to be particularly effective in the hydrolysis of regions of the ribonucleic molecule where several adenylic and/or uridylic acids followed one another.

B. Endonuclease of *Azotobacter agilis*

The non-specific endonuclease produced by *Azotobacter agilis* (Stevens and Hilmoe, 1960) exhibits very interesting properties. This enzyme has mostly been studied by using polyadenylic acid (poly A) as substrate (cf. nomenclature of polynucleotides synthesized by the action of poly-nucleotide phosphorylase, p. 99). The generalized reaction to which this enzyme leads when acting on a substrate of poly A is the following :

$$pApApA \downarrow pA...pApA \downarrow pApA...pApA \rightarrow$$
$$pApApA + pA...pApA + pApA...pApA$$

The end products of the reaction are di-, tri- and tetranucleotides.

1. Preparation of *A. agilis* nuclease

Two methods of preparing this nuclease have been described by Stevens and Hilmoe (1960). A crude extract is first prepared by disintegration of the bacteria and removing cell debris by centrifugation.

Following the first procedure, a treatment with zinc-ethanol allows the polynucleotide-phosphorylase (Ochoa, (1957) and the nuclease to be recovered from *A. agilis*. Fraction I of Ochoa's ethanol-zinc process is the starting point for procedure I; a protamine sulfate precipitation is carried out, followed by adsorptions on Cγ alumina and calcium phosphate gel. The specific activity rises from 38 units per milligram protein in the zinc-ethanol fraction to 1,333 units per milligram protein in the eluate from the column of calcium phosphate gel.

Following the second procedure for the preparation of *A. agilis* nuclease, the crude extract is subjected to fractional precipitation with ammonium sulfate, followed by precipitation with protamine sulfate and adsorption on Cγ alumina and on CM cellulose.

In this case, the specific activity rises from 30 units per milligram protein in the first ammonium sulfate precipitate to 1,000 units per milligram protein in the eluate from the CM cellulose column.

2. Properties of *A. agilis* nuclease

A hydrolysate obtained from polyA by the action of *A. agilis* nuclease, and which was 100 % acid-soluble, was analyzed by chromatography on DEAE-cellulose. The oligonucleotides pro-duced can be analyzed by the techniques described in the chapter on "methods". The oligonucle-otides produced by the nuclease are of the type

$$pA(pA)_n pA$$

with *n* being between zero and 3, so that the nucleotides vary from dinucleotides to pentanucle-otides. The structure of these oligonucleotides can be readily determined by alkaline hydrolysis, when each oligonucleotide will furnish 1 molecule of adenosine, *n* molecules of nucleotide Ap (adenosine 2'- or 3'-monophosphate) and one molecule of pAp. It is clear that *n* can be easily determined if the amounts of A, Ap and pAp are analyzed exactly.

A hydrolysate in which only 10 % of the polyA was acid-soluble was also chromatographed on DEAE-cellulose. In the latter case, oligonucleotides of higher molecular weight were obtained, the smallest of which was a tetranucleotide. This experiment shows that the enzyme does not act by dislodging small nucleotides from one end, but as a genuine endonuclease by causing cleavage in the middle of the chain.

The resistance of the terminal phosphodiester bonds is further illustrated by an experiment in which oligonucleotides isolated from an initial hydrolysis were submitted to the action of the enzyme; the pentanucleotide was hydrolyzed to a di- and a trinucleotide, the tetranucleotide was broken, but much more slowly, giving two equivalents of dinucleotide. Hydrolysis of other polymers than polyA has been examined, and it has become apparent that polyU, polyC and polyG are not hydrolyzed in conditions that result in total solubilization of polyA at the optimal Mg^{++} ion concentration. Increasing the enzyme concentration by a factor of 10 results in appreciable hydrolysis of polyU, this hydrolysis becoming a maximum when the Mg^{++} ion concentration corresponds to one equivalent per phosphate in the polyU. PolyC undergoes feeble hydrolysis when the enzyme concentration is 30 times more than that necessary for the polyA hydrolysis. PolyG is unhydrolyzed even at the highest enzyme concentrations.

The action of *A. agilis* nuclease on natural polynucleotides, RNA, m-RNA and DNA, is comparable to its action on polyA. The enzyme functions only as an endonuclease, hydrolyzing RNA and DNA with formation of oligonucleotides terminated by 5′-phosphate groups. The oligonucleotides obtained seem to be of the same order of size as those obtained from polyA, but their complexity has not allowed such an extensive study to be made.

The nuclease from *A. agilis* thus possesses some singular properties. Firstly, it shows strict specificity so far as the nucleotide sequences are concerned, since certain sequences such as polyG are resistant to the action of the enzyme, and secondly, it shows absolutely no specificity so far as the nature of the pentose is concerned, since it hydrolyzes indiscriminately both RNA and DNA, limiting itself, however, to the production of oligonucleotides. In neither case does it seem that the mononucleotides are liberated. *A. agilis* nuclease could have interesting applications in the preparation of ribonucleotide-5′-phosphates.

C. ENDONUCLEASE OF *Neurospora crassa*

An endonuclease from *Neurospora crassa* has been cataloged by Linn and Lehman (1965*a*, *b*) as being specific towards polynucleotides not having an ordered structure. The enzyme was prepared by the usual methods of extraction; fractionation with solvents and chromatography on various adsorbents, notably phosphocellulose and hydroxyapatite. In the course of the preparative procedure, the specific activity rose from 1.1 unit per mg to 11,500, a 10,000-fold enrichment.

This preparation hydrolyzes denatured DNA and ribosomal RNA at the same rate. These two activities would therefore seem to be catalyzed by the same enzyme. The enzyme is active over very wide temperature (25° — 65°) and pH (6-9) ranges and is unaffected by the presence or absence of divalent cations.

Specificity. The purified enzyme attacks natural DNA at one hundredth of the speed observed for denatured DNA. Similar results are observed with the synthetic polynucleotides (ribo and deoxyribo) existing respectively in helical or random coil form.

Analysis of the hydrolysis products shows that the enzyme has a distinct preference for guanosine or deoxyguanosine residues, since the hydrolysates contain a predominating amount of guanylic acid.

Part II

RIBONUCLEASES

I. PANCREATIC RIBONUCLEASE (Ribonucleate pyrimidine-nucleotide-2'-transferase (cyclizing). E.C.2.7.7.16.)

A. GENERAL REMARKS

The ribonucleases are widely distributed in animal and plant tissues; Kunitz in 1940 obtained from beef pancreas a crystalline ribonuclease (Kunitz, 1940; Northrop, Kunitz and Heriott, 1948), an enzyme which is a soluble protein of the albumin type, of molecular weight near 15,000. Kunitz also established that this ribonuclease (RNase) is stable within wide limits of pH and temperature; the activity is only slightly diminished irreversibly when the protein is heated at 100° and pH 2.0. Digestion of yeast RNA by RNase is accompanied by increasing formation of free acid groups without liberation of inorganic phosphoric acid. The hydrolysis products can no longer be precipitated either by glacial acetic acid or by 0.5 M hydrochloric acid, and they are dialyzable through a cellophane bag. It was later demonstrated that these fragments are nucleotides ending in 3'-phosphate group, arising from the cleavage of certain definite internucleotide bonds, namely those between the 3'-phosphoryl groups of the pyrimidine nucleosides and the 5'-phosphoryl groups of the purine nucleosides (Schmidt et al., 1951; Loring, Carpenter and Roll, 1947; Markham and Smith, 1952a, b, c; Volkin and Cohn, 1953; figure 35).

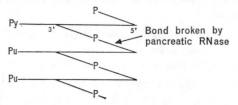

Figure 35. Schematic representation of the cleavages effected by RNase A

Pancreatic ribonuclease is the best known of all enzymes; as a protein, RNase has been much studied and its primary structure entirely elucidated by the work of Moore, Stein and co-workers (Spackman et al., 1960); its secondary and tertiary structures have been the subject of very elaborate schemes.

As an enzyme, RNase has also been the subject of a great deal of work, and recent studies have allowed a possible mechanism of enzymatic action to be defined.

The fact that pancreatic RNase hydrolyzes RNA is the property that enabled this enzyme, as well as several other RNases, to be discovered, but this fact constitutes only one particular facet of the RNase properties, its main role, as we shall see in the following pages, being to catalyze the migration of the 3'-5' phosphoryl RNA bond with transient formation of a 2'-3' cyclic ester. This is why this enzyme has been given the official name of [polynucleotide-2-oligonucleotido transferase (cyclizing)] and the nomenclature number 2.7.7.16, which corresponds to a transfer enzyme and not to a hydrolytic enzyme.

Besides innumerable original publications RNase has been the subject of many review articles namely by Northrop et al. 1948, Mc Donald 1955 a, Schmidt 1955 b, Scheraga and Rupley 1962, Irie 1964, Stein 1964, Moore 1964, Rabin and Mathias 1964, Witzel 1964, etc...

B. Preparation of crystalline RNase

Isolation of RNase in the crystalline state occurs essentially by fractional precipitation of the proteins of an acid extract of beef pancreas by ammonium sulfate. The greater part of the RNase is soluble in a medium of ammonium sulfate at 60 % saturation, and insoluble in a medium at 80 % saturation (Kunitz, 1940; Northrop et al., 1948; Mc Donald, 1948, 1955a).

Step 1. Preliminary Purification. About 20 pounds of fresh* beef pancreas is collected in ice-cold 0.25 N H_2SO_4. The glands are drained, freed of fat and connective tissue, and minced in a meat grinder. The ground pancreas is suspended in 2 vol. of ice-cold 0.25 N H_2SO_4 and left at 0 to 5º for 18 to 24 hours, with occasional stirring. The suspension is then strained through cheesecloth, and the strained fluid is saved. The residue is resuspended in an equal volume of cold 0.25 N H_2SO_4 and restrained after 1 hour. The residue is discarded. The combined extracts are brought to 0.65 saturation of $(NH_4)_2SO_4$ by the addition of 430 g. of salt per liter of strained fluid. The suspension is filtered by gravity through 50-cm. fluted filter papers (Eaton-Dikeman No. 612 or Whatman No. 12), at 0 to 5º, and the clear filtrate is saved. The residue is suspended in a volume of cold H_2O equal to that of the original minced pancreas, and 430 g. of $(NH_4)_2SO_4$ is added per liter of H_2O used. The mixture is refiltered through fluted paper. This filtrate** is combined which the first one, and 105 g. of $(NH_4)_2SO_4$ is added per liter of filtrate (final concentration of $(NH_4)_2SO_4$, 0.8 saturation). The resulting precipitate is allowed to settle for 2 days at 0 to 5º; the settling is greatly facilitated by occasional stirring of the mixture and

---

* Frozen pancreases, obtainable from any of the large slaughterhouses, can also be used if only ribonuclease (or deoxyribonuclease) is to be prepared. They should be thawed by leaving them immersed in 0.25 N H_2SO_4 at 5º.
** The residue on the paper can be used for the isolation of deoxyribonuclease (Kunitz 1950).

removal of foam during the first day of standing. The clear supernatant fluid is siphoned off and discarded; the remaining suspension is filtered through hardened paper (Schleicher and Schuell No. 576). The yield is about 4 g. per liter of ground pancreas used.

Step 2. Removal of Proteolytic and Potential Proteolytic Activity. Each gram* of filter cake is dissolved in 5 ml. of H_2O, and the resulting solution is poured into 20 ml. of boiling 0.2 saturated $(NH_4)_2SO_4$ previously adjusted with H_2SO_4 to pH 3.0 (methyl orange). The mixture is stirred for 5 minutes at 95 to 100°, cooled quickly to 25°, and left at 20 to 25° for approximately 1 hour. The suspension is filtered through soft paper (Eaton-Dikeman No 617) with the aid of 10 g. of Standard Super-Cel** per liter, and the filter cake is washed three times with small quantities of 0.2 saturated $(NH_4)_2SO_4$. The residue is discarded. The filtrate is brought to 0.5 saturation of $(NH_4)_2SO_4$ by the addition of 188 g. of salt per liter of filtrate; 10 g. of Standard Super-Cel is then added per liter, and the suspension is filtered with suction through soft paper. The residue is again discarded. The filtrate is brought to 0.8 saturation of $(NH_4)_2SO_4$ by the addition of 210 g. of salt per liter, and the resulting suspension is filtered on hardened paper; the yield is approximately 3 g./l. of ground pancreas used. The filtrate is discarded.

Each gram* of filter cake is dissolved in 5 ml. of H_2O, the pH of the solution is adjusted to 4.8 (methyl red or bromocresol green) with a few drops of 5 N NaOH, and 5 ml. of saturated $(NH_4)_2SO_4$ is added. The mixture is filtered through soft paper with the aid of 1 g. of Standard Super-Cel per 100 ml. of suspension. The residue is discarded. The filtrate is adjusted to pH 4.2 (bromocresol green) with 1 N H_2SO_4, after which 67 ml. of saturated $(NH_4)_2SO_4$ is added slowly with constant stirring for each 100 ml. of solution (final concentration of $(NH_4)_2SO_4$, 0.7 saturation). The suspension is filtered with suction on hardened paper. The yield is approximately 2 g./l. of mincel pancreas originally used. The filtrate is discarded***.

Step 3. Crystallization. Each gram of filter cake is dissolved in 1 ml. of H_2O. The solution is filtered through soft paper with the aid of 5 g. of Standard Super-Cel per 100 ml. of solution; the residue on the paper is washed several times with small quantities of H_2O and then discarded. The combined filtrate and washings are brought with H_2O to a final volume of 2 ml.; saturated $(NH_4)_2SO_4$ is then added *slowly*, with stirring, until a very faint turbidity appears (approximately 40 ml. per 100 ml. of solution is required), and the pH of the mixture is adjusted *immediately* to 4.6 (methyl red or bromocresol green) with a few drops of 1 N NaOH. The solution clears rapidly and is left at 20 to 25°. Crystals of ribonuclease gradually form****. They are filtered on hardened paper after 3 days; the yield is approximately 1.2 g/l of minced pancreas originally used. The filtrate is adjusted to pH 4.2 (bromocresol green) with 1 N H_2SO_4 and brought to 0.8 saturation of $(NH_4)_2SO_4$ by the slow addition, with constant stirring, of saturated $(NH_4)_2SO_4$. The suspension is filtered on hardened paper, and the filtrate is discarded. The yield of filter

---

* This expression denotes the relative amounts of material used. It does not mean that each gram of material is processed separately.

** Supplied by Johns-Manville, 22 East 40th Street, New York.

*** The yield of ribonuclease can be increased by adding $(NH_4)_2$ SO_4 to this filtrate to 0.8 saturation, filtering on hardened paper, and reworking the filter cake with the next batch of material being processed for the removal of proteolytic contaminants according to the second paragraph of step 2.

**** If too much (NH_2) SO_4 has been added, an amorphous precipitate will form rapidly. This may change within 1 or 2 days into a mass of fine crystals ; if not, water should be added dropwise until the amorphous material dissolves and typical "silkiness" is seen when the solution is stirred. Almost complete crystallization should then occur within the next 3 days. If no "silkiness" is seen the solution should be adjusted to pH 4.2, brought to 0.8 saturation with saturated $(NH_4)_2$ SO_4, and filtered with suction through hardened paper ; the filter cake should again be processed as described in step 3.

cake is about 0.4 g/l of minced pancreas. Additional ribonuclease crystals can be obtained by reprocessing this filter cake according to the second paragraph of step 2.

Step 4. *Recrystallization.* Each gram of filter cake of crystals is dissolved in 2 ml of H_2O. The solution is filtered through soft paper with the aid of 0.1 g of Standard Super-Cel. The residue is washed several times with small amounts of H_2O. The combined filtrate and washings are brought to 3 ml with H_2O. Saturated $(NH_4)_2SO_4$ is added *slowly*, with stirring, until the solution becomes very faintly turbid (about 4 ml per 10 ml of solution is required). The mixture is left at 20 to 25°; crystals form rapidly. They are filtered on hardened paper after 2 days; the yield is about 0.6 g/g of filter cake. The filtrate is adjusted to pH 4.2, and saturated $(NH_4)_2SO_4$ is added slowly to 0.8 saturation. The suspension is filtered on hardened paper, and the filtrate is discarded. The yield is about 0.3 g/g of filter cake. Additional ribonuclease crystals can be obtained from this filter cake by processing it as described in step 3.

Step 5. *Recrystallization in Ethanol.* Ribonuclease is recrystallized twice by means of $(NH_4)_2SO_4$, as described in the preceding section. Each gram of filter cake from the third crystallization is dissolved in 1.5 ml of H_2O, and the solution is dialyzed* in collodion or viscose dialyzing tubing at 0 to 5° against cold H_2O for 24 tours. The dialyzed solution is diluted with H_2O to 5 ml and cooled to 5°, and 60 ml of 95 % ethanol of the same temperature is added with stirring. A heavy amorphous precipitate is formed, which, on standing at 10 to 20°, changes within several hours into a mass of fine fan-shaped rosettes of rectangular or needle-shaped crystals. The crystals are filtered on hardened paper after 2 days and washed several times with cold 95 % ethanol. They are then dried for 24 to 72 hours over $CaCl_2$ in a desiccator. The dry powder can be stored in a cool place indefinitely; the yield is about 0.3 g of dry crystals per gram of filter cake.

At the present time, samples of crystalline RNase, prepared by this method, are commercially available, and are of quite sufficient purity.

Neurath and his co-workers (Keller et al., 1958; Neurath et al., 1960) have suggested a method of obtaining RNase, as well as all the other proteins from pancreatic juice by ion exchange chromatography of this juice. It does, indeed, appear more logical to utilize pancreatic juice as a source of enzymes rather than a pancreas mince, in which secondary enzymic reactions would naturally occur.

Prepared by one or the other of these methods, crystalline pancreatic RNase contains mostly two constituents, the major one on which almost all the work on RNase has been carried out, "RNase A", and a minor one, "RNase B", to wich we shall refer later (p. 211). RNase A samples become heterogenous during lyophilization or storage. Examination of samples liable to become heterogeneous can be carried out rapidly on columns of Amberlite IRC-50, Sephadex G-75 and sulfoethyl-Sephadex C-25. Changes can be avoided by storing the purified protein in a phosphate buffer at -20°. Salt-free samples can then be prepared as needed by de-salting on IRC-50 (acid form), passing the solution on Sephadex and lyophilization, starting with a dilute solution to avoid the formation of aggregates (Crestfield et al., 1963).

---

* M. Kunitz and H. Simms 641 (1927-28). If the dialyzer of Kunitz-Simms is not available, it is advantageous to dialyze with slow mechanical stirring for 48 hours against 2 l. of cold distilled H_2O which is changed twice daily.

C. Estimation of Ribonucleases

1. Determination of RNase by the so-called "soluble phosphorus" method

By this method, the total phosphorus in solution (not precipitable by acetic acid) is determined after the action of the RNase on yeast RNA. This "soluble phosphorus" is, of coure, present in the form of short nucleotides (Northrop, Kunitz and Herriot, 1948).

Tubes containing 0.5 ml of a 2 % yeast RNA solution in borate buffer of pH 8.0, and 0.5 ml of solution of the RNase under examination are placed in a water bath at 25° for 10 minutes. Then 10 ml glacial acetic acid are added, the mixture is shaken, and after 3 minutes, filtered through Whatman no. 42 paper. The total phosphorus per millilitre filtrate is measured by a standard method for phosphorus determination, such as that of Fiske and Subbarow (1925).

The results show that the addition of even one part RNase to 2,000 parts substrate causes 75 % of the total phosphorus in the substrate to form soluble phosphorus in 10 minutes at 25°. The final proportion hydrolyzed in the presence of a large excess of enzyme is 87 %.

This method has undergone many improvements. To obtain completely reproducible results, Kalnitsky et al. (1959) recommend the following procedure, developed from the method of Davidson and Waymouth (1944). It is necessary to start with a specially purified RNA as substrate (e.g. RNA prepared by the method of Crestfield et al. (1955), rather than commercially available RNA, which is known to suffer from the disadvantage of producing brownish solutions of unpleasing aspect).

The test tubes contain 1.0 ml 0.1 M acetate at pH 5.0 ($\mu = 0.065$) plus 0.01 ml of the RNase solution; 1 ml of the RNA solution (1 % in the acetate buffer) is added. This mixture is incubated for 4 minutes at 37°, after which 1 ml uranyl acetate (0.75 % in 25 % perchloric acid) is added. The mixture is cooled in an ice bath and centrifuged at 3°. Aliquots of 0.1 ml are rapidly taken from the supernatants and rapidly diluted with 3 ml water. The absorbance of the acid-soluble oligonucleotides is measured in quartz cells at 260 mμ.

Kalnitsky et al. have reported that the sensitivity of the method can be increased 10-fold if the estimation is carried out in phosphate buffer at pH 7.

2. RNase determination by the spectrophotometric method

Having noticed that yeast RNA hydrolysis was accompanied by a diminution of the absorbance of the solutions at 300 mμ, Kunitz (1946) proposed to use this phenomenon as the basis of a determination of RNase activity. This fall in the optical density at 300 mμ is probably caused by the fall in the Tyndall effect resulting from the RNA in colloidal solution.

Since the values for the absorbance E fall linearly with time, at least at the beginning of the reaction, the rate of fall is in general proportional to the concentration of the enzyme in solution, and it is therefore possible to write the expression

$$-\frac{dE}{dt} = KC\,(E - Ef),$$

where E is the absorbance after time t, E_f is the final absorbance (when maximum hydrolysis has been attained), and C is the concentration.

The RNase unit is defined as the amount of enzyme able to cause a 100 % fall in the $E_0 - E_f$ value in 1 minute at 25°. The substrate being a 0.05 % yeast RNA solution in 0.05 M acetate

buffer of pH 5.0, $E_0 - E_f$ is the maximum optical density change it is possible to obtain at 25°
and 300 mμ.

The practical details of the procedure are as follows.   A solution (2 ml) of a 0.1 % solution
of yeast RNA in 0.1 M sodium acetate buffer at pH 5.0 is rapidly mixed with 2 ml of a dilute
solution of RNase in distilled water.   The two solutions are at about 25°. and the determination
can be carried out at room temperature.   A stopwatch is started at the moment of mixing.
The mixing can either be done in the test-tube, or directly in a quartz cell 1 cm. thick.   A reading
at 300 mμ is taken every minute for about 10 minutes.   A blank solution consisting of 2 ml yeast
RNA and 2 ml distilled water is used as reference solution.   The activity of the RNase per milliliter is equal to

$$\frac{\Delta E/\text{minute}}{E_0 - E_f}$$

where E represents the average difference between two successive readings, and $E_0 - E_f$ is the
maximum difference possible between the solution at the beginning and finally after the action
of the RNase.

3. Detection and determination of RNase using synthetic substrates

The synthesis of large amounts of cytidine-2′ : 3′-cyclic phosphate has provided an excellent
substrate for the determination of RNase and for the measurement of its fundamental constants
(Crook et al., 1960).   Substrates of the same type have also been prepared by Shugar and his
co-workers by quantitative conversion of Up, Cp and Ap to the corresponding 2′ : 3′ cyclic phosphates.   These substrates were then used for histochemical localization of the ribonucleases
together with the exogenous phosphomonoesterase with the idea of dephosphorylating the monophosphates resulting from the RNase action.   The inorganic phosphate liberated is precipitated
wich calcium (Sierakowska and Shugar, 1960).

The same laboratory has reported that it is also possible to carry out the colorimetric determination and the cytochemical location of the RNase by using α-naphthyluridine-3′-phosphate.

For the colorimetric estimation of crystalline RNase activity, or for the RNase content of
tissue homogenates, 0.01 M substrate in 0.05 M tris-HCl buffer of pH 7.2 containing 0.003 M
$MgCl_2$ was incubated with either 0.05 — 0.20 μg RNase or 20 μl 0.1 % pancreatic tissue homogenate in a total volume of 180 μl.   The reaction was terminated by addition of 100 μl of a solution
containing 4 mg/ml of Fast red TR and 80 μl of a 0.2 M tris buffer at pH 9.   The resulting azo-
dye color was then photometered at 500 mμ against an enzyme-free control. (Sierakowska et al.
1965).

4. Turbidimetric method of RNase estimation

This method utilizes the principle of the formation of an insoluble complex between RNA
and neomycin sulfate (Altescu, 1964).   The practical details are as follows.   The reaction mixture
contains in 1 ml final volume at 25° : 1.0 mg LiRNA (purified), 10 — 100 mμg RNase and 10 μ moles
tris-HCl at pH 7.6.   The reaction is halted after 5 minutes by the addition of 4.0 ml neomycin
solution (2 %), and the resulting absorbance is read spectrophotometrically between 400 and
490 mμ.   Control blanks are carried out under the same conditions without enzyme.

5. Investigation of ribonuclease isoenzymes by an electrophoretic ultraviolet method

This elegant technique was devised by Ressler et al. (1965), in order to detect RNase isoenzymes in various tissues and secretions. After electrophoretic separation of the sample in agarose, RNA is added along the migration path and the sample is incubated while in contact with a dialysis membrane : the reaction products (mono-and oligonucleotides) selectively diffuse through the membrane into an agar layer on the other side. These products, corresponding to the initial places of the various RNase isoenzymes, are localized by UV. photograph at 260 mμ. The method may be performed at different pH values.

D. Properties of bovine pancreatic ribonuclease A

The optimum temperature for attaining maximum hydrolysis by the "soluble phosphorus" method is 65°. The rapid fall in the hydrolysis rate at temperatures above 65° is probably due to inactivation of the enzyme. The RNase acts in a pH range situated between 7.0 and 8.2 with the optimum value at 7.7.

By repeated crystallization, it is possible to obtain relatively pure RNase, and after 2 or 3 crystallizations, Kunitz found that the specific activity remained constant. Such samples of RNase appeared homogeneous on ultracentrifugation, but on the other hand, Hirs, Moore and Stein (1953), by chromatography of repeatedly crystallized RNase on Amberlite IRC 50-XE 64, observed the enzyme to be resolved into two active constituents, one principal constituent "A", and a constituent of lesser importance "B". The main constituent A appears to be the RNase whose specificity has been defined above, while constituent B seems to have a different specificity. In particular, Hakim (1957a, b) who isolated both constituents A and B in crystalline form by chromatography on Amberlite IRC 50, noted the following facts. By action of "ordinary" crystalline RNase, which is actually a mixture 1/0.2 of A + B, only 1.2 % of the total guanylic acid is liberated from yeast RNA, while RNases A and B liberate respectively 1.0 and 13.8 % of guanylic acid. Furthermore, RNase B hydrolyzes 2' : 3'-cyclic guanylic acid but RNase A does not. The properties so far attributed to RNase would therefore be the result of combined action by RNases A and B, naturally with RNase A predominating, since it is present in much larger amounts.

Redfield and Anfinsen (1956) believe that certain fresh preparations of commercial ribonuclease consist of almost entirely RNase A, the B component only making its appearance during storage at low temperatures. The two chromatographic species only differ by the presence of one more or less carboxyl (Tanford and Hauenstein 1956a, b), since the titration curves of the two enzymes are different. It is possible that one of the two enzymes loses an amide group in the course of the extraction or during storage. This apparently minute difference nevertheless seems able to cause a slight specificity difference between the two chromatographically different compounds A and B. Recent studies have indeed shown that the name RNase A should be reserved for the established holoprotein, the primary structure of which is shown on page 190, and the name RNase B for a glucoprotein that is only present in aqueous extracts of pancreas and in the pancreatic juice (cf p. 211).

1. Constitution of the ribonuclease

The aminoacid constitution and sequence have been examined in two laboratories, those of Anfinsen (Anfinsen et al., 1954; Redfield and Anfinsen, 1956; Potts et al., 1962), and of Hirs, Moore, Stein and their co-workers (Hirs et al., 1953-1960; Bailey et al., 1956; Spackman et al., 1960; Smyth et al., 1962, 1963; Moore, 1964).

RNase A, obtained by chromatography on Amberlite IRC 50 as a substance giving a single symmetrical peak in the course of a second chromatography, was used as starting material. The empirical RNase formula, corresponding to a molecular weight of 13,895 was given by Hirs, Stein and Moore (1954) as

Asp_{16}, Glu_{12}, Gly_3, Ala_{12}, Val_9, Leu_2, $Ileu_3$, Ser_{15}, Thr_{10}, $(Cys-)_8$, Met_4, Pro_5, Phe_3, Tyr_6, His_4, Lys_{10},

$$Arg_4, (-CONH_2)_{17}*.$$

By oxidation with performic acid, Anfinsen et al. did not notice any formation of peptide fragments, so they concluded that RNase consisted of a single chain folded on itself, the loops of which were linked together by disulfide bridges. Using in turn hydrolysis by trypsin, pepsin and chymotrypsin, Moore, Stein et al. obtained a number of peptide fragments that enabled them to arrive at the total structure of ribonuclease, including the positions of the disulfide bridges.

More recent work by Anfinsen's co-workers (Potts et al., 1962) and by Smyth, Stein and Moore (1962) has shown that the aminoacid sequence in positions 11-18, given at first as

Ser. Thr. Ser. Ser. Asp (NH₂). His. Met. Glu

should be replaced by a sequence involving the same aminoacids ,but placed in a different order :

11	12	13	14	15	16	17	18
Glu(NH₂).	His.	Met.	Asp.	Ser.	Ser.	Thr.	Ser

and a certain number of final modifications were made by Smyth et al. (1963).

The complete structure proposed by Spackman et al. and modified by Smyth et al. (1962, 1963) is given in fig. 36. This consists of a polypeptide chain of 124 aminoacids involving four intramolecular disulfide bridges.

Studies on the spatial configuration of the RNase molecule have been undertaken by Scheraga and his co-workers (Cha and Scheraga, 1960; Schildkraut and Scheraga, 1960; Scheraga, 1960). Based on the complete aminoacid sequence given below, Scheraga was able to construct a model of the primary, secondary and tertiary structures of the enzyme which was consistent with the contemporary data.

The first Scheraga model was discussed by Lindley, who proposed a model with a slightly different spatial configuration (1962) and in the same order of ideas, Saroff (1965), presented a structure of RNase derived from the clustering of its ionizable groups. Saroff's model is based 1) on the well established sequence of aminoacids, 2) on the known data concerning the active 'site (see p 208), 3) on the interpretation of proton and chloride binding yielding six clusters of five aminoacids each and 4) chemical evidence linking together distant parts of the polypeptide

---

* The formula determined after the complete structure was known is the following (1960-1962) :
Asp_{15}, Glu_{12}, Gly_3, Ala_{12}, Val_6, $Leu_2 Ileu_3$, Ser_{15}, Thr_{10}, $(Cys-)_8$, Met_4, Pro_4, Phe_3, Tyr_6, His_4, Lys_{10}, Arg_4, $(-CONH_2)_{17}$.
It can be seen that this includes only one less Asp and one less Pro than the empirical formula established by estimation of the aminoacids (1954).

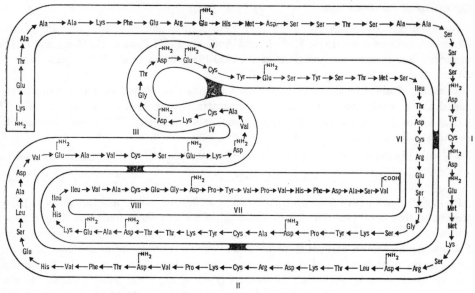

Figure 36. Two-dimensional schematic diagram of bovine ribonuclease A, showing the arrangement of the disulfide bridges and the aminoacid sequence. The arrows indicate the direction of the peptide chains starting from the amine end (from Spackman et al., 1960, modified by Smyth et al., 1962, 1963).

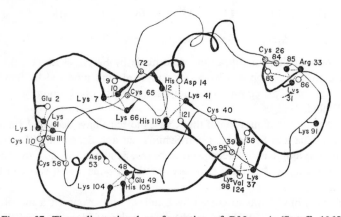

Figure 37. Three dimensional conformation of RNase A (Saroff, 1965)

backbone. This structure is illustrated in figure 37 reproduced from Saroff (1965). Recently Hammes and Scheraga (1966) have published a splendid multicolored model of RNase based on chemical evidence, summarizing the most recent information available on this matter.

2. Physicochemical modifications of RNase in connection with its enzymic activity; activation, inhibition

The action of metal ions on RNase has been studied, and the following facts have been established (McDonald, 1955a). Enzyme activity is inhibited by Mg^{++}, Ca^{++} and Mn^{++}, the minimum inhibiting dose being less than 5×10^{-4} M. The ions Na^+ and NH_4^+ stimulate RNase activity at concentrations of from 5×10^{-4} to 10^{-1} M, higher concentrations of these ions having, on the other hand, an inhibiting action. The RNase activity, measured by the liberation of free acid groups, is significantly inhibited by Cu^{++} or Zn^{++} at a concentration of 2×10^{-6} M, and weakly inhibited by Ni^{++} and Ag^+ at the same concentration. Co^{++}, Cd^{++}, Fe^{3+} and Hg^{++} have a negligible effect, but at higher concentrations (10^{-3} M) Co^{++} and Hg^{++} inhibit RNase.

Incubation of RNase with Na p-chloromercuribenzoate makes the enzymic activity decrease, then increase; incubation with iodoacetate, iodoacetamide, periodic acid, formaldehyde, ninhydrin or phenylisothiocyanate inactivates RNase (Zittle, 1946; Ledoux, 1953).

Even before the structure of RNase was completely elucidated, a search was undertaken to find out which molecular pieces, or which conformations of the polypeptide chain or its groups were essential for enzymic activity. The large number of experiments along these lines that were made have been reviewed and discussed by White and Anfinsen (1959) and by Kalnitsky et al. (1959).

RNase was submitted to certain reactions intended either to change the primary structure, i.e. to attack the continuity of the polypeptide chain by, for example, partial pepsin hydrolysis, or to alter the secondary and tertiary structures by, for instance, reducing the disulfide bridges or treatment with concentrated urea or guanidine, which is known to cause the molecule to unroll. Table XXV, reproduced from White and Anfinsen, represents the changes in enzymic activity of RNase in relation to the physical properties of the enzymes.

An interesting aspect of these physical properties is the UV spectrum of ribonuclease, which undergoes modification under the influence of certain reagents: an acid hydrolysate, for instance, shows the characteristic tyrosine absorption maximum at 2,760 Å.

The corresponding peak is displaced by about 15 Å towards higher wavelengths in the case of natural RNase, the total optical density becoming higher ($\varepsilon = 9,800$ for natural RNase, as compared with 9,390 for the hydrolysate). This effect is apparently due to hydrogen bonding between the hydroxyl groups of the tyrosine and carboxylic groups (Shugar, 1952; Sela and Anfinsen, 1957; Sela et al., 1957). The "attacks" capable of eliminating enzymic action by the RNase also eliminate in most cases the spectral shift observed in natural RNase, i.e. the spectrum becomes again that of tyrosine. The shift is not found after limited pepsin digestion, the products of which only differ from RNase by the absence of the C-terminal tetrapeptide. The shift is abolished by 8 M urea, but restored by the addition of 0.15 M phosphate.

Also in connection with the urea denaturation of RNase, Nelson and Hummel (1962) stated that the maximum denaturation is attained with 8 M urea at pH 7 and 30°. This denaturation follows the laws of a typical first order reaction. Renaturation of urea-denatured RNase also follows first-order kinetics, but it is insensitive to pH and temperature variations.

Nelson et al. (1962) have shown that the rate of denaturation of RNase by urea can be reduced by the following anions, placed in order of decreasing efficiency : pyrophosphate, 2'-cytidylate, phosphate, citrate, tartrate and sulfate.

According to Crestfield, Stein and Moore (1963a, b), alkylation of RNase by iodoacetic acid at pH 5,5 yields two inactive products, a major and a minor compound, the major one being present in 8 times the amount of the minor one. In the case of the major product, the alkylation occurs at the site of the His residue occupying position 119, giving 1-carboxymethyl-histidine-

RNase; in a similar way, these authors have demonstrated that the minor product is 3-carboxyme-thyl-histidine-12-RNase.

The conditions for this alkylation reaction have been studied; figure 38 shows the chroma-tographic behavior of RNase and its two alkylation derivatives. When the two derivatives, 1-carboxymethyl-His-119- and 3-carboxymethyl-His-12 are mixed in equal amounts, a large part of the enzyme activity is restored. This phenomenon appears to be due to the juxtapositioning of an unsubstituted His-12, furnished by the 1-carboxymethyl-His-119 derivative, and an unsubs-tituted His-119, furnished by the 3-carboxymethyl-His-12 derivative.

The information obtained in the course of this work lead to the conclusion that the imidazole

Table XXV Qualitative survey of activity changes compared with physical properties of RNase (White and Anfinsen 1959).

Treatment carried out	Changes compared with "natural" properties			
	Activity destroyed*	Spectral change**	Rise in optical rotation (negative) (1)	Rise in viscosity (1)
Performic acid oxidation	yes	yes	yes	yes
Reduction of up to $1\frac{1}{2}$ SH	weak	no	no	no
Reduction of up to 8 SH	yes	yes	yes	yes
Limited pepsin digestion	yes	yes	weak	weak
Complete pepsin digestion	yes	yes	yes	—
Methylation	yes	yes	yes	—
95 % Guanidation	yes	no (2)	no	—
Urea 8 M	no	yes	yes	yes
Urea 8M + phosphate 0.15M	no	no	no	no
Guanidine 2M	no	yes	yes	yes
Guanidine 2M + phosphate 0.15M	no	no	no	no
Guanidine 6M	yes	yes	yes	yes
Guanidine 6M + phosphate 0.15M	yes	yes	yes	yes
pH 12.7	yes	yes	—	—
pH 2	no	yes (3)	—	—
100° for 2 hours	yes	yes	—	—
Liquid NH₃	no	no	—	—
NH₄OH (28%)	no	no	—	—

* Complete or considerable destruction unless otherwise stated.
** Displacement of RNase UV spectrum towards that of the acid total hydrolysate. The absorption maximum of tyrosine shifts 15 Å towards shorter wavelengths and decreases in optical density.
1) Considered to be an indication of unfolding of secondary structures.
2) No shift of maximum, but decrease in optical density.
3) This shift is reversible; when the pH rises for the enzyme determination, the "natural" spectrum is restored, and the product possesses its whole activity.

rings of the histidines in positions 12 and 119 are at 5 Å distance from the active center of the enzyme.

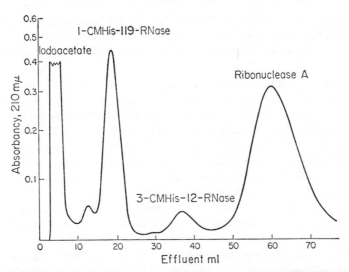

Figure 38. Chromatography of ribonuclease A, 1-CMHis-119-, and 3-CMHis-12-RNase on a column 0.9 x 15 cm) of IRC-50 with 0.266 molar NaCl as eluent at pH 6.47. The protein concentration in the effluent was monitored by measurement of absorption at 210 mμ. (Crestfield et al., 1963a, b)

Similar observations to those of Crestfield et al. were made by Yang and Hummel (1964), who found that the products of carbomethoxylation of RNase A at pH 5.6 using iodoacetic acid were separated into three components I, II and III, by chromatography on a column of Amberlite, IRC-50. Component I corresponded to unreacted RNase, component II (major) to 1-CMHis-119-RNase, and component III (minor) to 3-CMHis-12-RNase. Component II was completely devoid of activity, but component III possessed weak activity of the order of 0.45 — 0.55 % that of RNase A, this activity being measured by Kalnitsky and co-workers' method (p. 186) or Kunitz's method (p. 186). These two carboxymethyl derivatives are much more slowly denatured in 8 M urea at pH 5.5 than natural RNase. Spectrophotometric measurements show that neither of the carboxymethyl derivatives is able to form a complex with 2′-cytidylate. This phenomenon indicates that the presence of carboxymethyl groups on His-12 and His-119 not only destroys the anion and nucleotide-binding site at the active center, but also creates an electrostatic attraction between the carboxylate ion and the neighboring cationic residue, this attraction being responsible for the increased stability of the alkylated enzyme in acid media.

When the alkylation of RNase is performed at pH 8.5 instead of 5.5 somewhat different results are observed. Heinrikson (1966), for instance has subjected RNase to a series of homologous α-bromo acids and to iodo-acetamide; at pH 8.5 carboxylation occurs mainly at the three amino acids usually implied in the catalytic site of the enzyme : His-12, His-119 and Lys-41. The extent of the reaction depends on the structure of the alkylating agent : bromoacetic acid formed a derivative principally at Lys-41, and D-α-bromopropionate formed a derivative equally at Lys-41 and His-12, whilst the L-isomer showed only comparatively little reaction at Lys-12. With α bromobutyrate a marked increase at His-12 occured with the D-form. Alkylation with iodoacetamide at the same pH 8.5 furnishes a mixture of products of which mono-and dicarboxamido methylated derivatives of Lys-41 are prominent. The three products substituted at Lys-41 carboxymethyl, carboxamidomethyl and dicarboxamidomethyl, all are essentially inactive. It was also found that although the chemical modification of Lys-41 inactivates RNase, it does not markedly inhibit the alkylation of the His residues which have been implicated in the active site of the enzyme.

Continuing with the many attempts that have been made to modify the RNase molecule in connection with its enzymic activity, Cha and Scheraga (1963*a*, *b*) discovered the existence of buried tyrosyl residues within the molecule: iodination of RNase A with 6.1 moles iodine per mole RNase at pH 9.4 and 0° leads to modification of 4 out of 6 of the tyrosyl residues of RNase A, forming monoiodotyrosyl or 3,5-diiodotyrosyl residues. Chromatography of iodinated RNase on Amberlite IRC-50 partially resolves three fractions according to their iodine content. Nevertheless, all these fractions include two abnormal (non-iodinated) Tyr residues. Iodine in excess, reacting for a long time still results in complete iodination of the tyrosine in RNase. The activity of iodinated RNase is markedly lowered with respect to natural RNase, but not completely abolished. It is reported that the conformation of iodinated RNase is comparable to that of natural RNase.

By patient work, it has been possible to determine the position in the sequence of the amino-acids reacting with iodine with difficulty. The iodinated RNase was oxidized, after fractionation, and treated with various enzymes. Study of the different peptides obtained indicated that the buried tyrosine groups were to be found in the 25 and 97 positions.

Experiments devolving from those concerning the buried tyrosine groups have been carried out by Scheraga and co-workers concerning RNase methylation. Methylated RNase was prepared (Bromfield et al., 1965) essentially by Frankel-Conrat and Olcott's method (1945).

In the course of RNase methylation, it is found that 8 out of 11 of the carboxyl groups of the enzyme can be methylated. The three groups that are not esterified are the Asp-14, Asp-38 and Asp-83 groups.

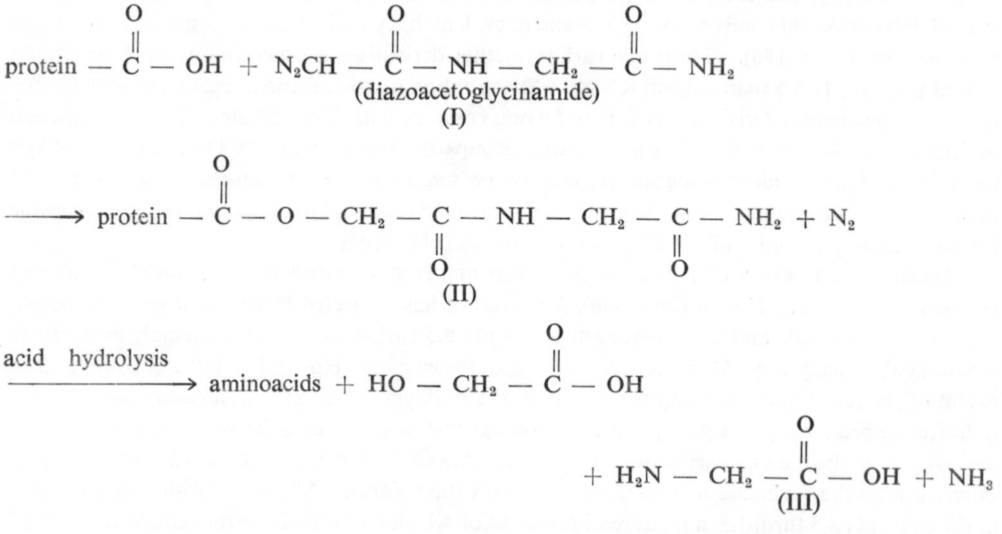

$$\text{protein} - \overset{\overset{\displaystyle O}{\|}}{C} - OH \; + \; N_2CH - \overset{\overset{\displaystyle O}{\|}}{C} - NH - CH_2 - \overset{\overset{\displaystyle O}{\|}}{C} - NH_2$$

(diazoacetoglycinamide)

(I)

$$\longrightarrow \text{protein} - \overset{\overset{\displaystyle O}{\|}}{C} - O - CH_2 - \underset{\underset{\displaystyle O}{\|}}{C} - NH - CH_2 - \underset{\underset{\displaystyle O}{\|}}{C} - NH_2 \; + \; N_2$$

(II)

acid   hydrolysis

$$\longrightarrow \text{aminoacids} \; + \; HO - CH_2 - \overset{\overset{\displaystyle O}{\|}}{C} - OH$$

$$+ \; H_2N - CH_2 - \overset{\overset{\displaystyle O}{\|}}{C} - OH \; + \; NH_3$$

(III)

Figure 39. Reaction of RNase with diazoacetoglycinamide (Riehm and Scheraga, 1965)

This methyl compound is supposed to have the same tyrosyl-carboxyl interactions as the natural compound (Riehm et al., 1965). We have already seen that the buried tyrosines of RNase A (Tyr-25 and Tyr-97) have been identified, so it ought therefore to be possible to pair these two tyrosines with the similarly buried carboxyls. Riehm and his co-workers concluded that Asp-83 and Tyr-25 would be paired in a hydrogen-bonded tyrosine-carboxylate link, while the second masked tyrosine will be with Asp-38, forming a Tyr-97 — Asp-38 hydrogen bond.

Another type of esterification proposed by Riehm and Scheraga (1965) consists in treating RNase A with diazoacetoglycinamide following the scheme (figure 39) :

This reaction results in the formation of one additional glycine per esterified carboxyl group.

The main derivative obtained by this reaction with RNase A contains four Gly residues per mole protein, i.e. one more than natural RNase. The peptide analyses subsequently carried out indicated that this derivative, which was 100 % active, is esterified on aspartic acid-53.

Among the other reagents applied to RNase we ought to mention also acrylonitrile and a water soluble carbodiimide (Riehm and Scheraga 1966 a, b). The reaction of RNase with acrylonitrile may be represented as follows :

$$\text{protein} - \underset{\underset{R}{|}}{N}H + CH_2 = CH\text{-}CN \longrightarrow \text{protein} - \underset{\underset{R}{|}}{N} - CH_2 - CH_2 - CN \xrightarrow[H_2O]{H^+}$$

$$\text{aminoacids} + R' - \overset{H}{\underset{\underset{R}{|}}{\overset{|}{N^+}}} - CH_2 - CH_2 - COOH + NH_4^+$$

In this scheme R and R' would be H and $HOOC - CH - (NH_3^+) (CH_2)_4$ respectively if the nitrogen-containing groups were lysine. Riehm and Scheraga were able to demonstrate that acrylonitrile reacted with the ε-aminogroups of lysine up to the extent where all ten residues had reacted. Although the fully reacted compound was inactive it did possess physicochemical properties similar to those of RNase.

The reaction of RNase with a water soluble carbodiimide (1-cyclohexyl-3-(2-morphilonoethyl) carbodiimide metho-p-toluene-sulfonate) at pH 4,5 produced a number of derivatives. Five of these derivatives designated by Riehm and Scheraga as B,D,F,G and H, have been isolated and examined : each of these compounds appears to differ from RNase in the number of carboxyl groups which have been modified.

Alkylation of the methionine residues has been studied by Stark and Stein (1964) using iodoacetate and iodoacetamide as the alkylating agents. Since the Met residues are buried in the natural protein, Stark and Stein were obliged to carry out the alkylation of RNase in 8 M urea so that the enzyme would be in a completely unfolded form. The rate of the RNase alkylation could be followed in 8 M urea at 40° by observing the amount of iodine liberated during the reaction, by means of a silver-silver iodide electrode. Under these conditions, the 4 Met residues of the RNase react at comparable velocities and the completely alkylated product is inactive. In view of the fact that it has not so far been possible to obtain homogenous partially alkylated products (e.g. monoalkyl-Met-RNase or dialkyl-Met-RNase), it is difficult to establish that a correlation between the degree of alkylation and enzymic activity, although it would appear the monosubstituted derivatives are at least partially active.

The action of 1-fluoro-2,4-dinitrobenzene, (F D N B), the well known reagent of proteins, has been studied by Hirs and his coworkers (Hirs et al. 1965, Hirs and Kycia 1965, Murdock et al. 1966). These authors have shown that the reaction at pH 8.0 and 15°, is limited in its initial stages to the modification of the lysine residues. The sites of attack are the α-amino group of the N-terminal Lys-residue and the ε-amino groups of the Lys residues in positions 7 and 41 ; the most reactive group is Lys-41. The 41-DNP-RNase 'A is inactive whereas modification of the terminal α-aminogroup gives rise to a product having 60 % of the activity of native RNase A. The principal products formed by action of F D N B on RNase A, 41-DNP-RNase, I-DNP-RNase, 7,41-bis-DNP-RNase and 7,41-bis-DNP-RNase may be separated over columns of IRC-50.

The action of a related reagent : 1,5-difluoro-2,4-dinitrobenzene (DFDNB) was studied by Marfey and coworkers (Marfey and King 1965, Marfey, Nowack, Uziel and Yphantis 1965, Marfey, Uziel and Little 1965). This reagent which is bifunctionnal, leads either to the formation of intramolecularly bridged derivatives or to dimeric derivatives. The major intramolecularly bridged monomer, obtained by action of DFDNB in dilute aqueous solutions, was found to possess a single cross link between the ε-amino groups of lysine residues 7 and 41. When the reaction was conducted by diffusion of DFDNB into RNase crystals, one monomer and two dimers were obtained. The monomeric RNase derivative although inactive toward cytidine-2' : 3'-cyclic phosphate, retained 2 % of the activity of RNase A toward RNA. The dimeric derivative was inactive toward both substrates.

Cleavage of the disulfide bridges by either performic acid oxidation or by reduction with compounds containing hydrosulfide groups causes a rise in the negative optical rotation and of the viscosity (both indications of unfolding of the secondary structure) as well as suppression of the spectral shift of the natural protein. These different effects demonstrate that fission of the disulfide bridges causes disorientation of the secondary structure as well as rupture of the tertiary configuration.

So far as the stepwise RNase reduction by thioglycolic acid is concerned, White and Anfinsen (1959) have shown that the enzyme is slowly inactivated until half the -S-S- groups are reduced, after which the inactivation is fast. It therefore appears as if the two bridges initially broken (out of the total of four) only have slight effect on the enzyme activity, while the two others are more intimately associated with the active center.

In the same way Epstein et al. (1962) from Anfinsen's laboratory have shown that reduction of RNase by β-mercaptoethanol can be carried out in 8 M urea in 20 hours at pH 8.2. After reduction, the reduced protein can be purified and separated from the reducing reagents by passage through a column of Sephadex G-25 equilibrated with 0.1 M acetic acid. Titration of the RNase reduced to this stage shows the presence of the expected number of hydrosulfide groups for total reduction, i.e. 8.0 ± 0.2. Reoxidation of the RNase can be achieved by leaving the reduced protein to stand at a concentration of 0.02 mg/ml in 0.09 M tris buffer at 24° and pH 8.2. The amount of reactivation is inversely proportional to the concentration of reduced protein. Under the most favorable conditions, some enzymic activity can be detected in the first five minutes, and complete restoration of the activity is obtained in 60 minutes.

Exactly the same results have been obtained by Givol et al. (1964) concerning the spontaneous reactivation of RNase reduced by β-mercaptoethanol, while Venetianer and Straub (1963, 1964) have found a thermolabile factor in pigeon and hen pancreas which catalyzes reoxidation of the reduced RNase.

Gublin et al. (1965), showed that the disulfide bridges of RNase may be titrated by a polarographic technique with parachloromercuribenzoate, after reduction by potassium borohydride. The results obtained by this technique confirm the well known presence of four disulfide bridges in RNase.

A further method intended to procure information about the conformation of the RNase molecule consists in studying the enzyme and some of its derivatives by the fluorescence polarization technique (Young and Potts, 1963). The principle consists of measuring the amount of fluorescence polarization emitted by a small fluorescent molecular species conjugated with the protein molecule. The fluorescent reagent chosen by Young and Potts is 5-dimethylamino-1-naphthalenesulfonyl chloride, and the radicals attached to the molecule are 5-dimethylamino-1-naphthalenesulfonyl groups (DNS). The absorption spectra of the RNase-DNS complex molecules in the region 260 — 280 mμ are essentially those of the unlabeled RNase A, and these molecules retain the enzymic activity of RNase A. The crude structure of the RNase does not appear to be affected either, since calculation of the relaxation times, from the volume of an ellipsoid of effective hydrodynamic revolution shows them to be in suitable accord with the experimentally measured values.

From changes in rotational relaxation time as a function of reduction and reduction-alkylation of RNase, evidence was presented for the existence of temperature, guanidine-HCl and urea-sensitive interactions in the reduced protein.

Another type of modification that RNase can be made to undergo consists in attaching a supplementary polypeptide chain, such as polyalanyl groups, to it. This was realized by Anfinsen et al. (1962) and Wellner et al. (1963) who examined the enzymic activity of polyalanyl-RNase (PAR), when they found that not only did it possess most of the enzymic properties of the natural enzyme, but that it also recovered all its original activity when the reduced form was reoxidized. The properties were compared by Wellner et al. (1963) between natural RNase and RNase enriched by a supplement of 94 (PAR 4D) and 130 (PAR 4E) alanine residues. A change in the curve of activity versus pH was observed, PAR 4D having an optimum pH for activity 0.8 units below that of natural RNase (using RNA as substrate). Using cyclic 2' : 3'-phosphate, the PAR activity is of the same order of size as that of RNase A. PAR preparations also have a lower isoelectric point than that of RNase in 0.1 M veronal buffer.

Scott and Scheraga (1963) have studied the thermal denaturation (or transition) of ₁RNase A in a pH range of 0.9 to 3.26 at an ionic strength of 0.16 by means of a special technique called "spectrophotometric stopped-flow". This technique allows changes in the UV absorption of the tyrosyl groups at 287 mμ to be measured, and we have seen that this is characteristic of the interactions between the tyrosyl and carboxyl groups. The results observed by Scott and Scheraga were fairly complex, but were interpreted in the following manner. The transition corresponds to two independent parallel transitions taking place in two distinct parts of the molecule; each of these regions contains an abnormal tyrosine which interacts with a carboxyl group by virtue of its hydrogen bonds, the different groups being buried in a hydrophobic environment. These tyrosines might well be the tyrosines 25 and 97 which we have seen to be resistant to iodination. The same group (Schrier and Scheraga, 1962; Schrier et al., 1965) has demonstrated that the thermal transition of the RNase is accentuated by the presence of alcohols, and that the lowering of the transition temperature for a given concentration of alcohol increases with the chain length of the alcohol (for alcohols with a linear chain). It has also been observed that plotted against the chain length, the molar transition temperature depressions follow, in the case of straight-chain alcohols, a smooth curve. The branched-chain alcohols gave molar depressions that fell on a straight line above the curve for the straight chain alcohols (figure 40; Schrier et al., 1965).

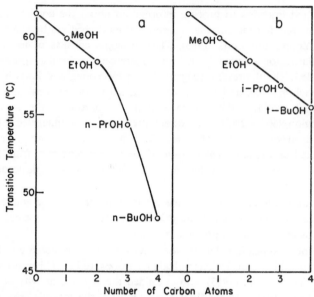

Figure 40. a) The transition temperature of ribonuclease in 1 M alcohol solutions (straight-chain). *b*) The transition temperature of ribonuclease in 1 M alcohol solutions (branched-chain), together with data for MeOH. and EtOH. (Schrier et al., 1965)

Various other techniques have been described to study the thermal transition of RNase. For instance von Hippel and Wong (1965; see an important bibliography of the work carried up on the study of thermal RNase transition in this reference) investigated this phenomenon by optical rotatory means : a number of transition parameters have been defined including the " melting temperature " (T_m), the size of the transition ($\Delta [\alpha]$), the breadth of the transition and the specific rotation of the pre- and post-transition states. Usually the experiments were conducted by placing the solution to be examined into a thermostated polarimeter tube and by raising the temperature in 3-8° steps, holding at each temperature for about ten minutes to achieve thermal equilibrium. Curves were then established by plotting temperature (abscissa) versus [α]. Such curves were drawn for control solutions of RNase and for solutions of RNase containing various classes of " structural perturbants " i.e. mainly inorganic salts and urea and guanidinium salts. In the course of a typical experiment, it was shown for instance that $CaCl_2$ is a rather potent destabilizer, for the melting point (T_m) is markedly shifted toward lower values as the concentration of this salt is increased; the same happens for guanidinium chloride. It is suggested that these reagents affect T_m by modifying the strength of intramolecular hydrophobic interactions which stabilize the enzyme in the native form.

The heat of transition of RNase A has been measured on 1.5 and 3 % (by weight) enzyme solutions between 20 and 60° (Beck et al., 1965), and was found to be 70 $\pm$ 1 kcal/mol.   These calorimetric results go towards confirming that the RNase transition is not a simple helix-coil polypeptide transition, nor is it a single-step transition.   Enthalpy measurements indicated a transition reaction involving more than one step.

Among the other physico-chemical agents capable of altering the structure of RNase A, the action of radiations was investigated by several authors.   Haskill and Hunt (1965), for instance, noticed that the reduction and reoxidation of RNase irradiated in oxygen provoked the appearance of hidden, sublethal damage following irradiation, wheras irradiation *in vacuo* produced no evidence of such damage.   The modifications of RNase structure by gamma irradiation was studied by Slobodian et al. (1965 *a*, *b*), who demonstrated that the irradiation of RNase A in aqueous solution produced 80-90 % inactivated samples.   Titration of the newly inactivated material indicated two -SH groups per molecule of enzyme : these results show that rupture of -SH bridges is one of the modifications introduced by irradiation.   The irradiated molecule also exhibits a greater sensitivity to trypsin as compared to native RNase.

3. Action of proteolytic enzymes on RNase; fragments retaining activity

Ribonuclease A is rather resistant to the action of the usual proteolytic enzymes, yet Huppert and Semmel (1965) reported that it can be inactivated as well as other RNases by pronase a *Streptomyces griseus* protease.

If the proteolytic enzymes such as trypsin and chymotrypsin do not attack natural RNase at room temperature, this happens at higher temperatures when the RNase undergoes its thermal transition (see above, p. 197). This hydrolysis yields fragments that can be separated by chromatography on IRC-50.   The intermediate compounds from the chymotrypsin hydrolysis are without activity, while those arising from the trypsin hydrolysis possess some activity (Rupley and Scheraga, 1963; Ooi et al., 1963).   In the course of this work that was also carried out in Scheraga's laboratory two active intermediates were obtained by partial RNase hydrolysis with trypsin, and were designated compound III and compound IV.   Compound IV, which can be obtained in fairly high yield, is a mixture of two molecular species each characterized by fission of a peptide link, namely Lys-31 — Ser-32 and Arg-33 — Asp (NH₂)-34 respectively.   Compound III is characterized by the fission of both these peptide links, and consequently no longer possesses the dipeptide Ser. 32 — Arg-33.   Compound IV digested more energetically with trypsin at room temperature yields eight compounds which were also fractionated on IRC-50.   These new compounds were numbered from 1 to 8, 8 being the starting compound IV, and 7 being the compound previously labeled III (Ooi et al., 1963).   In view of the fact that this hydrolysis does not cause the appearance of other fragments, it is evident that 5 peptide bonds that are in theory hydrolyzable by trypsin are not in fact broken, suggesting that at room temperature these bonds are less exposed to trypsin than the others are.   Some of the compounds obtained possess somewhat limited enzyme activity. Compounds IV (or 8) and III (or 7) obtained by controlled trypsin hydrolysis of RNase still have essentially the same conformation as RNase A, but with a somewhat looser structure (Ooi and Scheraga, 1964*a b*).

The action of pepsin on RNase has been studied first by Anfinsen (1956), who demonstrated that pepsin inactivated RNase (PIR) was obtained as the first digestion product when trypsin removes the C-terminal tetrapeptide (Asp. Ala. Ser. Val.); the hydrolysis was performed at pH

1.8 and 37°.   Later on Fujioka and Scheraga (1965) studied extensively the peptic digestion of RNase A at pH 2.0 and at 25°; in particular they separated all the intermediates by column chromatography.   The sites of peptic cleavage were shown to occur at Phe-Asp (120-121), Met-Ser (79-80), Thr-Phe (45-46), Glu (NH₂)-Ala (55-56), and Phe-Glu (8-9).   Iodination of PIR with 12 moles of I₂/mole PIR at pH 9.5 and 0°, iodinated 5 " exposed " tyrosyl groups but not the " buried " tyrosyl group.   Aminoacid analyses and spectral studies indicated the presence of one uniodinated tyrosyl group in iodinated PIR which was located as Tyr-25.

A very interesting observation was made by Richards (1958), who noticed that hydrolysis of RNase by the bacterial protease, subtilisin, yielded an active product containing only the N-terminal extremity of 20 aminoacids attached to a more important fragment, apparently by means of hydrogen bonds, this product exhibiting the spectral shift that is destroyed by urea and restored by phosphate.   Separation of the N-terminal fragment and the macromolecular fragment causes the disappearance of the spectral shift at the same time as complete loss of the activity.   The reaction seems principally to affect the histidine in position 12.

$$\text{RNase A} \xrightarrow{\text{subtilisin}} \text{RNase S} \begin{array}{l} \nearrow \text{ S-peptide \ (eicosapeptide)} \\ \searrow \text{ S-protein} \end{array}$$

RNase S′ = S-peptide + S-protein
              (reconstituted active "RNase")

Using Richards's nomenclature, the RNase A that is modified by the action of subtilisin is designated RNase S, the eicosapeptide obtained from RNase S is designated S-peptide, the protein component obtained from RNase S is called S-protein and the protein reconstituted by mixing equimolar amounts of S-peptide and S-protein is called RNase S′.

Potts and co-workers (1963) from Anfinsen's laboratory reported the reconstitution of completely active RNase S using the S-peptide degraded with carboxypeptidase.   Elimination of the five aminoacids from the terminal region is easy to effect with carboxypeptidase, and their removal from the S-peptide does not affect the ability of the latter to reconstitute a wholly active enzyme by equimolar recombination with RNase S.

Lys. Glu. Thr. Ala. Ala. Ala. Lys. Phe. Glu. Arg. Glu (NH₂). His. Met. Asp. Ser.

Ser. Thr. Ser. Ala. Ala

The diagram above shows, enclosed by a line, the sequence of the S-peptide, with the five aminoacids that can be removed by carboxypeptidase without loss of ability of the S-peptide to yield an active product.

Continuing their experiments in this direction, Potts et al. (1964) showed that loss of valine-124 from the terminal grouping in the S-protein does not modify the enzymic activity of this derivative after in vitro combination with the S-peptide to form RNase S.   Loss of serine-123 under the same conditions causes a 45 % loss of activity, while loss of the residues coming later (Ala-122, Asp-121, Phe-120) involves disappearance of enzyme activity even if an excess of S-peptide is added.

Hofmann et al. (1963) have published a note of an exceptional nature, since it describes experiments that represent the first partial synthesis of an enzyme in the laboratory.   They showed that addition of the S-protein to the synthetic peptide :

Lys. Glu(NH₂). Thr. Ala. Ala. Ala. Lys. Phe. Glu(NH₂). Arg. Glu(NH₂). His. Met.

which is close to, but not identical with the 13 *N*-terminal residues of RNase, restored 68-73 % of the RNase enzymic activity. The reconstructed enzyme attained maximum catalytic activity when ten peptide molecules were added per molecule of S-protein.

Subsequently Hofmann and his co-workers (1965*a*, *b*, *c*) synthesized several peptides, such as

H. Phe. Glu. Arg. Glu. OH

H. Phe. Glu. Arg. Glu. His. NH$_2$, etc.,

representing portions of the S-peptide sequence. They then examined the ability of these various peptides to regenerate RNase activity with S-protein (Finn and Hofmann, 1965). The most active fraction was :

Lys. Glu. Thr. Ala. Ala. Ala. Lys. Phe. Glu. Arg. Glu (NH$_2$). His. Met. NH$_2$.

The partially synthetic enzyme obtained in this way will hydrolyze yeast RNA, uridine-2′, 3′-phosphate and cytidine-2′, 3′-phosphate.

The shortest fraction able to activate S-protein using RNA as substrate is Phe. Glu. Arg. Glu (NH$_2$). His (amide).

Conformational studies of subtilisin-modified RNase were undertaken by Sherwood and Potts (1965 *a*, *b*) by means of optical rotatory changes and tyrosine difference spectroscopy. RNase A, RNase-S and S-protein were compared with respect to their denaturation behaviour : RNase A was the most resistant to unfolding, while S-protein was the most labile; S-peptide exhibited no evidence of ordered structure. RNase-S like RNase A was found to contain 3 buried tyrosines whereas only 2 were detected in S-protein. Addition of S-peptide to S-protein restored spectral abnormalities corresponding to a third tyrosine. Somewhat similar observations were made by Cowgill (1966 *a*, *b*) who submitted RNase A, RNase-S and S-protein to a variety of denaturing agents like : acid, heat, urea, dioxane, dodecyl sulfate, and cetyldimethylethyl ammonium bromide and suggested, as Sherwood and Potts, the following order of stability for the three forms : RNase A > RNase-S > S-protein.

The action on RNase A of another proteolytic enzyme : porcine pancreatic elastase was investigated by Klee (1965). By chromatography on Amberlite XE 64 of elastase treated RNase it was possible to isolate a new enzymically active form of RNase which was called RNase-E. Aminoacid analyses showed that RNase E differs from RNase S only in that an alanine residue has been eliminated from the carboxyl terminus of the peptide moiety.

4. Inhibition of RNase by anionic polymers and natural inhibitors

Among other agents able to cause inhibition of RNase, mention should be made of a series of anionic polymers such as heparin and polyxenylphosphate (cf. references given by Ukita et al., 1962). The experiments of Ukita et al. (1962) showed that heparin exerts the same degree of inhibition for both types of reaction catalyzed by RNase, namely "phosphotransferase" activity and "cyclic phosphatase" activity, the inhibition reactions being measured on synthetic substrates, e.g. ethylcytidine-3′-phosphate and cytidine-2′, 3′-phosphate (figure 41).

RNase inhibition is not caused simply by metallic ions and reaction products from the reaction with RNA, but there also exist cellular inhibitors of a protein nature in the tissues. Shortman (1961), for instance, has described the purification and determination of an inhibiting system for RNase isolated from rat liver. This inhibitor was purified by centrifugation of a

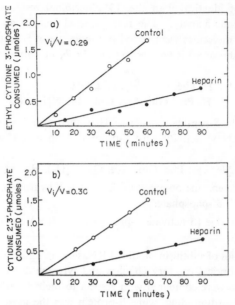

Figure 41. Effect of heparin on RNase-A activity on ethyl cytidine 3′-phosphate and cytidine-2′, 3′-phosphate. Reaction mixture : *a)* ethylcytidine-3′-phosphate, 4.5 μ moles. RNase-A 100 μg., heparin 1.5 mg., M/30 sodium phosphate buffer pH 7.6, 1.0 ml. *b)* cytidine-2′, 3′-phosphate 4.5/moles, RNase-A 10 μg., heparin 1.5 mg., M/30 sodium phosphate buffer pH 7.6 1.0 ml. Heparin was omitted from *a)* and *b)* for control experiment. Incubation was carried out at 37° (Ukita et al., 1962)

cell extract, chromatography on DEAE-cellulose and chromatography on calcium phosphate. Under these conditions an inhibitor is obtained in 20 % yield that is purified 6,000-fold compared with the starting extract.

RNase inhibitors have also been found in the livers of several other mammalian species besides the rat, e.g. mouse, hamster, guinea-pig, etc. On the other hand, no RNase inhibitor has been found in chicken or frog liver (Roth, 1962).

Some recent work by Wojnar (1965) describes the study of the RNase inhibitor obtained from the supernatants of normal rat liver, and supernatants from livers of rats fed with 2-acetyl-aminofluorene (a carcinogenic substance). A significant rise in the amount of RNase inhibitor was found in the animals fed with the carcinogen.

5. Further miscellaneous reactions of pancreatic RNase.

RNase being one of the best defined proteins that exist, it served as a model for Craig et al. (1963) in their studies on protein dialysis and membrane porosity.

Preliminary studies with RNase showed that the protein containing a small amount of sulfate dialyzed more quickly through some Visking cellophane membranes than when it was in pure water.

In order to plot the escape curves, the logarithm of the amount of enzyme remaining inside is taken as ordinate against time as abscissae, and a descending straight line is normally obtained if the product being examined obeys the laws of dialysis. An ideal curve would only be expected in the case of RNase when the system contained sulfate ions, and indeed it is found at ammonium sulfate concentrations of 0.0015 M.

RNase action being one of blocking RNA synthesis, as well as the syntheses of various analogous structures, it can give rise to the blocking of some cell multiplications. Plus (1965) has thus reported that RNase stops egg-laying by *Drosophila*, as does 5-fluorodeoxyuridine.

Loeb and Saroff (1964) have observed that chloride ions are effectively bound to RNase in the acid pH range in conditions normally pertaining during proton bond measurements.

The titration of acid RNase to its isoionic point has been carried out in 1.80 M KCl (Bull and Breese, 1965). From the value of the slope of the titration curve in the neighborhood of semi-neutralization, it was concluded that the influence of the electrical double layer around the protein ion on its behavior during titration is negligible at and above an ionic strength of 0.15.

Donovan (1965) has succeeded in carrying out a spectrophotometric titration of the imidazole groups in RNase.

It was shown by Hummel and Anderson (1956), that [RNase is strongly adsorbed at the water-glass interface, the enzyme being maximally adsorbed at pH 7.5. De la Llosa et al. (1966) demonstrated that the treatments which denature RNase like pH 12, performic acid oxidation, urea... affect the elution volume of this enzyme when fractionated on Sephadex G-100 columns. It was concluded that gel filtration may be used as a criterion for the type of denaturation affecting the secondary and tertiary structures of a protein. This type of chromatography may also be applied to the separation of the native protein from its denaturation products.

6. Pancreatic RNase specificity ; transfer and synthetic reactions catalyzed by the enzyme

It has been seen (p. 182) that pancreatic ribonuclease specifically hydrolyzes the bonds existing between the 3'-phosphoryl groups of the pyrimidine nucleosides and the 5'-hydroxyl groups of the purine nucleosides. The first step of the reaction involves the formation of nucleoside-2' : 3'-phosphates (or cyclic nucleotides) and simultaneous cleavage of the terminal phosphodiester bond, to lead finally to the nucleoside-3'-phosphate. It is therefore possible to isolate in the first stages of RNA hydrolysis by pancreatic RNase, cyclic pyrimidine nucleotides, and short oligonucleotides involving one or two purine nucleotides terminated by a pyrimidine nucleotide.

Chromatography of an RNA hydrolysate obtained by the action of RNase A, allows the isolation of fairly large amounts of cyclic mono nucleotides corresponding to C and U and smaller amounts of the cyclic purine nucleotides. Markham and Smith (1952a) gave the following evidence for the existence of cyclic nucleotides. So far as the cyclic pyrimidine nucleotides are concerned, Up! has been analyzed for its phosphorus and uracil content, which are present in the ratio 0.95/1 (theoretical 1/1). Cp! has a molecular ratio of 0.93/1 (theoretical 1/1). The chromatographic behavior in all solvent systems tried is identical to that of the synthetic substances prepared by Brown, Magrath and Todd (1952). The most striking proof of the identity of the natural and synthetic substances is the fact that both series are slowly hydrolyzed by crystalline RNase down to the free nucleotide state. In the case of the cyclic nucleotides, the phosphorus/adenine molecular ratio in Ap! has been found to be 1.00/1 (theoretical 1/1) and the phosphorus/guanine molecular ratio in Gp! to be 0.93/1 (theoretical 1/1). The general properties of the cyclic purine nucleotides are comparable to those of the cyclic pyrimidine nucleotides, with the exception that they are completely resistant to ribonuclease action. During hydrolysis with cold normal hydrochloric acid or normal sodium hydroxide, they yield mixtures of nucleotides *a* and *b*. Table XXVI

(Markham and Smith, 1952a) is a comparison of the properties of cyclic nucleotides, on one hand, and the corresponding 2'- and 3'-nucleotides, on the other.

Table XXVI Properties of cyclic nucleotides compared with those of the corresponding nucleoside 2'- and 3'-phosphates (after Markham and Smith, 1952a)

Cyclic Nucleotides	*Nucleoside 2'- and 3'-phosphates*
Higher R_f value in solvent 3*	Lower R_f value in solvent 3
Lower R_f value in solvent 1	Higher R_f value in solvent 1
Same electrophoretic mobility at pH 3.5	Same electrophoretic mobility at pH 3.5
Lower electrophoretic mobility at pH 7.4	Higher electrophoretic mobility at pH 7.4
Pyrimidine derivatives slowly hydrolyzed by RNase	Unchanged by RNase action
Exceedingly slow hydrolysis by prostate phospho-monoesterase	Rapidly dephosphorylated by prostate phosphomo-noesterase
Hydrolysis by cold NaOH to give a mixture of nucleoside 2'- and 3'- phosphates.	Unchanged by action of N NaOH.

* Solvent I has the following composition : $(NH_4)_2 SO_4$ in aqueous solution, 80 parts; 0.5 M CH_3COONa, 18 parts; isopropanol, 2 parts.   Solvent 3 : isopropanol 70 parts; water 30 parts (v /v), with the addition of 0.35 ml ammonia (d = 0.88) per liter gas space in the chromatography vessel.

As the result of their experiments, Markham and Smith (1952a, b, c) proposed as early as 1952 a possible ribonucleic acid structure that was in accord with their results. This structure can be represented in the following manner :

ApCp:Up:Cp:Up:Cp:Cp:ApGpApGpCp:Up:Cp:Cp:ApApGpUp:Up:
GpUp:Up:Cp:Cp:GpCp:Cp:Up:ApGpCp:Ap!

The colons represent points at which cleavage by RNase occurs, i.e. the bonds broken are pyrimidine-pyrimidine or pyrimidine-purine, but never purine-purine or purine-pyrimidine. The residues that can be dephosphorylated by prostate phosphomonoesterase are the terminal phosphoryl groups on each fragment except the last. Furthermore, the chain was said to be unbranched and terminated by a cyclic nucleotide.

Preliminary work by Schmidt et al. (1951) resulted in the conclusion that ribonuclease liberates about 60 % of the pyrimidines in the form of mononucleotides, the remainder of the pyrimidine nucleotides being attached to purine nucleotides by bonds other than 2'- and 3'-. All the mono-esterified phosphoryl groups were said to be attached to these free or combined pyrimidine nucleotides either in position 2' or in position 3'. From these facts, Schmidt et al. concluded that yeast RNA was formed of chains of purine nucleotides alternating with chains of pyrimidine nucleotides. The average length of each chain would be about 2 or 3 nucleotides, ribonuclease only hydrolyzing the bonds between two pyrimidine nucleotides.

Structural schemes for RNA such as those proposed by Markham and Smith and by Schmidt et al. were independently confirmed by experiments carried out by Volkin and Cohn (1953). These dealt at the same time with the RNA structure and the mode of action of RNase, two problems closely correlated. A figure reproduced from an article by Volkin and Cohn is given below (figure 42). This figure is entitled "Ion-exchange separation of the products of RNase digestion of calf liver ribonucleic acid", and it constitutes an application of the extensive work by Volkin and Cohn on nucleotide chromatography on ion exchange resins (Cohn and Volkin, 1951; Cohn, 1950a, b, 1951).   Upon examination of the nucleotides liberated by the action of ribonuclease and isolated by Volkin and Cohn, one is struck by the fact that they are all of the type Pyp or (Pup)$_n$Pyp, in which Py and Pu represent respectively a pyrimidine and a purine nucleoside, and p a phosphoryl group following the definition of nomenclature on p. 17.   In other words, RNase breaks the bonds — Py p — Py p- and -Py p — Pu p —, this fission occurring between the phosphoryl groups and carbon-5′, thereby liberating nucleotides terminated by a 3′-phosphate group.   The general structural scheme that Volkin and Cohn arrived at, is the same as that of Markham and Smith.

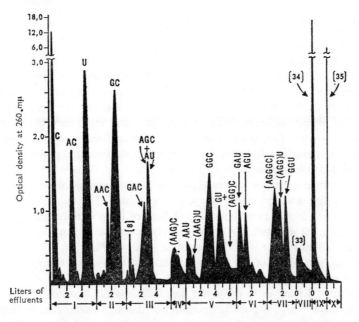

Figure 42. Ion-exchange separation of the products of RNase digestion of calf-liver RNA. Volume reagent (in liters) as abscissae, absorbance at 260 mμ as ordinates.   The parentheses on the graph indicate an unknown nucleotide sequence or a nucleotide mixture, the square brackets an empirical composition. The eluting agents were successively (I) 0.005 N HCl, (II) 0.01 N HCl, (III) 0.01 N HCl + 0.0125 M NaCl (IV) 0.01 N HCl + 0.025 M NaCl, (V) 0.01 N HCl + 0.05 M NaCl, (VI) 0.01 N HCl + 0.1 M NaCl, (VII) 0.01 N HCl + 0.2 M NaCl, (VIII) 0.01 N HCl + 0.3 M NaCl, (IX) 0.01 N HCl + 1 M NaCl, (X) 2 N HCl.   (After Volkin and Cohn, 1953)

Ribonuclease also hydrolyzes simple pyrimidine nucleoside-3′-phosphate esters, but not pyrimidine nucleoside-2′-phosphates, yielding a nucleoside-3′-phosphate and an alcohol, the cyclic nucleotide appearing transiently in the reaction (Brown and Todd, 1953).   Purine nucleotide esters and cyclic purine nucleotides are not affected by RNase.

All these results contribute towards showing that the depolymerizing activity of RNase is a reaction involving two successive steps, the first of which is a specific transphosphorylation, i.e. a transfer of the phosphodiester bond from the 5′-position to the 2′-position of a pyrimidine nucleotide by scheme (*a*) (figure 43).

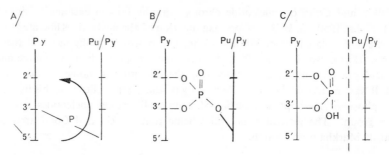

Figure 43. Three succesive steps occurring possibly during the hydrolysis of a phosphodiester bond by RNase (Szer and Shugar 1962)

The result is the formation of a cyclic pyrimidine nucleotide together with purine oligonucleotides terminated by a cyclic pyrimidine nucleotide. The second reaction step involves the opening of the cyclic phosphate groups and the formation of corresponding nucleosides terminated by a 3'-phosphate group. Szer and Shugar (1962) set out to examine the basic mechanism of this double reaction of transphosphorylation and hydrolysis, and more particularly, they wondered whether the cyclization and formation of an internal "triester" such as that shown in scheme (B) is in reality the first step of the RNase action, or whether the transphosphorylation occurs at the same time as the chain cleavage according to scheme (C).

The answer to these questions was made possible by the synthesis of methyl esters of uridine-2': 3'-cyclic phosphate and cytidine-2':3'-cyclic phosphate. The enzymatic experiments then carried out using these methyl esters showed that both of them were completely resistant to the action of the enzyme. This result would appear to indicate that enzymic hydrolysis of the internucleotide bonds does not occur with the formation of a cyclic triester, but that the depolymerization reaction (with breakage of the 3', 5'-phosphodiester bond) takes place at the same time as the formation of the 2': 3'-cyclic phosphate.

The specificity of RNase as we have just described it is not absolutely strict, and seems to be influenced by the size and spatial configuration of the macromolecules, as has been pointed out by Beers (1960) in the course of some work in which he showed that purine polynucleotides like polyA are hydrolyzed to the stage of mononucleotides.

Rushizky et al. (1961) have also clarified certain details about the stereospecificity of RNase, comparing the results obtained with partial and total hydrolysis of yeast and tobacco mosaic virus RNA. These authors noted that oligonucleotides containing one or more purines and a terminal pyrimidine are liberated before the pyrimidine mononucleotides. Furthermore, cytidylic acid is liberated before uridylic acid.

Application of RNase allowed Markham and Smith to develop a hypothesis about the structure of RNA (1952c) at the same time as it allowed them to isolate a whole series of new compounds, such as nucleoside-3'-phosphates, cyclic-2': 3'-phosphates, dinucleotides, oligonucleotides, more rapidly than would have been possible by synthesis. The same group (Heppel and Whitfeld 1955; Heppel, Whitefld and Markham, 1955; Whitfeld, Heppel and Markham, 1955) has also described exchange and synthetic reactions catalyzed by ribonuclease (and by spleen phosphodiesterase, cf. p. 267).

Ribonuclease can indeed catalyze the formation of certain pyrimidine alkyl esters starting either from cyclic nucleotides and the appropriate alcohol, or from the corresponding benzyl ester and the appropriate alcohol. Transfers of this type are illustrated by the following two reactions :

Cytidine-2': 3'-phosphate + methanol $\rightarrow$ cytidine-3'-methylphosphate (1)

Cytidine-3'-benzyl phosphate + methanol $\rightarrow$ cytidine-3'-methyl phosphate + benzyl alcohol (2).

Reaction (2) is also catalyzed by spleen phosphodiesterase, which is unable to catalyze the first.

In addition, reactions which are true *polynucleotide syntheses* are catalyzed by pancreatic RNase. For example, it is known that when cytidine cyclic-2': 3'-phosphate at a concentration of 0.02 M is incubated with RNase, it is hydrolyzed to give cytidine-3'-phosphate; if, however, the cytidine is present in solution at a concentration of 0.1 M, the formation of cytidylyl-cytidine, CpC, is observed. A series of experiments was undertaken in which the relative concentrations of cytidine 2': 3'-phosphate and cytidine were varied, as well as the incubation temperature. With high concentrations of the two substances ($>$ 0.1 M) the RNase catalyzed the formation of at least 4 other compounds, though in small amounts compared to CpC and cytidylic acid.

The products of this reaction were identified paper chromatographically as CpC, CpCp!, CpCpC, CpCpCp! and CpCp.

Of these five compounds, the formation of CpCp!, CpCpCp! and CpCp occurs in the absence of cytidine if a higher concentration than 0.1 M of cytidine 2': 3'-phosphate is used in the presence of a dilute solution of RNase at 2°. These synthetic reactions that have just been described can thus be summarized by the two following equations :

$$\text{Cp!} \xrightarrow{\text{RNase}} + \text{CpCp!} + \text{CpCpCp!} + ... + \text{(CpCp)} \qquad (3)$$

$$\text{Cp!} + \text{C} \xrightarrow{\text{RNase}} \text{Cp} + \text{CpC} + \text{CpCpC} + ... + \text{(CpCp)} \qquad (4)$$

The synthesis of polynucleotides from cyclic mononucleotides does not stop at the trinucleotide stage; paper chromatography of solutions resulting from the incubation of cyclic cytidylic acid and cytidine at high concentration (0.5 M) in the presence of ribonuclease show the presence of compounds that can be considered as polynucleotides containing more than three cytidylic acid residues.

Heppel et al. (1955) examined the possibility of using other acceptors than cytidine, and found that adenosine and adenosine-2':3'-phosphate can also function as acceptors.

$$\text{Cp!} + \text{A} \xrightarrow{\text{RNase}} \text{CpA} \qquad (5)$$

$$\text{Cp!} + \text{Ap!} \xrightarrow{\hspace{1cm}} \text{CpAp.} \qquad (6)$$

Conversely, it was also found that uridine-2': 3'-phosphate could function as donor in analogous reactions, RNase catalyzing the formation of the compound UpC in the presence of cytidine and cyclic uridylic acid.

Bernfield (1965, 1966) showed that not only RNase A, but also RNase S-protein (see p. 200), I-carboxymethyl-histidine-119-RNase, (see p. 193), and ε-dinitrophenylamino-lysine-41-RNase (see p. 196) actively catalyze the synthesis of oligoribonucleotides.

Enzymic parameters of RNase ; *mechanism of enzyme action.*

The kinetics of enzymic hydrolysis of various synthetic substrate by RNase have been the subject of a great deal of work. Studies of this nature are especially satisfying, since they deal with a perfectly defined enzyme, RNase, working on no less well-defined synthetic substrates. These kinetic studies have been made possible by the synthesis of an excellent substrate in large amounts, cytidine-2′: 3′-phosphate (Crook, Mathias and Rabin, 1960). Using solutions of known concentration of enzyme and substrate, and measuring the reaction velocity spectrophotometrically, all the usual parameerts have been determined (Herries, Mathias and Rabin, 1962). Concerning the hydrolysis of cyclic cytidylate, Winstead and Wold (1965), demonstrated that in the presence of high concentrations of salts, the rate of this reaction is enhanced whereas the contrary happens for the hydrolysis of RNA. Studies of the same sort have been carried out using uridine-2′ : 3′-cyclic phosphate as substrate by Witzel et al. (Witzel and Barnard, 1962; Witzel, 1963) and by Cheung and Abrash (1964). The latter have, in particular, determined the kinetic constants for the RNase hydrolysis of Up, in various conditions of temperature and pH. The tabular summary quoted by Cheung and Abrash represents results corresponding to 22 different experimental conditions. It is impossible to quote here all the constants established in this important work, and the reader is referred to the original publications.

The ionization and solubility constants of Cp and Cp! have been determined at an ionic strength of 0.1 M at various temperatures by Bahr et al. (1965), which has enabled the calculation of the appropriate thermodynamic constants for the hydrolytic process :

$$\text{Cytidine-2′: 3′-cyclic phosphate} + H_2O \xrightarrow{\text{RNase}} \text{Cytidine-3′-phosphate}$$

The standard enthalpy for hydrolysis of Cp! to Cp measured at 25° and an ionic strength of 0.1 M was found to be -2.66 $\pm$ 1.5 Kcal/mol taking the electrically neutral species as the standard state.

Systematic study of the hydrolysis of Cp! by RNase has led Rabin and co-workers to some interesting hypotheses about the mechanism of its enzymic action. The results obtained by varying the pH of the system at constant ionic strength at 25° are in agreement with a hypothesis according to which 2 ionizing groups are required by the active center, one of them in the basic form and one in the acid form (Herries, Mathias and Rabin, 1962).

Studies by the same group (Findlay, Mathias and Rabbin, 1962*a*, *b*) have shown that RNase is active in solutions containing high concentrations of organic solvents. Whifteld and Heppel's experiments (see above) had shown that synthetic cytidylic acid esters could be formed from cyclic phosphate in the presence of methanol. Findlay et al. have demonstrated that this "alcoholysis" of the cyclic phosphate may occur in the presence of a large number of alcohols. The initial rates of alcoholysis have been determined for many alcohols, and it has been found that glycerol is the most efficient of all the alcohols examined.

These experiments led to the conclusion that there is a site within the ribonuclease that fixes water or alcohol. Finally the inhibition of RNase by various systems, notably by Zn++ ions (Ross, Mathias and Rabin 1962), an inhibition varying with pH in the range 6-7, suggests that a histidine residue is blocked during this inhibition.

Based on the whole of Rabin and co-workers' studies, the enzyme-substrate complex is represented in figure 44*a*, where (I) is the imidazole group fixing either water or an alcohol, and

(II) is the imidazolium ion, site of the interactions with the oxygen atom at position 2′. Supplementary sites of interactions with the alcohol are at III, and the specific site is at IV, where it seems that interactions are also possible with the pyrimidine N_1 nitrogen. The interaction II weakens the P — O(2′) bond, making the phosphorus atom more sensitive to nucleophilic attack.

Figure 44a, b, c, d. Mechanism of the enzymic action of RNase (Rabin et al. 1962)

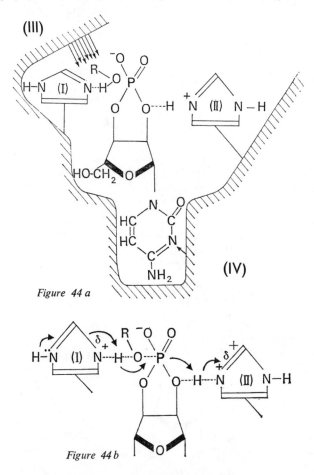

Figure 44 a

Figure 44 b

The transition state is represented in figure 44*b*, where the arrows indicate the directions of electron displacement. Alternatively, this figure can represent the shift of protons and the substituted phosphoryl group in the opposite direction to that shown for the electron displacements.

The enzyme-products reaction complex is illustrated in figure 44*c*, in which the acid-base groups can now be seen in their conjugated form. The opposite reaction proceeds by a complete reversal of the process just described, so that figure 44*c* represents in addition the enzyme-substrate complex for the cyclization reaction of a cytidine-3′-phosphate ester; if this ester is a ribonucleic chain, the enzyme-substrate complex will appear as shown in figure 44*d*.

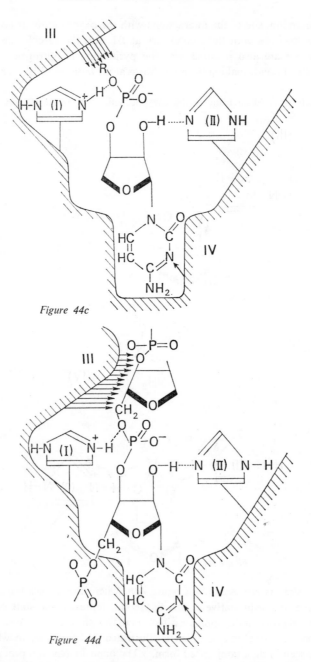

Figure 44c

Figure 44d

This work, completed by recent additions from the same authors (Deavin, Mathias and Rabin, 1966 a, b), is a outstanding example of an hypothesis on the mechanism of enzymic reactions, the function of two of the four histidine groups of RNase having been elucidated. The functioning of the remainder of the molecule, particularly that of the reactive lysine group, is still unclear.

The interactions between nucleotides and RNase are also demonstrated by the experiments of Myer and Schellman (1962) who have found that AMP is linked at two points to RNase, this nucleotide having an inhibiting action.

So far, we have only been considering the enzymic action of dissolved RNase in an aqueous solution of its substrate, which is itself in solution.   Several studies have been made on the enzymic activity of RNase and its derivatives in the form of suspensions, or in the crystalline state.   Doscher and Richards (1963), for instance, have shown that amorphous suspensions of RNase A, and crystalline suspensions of RNase, in an ammonium sulfate-rich medium are catalytically active in the hydrolysis of pyrimidine nucleoside cyclic-2′: 3′-phosphates.   The activity observed cannot be due to the enzyme in solution, nor to the enzyme existing on the surface of the molecular layer, so the enzymic activity must be due to enzyme molecules inside the crystal.   These molecules could have a catalytic activity without causing a break-up of the crystal lattice.   The kinetic constants are probably similar but not identical to those found for the enzyme in non-crystalline form.

Similar studies have been made by Bello and Nowoswiat (1965) on crystalline suspensions of RNase in a non-aqueous solvent, 2-methyl-2,4-pentanediol.   The activity of the enzyme per molecule on a synthetic substrate (which was cytidine-2′: 3′-cyclic phosphate) is between 1 and 10 times that of a molecule of RNase in aqueous solution dissolved in the medium.

E. Unusual forms of bovine pancreatic ribonuclease

RNase B, reported some time ago as a minor constituent of bovine pancreatic RNase was characterized by Plummer and Hirs (1963, 1964) as a glucoprotein related to RNase A, and like it, present in pancreatic juice.

RNase B has been mainly isolated from bovine pancreatic juice by chromatography on IRC-50 (figures 45, 46).

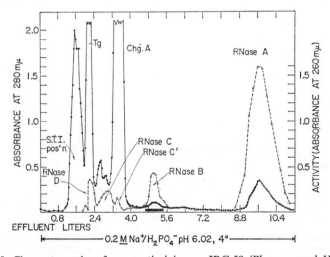

Figure 45. Chromatography of pancreatic juice on IRC-50 (Plummer and Hirs, 1963)

   The enzyme isolated in this way is homogenous by chromatography on carboxymethyl cellulose at pH 8, as well as by electrophoresis on polyacrylamide gel.   RNase B has the same activity as RNase A both on cyclic cytidylate and on yeast RNA.

   The overall aminoacid composition is identical to that of RNase A.   The molecular weight is 14,700 $\pm$ 300.   The difference with RNase A resides in the presence of five mannose residues and two glucosamine residues attached to each mole of protein.

   In fact RNase B has the same aminoacid structure as RNase A, the oligosaccharide fraction being fixed to the asparagine residue in position 34.   It is likely that this asparagine residue is situated near to the "surface" of the molecule, so that attachment of an oligosaccharide fragment at this point ought not to disturb the tertiary structure of the enzyme.   The relatively high molecular weight of the oligosaccharide part (1350) does not affect the activity of RNase B on yeast RNA (Plummer and Hirs, 1964).

   Figure 45 shows the cationic protein fraction of pancreatic juice, containing, besides RNase A and B, two other fractions in still smaller proportions, provisionally named RNase C and C', not yet having been the subject of much special attention.

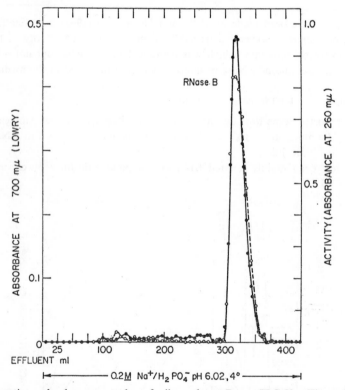

Figure 46. Preparative-scale chromatography of ribonuclease B on IRC-50.   The column measured 1.9 x 68 cm and was equilibrated with 0.2 M sodium phosphate buffer at pH 6.02 at 4°.   Approximately 25 mg of protein were chromatographed at a low rate of 3.2 cm per hour and the effluent was collected in 2 — 5 ml fractions.   Protein concentration (solid circles) was determined by the procedure of Lowry et al. (1951), and ribonuclease activity (open circles) was determined against yeast RNA as substrate (Plummer and Hirs, 1963)

By counter-current distribution of crystalline preparations of bovine pancreatic RNase A, Eaker, King and Craig (1965 *a*, *b*, *c*,) were able to isolate two new forms of RNase A which were subsequently proven to be respectively des-glutamyl- and des-lysylpyroglutamyl ribonucleases. The structure of these compounds was established both by aminoacid analyses and comparison of the tryptic peptides obtained from oxidized derivatives of RNase A and the two des-lysyl RNases. It appears that the des-lysyl-glutamyl enzyme is slightly less active and slightly more sensitive to trypsin digestion than RNase A, whereas the des-lysyl-pyroglutaminyl enzyme is considerably less active and more susceptible to digestion.

The preparation, properties and structures of two active forms of RNase dimer were discussed by Fruchter and Crestfield (1965 *a*, *b*). These authors showed that RNase A can be converted into active dimers with a yield of 50 % by lyophilizing the purified enzyme from 50 % acetic acid. The dimer fraction thus obtained can be separated into two components by chromatography on sulfoethyl-Sephadex in 0.115 M phosphate buffer. Both dimers are metastable and yield only RNase A when heated at 65° for 10 minutes.

F. BIOSYNTHESIS OF PANCREATIC RIBONUCLEASE

In the work carried out on the synthesis of specific proteins by living organisms, that of Morris and Dickman (1960) on the biosynthesis of ribonuclease in mouse pancreas should be mentioned. They followed the incorporation of L-valine-^{14}C into pancreatic RNase in the mouse under conditions leading to rapid synthesis of the protein, namely 18 hours after a pilocarpine injection.

The study of labeled pancreas cell fractions after injection of L-valine-^{14}C under optimal conditions for RNase synthesis shows that the greater part of the radioactivity incorporated into the pancreas during the first ten minutes is present in the microsome part of the cell, the radioactivity in this fraction being appreciable five minutes after injection of the labeled compound. The amount of valine-^{14}C present in the ribonuclease of various cell fractions after different time intervals was determined after chromatography of extracts from these fractions on Amberlite XE-64 following a purification method for RNase described by Hirs et al. (1953).

It can thus be seen that the rate of valine incorporation into the microsomes and into microsomal RNase is exceedingly rapid : Morris and Dickman reckon that about three minutes are necessary for the synthesis of the enzyme. Although Morris and Dickmann's observations were made on mouse RNase, it seems reasonable to extrapolate them to other animal species.

II. RNASE DISTRIBUTION IN ANIMAL AND PLANT TISSUES

Ribonucleases are widely distributed in both the animal and vegetal kingdoms, as Heppel and Rabinowitz (1958) have pointed out. They can be shown up histochemically on tissue sections by means of a technique of Sierakowska and Shugar (1960, p. 187). All the methods for estimating RNase which were described on p. 187 are applicable to the various RNases, on condition that they are adapted to the optimum pH of the particular enzyme under consideration.

The fact that these RNases have different specificities so far as their mode of attack on the ribonucleic structure is concerned, has caused them to be used for the determination of nucleotide sequences. One of the most remarkable examples of this kind of application was the determination of the complete sequence of consecutive nucleotides in yeast alanyl-t-RNA by Holley and his co-workers (1965, p. 302).

The search for enzymes having varied specificities that are usable for the investigation of nucleic acid structure has given rise to a great deal of work, the principal details of which will be summarized in the next pages.

A. ANIMAL RIBONUCLEASES

1. Human ribonucleases

One of the most studied nucleases from a human source was the one characterized from urine by Delaney (1960).

This RNase was purified by chromatography on Amberlite IRC-50 in a system including 0.2 M phosphate buffer and 0.12 M acetate buffer, the overall pH being 5.8. In this way, 20 mg protein were obtained from 3,000 liters urine, the final product being electrophoretically homogenous. Structural studies carried out on human urine RNase show that the peptide chain contains one less amide group and one more glutamic acid than bovine pancreatic RNase A. The N-terminal group is lysine as in RNaseA.

Later, the same authors (Delaney, 1963) obtained three highly purified RNases from human sources: RNases P and U were both isolated from urine by chromatography on an Amberlite IRC-50 column at pH 5.8, and an RNase was isolated from human spleen.

RNase P is precipitated by bovine pancreatic RNase (RNase A) antisera, and possesses properties that are closely related to those of RNase A, notably a similar molecular weight and aminoacid constitution (table XXVII). One important difference is in the number of amide groups.

Human urine RNase U exhibits different properties from RNase A and P; it is, in particular, not precipitated by RNase A antisera and its physicochemical properties are different (table XXIV). Chromatographically, human spleen RNase (RNase Sp) behaves similarly to RNase U on a phosphorylated cellulose column; it differs only slightly from RNase U in its molecular weight and aminoacid composition.

Two RNases have been isolated from human pancreas extracts by ion exchange chromatography (Ukita et al., 1964). One of these RNases, RNase HP.b was purified 500 times and exhibited properties comparable to those of beef pancreas RNase : optimum pH for activity 7.6, inhibition by Hg^{++}, Cu^{++} and Zn^{++} ions, specificity of action on RNA. The isoelectric point of this RNase, however, is higher than that of RNase A (pH 10.3). The second RNase, RNase HP.a, which has more acid properties than RNase HP.b, was only purified 46 times. Its pH for optimum activity is the same (7.6) as that of the first RNase. The ions Hg^{++}, Zn^{++} and Cu^{++} inhibit the activity to a comparable extent.

2. Ribonucleases of bovine origin

Besides the well-known beef pancreas ribonucleases, many other RNases have been characterized from the various tissues of this species, notably :

Table XXVII. The Amino Acid Composition of some Ribonucleases * (Delaney, 1963)

| | Amino Acid Residues | | | | Residues | | | |
| | 100 g Protein | | | | mole Protein | | | |
	A	P	U	Sp	A	P	U	Sp
Aspartic acid	13.0	13.0	16.4	15.1	15.4	15.4	26.1	24.1
Threonine	7.8	7.6	7.3	6.7	10.6	10.3	13.2	12.1
Serine	9.5	9.7	3.3	4.1	14.9	15.3	7.0	8.6
Glutamic acid	11.4	11.7	13.1	12.4	12.0	12.4	18,6	17.5
Proline	3.0	3.2	7.9	7.8	4.2	4.5	14.9	14.7
Glycine	1.3	1.3	1.2	1.7	3.2	3.1	3.7	5.5
Alamine	6.4	6.2	2.9	3.0	12.3	11.8	7.5	7.8
1/2 Cystine	5.3	5.6	4.6	4.6	7.1	7.5	8.3	8.3
Valine	6.2	6.3	5.7	5.4	8.6	8.7	10.6	10.0
Methionine	4.0	3.6	3.2	2.9	4.1	3.7	4.4	4.0
Isoleucine	2.6	2.8	4.9	5.0	3.1	3.0	8.0	8.1
Leucine	1.7	1.8	3.7	4.1	2.1	2.1	6.0	6.7
Tyrosine	6.8	7.0	4.8	4.2	5.7	5.8	4.8	5.4
Phenylalanine	3.0	3.3	4.8	4.8	2.8	3.0	5.9	6.0
Lysine	9.8	9.0	3.6	4.5	10.5	9.6	5.1	6.4
Histidine	3.8	3.9	4.5	4.4	3.8	3.9	6.0	6.0
Arginine	4.8	4.5	7.8	7.6	4.2	3.9	9.2	8.9
Tryptophan			1.0	1.0			1.0	1.0
Amide					18.1	14.4	32.9	(49.8)
Actual weight recovery	93	92	93	69				
Actual N recovery	96	100	96	92				

* The abbreviations used and molecular weights for each ribonuclease are as follows : A, bovine pancreatic ribo-nuclease A, and P, ribonuclease P, 13,680 ; U, ribonuclease U, and Sp, spleen ribonuclease, 18,320.

1) *Calf spleen ribonuclease.* Kaplan and Heppel (1956) prepared a RNase from calf spleen which strongly resembled pancreatic RNase; RNA is not completely hydrolyzed by it, and only pyrimidine nucleotides are formed. This enzyme has its optimum pH at 6.0 — 6.5, and is activated by Mg^{++} ions.

Maver et al. (1959) reported the presence of several RNases in calf spleen, a fact which is obvious when spleen "nuclease"* is chromatographed on DEAE-cellulose. The activities of these enzymes are characterized by their optimum pH, by the products liberated during their action on cyclic nucleotides and by their activity after heating. In the course of these systematic chromatograms on DEAE-cellulose, Maver et al. characterized the RNase described by Kaplan and Heppel as an alkaline RNase, which in its optimum activity pH, its stability to heat and its activity with Mg^{++} ions appeared to resemble liver RNase. Finally, several acid RNases having similar characteristics have been isolated and their chromatographic validity established by carrying out a second chromatogram on two of the fractions.

*A crude preparation having both RNase and DNase activities and called "spleen nuclease" (Maver and Greco 1956) served as the starting point in the experiments Maver et al. carried out on spleen RNases.

2) *Calf liver ribonuclease.* Liver contains an acid and an alkaline RNase (Reid and Nodes, 1959). According to observations by Lamirande et al. (1954) and by Roth (1954, 1957), these two RNases appear to be present in the mitochondria, the alkaline RNase also occurring in the supernatant fractions, but associated with an inhibitor. It could not be implied from these studies, however, that the RNases were a part of the mitochondria. The more detailed work of de Duve et al. (1955) has drawn attention to the fact that the acid RNases, as well as several other hydrolases, are not attached to the mitochondria but to the granules containing the acid phosphatases ("lysosomes"). In any case, Reid and Nodes showed that alkaline liver RNase acts on RNA to give cyclic pyrimidine nucleotides that are not attacked more extensively. Acid RNase furnishes cyclic nucleotides, both of the purine and pyrimidine series. Cyclic adenylic acid is hydrolyzed to 2′-adenylic acid, cyclic cytidylic acid being attacked, probably by a different enzyme, to yield 3′-cytidylic acid.

3) *Other ribonucleases of bovine origin.* An "acid" RNase has been reported in calf thymus by Bernardi (1961); it was purified chromatographically. The work carried out by D'Alessio (1963) also led to the characterization of a ribonuclease from bull seminal plasma. This enzyme has its optimum activity at pH 8.0, and exhibits high resistance to heat, it being necessary to heat it for 5 minutes at 100° for it to lose 97.5 % of its activity. This enzyme is fairly strongly inhibited by Zn^{++} ions, and also by Fe^{++} ions.

Other RNases of bovine origin were also reported to be present in bovine adrenal medulla (Smith and Winkler 1965), bovine thyroid gland (Dierick and Stockx 1965), bovine milk (Ibuki et al. 1965, Bingham and Kalan, 1966) etc... The properties of all these enzymes are sumarized in the final tables.

3. Ribonuclease from pigs

The purification and properties of an "alkaline ribonuclease II" from mitochondrial and soluble fractions of pig liver have been described by Beard and Razzel (1964). Pig liver homogenates in 0.25 M sucrose can be separated by centrifugation into a "soluble fraction" and a "mitochondrial fraction". More extensive purification of these two fractions by the same technique leads apparently to the same enzyme. This purification consists essentially of :
1) treatment with acid
2) treatment with papaïne
3) fractionation with ammonium sulfate
4) chromatography on carboxymethyl-Sephadex.

The specific activity of the enzyme rises from 2.8 units/mg in the soluble starting fraction to 6,700 units/mg in the "concentrated CM-Sephadex peak", i.e. an enrichment of over 3,000 times. The enzyme purified in this way is free from RNase I, acid RNase II, phosphodiesterases I and II and non-specific 2′: 3′-cyclic phosphodiesterase. The anti-RNase A antiserum does not inhibit this pig liver RNase.

This RNase has the following properties : its optimum pH is over a fairly wide range stretching from 6.7 to 8.5, and there is faster hydrolysis of RNA than of polyU and polyC, and there is no activity with polyA.

4. Rabbit reticulocyte RNase, or RR-RNase

This enzyme was described by Adachi et al. (1964), and isolated from rabbit reticulocytes by treatment at pH 2.5 followed by chromatography on CM-cellulose. In order to prepare a large quantity of reticulocytes, reticulocytosis was induced in rabbits by subcutaneous injection of phenylhydrazine. The reticulocytes are then collected by centrifugation at 3,000 r.p.m. for 30 minutes and washed three times with 0.9 % NaCl. Purification follows essentially the stages listed in table XXVIII, an approximately 5,000-fold enrichment being obtained.

Table XXVIII. Purification of rabbit reticulocyte RNase (Adachi et al., 1964)

Purification steps	Total RNase (units)	Total protein (mg)	RNase (S.A.) units/mg protein	Yield (%activity)	Purification factor
I : Solubilization	1088	3360	0.32	100	× 1
II : Acid and heat treatment	837	221	3.9	77	× 12
III : Chromatography on CM-cellulose	825	9.9	84	76	× 226
IV : Rechromatography on CM-cellulose	810	0.83	976	74	× 3030
(at peak)	(140)	(0.091)	(1540)	—	× 4880

The enzyme thus obtained is free from alkaline phosphatase, from phosphodiesterase and from DNase; its optimum activity occurs at pH 5.8. Reagents containing hydrosulfide groups are without action on it.

After exhaustive action of the enzyme on RNA, purine and pyrimidine nucleotides terminated by 2'-phosphate and 3'-phosphate groups are to be found in the hydrolysate.

Although rabbit reticulocytes are rich in RNase, the ribosomes extracted from these same reticulocytes are, on the other hand, practically without RNase activity under conditions where such activity in rabbit liver ribosomes can be demonstrated (Stavy et al., 1964).

Yet under certain conditions, these ribosomes may undergo self decomposition (Rosenthal et al. 1964). The latter authors demonstrated that optimal conditions for rabbit reticulocyte ribosomes self destruction were at pH 7.5 and 60-65°. This RNase activity appears to be pH dependent and shows a peak at pH 5.0 and a broad shoulder at pH 6.0-7.5, suggesting the existence of a second RNase.

5. Rat tissues ribonucleases.

Rat tissue ribonucleases have been the subject of a great deal of investigation. For instance, Beintema and Gruber (1965), isolated a RNase from the pancreas by a method similar to the method described by Kunitz for bovine pancreatic RNase (p. 183). Although the molecular weight of rat pancreatic RNase is comparable to that of RNase A, the aminoacid overall composition and sequence are very different.

Rat liver contains several RNases (Gordon 1965 *a*, *b*; 1966; Rahman 1966), whereas subcellular fractions of rat adrenals contain both RNase and inhibitor activities (Girija and Sreenivasan 1966).

RNases have been systematically sought in the adipose tissue of rat epididymal fat bodies

(Eichel et al., 1961) and two enzymes have been characterized : one is effective in the pH range 6.2 — 6.3, and the other in the range from 7.5 — 8.2.

6. Ribonuclease from *Vipera russelii* venom

An endonuclease accompanying the well-known phosphodiesterase was discovered by Mc-Lennan and Lane (1965) in the venom of *Vipera russelii*. This enzyme has properties comparable to those of RNase A, notably that it produces oligonucleotides of the general structure (Pu p)$_n$ Py p! (n = 1, 2, ... etc.), but does not produce mononucleotides.

7. Fish ribonucleases

Tomlinson (1958) reported the existence of RNase in the muscular tissue of many fish. Taking as an example the RNase extracted from the muscle of the cultus or ling-cod (*Ophidion elongatus*), the purification of the enzyme was carried out essentially by the following steps : preparation of an extract of muscle tissue and precipitation with 80 % saturated ammonium sulfate. The material precipitated by the 80 % saturated ammonium sulfate includes the greater part of the RNase activity. The proteins are redissolved in water and dialyzed, after which the contents of the dialysis bag are adjusted to pH 6.8 and centrifuged for 15 minutes at 25,000 g. The precipitate is discarded and the solution concentrated to a small volume by lyophilization. The concentrated extract is adjusted to pH 4.5 and the solution kept 1 hour at 25°. The precipitated proteins are removed by centrifugation, the pH of the solution being then brought to 9.0 and the solution maintained for 10 minutes at 58°. The precipitate is removed and the pH adjusted to 6.8. The extracts thus obtained can be preserved for several months at —20° without appreciable loss of activity.

This enzyme acts on yeast RNA and on fish RNA to give mononucleotides. It is inhibited by heat, acids and Zn^{++} and Cu^{++} ions, monoiodoacetate, formaldehyde and NaF. The optimum pH is 6.5.

The fact that the four RNA 3′-mononucleotides are liberated from RNA by *Ophidion* RNase indicates a different mode of action from that observed with RNase A, and would appear to eliminate from consideration any specificity concerning the sequence of purine and pyrimidine bases. Enzymes capable of hydrolyzing RNA as well as bis-(*p*-nitrophenyl)-phosphate, i.e. mixtures of RNase and phosphodiesterases, have been identified by Tomlinson in the muscle tissue of many fish, including spring salmon (*Onchorynchus tshawytscha*), lemon sole (*Paophys vetulus*), dogfish (*Squalus suckleyi*), herring (*Clupea pallasii*), etc...

B. PLANT RIBONUCLEASES

1. Soya germ ribonuclease

This enzyme was purified mainly by ammonium sulfate fractionation, and the specific activity rose from 26 to 1,300, a 50-fold enrichment with respect to the crude starting extract. The optimal activity is reached at pH 5.2 and the products obtained are 3′-phosphates.

Among the nucleotides remaining after enzyme action, 2′: 3′-cyclic purine and pyrimidine nucleotides have been found, together with 3′-mononucleotides. Adenosine 2′: 3′-cyclic phosphate is cleaved to the stage of the corresponding nucleotide 3′-phosphate, but cyclic pyrimidine nucleotides are resistant to the action of the enzyme (Merola and Davis, 1962).

2. Ribonuclease from maize seed (Zea mays). Comparison with RNases from other seeds

Two RNases have been isolated from the seeds of Z. mays by chromatography on CM-cellulose (Wilson, 1963a, b); one is RNase A with an optimum pH of 5.0, the other, RNase B with an optimum pH of 6.2.

Both RNases are stimulated at their optimum pH by KCl. RNase A is stimulated by $MgCl_2$ at pH 5.0 and inhibited at pH 5.8, while RNase B is stimulated at pH 5.8.

RNase A liberates oligonucleotides and 2′:3′-cyclic nucleotides, the amounts of which increase with time. RNase A is a polynucleotide 2-oligonucleotidotransferase (cyclizing) (E.C. 2.7.7.16). This enzyme, which resembles mung bean RNase, can be readily purified from commercial corn meal (Ingle, 1963). RNase B, on the other hand, is a nuclease that liberates 5′-nucleotides from RNA and DNA. It resembles the enzyme described as "mung-bean nuclease" by Sung and Laskowski (1962, p. 169).

Wilson's observations concerning Zea mays RNase agree with those of Ingle (1963); he thus agrees that an RNase can be extracted from corn meal. The enzyme is mainly characterized by a pH for optimum activity of 5.2.

Wilson and Shannon (1963) have systematically examined the comparative distribution of RNase in the seeds of various vegetables such as maize (Zea mays L.), cucumber (Cucurbis sativus L.) and soy bean (Glycine max. L. Merr.) and have given a list of results (table XXIX).

Table XXIX. Extraction of protein and RNase from plant tissue (Wilson and Shannon, 1963)

	Isolation Medium		Protein (mg/ml)			RNase (units/ml)		
Symbol	Composition	Corn	Cucumber	Soybeans	Corn	Cucumber	Soybeans
S	0.5 M sucrose	1.15	1.00	1.34	44	16.4	7.6
ST	0.5 M sucrose + 0.025 M tris-HCl (pH 7.5)	1.21	0.99	1.41	48	15.4	7.4
STK	0.5 M sucrose + 0.025 M tris-HCl (pH 7.5) + 0.5 M KCl	1.40	0.95	1.28	54	16.4	6.6
TK	0.025 M tris-HCl (pH 7.5) + 0.5 M KCl	1.21	0.89	1.43	47	23	7.9
SPE	0.5 M sucrose + 0.067 M potassium phosphate (pH 7.0) + 0.005 M EDTA	1.28	1.02	1.43	35	48	6.6
SE	0.5 M sucrose + 0.1 M EDTA (pH 7.3)	1.25	0.96	1.31	38	48	7.8

3. Phaseolus ribonuclease

Several fractions having a ribonuclease activity were characterized by Stockx and Vandend-riessche (1961) and Stockx et al. (1964) in the plant Phaseolus aureus Roxb. The extraction of these enzymes was effected by acid treatment of the plant, ammonium sulfate precipitation, adsorption on tricalcium phosphate gel and differential elution with phosphate buffer, then selective heat denaturation and finally chromatography on Amberlite XE-64. In this way the interfering enzymes are removed.

The three fractions isolated from *P. aureus* exhibit generally similar characteristics that give the impression that they are all derived from a single form of the enzyme. Their optimal ranges of activity are situated very close to one another (5.0; 5.2 and 5.6), while the optimum temperature for activity is at 45°.

4. Barley ribonuclease

The properties of barley RNase have been studied by Fiers and Vandendriessche (1961). The preparation could be completely freed from non-specific phosphodiesterase and from a great deal of the phosphomonoesterase by chromatography on hydroxyapatit. Barley RNase is a relatively thermostable enzyme, having its optimum activity at pH 6.1 (Fiers and Vandendriessche, 1961; Fiers, 1962).

5. Ribonuclease from *Nepenthes*

An interesting case is provided by the experiments of Matthews (1960), who studied the RNase activity found in the secretion of the "pitchers" of the carnivorous plants of the *Nepenthes* species. After several hours' incubation at pH 5 and 37°, this secretion degrades tobacco mosaic virus RNA almost quantitatively to the stage of the four 2′: 3′-cyclic phosphates.

6. Ribonuclease from germinating garlic

Various nucleases have been characterized from this material using methods of fractionation such as gel chromatography and electrophoresis.

The most highly purified enzyme is a ribonuclease having optimal activity at pH 7, a molecular weight of the order of 20,000, a sedimentation coefficient of 2.4 S, and similar properties to those of pancreatic RNase.

7. RNase activity of the basidiomycete *Agaricus campestris*

Extracts of the field mushroom *Agaricus campestris* possess both phosphodiesterase and RNase activity (Cuigniez et al., 1965). The ribonuclease-type activity could be purified by filtration on Sephadex G-25 gel and by chromatography on DEAE-Sephadex A-50. In the course of this purification Cuigniez et al. have been able to show the presence of two RNases of different properties, a first fraction with an optimum pH of 7.1 and a second fraction with an optimum pH of 4.6. Hydrolysis of RNA by one or the other of these RNases leads to formation of the four ribonucleoside-3′-phosphates through the intermediate corresponding cyclic nucleotides.

C. MICROBIAL RIBONUCLEASES

1. The T_1 and T_2 ribonucleases extracted from "Takadiastase" (*Aspergillus oryzae*)

The Japanese enzyme preparation called "Takadiastase" contains, amongst other enzymes, two ribonucleases, RNase T_1 and RNase T_2. The first of these ribonucleases, RNase T_1, has been defined by the International Enzyme Commission as a "Ribonucleate 3′-guanidohydrolase" (specific for the hydrolysis of Gp X bonds) and given the reference number E.C.3.1.4.7. In view of its well-defined specificity and possible applications to the structural investigations of ribonucleic acids, RNase T_1 has been the subject of a considerable amount of work, mainly by Sato, Egami et al. (1957-1964), Rushiszky, Sober et al. (1962a, b, 1963); Kasai (1963), Whitfeld and Witzel (1964); Staehelin (1964). The most remarkable applications of RNase T_1 have been the recent studies of Holley et al. (1965) on the structure of alanyl-t-RNA (p. 302). The comparitive properties of RNase T_1 and RNase T_2 have been reviewed by Egami et al. (1964).

a. *Ribonuclease T_1*

At first, RNase T_1 was purified by a four-step method involving acid treatment, acetone fractionation and chromatography on DEAE-cellulose; an approximately 400-fold purification with a 33 % yield could be obtained (Rushiszky and Sober, 1962a). Chung and Mandeles (1964) have described a more extensive method of purification of RNase T_1 that enables the high cellulase activity still found in purified preparations of RNase T_1 to be eliminated. The new and efficient method proposed for the RNase T_1 purification is as follows. The crude RNase T_1 solution first follows two cycles of phenol extraction and precipitation with acetone followed by passage of the extract through a 4 × 50 cm column of CM-Sephadex G-25 (coarse) at pH 4.0. This treatment results in the elimination of all detectable cellulase activity, and yields an enzymatic preparation ready for fractionation with ammonium sulfate or chromatography on DEAE-cellulose (table XXX).

Table XXX. Purification of T_1 ribonuclease (Chung and Mandeles, 1964)

Stage	Protein content (g)	Total activity*	Specific activity**	Recovery (%)
Water extract	45.6	1390	0.030	100
Sulfuric acid precipitation	28.8	1120	0.039	81
Ammonia neutralization	20.7	940	0.045	67
Phenol extraction, acetone precipitation, twice	10.5	810	0.077	58
CM-Sephadex	2.38	770	0.32	51
DEAE-cellulose-1	0.163	590	3.6	42
DEAE-cellulose-2	0.043	510	11.9	37
DEAE-cellulose-3	0.016	400	25.0	29

* Microequivalents alkali consumed per min. at 30°.
** Total activity per protein content. Protein content measured by method of Lowry et al., (1951).

Chung and Mandeles have also described a titrimetric method for the determination of RNase T_1.

Egami et al. (1964) have also described a method for the purification of RNase T_1 in seven steps, allowing 100-200 mg enzyme to be obtained from 1 kg Takadiastase.

RNase T_1 has a molecular weight of 11,000 (Kasai, 1963; Egami et al., 1964) and an optimum pH of 7.5. It is inhibited by Cu^{++} and Zn^{++} ions (as is RNase T_2). Dissolved in 8 M urea and reduced with mercaptoethanol, RNase T_1 loses some of its activity with the appearance of free

-SH groups.   Reduced RNase T_1 can be precipitated by cold acetone and separated from the urea and mercaptoethanol, when it can be readily redissolved in a buffer above pH 6.   When it is reoxidized by air in an appropriate tris or phosphate buffer of pH 7.7 — 8.7, the enzymic activity reappears.   This reaction is completely inhibited by p-chloromercuribenzoate and by mercaptoethanol.   The principal physical and chemical properties of RNase T_1 are listed in tables XXXI and XXXII, compared with those of RNase T_2 and pancreatic RNase (RNase I A).

Takahashi (1965) has recently determined the total aminoacid sequence of RNase T_1 (figure 47).

The RNase T_1 specificity has been studied by the conventional method, i.e. by examination of the oligonucleotides (and the internucleotide bonds) remaining unattacked after exhaustive action of the enzyme on RNA.   The oligonucleotides that resist the action of the enzyme were isolated by preparative paper chromatography, and all were analysed.   Only di- and tri- nucleotides of the XpGp or XpYpGp type were found, in other words the Xp-Gp bond appears to be resistant to the action of RNase T_1 (Rushiszky and Sober, 1962b).   Later, more detail was given about RNase T_1 specificity, particularly by Staehelin (1964), who showed that the phosphodiester bond of 2-methylguanylic acid is instantaneously attacked by the enzyme but that the 1-methylguanylic bond is not attached.   Linkages involving 2-methylguanylic |acid are immediately cleaved, but the terminal cyclic group is not converted to an open-chain 3′-group.

Table XXXI. Physical and Chemical Properties of RNase T_1 T_2, and A (Egami et al., 1964)

Properties	*RNase T_1*	*RNase T_2*	*RNase A*
Sedimentation diffusion	11,000	—	—
Sedimentation equilibrium	—	36,200	14,000
Amino acid analysis	14,127	36,700	13,683
s_{20}, w	1.62S	3.36S	1.85S (s_{25})
D_{20}, w	12.0 M 10^{-7} cm^2 sec^{-1}	—	13.6 M 10^{-7} cm^2 sec^{-1} (D_{25})
f/f_0	1.21	—	—
Electrophoretic mobility	-2.82×10^{-4} cm^2 volt^{-1} sec^{-1} (pH 7.0)	—	—
($\mu = 0.1$)	$-0.71_3 \times 10^{-4}$ cm^2 volt^{-1} sec^{-1} (pH 4.0)	—	—
	$+0.25_1 \times 10^{-4}$ cm^2 volt^{-1} sec^{-1} (pH 2.5)	—	—
Isoelectric point	pH 2.9	ca. 6	7.8
Absorption maximum	277-278 mμ	281 mμ	277.5 mμ
Absorption minimum	251-252 mμ	252 mμ	—
E_{max}/E_{min}	3.0_1	2.5_2	—
$E_{max\ 1\ cm.}^{0.1\%}$	1.9_1	1.9_9	0.71_6
$[\alpha]_D^{20}$	-15.7°	—	-71.7°
Nitrogen content	16.5 %	—	16.5 %
Amino terminal	Alanine	Glutamic acid (or glutamine)	Lysine
Carboxyl terminal	Threonine	—	Valine

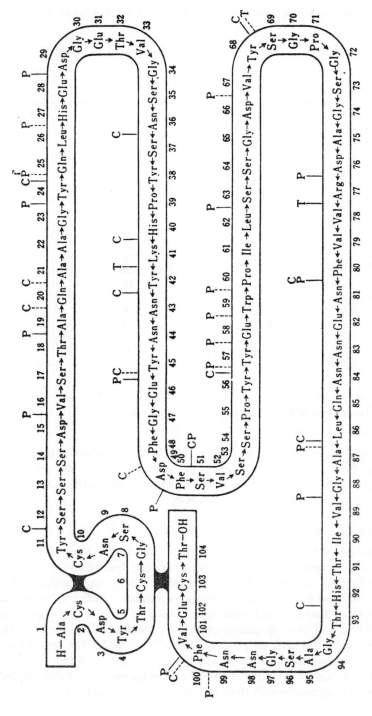

Figure 47. The amino acid sequence of ribonuclease T₁. The points of hydrolysis by trypsin and chymotrypsin in the performic acid-oxidized protein and by pepsin in the heat-denatured protein are marked by *T*, *C*, and *P*, respectively. The *solid lines* represent extensive or rapid hydrolyses, and the *dashed lines*, incomplete or slower hydrolyses (Takahashi 1965)

Table XXXII. Amino Acid Composition of RNases T_1 T_2, and A (Egami et al., 1964)

Amino acid	Number of residues per molecule		
	RNase T_1	RNase T_2-A*	RNase I-A
Asp	15	39	15
Thr	6	25	10
Ser	17	32	15
Glu	10	39	12
Pro	4	23	4
Gly	12	28	3
Ala	7	19	12
Cys	4	11	8
Val	7	7	9
Met	0	1	4
Ileu	2	19	3
Leu	3	18	2
Tyr	8	14	6
Phe	4	10	3
Lys	1	23	10
His	3	6	4
Arg	1	4	4
Try	1	7	0
(Amide NH_2)	(11)	(63)	(17)
Total	105	325	124

* The aminoacid composition of RNase T_2-A was calculated by assuming the presence of one residue of methionine per molecule.

Whitfeld and Witzel have examined the relative hydrolysis velocities of various substrates by RNase T_1. Even for bonds of the GpX type, which theoretically are preferentially broken by RNase T_1, there are notable differences in the hydrolysis rates (table XXXIII); for example, GpCp is hydrolyzed four times as quickly as GpUp.

b. *Ribonuclease T_2; comparison between RNases T_1 and T_2*

This RNase can be prepared like RNase T_1 from "Takadiastase Powder" (Sankyo Ccmpany, Tokyo). Purification methods for this enzyme have been described by Rushiszky and Sober (1963) and by Egami et al. (1964). The highly purified enzymic preparations obtained by these authors were considered sufficiently homogeneous for structural studies to be undertaken (tables XXXI and XXXII). Rushiszky and Sober claim that RNase T_2 purified by two chromatographies on DEAE-cellulose and two chromatographies on CM-cellulose was enriched 770-fold with respect to the starting Takadiastase powder, and in 29 % yield. The material obtained was homogeneous on ultracentrifugation, and had a molecular weight of 30,500.

The results obtained by Rushiszky and Sober concerning the physical and chemical properties of this RNase are in agreement with those of Egami et al. (table XXXI).

The specificity of RNase T$_2$, initially believed to be for Ap | Xp bonds, does not appear to be as strict as was thought, and there seems merely to be a "preference" for Ap | Xp bonds.

Table XXXIII. Relative rates of splitting of different substrates by ribonuclease T$_1$ (Whitfeld and Witzel 1963)

Compound	Relative rate
GpCp	1100
GpC	800
GpA	550
GpG	450
GpU	250
IpC	150
XpC	10
Glyoxal-GpC	5
G-cyclic-P	2

2. Extracellular ribonuclease from *Bacillus subtilis*

The preparation of this enzyme in crystalline form and the description of its principal properties are the work of Nishimura et al. (Nishimura, 1960; Nishimura and Ozawa, 1962). According to these workers, *B. subtilis* RNase bears a formal analogy with RNase A in that it possesses analogous chromatographic behavior, an optimum activity at pH 7.5 and a sedimentation constant of 1.4 S. As we shall see, however, its specificity is different.

Rushiszky et al. (1963) have demonstrated that the RNase of *B. subtilis* can also be purified to a very high degree by a series of chromatographies on DEAE and CM-cellulose. Starting from a bacterial medium, a final yield of 11 % is obtained, the enzymic activity rising from 106 units in the starting medium to 446,000 in the richest fractions — an approximately 4,200-fold enrichment.

The enzyme obtained in this way appears homogenous by the following criteria : molecular weight determined by ultracentrifugation, electrophoresis on polyacrylamide gel and chromatography on Sephadex G-75. The molecular weight reported by Hartley et al. (1963), is 10,700 ± 400, and the sedimentation cœfficient is 1.5 S. Comparative experiments carried out on RNase A gave a cœfficient of 1.9 S. Nishimura and Ozawa (1962) observed that the aminoacid composition of *B. subtilis* RNase was clearly different from that of RNase A; in particular, cystine is absent, and in addition, preliminary proteolytic hydrolysis experiments showed that the fragments obtained from *B. subtilis* RNase were all different from those given by pancreatic RNase. Photooxidation in the presence of methylene blue results in inactivation as well as damage to the histidine groups, which therefore seem to play an important part in the enzymic activity.

The experiments of Hartley et al. (1963) have also shown that methionine and cystine are absent in *B. subtilis* RNase.

According to Nishimura, the specificity of this enzyme can be defined as "hydrolysis of purine-riboside-3'-phosphate phosphoric esters", and he has also noted that 3'-guanylic acid is liberated from the corresponding 2': 3'-cyclic compound.

Rushiszky et al. (1963) report that this enzyme hydrolyzes -Gp | Gp- and -Gp | Ap- about

100 times quicker than other phosphate bonds, but this specificity is not complete, since only mono- and dinucleotides are found after hydrolysis of macromolecular RNA.

According to Whitfeld and Witzel (1963), *B. subtilis* RNase hydrolyzes ribonucleic polymers in the following order of decreasing rate :

$$\text{polyI} > \text{polyA} > \text{polyU} > \text{polyC,}$$

polyC being almost resistent to hydrolysis.

Hydrolysis of the polynucleotide gives mainly di- and trinucleotides terminated by a cyclic nucleotide. Final arrival at the cyclic mononucleotide is a slow process. As an example of a hydrolytic process, these authors indicated the following scheme for hydrolysis :

```
                fast
Poly A  ─────────────→  ApApAp! + ApAp! + Ap!
                        ↓ slow       │ very slow
                        ApAp! + Ap!↓
                        very ─────→  2 Ap.
                        slow
```

The hydrolysis of TMV RNA fits the expected results that were provided by the hydrolysis of reference polynucleotides of known structure.

3. Ribonucleases from *Escherichia coli*

According to Spahr (1964) and Anraku and Mizuno (1965), four types of enzymes able to degrade RNA have been described in *E. coli* :

1) The well-known polynucleotide phosphorylase (p. 100).

2) An RNase called "RNase I", bound to the 30 S ribosomes in the form of a latent enzyme. When this RNase is freed from the ribosomes, it attacks RNA yielding nucleoside-3'-phosphates via the corresponding 2'-3'-cyclic nucleoside intermediates.

3) An RNase called "RNase II" liberating nucleoside-5'-phosphates.

4) An RNase isolated from *coli* cell debris called "Debris-RNase".

1) The polynucleotide phosphorylase from *coli* has been abundantly described in the previous chapters, and we do not intend to add anything further here.

2) *Coli* RNase I has been the subject of a number of studies (Tal and Elson, 1963; Neu and Heppel, 1964; Anderson and Carter, 1965; Carter and Anderson, 1965, Wade and Robinson 1965).

This RNase is localized internally in the ribosomes, and within the ribosomes it is concentrated in the 30 S particles, but absent from the 50 S particles. This RNase has been purified by a perchloric acid fractionation of the ribosomes; the enzyme is found in the fraction soluble in dilute perchloric acid. The enzyme thus extracted exhibits a high activity at pH 8.0, and its molecular weight seems to be situated between 10,000 and 30,000.

This enzyme hydrolyzes phosphodiester bonds of ribonucleic compounds to the 3'-phosphate stage, going through the corresponding cyclic nucleotide intermediates. If the activity is arbitrarily fixed at 48 for poly C, it is 10 for poly A and 5 for t-RNA, the ultimate stage in the RNA hydrolysis being the formation of the four mononucleotide-3'-phosphates.

3) RNase II of *coli*. This enzyme is the one that was previously called *coli* phosphodiesterase by Spahr and Schlesinger (1963). The purification of the enzyme was effected in four steps involving chromatography on Amberlite CG-50, filtration on Sephadex G-200 gel, chromatography

on DEAE-cellulose.   Under these conditions, the specific activity rises from 200 units/mg. protein to 6,100, or an enrichment of about 27 times (Spahr, 1964).   Purified RNase II is free from *coli* RNase I and polynucleotide phosphorylase.   It has no further action on DNA.

For its activity, RNase II requires both a monovalent (K^+ or NH_4^+) and a bivalent cation. It is completely inhibited by M urea.   The optimum pH is between 7 and 8 and the Michaelis constant for polyuridylic acid is 7.5×10^{-3} M.

The action on RNA is both that of an exonuclease and an endonuclease, with liberation of 4 mononucleoside-5'-phosphates.   This enzyme is particularly interesting, since it represents a very rare, if not unique, case of a nuclease liberating 5'-phosphates from RNA, but being without action on DNA.

According to Singer and Tolbert (1965), this RNase is specific for single stranded polyribonucleotides; helical forms do not appear to be hydrolyzed, nor do they inhibit the hydrolysis of single stranded sequences.

4) RNase from *Escherichia coli* débris.

The cell débris of *E. coli*, obtained after blending the cells with sand and centrifuging, contains high RNase activity that is distinct from the activities already described.   This RNase appears to have properties similar to those of RNase I from *E. coli* so far as its action on ribonucleic polymers is concerned, but it is differentiated from it by its chromatographic behavior.   The difference between the two enzymes is also demonstrated by comparison of the initial rates of depolymerization by ribosomal and débris RNases.

4. *Saccharomyces* ribosomal ribonuclease

A further latent RNase was discovered in yeast ribosomes by Danner (1965), who also studied its variation during the growth of the microorganism.

The RNase is present in latent form in the ribosomes, from which it can be released by 0.5 M NaCl at pH 5.

After being liberated from the ribosomes in this way, the RNase is purified by chromatography on the ion exchange resin Amberlite CG-50.

The final products of ribosomal RNA degradation by this enzyme are the 2'- and/or 3' isomers of AMP, GMP, CMP and UMP.   This enzyme is involved in the yeast cycle.

5. Ribonuclease from *Streptomyces erythreus*

A thermostable RNase has been partially purified from *S. erythreus* (Tanaka, 1961).   This enzyme resembles RNase T_1.

Results of later work (Tanaka and Cantoni, 1963) confirm that *Streptomyces* RNase can, like RNase T_1, hydrolyze all the Gp secondary phosphoric esters, but that, unlike RNase T_1, it can also cleave all the secondary phosphoric esters of methylguanine nucleoside-3'-phosphate in m-RNA.

6. Ribonuclease from *Ustilago sphaerogena*

This enzyme has been purified by the following series of operations (Glitz and Dekker, 1964*a*) :

1) microorganism culture and removal of cells by centrifugation,
2) concentration of the extracellular fluid in vacuum,
3) fractionation on Sephadex G-25,

4) fractional precipitation with ammonium sulfate,

5) chromatography on DEAE-cellulose,

6) a second ammonium sulfate fractionation,

7) phenol extraction.

Under these conditions, the enzyme is purified about 300-fold, and its activity is comparable to that of other highly purified nucleases. The enzyme is essentially pure by ultracentrifugation and electrophoresis. It exhibits properties comparable to those of RNase T_1, in particular a sedimentation constant of 1.6 S, an optimum pH of 7.0 — 7.5 and stability towards heat and acids. A remarkable fact is that it is inhibited by NaCl and $MgCl_2$. Studies on the specificity have shown that Xp ⎪ Gp bonds are broken preferentially. The enzyme acts by first forming guanosine-2′:3′-cyclic phosphate, then hydrolyzing this further, resulting in the 3′-nucleotide. Polyadenylic acid is hydrolyzed at 0.002 % of the speed of RNA, while poly U, poly C, DNA and bis-p-nitrophenylphosphate are completely resistant to the action of the enzyme (Glitz and Dekker, 1964a, b).

Part III

DEOXYRIBONUCLEASES

1. INTRODUCTORY REMARKS, ESTIMATION

Older observations (Araki, 1903; Abderhalden and Schittenhelm, 1906; de la Blanchardière, 1913; Feulgen, 1935) had already shown that many tissue and secretion extracts, such as from pancreatic juice, had the property of liquifying DNA gels without liberating either inorganic phosphate or purine and pyrimidine bases, but with liberation of "oligonucleotides". It is now known that deoxyribonucleases, or DNases, are responsible for these hydrolyses of DNA. The best known among these enzymes, pancreatic DNase, was isolated in crystalline form by Kunitz in 1950. In the same publication as the one where the crystallization |of DNase is described, Kunitz added the following observations: this enzyme depolymerizes thymus DNA without liberation of inorganic phosphate and requires the presence of bivalent ions (Mg^{++}, Mn^{++}, Co^{++}) for its activation. This DNase has no action at all on ribonucleic acid.

DNase activity of tissues, secretions, bacterial cultures, etc., can be measured by one of the following methods.

A. VISCOMETRIC METHOD

This method is sensitive and speedy, and has the advantage over spectrophotometric methods of being usable with solutions that are strongly absorbing in the ultraviolet (Laskowski and Seidel, 1945).

The experimental details are as follows. DNA is prepared by the method of Hammarsten (1934) or of Kay, Simmons and Dounce (1952) (cf. p. 115). Five ml DNA solution in 0.2 M borate buffer at pH 7.0 are placed in an Ostwald viscometer immersed in a water bath at 37°. The enzyme extract under examination is diluted with the same buffer to a suitable concentration and heated to the same temperature. At the time of the determination, 3 ml of the diluted enzyme are rapidly added to the viscometer, vigorously shaken and the viscosity at zero time is measured.

In the next 30 minutes, the viscosity is measured at 5 minute intervals. The viscosity constant of a unimolecular reaction is calculated from the formula

$$K = \frac{1}{t} \log \frac{\eta_0}{\eta_t}$$

where η_0 = relative viscosity after zero time,
η_t = relative viscosity after time t.

The DNase unit is defined as the amount of enzyme which under the conditions just described gives a K value of 1.0×10^{-3}. A table of experimental values has been reproduced from Laskowski (table XXXIV) that illustrates perfectly the sequence of operations just described, together with the calculations necessary.

Table XXXIV : Viscometric estimation of DNase I (Laskowski and Seidel, 1945).

	Incubation (min)	Time elapsed (sec)	Relative viscosity	$\dfrac{\eta_0}{\eta_t}$	$\log \dfrac{\eta_0}{\eta_t}$	K
Water	—	34	1.00	—	—	—
DNA + extract	0	124	3.66	—	—	—
	5	120	3.53	1.03	0.0128	0.00256
	10	118	3.47	1.05	0.0212	0.00212
	15	113	3.32	1.10	0.0414	0.00276
	20	107	3.15	1.16	0.0645	0.00322
	25	105	3.08	1.19	0.0755	0.00302
	30	100	2.98	1.22	0.0864	0.00288
Average						0.00276
Units						2.76

B. SPECTROPHOTOMETRIC METHOD

Having noticed that the action of DNase on a DNA solution was accompanied by a rise in optical density at 260 mμ reaching a maximum of 30 % after 10 minutes, Kunitz (1950) proposed to use this phenomenon as a method for the determination of DNase. This actually consists in measuring a phenomenon that has since been extensively studied, namely the hyperchromic effect resulting from modification of the DNA spatial conformation (cf. p. 67).

Experimentally, the following solutions are used:

1) Stock solution of sodium deoxyribonuclease, 2 mg/ml in distilled water. This solution is stable for several weeks in the refrigerator at 4°.

2) Spectrophotometric substrate solution: 2 ml of the stock Na DNate solution are mixed with 10 ml 0.05 M $MgSO_4$ and 10 ml 1.0 M Na acetate buffer at pH 5.0, the mixture being made up to 100 ml with distilled water. This solution can be kept in the refrigerator for at least a week.

At the time of the measurement, several tubes each containing 3 ml of the substrate solution are placed in the water bath at 25° for about five minutes (in point of fact the determination works just as well at room temperature, and one thereby avoids the trouble of having a thermostat at 25°).   One ml water is added to one of these tubes, and the mixture is then transferred to the first quartz cell of the spectrophotometer.   This mixture is the reference solution.   A 1 ml sample of the DNase solution in distilled water, containing 5 — 10 μg DNase/ml is added to another tube containing 3 ml substrate solution.   The solutions are mixed at the same time as a stopwatch is set in motion, when the solution is transferred to the second quartz spectrophotometer cell. Optical density readings at 260 mμ are made of the solution in the second cell at one minute intervals for about five minutes.

The unit of activity is the amount of enzyme able to cause a rise in the optical density at 260 mμ of 1.0/min in the exactly defined conditions just described :

$\Delta\ E_{260}$/min = number of units in the sample

$\Delta\ E_{260}$/min/mg protein = specific DNase activity of the preparation examined.

Kunitz's method is only applicable when the solution to be estimated does not contain anything absorbing at 260 mμ (other than the DNA).

C. Methods utilizing the estimation of soluble nucleotides

These nucleotides are nucleotides produced by the action of DNase, and which are soluble in the presence of lanthanum salts or trichloracetic acid.

It is known that highly polymerized nucleic acids can be readily precipitated as lanthanum salts (see, among other references, Davidson and Waymouth, 1944).   This phenomenon can therefore be used to follow the appearance by DNase action of nucleotides soluble in the presence of lanthanum salts.   The experimental details of this method have been supplied by Boman and Kaletta (1957).

Laskowski (1946) has developed a comparable method involving the estimation of "soluble phosphorus" in the presence of 10 % trichloracetic acid (cf. also a detailed description of this method in McDonald, 1955b).

D. Methods involving diffusion in agar gel

The method using diffusion in an agar gel was described by Le Talaer et al. (1963), and is of considerable sensitivity using a very small sample; it also allows the simultaneous determination of a large number of samples.

1. Principle

Agar gel contains deoxyribonucleic acid, the hydrolysis of which is effected in situ during diffusion of the enzyme.   The diffusion zones can be revealed in a variety of ways; in the experimental conditions chosen, the diameter of the diffusion zone is proportional to the logarithm of the enzyme concentration, this relation allowing a semi-quantitative study of the "enzymic activity" to be made.   It is clear that a certain number of conditions must be respected, and to remember, in particular, that neutral DNase activity is maximal at pH 7.5 and in the presence of Mg^{++}.

2. Description of the method

a. *Materials*

Petri dishes (flat-bottomed), diam. 15 cm.
Oven at 37°.
Boiling water bath
50 μl micropipettes, accurate to 1/1,000
Paper disks (9 mm diameter, filters)

b. *Reagents*

R.1 : powdered gelose (purified Agar-Difco).
R.2 : Solution of trishydroxymethylaminomethane (Tris, 0.4 M at pH 7.5).
R.3 : 2 mg/ml DNA solution in 0.14 M sodium chloride solution.

One ml of a 1 % merthiolate solution per 100 ml is added, and the mixture kept at 4°. DNA is prepared in the laboratory by a method involving direct action of papain on calf thymus. The concentration of the solution is measured both by determination of the deoxyribose and by measurement of the absorption at 260 mμ.

R.4 : 1 M aqueous magnesium chloride solution.
R.5 : Aqueous solution of methyl green, 4 °/oo.

This dyestuff, derived from triphenylmethane, is often contaminated with related products, especially with crystal violet, which is eliminated by chloroform extraction. A preference for "Merck" methyl green is given.

R.6 : Revealing solution.
Methyl green solution, 4 °/oo (R.5) .... 250 ml
0.4 M tris buffer solution, pH 7.5 .... 125 ml
Sodium citrate. 5.5 H₂O .... 18 g
Distilled water .... to make 1000 ml.

R.7 : Standardized Kunitz DNase solution, 100 μg/ml in 0.14 M sodium chloride. This solution is divided into 0.4 ml fractions in sealed ampules which are frozen in a dry ice — acetone mixture and kept at — 20°.

The dilutions are always freshly prepared in a 0.14 M NaCl solution, the DNase ampules not having been thawed out several times.

R.8: 1 % merthiolate solution.
R.9: Gel substrate.

The substrate used is an Agar gel (1 %), containing 300 μg/ml DNA in the presence of a 0.02 M magnesium chloride concentration, and buffered at pH 7.5.

In 100 ml medium, there are :
Powdered gelose (R.1) .... 1 g
MgCl₂ solution (R.4) .... 2 ml
Buffer solution (R.2) .... 20 ml
Distilled water .... 47 ml
DNA solution (R.3) .... 30 ml
1 % Merthiolate solution (R.8) .... 1 ml

The gelose is dissolved in the water together with the magnesium chloride and the buffer solution on the boiling water bath (about 1 hour).   After cooling to 60°, the 30 ml DNA solution is added.   The solution is stirred for a short while with a magnetic stirrer, and the mixture (R.9) is rapidly poured into Petri dishe with absolutely horizontal flat bottoms to have 1 mm thickness.   Preservation at 4° is good for several weeks without microbial growth.

3. Experimental

Distribution and impregnation of the disks; diffusion.   Five 9 mm filter paper disks are placed with forceps at regular distances on the Petri dishes just described.   Each disk is impregnated by means of a micropipette with 30 µl of the solutions to be examined, then the closed dishes are placed in the oven at 37°, taking care to invert them in order to avoid deleterious effects of water condensation on the gelled medium.

Colouring.   After 18 hr., the disks are removed with forceps and the diffusion zones of the enzyme are coloured by covering the gelose with a methyl green solution (R.6) for 1 hr., after which time the agent is removed.

Reading.   The diameter of the diffusion zones is measured to within 0.5 mm in two perpendicular directions.

Standard curve expression of results.   The crystalline DNase of Kunitz (DNase I, p. 236) is used as standard, the activity of different batches being checked with one of the conventional reference techniques.   In order to establish a complete range of reference, freshly prepared dilute DNase solutions in 0.14 M NaCl solution are prepared, titrating for respectively 40, 20, 10, 5, 2.5, 1.25, 0.625 µg enzyme per ml.

In this concentration range, and for the described conditions, a linear relation between the diameter of the diffusion zones and the logarithm of the concentration is observed (figure 48). When the enzyme concentration doubles, the diameter increases by 2 mm.

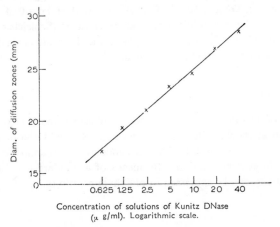

Figure 48. Linear relation between the diameter of the diffusion zones and the logarithm of DNase concentration (Le Talaer et al. 1963)

The measurements carried out at each assay are referred to this reference curve, and the results expressed in µg Kunitz DNase per ml solution.

A method of the same type has been described by Osowiecki and Dobrzánski (1963) to measure the DNase production by *Staphylococci*.

Table XXXV : Relation between the concentration of gelose in the medium and the diameter of the diffusion zones (Le Talaer et al., 1963)

Gelose (g %)	Diameter (mm)	Number of experiments
0.7	29.9 ± 0.4	4
1	30.2 ± 0.8	4
2	29.8 ± 1.0	3

Substrate : DNA 300 μg/ml, 0.02 M MgCl$_2$, 0.08 M Tris buffer pH 7.5, thickness of medium 1 mm.   Solution of Kunitz DNase 40 μg/ml, 30 μl per disk of 9 mm diameter.   Diffusion time 18 hr at 37°.

E. Ultrafiltration method

This method was described by Geiduschek and Daniels (1965) and makes use of the property of nitrocellulose filters of allowing the passage of low molecular weight fragments and only retaining polynucleotides of high molecular weight.   The experimental procedure is as follows.

When heat-denatured bacteriophage T2 DNA-^{3}H or *B. subtilis* DNA-^{32}P is incubated with pancreatic endonuclease, the resulting phosphodiester cleavage and depolymerization decreases retention of DNA by nitrocellulose filters.   After incubation for 15 min at 37° of 5 μg denatured T2 DNA-^{3}H, 1.5 μ moles MgCl$_2$, 5 μ moles Tris Cl pH 7.5 and 100 μg bovine serum albumin with varied amounts of pancreatic DNase, 10 ml of 0.5 M KCl- 0.01 M Tris- 0.01 M EDTA are added. The mixture is then filtered through nitrocellulose membranes (Schleicher and Schuell, Grade B6, soaked before use in 0.5 M KCl- 0.01 M Tris, pH 7.5) and the filters washed with 50 ml KCl-Tris-EDTA.   The filters are then dried and counted.

F. Fluorimetric method

After the action of DNase on DNA, an acid-soluble supernatant is obtained by treating the samples withdrawn at regular intervals with HClO$_4$.   The addition of EDTA and bromine water converts the thymine into acetol which is condensed with aminobenzaldehyde, resulting in the formation of a fluorescent solution.   By means of a standard curve (thymine vs. fluorescence) the enzymic activity can be expressed in mg thymine/min/unit of enzyme (Hathaway and Frajola, 1965).

G. Turbidimetric method

This method described by Houck (1959) is based on the finding that highly polymerized DNA in the presence of acidified serum albumin forms an opaque and stable colloid.   The optical density of the opacity is proportional both to the degree of polymerization and to the DNA concentration.   These conclusions are valid both for the DNA-DNase system and for the RNA-RNase system (Houck, 1958).

The determination is made simply by incubating aqueous solutions containing varied amounts of DNase or serum at respectively 26° and 37° for 30 minutes with 0.60 mg/ml DNA and determining the depolymerization of the substrate by a reading at 450 mμ.

H. CRITICISM OF VARIOUS DNASE ESTIMATIONS

It is clear that since the methods which have been described do not measure the same phenomenon, the results obtained must be interpreted with care.

This warning has been particularly well illustrated by Oth, Frédéricq and Hacha (1958) who plotted on the same scale the percentage degradation of the same DNA under the influence of the same DNase (from thymus) against time, as measured by three different methods, and found that the curves were not coincident (figure 49).

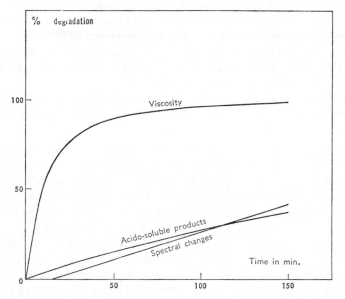

Figure 49. Percentage degradation of DNA with time, measured by three different methods (Oth, Frédéricq and Hacha, 1958)

The estimation of DNase activity by viscometric methods of a highly purified preparation of phosphodiesterase led to suppose the absence of any action by this enzyme on intact DNA (Privat de Garilhe and Laskowski, 1955a).   Laskowski, Hagerty and Laurila (1957) were obliged to revise this idea, since phosphodiesterase in fact acts on DNA as an exonuclease, i.e. by removing the mononucleotides one by one, beginning from one end.   Although no fall in the viscosity is observed in the first stages of the reaction (up to the moment when 10 % of the internucleotide bonds have been broken), during the same time fragments soluble in lanthanum salt solutions appear, these being mainly mononucleotides, as was shown by column chromatography of the lanthanum salt-soluble fraction.   It will naturally be realized that the breakage of several bonds within the chain will suffice to cause a considerable fall in the viscosity without the appearance of La-soluble fragments (endo-enzymes like DNase I and DNase II in the initial stages of their action) whilst step-wise degradation causes, on the other hand, a large production of La-soluble fragments without altering the viscosity.

There is, therefore, every reason to use at least two methods of determination of the nucleo-lytic enzymes during their purification.

II. DEOXYRIBONUCLEASES OF ANIMAL ORIGIN

A. BOVINE   PANCREATIC   DEOXYRIBONUCLEASE, OR DNASE I (E.C. 3.1.4.5)*

1. Isolation of crystalline pancreatic DNase

Pancreatic DNase or DNase I is isolated from beef pancreas by extraction with a dilute sulfuric acid solution, then fractionally precipitated with ammonium sulfate.   The DNase occurs in the fraction precipitated with 20 — 40 % saturated ammonium sulfate.

The yield of crystalline DNase in this process is low on account of the extensive denaturation taking place at pH 2.8 during the crystallization.   Starting with 1 kg of minced pancreas, 3-5 mg of dry crystals are obtained in the first crystallizate.

The saturated solution of ammonium sulfate is prepared at 20-25° (760 g salt/liter water). All filtrations are by suction unless otherwise stated (Kunitz, 1950; McCarty, 1946; McDonald, 1955b).

Step 1.   Preliminary Purification Fresh** beef pancreases are collected in ice-cold 0.25 N H_2SO_4.   The glands are drained, cleaned of fat and connective tissue, then minced in a meat grinder.   The minced pancreas is suspended in an equal volume of ice-cold H_2O, and ice-cold 0.25 N H_2SO_4 is added with stirring until the pH of the suspension is approximately 3.0 (tested with 0.01 % methyl orange on a test plate); a volume of acid equal to half that of the H_2O added is generally required.   The suspension is left at 2 to 5° for 18 to 20 hours.   It is then strained through cheesecloth,   The residue is resuspended in 1 vol. of ice-cold H_2O and again strained. The residue is then discarded, and the combined filtrates are brought to 0.2 saturation of $(NH_4)_2SO_4$ by the addition of 114 g. of salt per liter of filtrate.   The precipitate formed is filtered through a rapid filtering paper (such as Eaton-Dikeman No. 617) with the aid of 10 g. of Celite No. 503*** and 10 g. of Standard Super-Cel*** per liter of solution.   The filter cake is discarded.   The clear filtrate is brought to 0.4 saturation of $(NH_4)_2SO_4$ by the addition of 121 g. of salt per liter and refiltered with the aid of 3 g. of Celite No. 503 per liter through double paper, E-D No. 612 on top of No. 617.   The residue**** is suspended in five times its weight of water, the suspension

---

* Cunningham and Laskowski (1953) have suggested a broad distinction between two types of DNase, one (type I) with an optimum pH around 7.0 and requiring Mg^{++} ions for activity, and another (type II) with an optimum pH in the acid region.
** Frozen pancreas, obtainable from any of the large slaughter-houses, can also be used if only deoxyribonucleose (or ribonuclease) is to be prepared.   They should be thawed by lea ving them immersed in 0.25 N H_2SO_4 at 5°.
*** Supplied by Johns-Manville, 22 East 40th Street, New York.
**** The filtrate, when adjusted to 0.25 N H_2SO_4 by the addition of 7 ml of concentrated H_2SO_4 per liter of H_2O used in the extraction and washing of the ground pancreas, can be utilized for the preparation of chymotrypsinogen, trypsinogen, trypsin, trypsin-inhibitor compound.

is brought to 0.3 saturation of $(NH_4)_2SO_4$ by the addition of 176 g. of salt per liter of H_2O used and refiltered on E-D No. 617 paper; the filtrate is discarded.

Step 2. Incubation at 37° Followed by Fractionation with Ammonium Sulfate. The residue is suspended in ten times its weight of H_2O, and the suspension is brought to 0.15 saturation of $(NH_4)_2SO_4$ by the addition of 83.7 g. of salt per liter of H_2O. The solution is titrated to pH 3.2 (glass electrode) with about 2 ml. of 5 N H_2SO_4 per liter. It is heated to 37° and left for 1 hour at that temperature. It is then cooled to 20° and filtered through E-D No. 617 paper with the aid of an additional 5 g. of Celite No. 503 per liter of suspension. The residue is discarded. The filtrate is titrated to pH 5.3 (glass electrode) with 5 N NaOH (about 2 ml./l.) and brought to 0.5 saturation of $(NH_4)_2SO_4$ by the addition of 220 g. of salt per liter. The precipitate formed, designated 0.5 precipitate, is filtered on E-D No. 617 paper with the aid of 5 g. of Celite No. 503 per liter of solution. The clear filtrate is titrated with a few drops of 5 N H_2SO_4 to pH 4.0 (tested with bromocresol green on a spot plate) and brought to 0.7 saturation of $(NH_4)_2SO_4$ by the addition of 135 g. of salt per liter. The scant precipitate formed, designated 0.7 precipitate, is filtered on E-D No. 612 paper with the aid of 2. g of Standard Super-Cel per liter and stored. The filtrate is discarded.

The 0.5 precipitate is resuspended in three times its weight of water and step 2, including the incubation at 37°, is repeated several times until no appreciable 0.7 precipitate is formed.

The 0.7 precipitates are combined and suspended in ten times their weight of H_2O and filtered through E-D No. 612 paper. The residue is washed with H_2O until the washing is water clear.

Step 3. Fractionation with Ethanol. The combined filtrate and washings are diluted with H_2O to a concentration of approximately 1 % protein (the approximate concentration of protein can be determined spectrophotometrically at 280 mμ, the optical density being 1.2 per milligram of protein per milliliter). The pH of the solution is adjusted with 5 N H_2SO_4 to pH 3.8 (tested with methyl orange on a spot plate), and 2 ml. of saturated $(NH_4)_2SO_4$ are added per 100 ml. of solution. The mixture is cooled in an ice-salt bath to 2°, and one-quarter of its volume of ice-cold 95 % ethanol is added slowly, with stirring, keeping the temperature of the solution between 2 and 5°. The mixture is stored for 24 hours at 2 to 5° and is then centrifuged at the same temperature. The residue is discarded, and the clear supernatant is left at — 10° for 24 hours, after which it is centrifuged at the same temperature. The supernatant is discarded.

Step 4. Crystallization. The precipitate is dissolved in approximately ten times its volume of ice-cold H_2O, after which it is brought to 0.38 saturation by the addition of 60 ml. of saturated $(NH_4)_2SO_4$ per 100 ml. of solution. The precipitate formed is filtered with suction on hardened paper (such as Schleicher and Schuell No. 576) at 5 to 10°. It is then suspended in three times its weight of ice-cold H_2O and dissolved by the slow addition of several drops of 0.25 N NaOH, keeping the pH of the solution below 4.8. If the solution is turbid it is centrifuged clear at about 5°, then adjusted to pH 2.8 (glass electrode) with several drops of 0.2 N H_2SO_4. The heavy precipitate, which usually forms at approximately pH 3.5, dissolves readily as the pH of the solution reaches 3.0 or lower. The clear solution is left at 5° overnight and then at approximately 20° for 6 to 8 hours. Crystals appear during the latter step.

Step 5. Recrystallization. The suspension of crystals is centrifuged. The residue is suspended in approximately 3 vol. of 0.02 saturated $(NH_4)_2SO_4$ and dissolved with the aid of a few drops of 0.2 N NaOH at a pH of about 4.6. The solution is centrifuged if turbid, titrated to pH 2.8 (glass electrode), and left at 20°. Crystals of DNase form within an hour. They are filtered on hardened paper at 5°, then washed, first with ice-cold acidified 30 % ethanol (1 drop of 5 N H_2SO_4 per 100 ml.), then with ice-cold acetone, and dried at room temperature for several hours.

The mother liquors in steps 4 and 5 yield additional crystals when treated as follows : the solution is diluted threefold with ice-cold H_2O and titrated with 0.2 N NaOH to pH 4.6 (tested with bromocresol green on a spot plate). Any insoluble material formed is removed by centrifugation. The clear supernatant is titrated with 0.2 N H_2SO_4 to pH 4.0 and then brought to 0.38 saturation of $(NH_4)_2SO_4$, as described in step 4 which is then followed through in every detail.

Neurath et al (Keller et al., 1958; Neurath et al., 1960) obtained a DNase peak that was fairly well defined by chromatography of bull pancreatic juice on DEAE-cellulose; this fraction can also serve as starting point in the purification of DNase.

It was found by Zimmerman and Sandeen (1966) that commercial samples of crystalline DNase I still retain some RNase activity. DEAE cellulose chromatography reduces the RNase activity by 90 % and removes inactive protein material. A subsequent treatment with Na Iodoacetate reduces the RNase activity to 0 % and the DNase to 60 %.

2. Properties of DNase I

DNase I is a protein with a molecular weight in the neighborhood of 62,000*; its aminoacid composition has been given by Gehrmann and Okada (1957) as :

$$Asp_{65}, Thr_{36}, Ser_{62}, Pro_{19}, Glu_{43}, Gly_{26}, Ala_{35}, Val_{42}, (Cys-Cyste)_3, Met_{12}, Ileu_{21}, Leu_{41}, Tyr_{29},$$
$$Phe_{20}, Lys_{33}, His_{22}, Try_5, Arg_{26}, (CONH_2)_{83}.$$

DNase rapidly depolymerizes DNA gels. It is possible to obtain a closer insight into the actual hydrolysis by examining the reaction products. In the course of a typical reaction, 200 mg DNA are suspended in 10 ml 0.1 M Na borate buffer pH 7.0 and 0.025 M Mg^{++}. Crystallized DNase I (2 mg) is added and the solution is placed in a water bath at 37° for 4 to 5 hours. The DNA, which is a cotton-like insoluble mass, first forms a viscous gel, then gives a solution that becomes increasingly fluid. The products from the incubation are entirely dialyzable against distilled water.

When such a hydrolyzate is chromatographed on a Dowex 1-X2 column carrying out the elution with ammonium formate buffers at pH 4.5, and with increasing ionic strength, an elution diagram like the one in figure 50 is obtained.

The two first peaks eluted by 0.1 M formate buffer are 1) d-pC and 2) d-pT; these are the only mononucleotides. From the quantitative point of view they represent less than 1 % of the total. Next come the dinucleotides 3) d-pCpC, 4) d-pCpT, 5) d-pCpA. Peaks 6 — 10, eluted with 0.25 M buffer are mixtures of dinucleotides that can be resolved later by evaporation of the buffer and column chromatography under different conditions. Peaks 11 — 15 are mixtures of di- and trinucleotides; the predominating fraction from a quantitative point of view being the fraction eluted with 1 M buffer. Finally it may be pointed out that the whole (over 95 %) of the hydrolysate can be eluted with buffers of molarity equal to, or less than 2 M.

---

* More recent determinations effected by Lindberg (1966) indicate a molecular weight of 33,200 and therefore the possible appearance of dimeric forms.

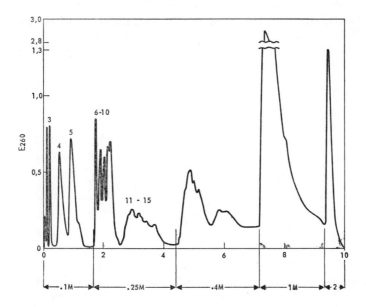

Figure 50. Elution diagram of a hydrolysate of 200 mg DNA by DNase I. Column : Dowex 1-X2, 0.8 × 10 cm. Eluent : ammonium formate at pH 4.5, volumes and molarities as indicated. The two first peaks, unnumbered and only visible with difficulty on the figure are : 1) d-pC, 2) d-pT. Later come 3) d-pCpC, 4) d-pCpT, 5) d-pCpA. Peaks 6 to 10 are dinucleotide mixtures, peaks 11 to 15 are di and trinucleotide mixtures (after Privat de Garilhe and Laskowski, 1955*b*)

According to Kunitz, the average dimensions of the fragments produced by the action of DNase I are those of tetranucleotides, so that, on the whole, we can suppose that one bond in four will be broken. The mononucleotides produced by DNase I are easily dephosphorylated by 5′-nucleotidase, an enzyme to be found in the venom of *Crotalus adamanteus*, and which specifically dephosphorylates nucleotides ending with a 5′-phosphate (see p. 262). It would thus seem that DNase I hydrolyzes bonds joining the hydroxyl group in C-3′ and the phosphate, to yield mononucleotides and oligonucleotides terminated by a phosphoryl group in the 5′-position.

A detailed discussion has already been given (p. 285) of the analysis of the dinucleotides arising in a thymus DNA hydrolysate from the action of DNase I, when it was noted that there were only traces of dinucleotides of the d-pPu-pPy type, which led to the supposition that this type of bond was preferentially broken by DNase I (Table XXXVI).

Vanecko and Laskowski (1961*a*, *b*) have extended the investigations on DNase I specificity by systematically studying the action of the enzyme on a series of oligonucleotides, some carrying a monoesterified phosphoryl group in the C-3′ position, others a monoesterified group in the C-5′ position.

Let us first see what happens when oligonucleotides carrying a monoesterified group in the C-3′ position are hydrolyzed by DNase I. This work followed an observation by Privat de Garilhe and Laskowski (1955*b*) in which oligonucleotides liberated by the action of DNase II (terminated by 3′-phosphate groups, see below) are nevertheless hydrolyzable by pancreatic DNase.

16

Table XXXVI. Dinucleotides characterized and estimated from a total hydrolysate of DNA by DNase I (Sinsheimer, 1954)

	A	C	G	T
A	pApA 0.46	pApC 0	pApG 0.20	pApT 0.10
C	pCpC 3.22	pCpC 1.11	(pMpG) pCpG 1.15	pCpT 2.34
G	pGpA 0.97	pGpC 0.75	pGpC 0.83	pGpT 0.16
T	pTpA 1.36	pTpC 0.78	pTpG 2.61	pTpT 1.38

The nucleotides are isolated by chromatography on ion exchanger and estimated by spectrophotometry; They are expressed as % of the total hydrolysate. The paucity of dinucleotides of the type d-p-purine-p-pyrimidine (boxes crossed with a diagonal line) seems to indicate that this type of linkage is preferentially broken by DNase I.

It was also shown that the trinucleotide d-ApApTp was hydrolyzed by DNase I with formation of ApA + pTp (Potter, Laurila and Laskowski, 1958). The work of Vanecko and Laskowski led to the conclusion that all trinucleotides would be hydrolyzed by the same scheme as d-ApApTp.

Hydrolysis of the tetranucleotides can take place by two different pathways :

$$d\text{-}XpYpY'pZp \nearrow\quad d\text{-}XpY + pY'pZp$$
$$\searrow\quad d\text{-}XpYpY'p + pZp$$

Which of these two paths will be followed cannot yet be decided with complete certainty, but in any case the first reaction to occur prevents the second, since both types of product, pY'pZp and XpYpY', are resistant to further DNase I action.

Two alternatives are possible in the case of the pentanucleotides :

$$\overset{1}{\downarrow}\quad\overset{2}{\downarrow}$$
$$d\text{-}XpYpY'pY''pZp \nearrow\quad d\text{-}XpY + d\text{-}pY'pY'' + d\text{-}pZp$$
$$\underset{3}{\uparrow}\qquad\searrow\quad d\text{-}XpYpY' + d\text{-}pY''pZp$$

If the fission occurs at the arrow 1 or the arrow 2, the second fission will then be possible, since in both cases the larger fragment is sensitive to DNase action. If, on the other hand, the initial cleavage occurs at the arrow 3, no other cleavage is possible, both products formed being resistant to DNase action.

Examination of the compounds occurring in a DNase I hydrolysate of oligonucleotides carrying 3'-phosphate groups leads to the conclusion that all the fragments with two units, and certain fragments with three units are resistent to action by the enzyme, whatever their base composition. This observation makes it even more difficult to account for the presence of mononucleotides in the total hydrolysate of DNA by DNase I.

Hydrolysis of oligonucleotides carrying phosphoryl groups in the C-5' position also yields interesting information about the specificity of DNase I; in particular, length for length, oligonucleotides terminated by a 3'-phosphate group are better substrates than oligonucleotides terminated by a 5'-phosphate group.

The last oligonucleotides which are produced in the course of DNA hydrolysis by DNase I act as inhibitors of the DNA hydrolysis, but they can function as substrates provided that massive doses of DNase are used with respect to them; for instance, if a concentration of enzyme equal to that of the oligonucleotides of the substrate is used, it is possible to obtain a hydrolysate containing 60 % trinucleotides and 25 % dinucleotides.

The conclusions of Vanecko and Laskowski agree with those of Frédéricq (Frédéricq, 1959-1961; Frédéricq, Oth and Desreux, 1960), who suggested that the hydrolysis of oligonucleotides by DNase I is more difficult than that of macromolecular DNA, and that in general the shorter the fragments, the more difficult the hydrolysis.

Conclusions that were in accord with these were obtained by Ralph et al. (1962), who examined the action of DNase I on synthetic substrates of known structure. The substrates used were homopolymers such as poly T, poly d-C and poly d-A, in addition to the nucleotide d-TpApC. DNase activation was achieved by manganous ions, which are more efficient than Mg^{++}. In the standard conditions used (especially a large excess of enzyme), all the tetranucleotides and higher nucleotides carrying a 5'-phosphate group were attacked. Di- and trinucleotides having 5'-phosphate groups, and the trinucleotide d-TpApC were resistant to action by the enzyme. The mode of action is identical in the whole series of 5'-phosphates, endonucleolytic fission occurring preferentially. Thus the tetranucleotides give mainly dinucleotides, the pentanucleotides give mainly di- and trinucleotides, etc. With the pentanucleotide d-TpTpTpTpTp, carrying a terminal 3'-phosphate group, an additional exonucleolytic cleavage is observed, with liberation of pTp and TpTpTpT. In each homologous series, the rate of degradation increases with increasing chain length. The study of the behavior of the three analogous pentanucleotides, $d-p_5T_5$, $d-p_5C_5$ and $d-p_5A_5$ showed that the latter is attacked more rapidly than the corresponding pyrimidine oligonucleotides.

Bollum (1965) has examined the action of DNase I on deoxyribonucleic homopolymer complexes such as poly d-A: d-T, poly d-I: d-C and poly d-G: d-C. This reaction results in the formation of oligomers corresponding to the various purine and pyrimidine bases. These oligomers can be separated by chromatography on DEAE-cellulose by standard methods. This observation excludes any strict DNase specificity, since all types of bond are broken. Difficulties were encountered in the hydrolysis of poly d-I: d-C containing a resistant and a non-resistant chain, a surprising fact considering the hypothesis by which pyrimidine-pyrimidine links are relatively easily accessible to DNase action. These difficulties can be removed by the addition of Ca^{++} to the DNase I activated by Mg^{++}, or by replacing Mg^{++} by Mn^{++}.

All the experiments carried out with DNase I acting on oligonucleotides and synthetic polynucleotides of known structure demonstrate that the hypothesis by which the enzyme preferentially attacks bonds of the d-p purine — p pyrimidine type represents only a *preference* of the enzyme and not a strict specificity. The DNase I specificity is far from being as well defined as that of RNase A or RNase T_1.

According to Bernardi and Sadron (1961), hydrolysis by the DNases of DNA can be conducted in such a way that high molecular weight fragments (7 and 9 × 10^5) are obtained, by causing only a few breaks in the middle of the chain. These fragments, that could subsequently be isolated by standard methods of purification, would offer a great deal of interest in view of their possible application to the structural determination of nucleic acids.

Activation and Inhibition of D Nase I. Studies on the Active Center.

It has been known for some time (McDonald, 1955a) that Mg^{++} ions (or other bivalent cations) are essential for the enzymic activity of DNase I. The same enzyme is, on the other hand, inhibited by the following anions : fluoride citrate, arsenate, borate and selenite, probably on account of their reaction with the Mg^{++} ions. Among the other principal inhibitors, might be mentioned the heavy metals such as Cu^{++}, Zn^{++}, Fe^{++}, Fe^{+++}, Cr^{++} and Ni^{++}.
The action of metallic ions has been extensively studied, notably by Becking and Hurst (1963), who showed that the specificity of the enzyme could be modified by the addition of manganous ions. Hydrolysis of DNA by DNase I in the presence of manganous ions results in increased formation of mono- and di-nucleotides, which now represent 5 % and 49 % respectively of the total nucleotide phosphorus. The relative proportions of the isomeric dinucleotides are different from those observed in the presence of Mg^{++} ion activation. The study of the nature of the products formed indicates random endonucleolytic attack, with a few preferred points. The experimental results suggest that the Pu/Pu type of bond is stable, and that the increased liberation of purine nucleotides with a terminal 5′-phosphoryl group is due to the hydrolysis of pPy-pPu links.

Shack and Bynum (1964) have studied the synergic effect of various bivalent cations, and have shown in particular that the highest potentiation of hydrolysis, obtained with the best combinations of Mg^{++} + either Ca^{++}, Ba^{++} or Sr^{++}, in certain cases equals, but never surpasses, the maximum activation obtained with Mg^{++} alone. Ca^{++}, Ba^{++} and Sr^{++} are all weakly active by themselves, but do not exhibit any synergic effect between themselves, or with Mn^{++}. Mg^{++} and Mn^{++} show no synergic effect between each other, although it has already been stated (Ralph et al., 1962) that manganous ions were vastly superior activators compared with Mg^{++} ions.

Finally, Festy et al. (1965) have recently demonstrated the remarkable inhibition of DNase by beryllium ions. The mechanism of this inhibition is believed to be due to the formation of a DNA-Be complex which is the real inhibitor of the enzyme. Under the conditions described by these authors, a $BeSO_4$ concentration of the order of 10^{-4} M is enough to cause a 50 % inhibition of the enzyme.

Considerable work has been carried out by the team of Okada to try and determine the nature of the active center of DNase I (Okada, 1957a, b, c; Okada and Gehrmann, 1957; Okada and Fletcher, 1959, 1961, etc). These experiments were conducted by examining the various known specific inhibitors, and by considering the relation between the degradation of certain aminoacids by irradiation, and the associated loss of enzyme activity. In this way, it was noted that iodoacetate and bromoacetate which bind specifically to the histidine groups of ribonuclease are without action on DNase I. In addition, histidine residues are not affected by irradiation; these two facts suggest that histidine residues are not involved in the active center. Inhibitors of SH groups such as *p*-chloromercuribenzoate and iodoacetate are without action on the enzymic activity of DNase, suggesting that SH groups are not effectively involved in the active center, a conclusion that is also supported by the observation that DNase that has been inactivated by irradiation is not reactivated by the addition of reduced glutathione.   It is also found that diiso-propylfluorophosphate, which acts as a trypsin inhibitor by blocking the serine groups, is without action on DNase I, indicating that the serine residues do not participate in the active center.   N-bromosuccinimide, on the other hand, which inhibits trypsin by destroying the tryptophane groups, strongly inhibits DNase too.   The degree of tryptophan destruction by different N-bromosuc-cinimide concentrations is directly related to the percentage inactivation of the enzyme.   Similarly, inactivation of DNase by irradiation is accompanied by the destruction of the tryptophane groups. The experiments carried out with specific inhibitions and irradiation thus demonstrate that tryptophane is implicated in the active center of the DNase.   DNase I therefore seems to function by a different mechanism from RNase, for which we have seen that histidine groups play a vital part.

Concerning the same class of inhibitors, mention must be made of the work of Eron and McAuslan (1966) who demonstrated that both actinomycin D and ethidium bromide inhibited DNase I activity.   The authors suggest using the latter as a useful tool for examining the biolo-gical function of DNases.

Many other systems able to activate or inhibit DNase I have been described.

Naturally, like most biologically active proteins, DNase is rapidly destroyed by the known proteolytic enzymes such as trypsin, chymotrypsin, ficin, bromelain, papain etc. (Maxwell et al., 1963); this phenomenon can be utilized, if so desired, to halt the action of DNase, for example during its therapeutic application.

Le Talaer et al. (1962) have studied the action of calf liver RNA on the hydrolysis of DNA by DNase I and shown that the RNA slightly raises the amount of degradation of the DNA.

B. DEOXYRIBONUCLEASE FROM CALF THYMUS, DNASE II, OF OPTIMUM pH FOR ACTIVITY IN THE ACID RANGE (E.C.3.1.4.6)

The most extensively studied DNases of this type are those of calf thymus and spleen reported as early as 1949 by Maver and Greco in cathepsin preparations obtained from these organs.

A method for the partial purification of thymus DNase was described by Laskowski et al. (1954), which allowed the preparation of an enzyme with a specific activity, measured spectro-photometrically, of 2 (crystalline DNase I = 10). Frédéricq and Oth (1958), improving on the method of Laskowski et al. by adding calcium phosphate (hydroxyapatite) chromatograms, achieved definite progress in the DNase II purification, since their best preparations had a specific activity of 100.

In spite of this, DNase II is relatively little known as a protein.   The most remarkable aspects of its enzymic propreties are that its pH for optimum activity is situated around 4.5, and that divalent cations have a rather odd effect, being activators at low concentrations and inhibitors at high ones.   At optimal concentration which, in the case of Mg^{++} is from 0.002 — 0.0025 M the activation is 100 % with respect to a control experiment carried out without addition of the bivalent cation (Oth et al., 1958).

Let us now see what happens when thymus DNA is hydrolyzed by a purified preparation of thymus DNase (Privat de Garilhe and Laskowski, 1955 b; figure 51).

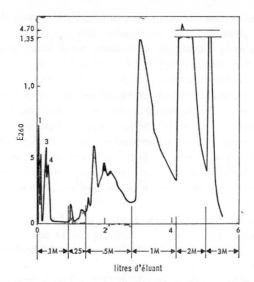

Figure 51. Elution diagram of a hydrolysate by DNase II of 200 mg DNA.   Column : Dowex 1-X2, 0.8 м 10 cm.   Eluent : ammonium formate at pH 4.5.   Volumes and molarities as indicated.   The four first peaks eluted are : peak 1 d-Cp, peak 2 d-Tp, peak 3 d-Ap, peak 4 d-Gp (after Privat de Garilhe and Laskowski, 1955*b*)

The hydrolysate was made under conditions analogous to those employed for DNase I, except that an acetate buffer at pH 5.0 was used instead of borate at pH 7.0, and no Mg^{++} was added. The elution diagram differs in a surprising way from the earlier one, four mononucleotides being present in the following order : 1) d-Cp, 2) d-Tp, 3) d-Ap, 4) d-Gp.   There are few dinucleotides and trinucleotides, but a considerable amount of higher molecular weight oligonucleotides.   The 2 м fraction is much more important than in the previous diagram, and finally, a 3 м buffer is necessary of elute all the polynucleotides.   On comparison of the two diagrams, it is evident that few to the fragments isolated from the two hydrolysates are identical, from which fact stems the idea of a specificity difference between DNase I and DNase II with the same substrate.   At the time, this was a novel idea.

Experiment showed that oligonucleotides that were resistant to DNase I action were also resistant to DNase II.   On the other hand, the 2 м and 3 м fractions resisting DNase II are readily hydrolyzable by DNase I.

The question then arises as to whether the break occurs between the C-3′ position and the phosphate as in DNase I, or whether it is between the phosphate and C-5′.   Experimentally it is found that the fission occurs between the phosphate and the C-5′ position.   The 4 mononucleotides produced in small yield by DNase II were worked up individually by chromatography on Dowex I, then submitted to the action of 5′-nucleotidase.   In no case was there any dephosphorylation, so the monophosphates are 3′-phosphates, and the cleavage occurs at a different position to that with DNase I.

Laurila and Laskowski (1957) systematically studied the position of the terminal phosphoryl groups of the mono- and dinucleotides produced by the action of thymus DNase II, and realized hat none of these nucleotides is dephosphorylated by *Crotalus adamanteus* venom, which is used as a source of 5′ nucleotidase. This fact indicates that the terminal phosphoryl groups are in the 3′-position.

Furthermore, the following nucleotides were isolated and their structures determined : dinucleotides d-CpCp, d-CpTp, d-ApTp, d-ApAp, d-GpAp, trinucleotide d-GpApCp.

It will be noticed that among all these nucleotides the Pyp-Pup type sequence is absent, which induced Laurila and Laskowski to conclude that it would be preferentially broken up by thymus DNase II.

C. BOVINE SPLEEN DEOXYRIBONUCLEASE (DNASE OF TYPE II)

A DNase having comparable properties to those of thymus DNase, i.e. with its optimum activity in the acid range, was reported by Maver and Greco (1949, 1954), partially purified by McDonald (1955b) and finally thoroughly examined by Koerner and Sinsheimer (1957a, b).

During the purification of spleen DNase, Koerner and Sinsheimer's primary object was to free it from spleen phosphodiesterase (cf. p. 267). This aim was realized by the following series of operations (Koerner and Sinsheimer, 1957a) : mincing calf spleen (or the spleens of bovine origin generally), extracting the mince with salt solutions, heating the extract at 58 — 60° for 15 minutes to remove by denaturation certain inactive proteins, fractionating with ethanol and finally chromatographing on Celite. The proteins adsorbed on the Celite were eluted with solutions of 0.05 M Tris-acetate buffer at pH 8.5 containing 0.001 M ethylene diamine tetraacetate, and increasing amounts of NaCl. The DNase is eluted in the first tubes, while phosphodiesterase and phosphatase are more strongly adsorbed.

By this method, a DNase fraction is finally obtained at the exit of the column that is some 100-fold enriched in respect to the tissue extract.

A method for the purification of spleen DNase has also been described by Shimomura and Laskowski (1957); the product obtained appeared to have the same specific activity as that of Koerner and Sinsheimer.

Hodes and Swenson (1962) have proposed a new method for the purification of calf spleen DNase which constitutes a simplification of the methods already described (Sinsheimer, Laskowski, etc.).

This method involves the following steps :

1) extraction

2) heating for 1 hour at 60°

3) two successive chromatograms on carboxymethyl-cellulose. The enrichment obtained was 580-fold, and the enzyme contained no phosphatase and *little* phosphodiesterase.

The properties of spleen DNase are comparable to those of thymus DNase II. The optimum activity pH is very definitely on the acid side, between 4 and 5, with slight differences depending on the nature of the ions contained in the buffer used — a phenomenon frequently met with in enzymology. An important activation of the enzyme is found at pH 4.5 with potassium chloride and magnesium chloride, but on the other hand several polyvalent anions like sulfate, phosphate and arsenate are inhibitors.

The kinetics of the action of spleen DNase on thymus DNA have been mainly studied using the methods Sinsheimer himself described (1954) for DNase I, with an additional new method called the determination of "monoesterified phosphate". This method consists in liberating the monoesterified phosphate with prostate phosphatase, then estimating the inorganic phosphate under special conditions to avoid the complex formation that occurs with high molecular weight polynucleotides.

By following the appearance of (terminal) monoesterified phosphate, Koerner and Sinsheimer noticed that there was a clear-cut and rapid degradation of the DNA until about 10 % of the internucleotide linkages were broken. Slower degradation continued until 20 % of the linkages were broken, when it was finally found that with very high concentrations of enzyme the degradation continued still further, and although in one experiment more than 30 % of the linkages were broken, the hydrolysis appeared to go on indefinitely.

This apparently indefinite hydrolysis cannot be attributed to the presence in the DNase of phosphodiesterase, since a comparison of preparations in which the DNase has been selectively inactivated after chromatography shows that at a given DNase concentration, the same slow rates of degradation are observed, whatever the residual phosphodiesterase concentration. Since the slow degradation is independent of the phosphodiesterase concentration, and since it is related to the DNase activity in the course of its purification, it can be considered that this is an intrinsic property of DNase and not of a contamination.

In addition, the secondary degradation of thymus DNA spleen DNase hydrolysates by prostate phosphatase, by phosphatase plus spleen phosphodiesterase and by snake venom phosphodiesterase, followed by ion exchange chromatographic analysis of the products, has shown that the polynucleotides yield a (terminally) monoesterified phosphate at the C-3′ position. There seems to be no preferential cleavage because of the presence of any particular purine or pyrimidine base. The phosphodiesterase of *C. adamanteus* venom (a 5′-former) can degrade completely and sufficiently long oligonucleotides including, for example, n residues, to give 1 nucleoside, 1 nucleoside diphosphate and (n—2) mononucleotides ending with 5′-phosphate groups, whereas spleen phosphodiesterase (3′-former) yields only n mononucleotides ending with 3′-phosphate groups.

The very high resistance to the action of venom phosphodiesterase of short oligonucleotides terminated by 3′-phosphate groups, and the very high resistance of the dinucleotides in particular, is in agreement with the observations of Privat de Garilhe et al. (1956) concerning oligonucleotides of the same type isolated after the action of the nuclease from *Staphylococcus pyogenes*.

Young et al. (1965) have compared the action of DNase II and DNase I on material that possessed biological activity, namely infectious DNA from the phage λ. The λ phage b2b5c DNA can be prepared in such a way that the molecule undergoes no fission of its chain. DNase II degrades this λ DNA by simultaneous cleavage of the polynucleotide λ chains at the same point, or near the same point. This observation is in agreement with the suggestion by Bernardi and Sadron (1961a). A single one of these fissions is enough to destroy the activity.

So far as pancreatic DNase is concerned, an average of 4 phosphodiester bonds can be broken (scissions of a simple chain) by DNase I without the activity being lost.

Work by Jacquemin-Sablon et al. (1964) has shown that RNA can function as a competitive inhibitor of bovine spleen DNase II; this phenomenon has been observed with rat liver and calf liver, and it depends on the molecular weight of the RNA without it being possible to note any specificity concerning the species. Inhibition of the DNase II could be explained by complex formation between this enzyme, whose isoelectric point is very high, and RNA, which is able to form complexes with many basic proteins.

D. DEOXYRIBONUCLEASE FROM PIG SPLEEN (DNASE OF TYPE II)

This DNase has been mostly studied by Bernardi and co-workers, and exhibits very close analogies with bovine spleen DNase.   It has been prepared in a very high state of purity (Bernardi et al., 1963; Bernardi and Griffé, 1964) by a series of chromatograms on various adsorbants : DEAE-cellulose, hydroxyapatite, Amberlite IRC-50.   The specific activity rises from 3.9 units in the starting material to 302 in the purest product, an almost 80-fold enrichment.   The final material appears homogeneous by the usual physical criteria (sedimentation and electrophoresis on cellulose acetate at different pH values), by analysis of the aminoacids, centrifugation in a density gradient (figure 53) and by enzymological criteria.

Properties of pig spleen DNase II.

This DNase is active both on DNA and on a series of *p*-nitrophenylphosphodiesters.   The DNase hydrolyzes natural DNA and denatured DNA, although the formation of acid-soluble nucleotides is slower in the latter case.   The optimum pH is close to 4.8; magnesium is slightly inhibiting above pH 4.5 and alters the optimum pH so that it falls to 4.4.

This enzyme exhibits activity on $Ca[bis(p\text{-nitrophenyl})\text{-phosphate}]_2$ and on thymidine-deoxyguanosine- and deoxycytidine-3'-phosphate *p*-nitrophenyl esters.

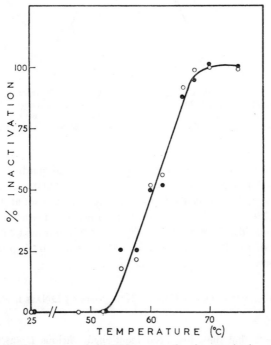

Figure 52. Thermal inactivation curve.   Acid DNase samples in standard acetate buffer were kept 20 minutes at the temperatures indicated in the abscissa; they were chilled in ice bath and assayed at 37° for both DNase (open circles) and "phosphodiesterase" activity (solid circles).   (Bernardi & Griffé 1964)

Both the DNase and the phosphodiesderase activities are due to the same protein molecule, since it is impossible to dissociate them in the course of three different treatments : chromatography on Amberlite IRC-50, thermal inactivation and centrifugation in a sucrose gradient. During all these three types of treatment a completely identical behavior of the two activities is observed (figures 52, 53, 54).

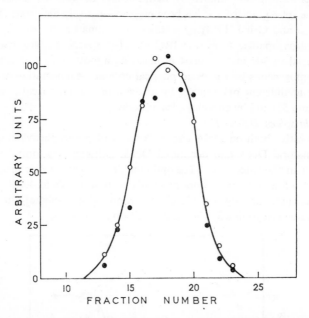

Figure 53. Sucrose-gradient centrifugation of acid DNase. A total of 32 fractions was collected. Circles indicate the DNase activity; points indicate the "phosphodiesterase" activity. Bottom of the cell to the left. A linear molarity gradient was obtained using 5 % and 20 % sucrose solutions in standard acetate buffer. Centrifugation was carried out for 16 hours at 4° at 38,000 rpm using a SW-39 rotor and a Spinco Model L ultracentrifuge (Bernardi & Griffé 1964)

Other properties of this DNase were later on described by Bernardi et al. (1965) : for instance it was shown that hog spleen DNase has a molecular weight of 38,000 calculated from the diffusion coefficient. The sedimentation coefficient is 3.4 S, the isoelectric point at pH 10.2 and the extinction coefficient 12.1 at 280 mμ. The total hydrolysis shows the presence of glucosamine in addition to the usual aminoacids, therefore this enzyme is a glucoprotein capable of simultaneous attack on each strand of the DNA double helix. This " single hit " process will be discussed below for it is a property common to all acid DNases.

E. OTHER "ACID" DEOXYRIBONUCLEASES (DNASE IIS), COMMON DNASE II PROPERTIES, COMPARISON WITH DNASE I.

In addition to those that have just been mentioned, various DNases with their optimum activity in the acid range of pH have been discovered in the tissues of higher animals. For example, the distribution of these DNases in the tissues of the guinea-pig, rat and mouse was studied by

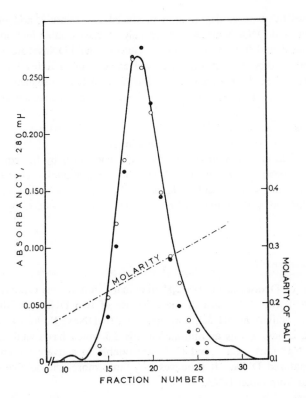

Figure 54. Chromatography of acid DNase on IRC-50. The enzyme was eluted by a molarity gradient of phosphate buffer, pH 6.0. The solid line gives the absorbancy at 280 mμ (left ordinate); the broken line indicates the molarity (right-hand ordinate). Circles indicate the DNase activity, points the "phosphodiesterase" activity; both activities are given in arbitrary units   (Bernardi & Griffé 1964)

Tempel and Roessner (1965).   The values obtained for the optimum pH of the brain DNases was 5.2 for the three species mentioned.   The corresponding values found for the spleen of the guinea-pig and rat were respectively 5.2 and 5.0.

A DNase II from lamb spleen has also been reported by Slor and Hodes (1965).   This enzyme has an optimum pH of 4.5.   An enzyme of the same type, having an optimum activity at pH 5.5 was also found in the mammary mouse tumor C_3H (Georgatsos and Symeonidis, 1965).

All the acid DNases possess common properties so far as their mode of DNA hydrolysis is concerned.   This is clear from a publication by Bernardi and Sadron (1964) in which they report the results of experiments carried out on the mechanism of degradation of DNA from various sources (chicken erythrocytes, calf thymus, *E. coli*) by acid DNases extracted from, respectively, chicken erythrocytes, calf thymus, calf spleen and pig spleen.   The hydrolysis of the DNA by these various DNases was followed by measuring the molecular weight of the DNA by light scattering during the hydrolysis.   Natural DNA is degraded following two kinetic pathways corresponding to a "single hit" and a "double hit".   Degradation of the "single hit" type takes place by simultaneous scission of the two chains at the same point.   The "double hit" type of degradation resembles the type of degradation produced by DNase I, and only occurs after a latent period.   Denatured DNA is attacked essentially by the "double hit" mechanism.   These observations led Bernardi and Sadron to a hypothesis in which acid DNases are taken to be proteins with two active centers; these enzymes are believed capable of breaking both DNA chains at the same time at sites where the preferentially hydrolyzed nucleotide sequences are found in the two opposing chains, or else to break only one chain when the sensitive site occurs on only one of the chains.

This concept was strengthened by the dimeric structure and allosteric properties of hog spleen acid DNase discovered by Bernardi (1965).   The dimeric structure of DNase II was suggested first by the even repartition of aminoacid residues and confirmed by the complete dissociation into monomers which occurs in 8M urea—0.1 M 2-mercaptoethanol.   Therefore the single hit mechanism of DNA hydrolysis by acid DNases can be explained by the simultaneous attack of opposite bonds, located at the same level on the DNA double helices, by the active centers of the dimeric enzyme.

F. Mouse tumor deoxyribonucleases

The distribution of DNases in mouse C_3H mammary tumors was examined by Georgatsos and Symeonidis (1965) who demonstrated the existence of two DNase activities in this tissue. One had an optimum activity at pH 5.5, corresponding to DNase II, known to occur in many animal tissues, and a DNase having an optimum at pH 8.5 which has a vital need of Mg^{++} ions, and is inhibited by Na^+ ions. Ca^{++} and Co^{++} are unable to activate the enzyme, which acts preferentially on denatured DNA.   It produces $2\frac{1}{2}$ times more acid soluble deoxyribose from denatured DNA than from intact DNA.

G. *Mustelus canis* deoxyribonuclease

The work of Ashe et al. (1965) concerns the characterization of the *Mustelus canis* DNase. It is an enzyme that hydrolyzes thermally denatured DNA, such as for instance the DNA isolated from the bacteriophage T_4.   The enzyme is extracted by standard methods from the liver of this elasmobranch.

Its activity on denatured DNA (on which it acts preferentially to native DNA) is optimal in 0.1 M NaCl.   The need for bivalent cations can be met by Mg^{++}, Mn^{++} or Co^{++}.   The optimum pH is at 8.0 and the hydrolysis process is reported to be endonucleolytic.

H. "Alkaline" deoxyribonuclease from crab testes

This enzyme has been worked up from testes of the crab *Neptunus astatus* by the following series of operations (Georgatsos, 1965) :
1) Extraction.
2) Preparation of an acetone-insoluble powder.
3) Ammonium sulfate fractionation.
4) Filtration on Sephadex G-100 gel.

5) Filtration on Sephadex G-200.

The optimum activity is at pH 8.5 in the presence of 10^{-3} M Mg $^{++}$. A synergism between Ca^{++} and Mg^{++} exists, the enzyme being optimally activated in the presence of 7.5×10^{-4} M Mg^{++} and 2.5×10^{-4} M Ca^{++}. The enzyme acts endonucleolytically, and the reaction products are 3'-phosphates. Preferential cleavage of XpTp is observed, XpCp being the most resistant type of bond towards *N. astatus* DNA.

1. Deoxyribonucleases from various marine invertebrates : comparison with vertebrate DNase II (DNase II from bovine spleen)

Russel et al. (1964) undertook some investigations of DNases from the tissues of various phyla specially picked from the marine invertebrates. On one hand annelids, arthropods and molluscs were chosen, since they constitute a natural group of phyla related to, though differing from the vertebrates, and on the other hand echinoderms were chosen as representing a phylum having affinities with the chordates, and consequently with vertebrates. The DNases from these various invertebrates were compared with the DNase II that is widely distributed in vertebrate tissue (see above). Bovine spleen was the tissue selected as the source of vertebrate DNase II. The work of Russel et al. can be summarized as follows :

The acid DNases extracted respectively from the annelid *Tubifex tubifex*, the mollusc *Mercenaria mercenaria* and the arthropod *Homarus americanus* represent a different class of enzymes from those including vertebrate DNase I and DNase II. The distinction between the two classes of enzymes was established by the fact that their response to activation or deactivation by metallic ions is different. This new class of enzymes can be defined as *deoxyribonucleotidases* that are active in the acid pH region, and that are activated by bivalent cations and anions at concentrations which inhibit DNase II. The behavior of the acid DNase extracted from the sea urchin *Strongylocentrotus droehbachiensis* allows it to be classed as a DNase of type II; the enzyme has an optimum pH of about 5, it is inhibited by sodium sulfate and MgCl$_2$ at concentrations of from 0.01 M to 0.04 M and MnCl$_2$ at a concentration of 0.04 M inhibits the enzymic reaction to the extent of 30 %. These facts are considered by the authors as supplementary evidence for the postulated phylogenetic affinities between the echinoderms and the chordates.

III. DEOXYRIBONUCLEASES OF MICROBIAL ORIGIN

A. *Clostridium* deoxyribonucleases

In a series of articles that appeared between 1959 and 1962, Meisel et al. described the properties of a DNase (β-antigen) produced by multiplying cells of *Clostridium septicum*. This DNase does not appear to be influenced by a variable concentration of magnesium ions, but it is inhibited by manganese ions. The authors were able to characterize a DNase activity in disintegrated cells of *Cl. septicum*, but the activity thus demonstrated was quantitatively inferior to that found in the culture fluid. The DNase extracted from *Cl. septicum* is completely and specifically neutralized by the antitoxic serum of *Cl. septicum*. The antitoxic serum of *Cl. chauvoei* partially neutralizes the *Cl. septicum* activity, while the antitoxic sera of *Cl. perfringens* type A and *Cl. histolyticum* do not exert any neutralizing action on the enzyme, even at elevated concentrations. The latter two sera thus behave towards *Cl. septicum* DNase in the same way that ordinary horse serum does.

B. *Escherichia coli* DEOXYRIBONUCLEASES

Deoxyribonucleases are widely spread in enterobacteriacaæ to such a point that Rothberg and Swartz (1965) suggested using this property as a criterion to distinguish the members of this family. *Escherichia coli* as usual, was much favored by the number of investigations achieved on its DNase equipment. According to Kersten et al. (1965), who measured DNase activity in *E. coli* crude cellular extracts, the free DNases are to be found mainly in the ribosome-free supernatants.

Lehman (1963) and Jorgensen and Koerner (1965) have reported evidence for the existence in cell-free extracts of *Escherichia coli*, strain B, of six distinct hydrolytic enzymes attacking specifically deoxyribonucleic chains. Among these enzymes, the predominating one is an endonuclease, called *E. coli* endonuclease I, which acts preferentially on natural double-stranded DNA. The other five enzymes are exonucleases attacking the polydeoxyribonucleic chain from the end carrying the terminal 3'-hydroxyl group, and liberating one after the other nucleoside-5'-phosphates. The most active of these enzymes is exonuclease I, which possesses an almost total specificity for single stranded denatured DNA. The two following exonucleases (II and III), on the other hand, prefer the double chains. Exonuclease II is the nuclease associated with highly purified DNA polymerase preparations; exonuclease III, also called DNA phosphatase exonuclease by Lehman and his coworkers, is associated with specific phosphomonoesterase activity on the DNA, liberating not only a 5'-nucleotide residue from the terminal 3'-hydroxyl end of the DNA, but also any monoesterified phosphoryl group in this position. Concerning the exonucleases IV and V of *E. coli* B, the existence of which was demonstrated by Jorgensen and Koerner (1965), they have only slight activity on highly polymerized deoxyribonucleic chains, either single- or double-stranded. An excellent substrate for these two exonucleases is the oligonucleotides obtained after action of pancreatic DNase I on DNA. Although they are fairly closely related, these two exonucleases can be separated by chromatography on DEAE-cellulose.

In this chapter we intend to deal only with the true DNase of *E. coli* (Lehman's "endonuclease I", despite its being specific for DNA) and the discussion of the *E. coli* exonucleases will be postponed to the chapter dealing with exonucleases (p. 270).

It has been mentioned that the enzyme, characterized by Lehman, Roussos and Pratt (1962*a*, *b*) in cell-free extracts of *E. coli* preferentially hydrolyzes double helical DNA to yield oligonucleotides, the size of which is generally superior to the pentanucleotide stage. The enzyme proceeds by cleaving at a number of points within the chain, and must therefore be classed as an endonuclease. Its optimum activity, measured in Tris buffer, lies between pH 7.5 and 8.5, this optimum being observed in the presence of Mg^{++} ions. This DNase is strongly inhibited by ribonucleic acids from various sources.

The purification of the enzyme was realized by the following stages :
1) Extraction
2) Adsorption on protamine sulfate then elution
3) Fractionation with ammonium sulfate

4) Fractionation on DEAE-cellulose

5) Chromatography on CM-cellulose

Under these conditions, the specific activity rises from 10.2 units per milligram protein at the beginning of the purification to 6,300 units per milligram protein at the end, an enrichment of about 600-fold. In the course of this purification, dissociation of the two activities initially present RNase and DNase, is observed.

Naber et al. (1965, 1966), noticed that agarose binds proteins, especially endonuclease I from *E. Coli* strain B extracts, and proposed a new method for preparing this enzyme by adsorption to and elution from agarose followed by chromatographies on DEAE- and CM-celluloses.

So far as the specificity of *E. coli* DNase is concerned, Lehman et al. have observed that its action on DNA results in the formation of oligonucleotides having an average chain length corresponding to 7 nucleotides and carrying a phosphomonoester in the C-5′ position. The oligonucleotides with a lower chain length are resistant to the action of this DNase, and bonds of the d-pApX type are apparently relatively resistant.

The four deoxyribonucleodepolymerases characterized by Lehman and co-workers in *E. coli* B have been studied by the same authors (Shortman and Lehman, 1964) in different physiological conditions. In particular, it was noticed that the activities of the four enzymes were higher during the exponential growth phase, diminishing to varying extents during the stationary phase.

Bernardi and Cordonnier (1965) have demonstrated that *E. coli* DNase I (or endonuclease I) hydrolyzes DNA in both chains at the same time and in the same place ("single hit"), by a comparable process to that found with spleen DNase II. These two DNases differ, nevertheless, in the nature of the nucleotides formed, which are 5′-phosphates for *coli* DNase and 3′-phosphates for spleen DNase. According to the same authors (Cordonnier and Bernardi 1965), *E. coli* endonuclease I should be localized near to the bacterial surface.

Weissbach and Korn (1963) have studied the distribution of DNases in another strain of *Escherichia coli*, namely K_{12} λ (lysogenic bacterium). The DNases were prepared from the K_{12} λ strain by extracting the cells by standard methods and finally purifying by chromatography on DEAE-cellulose. These authors obtained in this way four chromatographic peaks corresponding to four distinct enzymic activities, which they called DNase I, II, III and IV from *E. coli* K_{12} λ. The I and II DNases possess properties comparable to those of *E. coli* B DNase, or Lehman's *E. coli* B endonuclease (Lehman, Roussos and Pratt, 1962a, b; Lehman, 1963), i.e. endonucleolytic activity causing the appearance of higher fragments than pentanucleotides, inhibition by RNA, optimum activity between pH 7 and 8. The III and IV DNases, corresponding to the third and fourth chromatographic peaks, have somewhat different properties; they are not inhibited by RNA. DNase III degrades denatured DNA 13 times faster than it does double stranded DNA. The main products of the action of these DNases III and IV appear to be mononucleotides. The two nucleases III and IV have optimum activity at pH 8.5 — 9.0.

Korn and Weissbach (1963) have shown that lysogenic induction of K_{12} λ by mitomycin causes the appearance of a new DNase not found in normal K_{12} λ cells.

Following up this idea, Koerner and co-workers (Oleson and Koerner, 1964; Short and Koerner, 1965) observed the appearance during infection of *E. coli* by the T_2 phage, of nucleases that could be distinguished from the known nucleases normally found in uninfected *E. coli* cells.

C. STREPTOCOCCAL DEOXYRIBONUCLEASES

Among bacterial DNases, one of the most examined enzymes is certainly the so-called "strep-todornase" (abbreviation of streptococcal deoxyribonuclease) produced by *Streptococci*. There are partially purified streptodornase preparations commercially available, and such a preparation was the starting point for Potter and Laskowski's experiments (1959). As in the case of the DNases I and II, the hydrolysate from thymus DNA (at pH 7.0 in the presence of Mg^{++} ions) was chromatographed on Dowex I. There were few mononucleotides, but two dinucleotides could be isolated :

$$d\text{-pCpC of the type pPy} - pPy$$
$$d\text{-pApC of the type pPu} - pPy.$$

Streptodornase thus favors the appearance of at least one dinucleotide with a purine-pyrimidine linkage (the reverse sequence to that produced by DNase I, which is pC — pA). It would therefore seem that the type of bond that is preferentially broken is pPy — pPu. The nucleotides produced are terminated by 5'-phosphoryl groups.

Later, Stone and Burton (1961) showed that there is a synergic action of certain bivalent cations on streptodornase. The sample that these authors used was an extracellular commercial preparation of DNase from *Streptococcus haemolyticus* in general activated by Mg^{++} ions. They confirmed that the hydrolysis occurred at the position of the phosphodiester bonds attached to the nucleotide C-3' position, i.e. the liberated oligonucleotides are terminated by 5'-phosphate ester groups. According to Stone and Burton, DNA depolymerization involves two sites linked to metals, or two groups of sites, one requiring Mg^{++}, Mn^{++} or Fe^{++}, and the other Ca^{++} or Sr^{++} ions.

It was as a result of these observations that Georgatsos, Unterholzner and Laskowski (1962) wondered whether the optimal activity of the enzyme would not provoke new ruptures, i.e. whether the synergic action with two bivalent metal ions would not modify the streptodornase specificity.

Purification of the enzyme was effected by the latter authors from the commercial preparation by dialysis and chromatography on DEAE-cellulose; in this way, the specific activity was multiplied by six.

Exhaustive hydrolysis of DNA by this purified enzyme leads to formation of not more than 1.5 % mononucleotides, 90 % of the hydrolysate consisting of oligonucleotides with from 3 to 10 mononucleotides. Examination of the frequency of nucleotides in the terminal position shows that guanylic acid predominates at the end, carrying a 5'-phosphate group (about 50 %), while at the end with a free 3'-hydroxyl group, the distribution is nearly random, although it was noted that thymidylic + adenylic represented about 60 % of the extremities.

Starting from *Streptococcus pyogenes*, Winter and Bernheimer (1964) were able to isolate four different DNases by continuous-flow (= "curtain") electrophoresis, and electrophoresis in a sucrose gradient.

The four streptococcal DNases resemble pancreatic DNase in that they are endonucleases attacking double-stranded DNA at a greater rate than denatured DNA, producing oligonucleotides terminated by 5'-phosphate groups, and requiring bivalent cations to be active. The combined presence of Mg^{++} and Ca^{++} increases the activity of all four of these nucleases.

Determination of the optimal pH for the four enzymes in the presence of Mg^{++} and Ca^{++} using the standard system of estimation gave the following results : DNase A, 8 — 9; DNase B, 8 — 9; DNase C, 5 — 6; DNase D, 6 — 7.

DNases A and B cleave pXpG sequences preferentially. DNase D acts preferentially on pXpA linkages, and DNase C, judging by the results of limited hydrolysis, is relatively unspecific so far as the sequence of bases attacked is concerned.

IV. DEOXYRIBONUCLEASE INHIBITORS (MOSTLY OF PROTEIN NATURE)

DNase inhibitors have been shown to exist in various animal tissues such as the hypertrophic tissue of pigeon crop gland (Dabrowska and Laskowski, 1949; Cooper et al., 1950), human leucocytes and cells of human bone marrow (Henstel and Freedman, 1952; Henstel et al., 1952), various constituents of human blood such as white blood cells, red cells and serum (Gupter and Herriott, 1963), the serum of various animals, especially rat (Berger, 1965) and calf spleen (Lindberg, 1964, 1966). Other inhibitors have also been described from yeast extracts (Zamenhof and Chargaff, 1948).

Inhibition of pancreatic DNase and RNase can also be realized by polyanionic polymers of conventional types such as 1) the products obtained by condensation of carbonyl or sulfonic phenolic derivatives with aldehydes, 2) polymers arising by condensation of products of type 1 with phenolic acids under oxidizing conditions, 3) polymers resulting from the oxidative polymerization of products of the phenol or hydroquinone type (Heyman et al., 1958). All these polyanionic polymers act by forming complexes with DNases or RNases, which can be considered as polycationic proteins, similarly to the way that RNA is considered as a polyanionic polymer inhibiting *E. coli* DNase I (endonuclease I) (Lehman et al., 1962, p. 252).

Among the inhibitors of protein origin that occur naturally in tissues, we propose first to give some information about the DNase inhibitor in pigeon crop gland, which seems to be the first known from a historical point of view. The way in which Dabrowska et al. (1949) discovered the inhibitor was through the consideration that the epithelium of this gland undergoes alternative hypertrophy and desquamation, so that it was logical to think it might contain a high amount of DNase. To examine the DNase content, 0.1 to 0.4 g amounts of tissue were taken by biopsy during development and while at rest. The tissue was minced with water and centrifuged, and the extract analyzed for its DNase activity. No activity was found at any stage. From this point to that of believing the gland to contain an inhibitor was only a short step, and it was soon realized that extracts of normal or hypertrophied pigeon crop possessed the property of inhibiting pancreatic DNase in variable proportions depending on the state of activity of the gland. Partially purified fractions of this inhibitor made it possible to attain 100 % inhibition of the DNase under the experimental conditions described by Dabrowska et al. This inhibitor is a protein, since it is rapidly destroyed by heat, exposure to pH 3.0 and trypsin, and it is not dialyzable.

Among the other inhibitors mentioned in the literature, we might quote those occurring in the cellular components of human blood. Gupter and Herriott (1963) claim that white cells contain a DNase inhibitor which is liberated into the medium when the cells are incubated. The same authors have also been able to show that during lysis of red cells, a significant amount of a DNase inhibitor and comparatively little RNase inhibitor are present. During human serum incubation, the DNase activity disappears little by little, and Gupter and Herriott showed that this phenomenon was due to the appearance of an inhibitor that was sufficiently active to reduce the activity of the foreign pancreatic DNase which can be added to the medium. DNase inhibitors are also found in rat serum, and Berger (1965) has been able to show that the amount of inhibitor

varies with the animal's age; the amount is low at birth, passes through a maximum at about
6 — 7 weeks, and then slowly diminishes (figure 55).

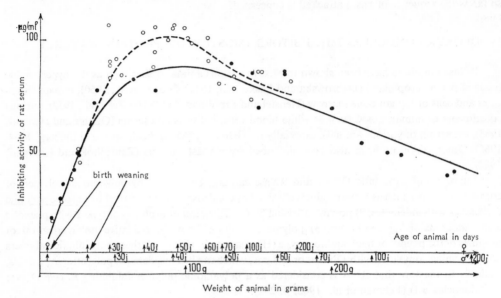

Figure 55. Inhibiting ability of rat serum against DNase I as a function of the weight and age of the
animal (Berger, 1965).
   1) Male animals (—●—)
   2) Female animals (...O...)
   The inhibitor concentration is expressed in micrograms DNase inhibited per ml serum, under the
conditions of the determination

    The DNase inhibitor occurring in calf spleen has been prepared in a high state of purity
by Lindberg (1964) by a series of treatments involving ammonium sulfate fractionation, chromatography on alumina Cγ and chromatography on DEAE-Sephadex. In the course of this purification the specific activity rose from 880 units in the crude starting extract to 35,000 in the product
obtained after chromatography on DEAE-Sephadex, or a 40-fold enrichment, in 13 % yield.
Lindberg also noted that several bovine organs such as spleen, thymus, testes, brain and liver
contain DNase inhibitors, but that the spleen contained the greatest amount (nearly 10 times
the amount in the liver).

    More recently, the same author (Lindberg 1966), succeeded in crystallizing from calf spleen
two inhibitors of DNase I designated inhibitors I and II. This was achieved by subsequent purification of the fraction coming from the DEAE-Sephadex chromatography : this fraction was
submitted to gel filtration through a column of Sephadex G-100 followed by a chromatography
on hydroxyapatite. The last step of the purification procedure is represented in figure 56.

    The highly purified inhibitor from bovine spleen possesses the general properties associated
with proteins; it is thermostable with a stability optimum at pH 7.6, and a "typical" U.V.
spectrum between 250 and 350 mμ; it is stabilized by compounds containing -SH groups, and
issensitive to the action of trypsin.

Preliminary studies on the mechanism of the inhibition indicate that the inhibitor works by becoming bonded to the DNase with which they form stable complexes. In the case of inhibitor II it was shown that the complex (molecular weight 88, 200) consisted of one mole of DNase I (molecular weight 33,200) and one mole of inhibitor (molecular weight 57,400).

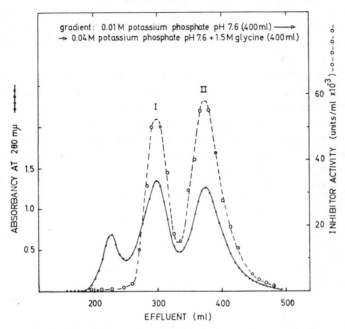

Figure 56. Chromatography of inhibitors from spleen on hydroxyapatite (Lindberg, 1966). Before the protein sample (100 mg) was applied to the column (4 × 9 cm), it was dialyzed against 0.005 M potassium phosphate. pH 7.6, for 3 hours (2 × 2 liters). After the dialysis, the sample was diluted with water to give a protein concentration of 10 mg per ml. The column was eluted with linear gradient as shown in the figure

V. DEOXYRIBONUCLEASES AS GROWTH FACTORS

The observations made by Brody (1958) were the first to draw attention to the fact that tissues that were undergoing rapid multiplication had an increased deoxyribonuclease content. These facts led Zahn (1959) to wonder whether the DNase itself could, as such, have an influence on the rate of cell multiplication. Experiments undertaken on *Euglena gracilis*, in the course of which the DNase action was examined, did indeed show that at doses of about a microgram, the growth of this organism could be doubled under the influence of the enzyme.

This phenomenon is a general one, since at DNase I concentrations of from 10^{-8} to 10^{-5} grams per milliliter, organisms such as fertilized eggs of sea urchin, *Turbellaria* and frog, and microorganisms such as *Micrococcus*, *Euglena gracilis*, *Glaucoma piriformis*, as well as human cells in tissue culture all show a clear rise in cell division (Zahn, 1960). This action on cell division is not limited only to pancreatic DNase, since a series of other DNases such as streptodornase, *S. pyogenes* DNase and the DNase from pig spleen exhibit the same activating effect. Pig spleen DNase II turned out to be at least 10 million times more active than the other DNases.

One objection that can be raised against these experiments is as follows; how far are the products of DNA hydrolysis by DNases in the extracellular medium themselves growth factors? The objection can be met if experiments are carried out showing that the biological action of the enzymes is not influenced by products like DNA from identical dead or foreign cells. This addition even has the opposite effect of increasing the DNase action, whilst the addition of various nucleotides has no action at all.

The proposition is therefore that DNases, or some essential parts of them, are able to penetrate into the interior of cells. The fact that the addition of surface-active agents greatly potentiates the DNase action supports the latter hypothesis, and this would be one further example of the active penetration of macromolecules into the cell interior.

Inside the cells, the site of the DNase action is closely linked to mitotic mechanisms, since the mitogenic hormone 17 β-estradiol potentiates the effect of DNase. This is a highly specific effect, 17 α-estradiol not causing this response.

These experiments taken together show that DNases behave throughout as growth factors.

"Non-specific" and specific phosphodiesterases
(exonucleases-phosphodiesterases)

I. GENERAL REMARKS, CHARACTERIZATION METHODS, ESTIMATION

These enzymes form part of the Phosphoric Diester Hydrolases (E.C.3.1.4) and have been officially named by the Enzyme commission "Orthophosphoric diester phosphohydrolases" (E.C.3.1.4.1). The suggested trivial name is "Phosphodiesterases". Considering these enzymes from the point of view of their action on the nucleic acids, they are in principle enzymes able to hydrolyze the polynucleotide chain in a stepwise manner by successively detaching mononucleotides one after the other from one end of the chain. Most of these enzymes have been known for long time under the name of *phosphodiesterases**, i.e. enzymes hydrolyzing all phosphodiesters without distinction between the type of residue esterifying the phosphoryl group, so that such enzymes will also effect stepwise hydrolysis of the polynucleotides (e.g. snake venom phosphodiesterase). For this reason we have provisionally retained a single chapter for exonuclease and phosphodiesterases, although the recent discovery of phosphodiesterase-exonucleases where the action is limited to nucleic acids forces attention to be drawn to this class of enzyme, and also requires two enzyme classes to be mentioned, that could later give rise to two separate headings:

1) Phosphodiesterase-exonucleases, unspecific towards the nature of the residues esterifying the phosphoryl group, and whose action extends to all phosphodiesters. Example : snake venom phosphodiesterase.

2) Phosphodiesterase-exonucleases, specific towards the nature of the residues esterifying the phosphoryl group, and whose action is limited to polynucleotide phosphodiesters. Example : the exonuclease I from *Escherichia coli*.

It is also convenient to distinguish in each phosphodiesterase category between those producing nucleoside-3′-phosphates and those producing nucleoside-5′-phosphates, which is actually the only certain criterion for distinguishing the nucleases, since there has so far never been found

---

* It may be seen how unsatisfactory this name is if one considers that all nucleases are, in fact, phosphodiesterases.

a nuclease able to produce sometimes 3'-phosphates and sometimes 5'-phosphates. Apart from this, all phosphodiesterases catalyze overall reactions of the type.

$$O = \overset{\displaystyle OH}{\underset{\displaystyle OR_2}{P}} - OR_1 + H_2O \longrightarrow O = \overset{\displaystyle OH}{\underset{\displaystyle OR_2}{P}} - OH + R_1OH$$

where R_1 and R_2 represent either alcohol or phenol groups or nucleosides. They catalyze this type of reaction as opposed to the phosphomonoesterases or phosphatases which hydrolyze phosphomonoesters with the production of alcohol or phenol and free inorganic phosphate. It is by this scheme that, for example, diphenylphosphate is hydrolyzed to monophenylphosphate and phenol, without the hydrolysis going any further.

It does not appear that phosphoric acid triesters can be hydrolyzed by any of the animal or vegetable phosphatases.

Although monophosphatases have been known for half a century, it would seem that phosphodiesterases were only discovered around 1929-1930 by a number of Japanese workers. Azakawa (1929), attempting to hydrolyze a wide variety of phosphoric esters including some phosphodiesters with crude phosphatase preparations from kidney and takadiastase, noted that the diesters were slightly hydrolyzed, but does not seem to have attributed this weak hydrolysis to a different enzyme from the phosphomonoesterases already known. Uzawa (1932) and Takahashi (1932), studying the venom from the Japanese "habu" snake (*Trimesurus flavoviridis*), showed that the venom was without action on monophenylphosphate, but that it was able to hydrolyze diphenylphosphate with liberation of monophenylphosphate and phenol. In 1938, Gulland and Jackson examined the distribution of phosphomonoesterases and phosphodiesterases in the bones of a large number of mammals, and in twelve snake venoms. They showed that some of these venoms were exceptionally rich in phosphodiesterase, pointing out the interest of *Crotalus adamanteus* venom, which contains phosphodiesterase but no phosphomonoesterase. Since that time, *C. adamanteus* venom has been used by several groups as a source of phosphodiesterase. It was also found that although this venom did not contain a non-specific phosphomonoesterase, it did contain a "5'-nucleotidase". It is necessary to free it from the latter enzyme if dephosphorylation of all the nucleotides terminating in a 5'-phosphate is to be avoided when it is used for oligonucleotide analysis.

It was finally realized that most tissues and microorganisms contain exonucleases and exonuclease-phosphodiesterases.

Demonstration of the phosphodiesterase activity.

The estimation of phosphodiesterase activity is carried out as a routine method using Ca [bis(*p*-nitrophenyl)phosphate]$_2$ as substrate, following the directions of Yoshida (1941). This material constitutes a convenient substrate for phosphodiesterase estimation, because it results in the liberation of yellow-colored nitrophenol in the reaction medium, but many other products can also serve as substrates for phosphodiesterase estimation (table XXXVII, p. 263).

Example of phosphodiesterase determination: estimation of C. adamanteus venom phosphodiesterase.

The liberation of *p*-nitrophenol is directly measured with a spectrophotometer fitted with a thermostated cell cavity at 37°. The wavelength chosen is 440 mμ.

Into a suitable glass cell is measured : 1 ml 0.3 M glycine — NaOH buffer at pH 9.0, 1.5 ml

0.001 M Ca[bis(p-nitrophenyl)phosphate]$_2$* solution. Independently, an enzyme solution containing 0.01 to 0.25 units phosphodiesterase per milliliter (cf. below for definition of a phosphodiesterase unit) is heated. After 5 minutes equilibrating time, 0.5 ml of the enzyme solution are pipetted into the glass cell. Readings are taken every 3 minutes for 15 to 30 minutes.

Under theses conditions, a zero order reaction persists for at least 30 minutes. A direct relation has been observed between the activity and the amount of enzyme, at least within the limits recommended for the estimation.

The phosphodiesterase activity is expressed by the rise in optical density at 440 mμ at 3 minute intervals. A phosphodiesterase unit has been defined as the amount of enzyme which, under the conditions indicated, results in the hydrolysis of 1 micromole of the substrate per minute at 37°.
A slight variation of the method described consists in making the final optical density readings at 400 mμ. instead of 440 mμ.

Demonstration of the presence of nucleolytic enzymes in general and ribonucleases and phosphodiesterases in particular within tissues can be effected by a micro-method developed by Sierakowska et al. (1964). This method is based on microdissection of individual cells in a non-aqueous medium, incubation of the isolated cell fragments with specific substrates and micro-electrophoresis of the products resulting from enzymic hydrolysis. This method is relatively independent of artefacts arising from enzyme diffusion and will allow a whole range of nucleolytic enzymes to be listed, according to the nature of the substrates used.

Exonucleases that are specific for ribonucleic or deoxyribonucleic polynucleotides are without action on phosphoric diesters such as diphenyl phosphate or Ca[bis(p-nitrophenyl)phosphate]$_2$, and often without action on macromolecular nucleic acids too. They must then be determined by using polynucleotides obtained by partial degradation of nucleic acids as substrates, and by adapting the methods described for the determination of the nucleases. In this way, the exonuclease of *Escherichia coli* can be determined by a method utilizing precipitation of the nucleotides in acid medium with a partially degraded thymus DNA as substrate (Lehman, 1960, cf. p. 271); ribonucleic exonucleases can similarly be determined using as substrate the RNA core left by RNase A, following the method described by Heppel and Hilmoe (1955b). Special methods, adapted to each enzyme, will be described below with the corresponding exonucleases.

II. PHOSPHODIESTERASE — EXONUCLEASES FROM SNAKE VENOMS

A. PHOSPHODIESTERASE — EXONUCLEASE OF *Crotalus adamanteus*

1. Purification of the phosphodiesterase of *C. adamanteus* venom

Hurst and Butler (1951) proposed the use of cellulose powder columns for the fractionation of snake venoms and thereby obtained fractions that were rich in phosphodiesterase and practically

---

* This material may be purchased ready-made from some suppliers or synthesized following the technique of Privat de Garilhe and Laskowski (1955a).

free from phosphomonoesterase (5'-nucleotidase). Sinsheimer and Koerner (1952b) attained the same end by employing a series of acetone fractionations. It does not appear that these authors were concerned with contamination of the phosphodiesterase samples obtained by enzymes other than 5'-nucleotidase. Privat de Garilhe and Laskowski (1955) developed a method utilizing a series of chromatograms on cation exchangers, which, although tedious and lengthy, does result in obtaining chromatographically pure samples of phosphodiesterase, i.e. samples from chromatographic peaks in which all points have the same specific activity.

More extensive studies made in Laskowski's laboratory (Felix et al., 1960) have shown that the method can be simplified by using the following technique in four stages : 1) fractional precipitation with acetone; 2) fractional precipitation with alcohol; 3) chromatography on CM-cellulose; 4) chromatography on DEAE-cellulose.

Boman and Kaletta (1957) have obtained interesting results concerning the purification of phosphodiesterases, using mostly DEAE-cellulose, and Razzel and Khorana (1959a) have proposed an eclectic scheme of purification drawn from the various methods described above.

The fact that all these methods and modifications have been proposed, shows that the problem of the purification of C. adamanteus venom is difficult, this being for a number of reasons. Firstly, the relative scarcity of the starting material, and the inconstancy of its composition make the experiments poorly reproducible, and they are complicated by the presence of the many enzymes with closely related properties.

2. Properties of the phosphodiesterase

a. *Stability, optimum activity pH*

The purified phosphodiesterase is unstable in dilute aqueous solution. In 0.1 M NaCl solution, on the other hand, it can be stored for several weeks in the refrigerator without notable loss of activity. In the frozen state and in 0.1 M NaCl solution it can be stored for months in the freezer at—20°.

The range of activity, determined by the reaction on Ca[bis(p-nitrophenyl)phosphate]$_2$ in buffers of varying pH, is situated on the alkaline side between 7 and 10, with an optimum at pH 8.6.

b. *Specificity*

α. *General appearance, hydrolysis of various phosphodiesters.*

Phosphodiesterase from C. *adamanteus* in principle specifically catalyzes the hydrolysis of internucleotide linkages with formation of mononucleotides terminated by a 5'-phosphate group (Sinsheimer and Koerner, 1952b; Privat de Garilhe and Laskowski, 1955a; Heppel and Rabinowitz, 1958).

It is found, for instance, that the oligonucleotide fractions resulting from the hydrolysis of calf thymus DNA by pancreatic DNase are rapidly hydrolyzed by phosphodiesterase to the stage of the corresponding nucleoside-5'-phosphates.

The action of phosphodiesterase on other substrates than oligonucleotides has been examined In particular, it was noted that the highly purified enzyme was without action on :

deoxyadenosine-5′-phosphate
thymidine-5′-phosphate
thymidine-5′-diphosphate.

Table XXXVII : Specificity of venom phosphodiesterase* (Razzel and Khorana, 1959a)

Substrate	V_m moles/h/mg protein	K_m moles/l
Nitrophenyl-pT	36,500	5.0×10^{-4}
pTpT	6,840	2.1×10^{-4}
Nitrophenyl-pU	1,275	5.4×10^{-4}
TpT	278	5.3×10^{-4}
Di-p-nitrophenyl phosphate	39	7.7×10^{-4}
Benzyl-p-nitrophenyl phosphate	315	6.8×10^{-3}
Methyl-p-nitrophenyl phosphate	714	1.2×10^{-3}

* The phosphodiesterase source was 50 µg venom ; this was dissolved in Tris buffer (0.002 M at pH 8.9) at a concentration of 200 µg per ml and allowed to stand overnight at 4°.

Razzel and Khorana (1959a) have tested the activity of the enzyme against a series of natural and synthetic phosphodiesters (cf. table XXXVII); it can be seen that the dinucleotide pTpT is an excellent substrate, as are the synthetic products nitrophenyl-pU and nitrophenyl-pT; di-p-nitrophenyl phosphate, the most used compound for the determination (as its calcium salt), on the other hand, is only slowly hydrolyzed. Baev et al. (1963) have reported that dimethylated dinucleotides are hydrolyzed much more slowly than the corresponding unmethylated dinucleotides.

β. *Action of phosphodiesterase on macromolecular DNA*

Its action on thymus DNA originally gave rise to some controversy (Laskowski, Hagerty and Laurila, 1957; Boman, 1957) that has since been settled. Phosphodiesterase action on thymus DNA, measured viscometrically, led to the conclusion that the enzyme was without action since no fall in the viscosity was observed. One could well imagine, however, that the enzyme caused a stepwise removal of the mononucleotides from one end of the chain, giving rise to the appearance of material soluble in lanthanum salts, without resulting in a significant fall in the viscosity. Laskowski et al. (1957) did indeed show that it was possible to hydrolyze in this manner stepwise up to 10 % of the terminal linkages without altering the viscosity. When the mononucleotides produced in the course of this stepwise hydrolysis are analyzed by column chromatography, it is found that 90 % of them are in the mononucleotide form. The stepwise nature of the phosphodiesterase hydrolysis of oligonucleotides is an interesting phenomenon suitable for many applications in structural investigations of nucleic acids in general.

Later experiments carried out by Williams, Sung and Laskowski (1961) using a highly purified phosphodiesterase, confirmed that the enzyme degraded macromolecular DNA to the mononucleotide stage without it being possible to detect other products. The reaction rate depends on the concentrations of $MgCl_2$ and $CaCl_2$; this reaction is inhibited by a high concentration of NaCl or substrate. The DNA degradation by phosphodiesterase was followed spectrophotometrically, viscometrically and titrimetrically. The degradation takes place in the expected way for an exonucleolytic reaction, and in particular differs fundamentally from the type of reaction encountered with DNase I.

γ. Hydrolysis of transfer RNA

The stepwise hydrolysis of transfer RNA by *C. adamanteus* venom has been studied by Keller (1964) using a titrimetric method. This hydrolysis was effected at pH 7.4 in order to avoid spontaneous hydrolysis of the t-RNA which is already considerable at pH 8.8, i.e. in the neighborhood of the optimum pH of the enzyme. Hydrolysis of the t-RNA exhibits an initial rapid phase during which 10 % of the phosphodiester bonds are broken. This phase is followed by a much slower hydrolytic process, possibly owing to the stability of the secondary t-RNA structure in the presence of Mg^{++} ions.

δ. Stepwise oligonucleotide hydrolysis

Preliminary experiments effected as long ago as 1956 led to the hypothesis of a stepwise oligonucleotide hydrolysis by phosphodiesterases (Privat de Garilhe and Laskowski, 1956); but this work did not show from which end of the chain the hydrolysis occurred. This problem was successfully resolved by the work of Razzel and Khorana (Khorana et al., 1958; Razzel and Khorana, 1958, 1959a, b).

Chemical polymerization of thymidine-5'-monophosphate, pT, yields a certain number of oligonucleotides p_nT_n carrying terminal 5'-phosphoryl groups. Using these compounds, and those of the corresponding series $p_{(n-1)}T_n$, obtained by dephosphorylation of the first series with prostatic phosphatase, Khorana et al. obtained new insight into the mode of action of venom and spleen phosphodiesterases (Razzel and Khorana, 1958).

Incubation of TpTpTpTpT with *C. adamanteus* phosphodiesterase (purified), led to the successive formation of :

$$
\begin{array}{ll}
\text{TpTpTpTpT} & \\
\text{TpTpTpT} & + \ \text{pT} \\
\text{TpTpT} & + \ \text{2pT} \\
\text{TpT} & + \ \text{3pT} \\
\text{T} & + \ \text{4pT}
\end{array}
$$

It can be seen that the phosphodiesterase removes one 5'-thymidylic acid at a time from the end carrying a 3'-hydroxyl, while pT accumulates; the last product to appear in the course of the hydrolysis (which is followed by chromatography, for example) is, as might be expected, thymidine. Degradation of oligonucleotides p_nT_n is much faster, and takes place also in a stepwise manner; moreover, during the hydrolysis of p_4T_4 acetylated in the 3'-position, the first mononucleotide liberated is 3'-acetyl-pT.

Spleen phosphodiesterase has also been studied by the same method, i.e. by its action on compounds of the $p_{(n-1)}T_n$ type.   The degradative scheme appears to be as follows :

$$
\begin{array}{rcl}
 & & \text{TpTpTpTpT} \\
\text{Tp} & + & \text{TpTpTpT} \\
\text{2 Tp} & + & \text{TpTpT} \\
\text{3 Tp} & + & \text{TpT} \\
\text{4 T} & + & \text{pT}
\end{array}
$$

i.e. the mononucleotide that accumulates is thymidine-3'-phosphate as in the ribonucleotide series.

The action of spleen phosphodiesterase thus also takes place by stepwise degradation, but this time it starts at the end carrying the 5'-terminal hydroxyl group.   It is obvious that such a system of two stepwise phosphodiesterases is of great interest for the study of nucleic acid and nucleotide composition.   It has, in particular, attracted much attention for the study of large oligonucleotides such as those obtained by controlled hydrolysis of nucleic acids.   Holley et al. (1964) have described a new method for sequence determination of large oligonucleotides. which uses the partial degradation of large oligonucleotides with snake venom phosphodiesterase.   This degradation takes place in stepwise manner and the identification of the terminal nucleosides obtained from these products can be utilized to establish the oligonucleotide sequence.   In their publication, these authors describe the application of method to the sequence determination of the following oligonucleotides :

Ap Up Up Cp Cp G(p)   hexanucleotide (dephosphorylated)
Gp Gp Gp Ap Gp Ap Gp U(p)   octanucleotide (dephosphorylated).

Separation of the various reaction products was effected by chromatography on DEAE-cellulose in a linear gradient formed by sodium acetate buffer at pH 7.5 in 7 M urea.   Each fraction was desalted by adsorption on a short DEAE-cellulose column followed by elution.

Figure 57 shows the various products from the oligonucleotide degradation, and how the step by step identification of these products allowed reconstitution of the starting oligonucleotide.

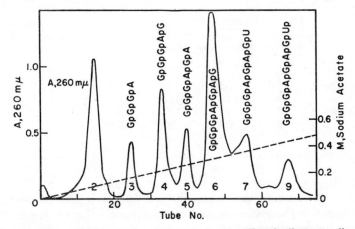

Figure 57. Chromatography of products of partial snake venom phosphodiesterase digestion of GpGp GpApGpApGpU. (Holley et al., 1964)

c) *Optical phenomena accompanying phosphodiester hydrolysis of oligonucleotides*

It has been seen that the DNase hydrolysis of thymus DNA in aqueous solution is accompanied by a rise in the optical density of the solution, the rise reaching 30 % at 260 mμ (Kunitz, 1950). The same phenomenon occurs when oligonucleotides are hydrolyzed with phosphodiesterase (Privat de Garilhe and Laskowski, 1956).

B. PHOSPHODIESTERASE — EXONUCLEASES FROM OTHER SNAKE VENOMS

As long ago as 1938, Gulland and Jackson had shown that phosphodiesterases as well as phosphomonoesterases were present in most snake venoms. More recently, Laskowski and co-workers (Richards et al., 1965) have studied the distribution of several related enzymes : phosphodiesterase, phosphomonoesterase, ("non-specific") 5′-nucleotidase and endonuclease (cf. table XXXVIII). Their results showed a high phosphatase content in the venom of the cobra *Naja nigricollis*, a fact that eliminates it as a source of phosphodiesterase. For the four other snakes examined, all belonging to the pit viper family, the relative distribution of the four enzymes is of the same order of magnitude, but with variations in the absolute content of the individual enzymes. *Bothrops* and *C. adamanteus* are rich in nucleolytic enzymes, *Agkistrodon* and *C. atrox* being relatively poor in these components. *Bothrops* and *C. adamanteus* thus represent *a priori* the most favorable sources for the purification of the various nucleolytic enzymes mentioned, provided it is possible to obtain adequate supplies.

B. *atrox* venom was Bjork's (1963) starting point for the preparation of a highly purified phosphodiesterase in six consecutive steps. The enzyme, purified in' this way, was free of all contamination by 5′-nucleotidase, which had been removed beyond detectable limits.

Table XXXVIII. Levels of enzymes in five snake venoms. (Richards et al., 1965)

Species of Venom	Units of Enzyme $\times 10^3$ per mg Dry Venom				Ratio of Enzymes : Phosphodiesterase = 1.0		
	Phospho-diesterase	Nonspecific Phosphatase	5′-Nucleo-tidase	Endo-nuclease	Nonspecific Phosphatase	5′-Nucleo-tidase	Endo-nuclease
Agkistrodon piscivorus	7.8	0.55	495	3.3	0.070	64	0.42
Bothrops atrox	36	1.8	1070	3.4	0.050	30	0.095
Crotalus adamanteus	25	1.3	1390	8.8	0.052	56	0.35
Crotalus atrox	8.7	0.39	860	2.8	0.045	99	0.32
Naja nigricollis	17	54	360	1.1	3.2	21	0.065

The venom of the Russian snake "Gurza" (*Vipera lebetina*) enabled Nikolskaya et al. (1963, 1964, 1965) to prepare a phosphodiesterase that was without action on double stranded DNA, but specifically hydrolyzed denatured DNA.

A similar type of experiment undertaken by Pfleiderer and Ortander (1965) allowed a simple method to be developed for the preparation of a phosphodiesterase from the venom of *Naja nivea*. The enrichment found in the best fractions was 60 — 80-fold, and it was noted during the purification that the amounts of phosphodiesterase and ATP-pyrophosphatase remained in constant ratio. The identity of the two enzymes was also confirmed by electrophoresis. The nucleoside-di- and triphosphates are hydrolyzed at the α-β bond of the pyrophosphate.

III. PHOSPHODIESTERASE — EXONUCLEASES FROM ANIMAL TISSUES

A. BOVINE SPLEEN PHOSPHODIESTERASE (E.C.3.1.4.1)

Spleen contains several phosphodiesterases, one of these fractions having been particularly studied, and it is usually this one that is referred to when one talks of "spleen phosphodiesterase" (Heppel and Hilmoe, 1955; Heppel and Whitfeld, 1955; Heppel, Whiteld and Markham, 1955; Whitfeld, Heppel and Markham, 1955; Razzel and Khorana, 1958, 1961; Hilmoe, 1960).

1. Estimation

Principle. This method of determination was suggested by McFadyen (1934) and described by Heppel and Hilmoe (1955*b*), using spleen phosphodiesterase, but it is naturally equally valid for all phosphodiesterases. The principle consists in the hydrolysis of a polynucleotide fraction with phosphodiesterase, and measurement of the increase of nucleotides soluble in a perchloric acid solution of uranium acetate.

Reagents. The RNase-resistant nucleotide fraction (the "core") is prepared by exhaustive hydrolysis of yeast sodium nucleate with RNase A, followed by dialysis for two days at 2° against distilled water. The dialyzed solution is concentrated by lyophilization, neutralized to pH 7.0 and brought to a concentration of 17 milligrams per liter. It can be stored for several months at —10°.

Uranium acetate — perchloric acid. 250 mg uranium [a]cetate are dissolved in 4.17 ml 60 % perchloric acid (aqueous) and the solution brought to 100 ml.

Succinate buffer. 0.25 M at pH 6.5

Procedure. Into a 10× 75 mm test-tube are measured 0.04 ml succinate buffer and 0.05 ml polynucleotide solution ("core"), and 0.04 - 0.07 units enzyme are added, the whole being brought to a final volume of 0.2 ml. The test-tubes are stoppered and the mixture incubated for 30 minutes at 37°. After the incubation 0.2 ml of the uranium acetate — perchloric acetate solution is added with shaking. The test-tube is placed in an icebath for 5 minutes, then centrifuged for 5 minutes at 2,000 r.p.m. The supernatant is then diluted to 4 ml., and the optical density is measured with a spectrophotometer, at 260 mμ in quartz cells of 1 cm thickness. With each series of determinations, a blank is run containing only the buffer and " core ".

A unit of enzyme is defined as the amount inducing a change of 2.0 at E_{260} (ΔE_{260}) under the above condiditons. The specific activity is expressed in units per milligram of protein.

2. Purification

Following a method described by Heppel and Hilmoe (1955*b*) the purification procedure involves five stages: 1) preparation from calf spleen of an acetone powder, 2) first ammonium sulfate fractionation, 3) heating and dialysis, 4) second ammonium sulfate fractionation, 5) adsorption on alumina Cγ gel and elution.

3. Properties of spleen phosphodiesterase

a. *Stability, optimum activity pH*

In the frozen state, solutions of this enzyme can be stored for a year without loss of activity; incubation at 60° for twenty minutes destroys the greater part of the activity, both in neutral and in acid medium.   The optimum pH is about 7.0.

b. *Specificity*

The experiments of Razzel and Khorana on the comparative specificities of snake venom phosphodiesterase and spleen phosphodiesterase have already been described, especially so far as the action of the two enzymes on polythymidylic acids of the $p_{(n-1)}T$ type is concerned.

Phosphodiesterase action is stepwise, and the attack begins on the end with a 5′-terminal hydroxyl group :

$$\text{TpTpTp...} \quad \longrightarrow \quad \text{Tp} \quad + \quad \text{TpTp... etc.}$$

The mononucleotides liberated by hydrolysis of the oligonucleotides carry a phosphoryl group in the C-3′ position.   Spleen phosphodiesterase, however, possesses the curious property of hydrolyzing cyclic phosphodiesters in a different way from that found with the other phosphodiesters; compounds of the type cytidine-2′: 3′-cyclic phosphate are hydrolyzed with production of 2′-cytidylic acid.

Like ribonuclease, spleen phosphodiesterase is able to catalyze certain exchange and synthesis reactions.   Thus the formation of cytidine-3′-methyl phosphate from cytidine-3′-benzyl phosphate and methanol can be observed, according to the equation :
cytidine-3′-benzyl phosphate + methanol $\longrightarrow$ cytidine-3′-methyl phosphate + benzyl alcohol.

In the presence of cytidine as acceptor, adenylyluridylic acid (ApUp) reacts to yield the dinucleotide monophosphate ApC and uridylic acid :

$$\text{ApUp} + \text{C} \longrightarrow \text{ApC} + \text{Up.}$$

Finally, it has been established that the hydrolysis of polynucleotides (the "core", left by ribonuclease) results, if it is carried out in the presence of cytidine, not only to the formation of nucleoside 3′-phosphates but also in the formation of dinucleoside monophosphates.

All reactions led Heppel et al. (1955) to conclude that, as in the ribonuclease case, the presence in cells of enzymes of this type could be in order to effect synthetic rather than hydrolytic reactions.

B. PHOSPHODIESTERASE FROM BOVINE INTESTINAL MUCOSA

In addition to the phosphodiesterase of calf spleen that has been extensively examined, and which we have described above, there exists a phosphodiesterase in the intestinal mucosa of calves, which has properties comparable to those of spleen phosphodiesterase (optimum pH 7.0) and which can be partially purified by a procedure described by Heppel and Hilmoe (1955*b*); this procedure is essentially an ammonium sulfate fractionation at controlled pH.

The purified preparation of intestinal phosphodiesterase acts on RNA to yields nucleoside-3'-phosphates. The four cyclic mononucleotides are rapidly hydrolyzed by this enzyme to the corresponding 3'-phosphates.

C. Phosphodiesterase from Pig Kidney

Another phosphodiesterase of animal origin, and with properties that are fairly close to spleen phosphodiesterase, has been isolated by Razzel (1961*b*) from pig kidney. This enzyme, which hydrolyzes nitrophenyl-pT to produce nitrophenol and 5'-thymidylic acid, belongs to the category of phosphodiesterases liberating 5'-phosphates. It is present in the lysozome-microsome fraction from extracts of pig kidney.

The purification of this enzyme is carried out in the following stages :

1) homogenization of the tissue,
2) centrifugation and recovery of the supernatant,
3) treatment with trypsin,
4) precipitation with acetone,
5) chromatography on ECTEOLA-cellulose.

The enrichment obtained is between 100 and 200-fold.

Razzel (1961*a*) has proposed the classification of phosphodiesterases into two large categories according to the nature of the substrates attacked and the products formed.

1. Phosphodiesterase I type enzymes effect the following reaction :

$$\text{Nitrophenyl-pT} \xrightarrow[\text{(from venom)}]{\text{phosphodiesterase I}} \text{Nitrophenol} + \text{pT (5'-phosphate)}$$

2. Phosphodiesterase II type enzymes effect the following reaction :

$$\text{Tp-nitrophenol} \xrightarrow[\text{(from spleen)}]{\text{phosphodiesterase II}} \text{Tp (3'-phosphate)} + \text{nitrophenol}$$

We feel that it would be equally reasonable to make a distinction between phosphodiesterases specific for nucleic acids, e.g. such as phosphodiesterases from leukemic mouse cells and from *E. coli*, and phosphodiesterases acting without distinction on a number of phosphoric diesters not necessarily belonging to the nucleic acids (see general remarks).

D. Exonuclease from Leukemic Mouse Cells

So far, several phosphodiesterases have been described which have been defined as exonucleases, but which we have also seen are able to hydrolyze a wide variety of phosphodiesters. This they certainly do at different velocities, depending on the nature of the alcoholic or phenolic groups esterifying the phosphate residue, but they nevertheless have qualitatively the same action, namely that of hydrolyzing any phosphodiester with the production of a phosphomonoester and alcohol or phenol. With the exonuclease from leukemic mouse cells, we meet a more specific kind of phosphodiesterase which is without action on the more usual diesterase substrates such as benzyl or *p*-nitrophenyl esters of nucleotide-5'-phosphates, and whose action is limited to the phosphodiester linkages of the sort where two hydroxyls of the phosphate group are esterified by two nucleoside residues. This second kind of phosphodiesterase thus has its action restricted to the nucleic acids.

In view of the absence of action by this enzyme on the standard phosphodiesterase substrates, Anderson and Heppel (1960) have developed a method of estimation that utilizes the formation of acid-soluble nucleotides from polyadenylic acid.

The purification of the enzyme results in samples in which the specific activity has not risen a geat deal, but which are free from foreign enzymes having other activities. The leukemic cells are first disintegrated by high frequency vibrations, and the extract obtained treated by heat, which results in a slight loss of diesterase activity, but also eliminates the adenosine 5'-phosphate deaminase. The heat-treated extract may then undergo either a protamine sulfate fractionation, or chromatography on DEAE-cellulose. The best preparations obtained after chromatography on DEAE-cellulose are enriched at least 20-fold over the crude extract.

The properties of the exonuclease from leukemic mouse cells are very interesting; for instance, it is found that it hydrolyzes poly A, poly AU, RNA (very slowly), and oligonucleotides with a monoesterified phosphoryl group at C-5', giving rise to nucleoside-5'-phosphates. Ribonucleotides such as pApA, pApApA and pUpU are hydrolyzed, as are deoxyribonucleotides like pTpT. In this respect, the enzyme exhibits a specificity comparable to that of venom phosphodiesterase. It is distinguished from the latter, however, by being unable to effect the hydrolysis of simple esters such as benzyl adenosine-5'-phosphate and p-nitrophenyl thymidine-5'-phosphate.

IV. PLANT TISSUE PHOSPHODIESTERASES — EXONUCLEASES

A phosphodiesterase from germinating barley was purified by Georgatsos (1963). He obtained a 600-fold enrichment during the carrying out of the following operations :

1) fractional precipitation with ammonium sulfate at pH 4.0,
2) filtration on Sephadex G-50 gel,
3) fractionation with methanol in the presence of M KCl,
4) chromatography on DEAE-cellulose.

This enzyme has an activity optimum at pH 5 — 6 in a 0.05 M acetate buffer. In the purified state it is active neither on DNA (intact or denatured), nor on "core" DNA, nor on yeast t-RNA.

According to Razzell (1966), plant tissues of various origins possess two kinds of enzymes related to phosphodiesterases : one corresponding to the animal tissue phosphodiesterases and the other to the potato nucleotide pyrophosphatase (Kornberg and Pricer 1950a). Both enzyme activities were investigated, found and compared in pea seedlings, corn seedlings and potato.

V. MICROBIAL PHOSPHODIESTERASES — EXONUCLEASES

A. THE EXONUCLEASES FROM Escherichia coli

It has been seen that to date five exonucleases with different properties have been detected in Escherichia coli extracts.

Exonuclease I, formerly called *E. coli* phosphodiesterase by Lehman (1960). This enzyme is apparently the most active of the *coli* exonucleases, and possesses an almost total specificity for denatured single-stranded DNA.

Exonuclease II, which is the nuclease associated with highly purified preparations of *coli* DNA polymerase (Lehman and Richardson, 1964).

Exonuclease III (DNA-phosphatase-exonuclease). This exonuclease is associated with a DNA-specific phosphatase activity. It liberates not only a 5′-nucleoside residue from the 3′-hydroxyl end of a DNA chain, but also any monoesterified phosphate in this position (Richardson and Kornberg, 1964).

Exonuclease IV, clearly different from the three previous ones in its chromatographic enzymatic and properties (Jorgensen and Koerner, 1965).

Exonuclease V, clearly separable from the previous ones by chromatography on DEAE-cellulose (Jorgensen and Koerner, 1965).

1. Exonuclease I from Escherichia coli

This enzyme is obviously an exonuclease, since it acts in a stepwise manner on DNA, and very slightly on RNA. It exhibits strict specificity so far as the pentose is concerned, but not so far as the nucleotide sequence is concerned, the exactly opposite situation from that of *Azotobacter agilis* nuclease (p. 180).

a. *Estimation*

Since *E. coli* exonuclease I is without action on Ca[bis(*p*-nitrophenyl)phosphate]$_2$, it was necessary to find another way of determining it.

The method proposed by Lehman (1960) consists in measuring the conversion of a partially degraded (but acid-insoluble) DNA labeled with ^{32}P, to acid-soluble fragments.

The incubation mixture (0.30 ml) contains 20 µmoles glycine buffer at pH 9.2, 2 µmoles MgCl$_2$, 10 µmoles partially degraded ^{32}P-DNA*, i.e. having undergone rapid treatment with pancreatic DNase (2 µc/µmole P) and 0.05 — 0.25 units enzyme. The mixture is incubated at 37° for 30 minutes, when 0.2 ml of a solution of thymus DNA (2.5 mg/ml) is added as "carrier", then 0.5 ml of cold 0.5 M perchloric acid. After 5 minutes at 0°, the precipitate is removed by centrifuging at 10,000 g for 3 minutes, and 0.2 ml supernatant is removed. After the addition of one drop of N KOH, the solution is taken to dryness and the radioactivity determined. The supernatants obtained from blank experiments (without enzyme) contain 0.3 to 0.4 % added radioactivity.

The unit of enzyme is defined as the amount of enzyme causing the production of 10 µmoles acid-soluble ^{32}P in 30 minutes. The acid-soluble radioactivity is proportional to the enzyme concentration at levels of from 0.05 — 0.25 units of enzyme; subsequently, after addition af 0.005,

---

* Preparation of partially degraded DNA : effected by treating *E. coli* DNA labeled with ^{32}P (Kornberg, quoted by Lehman, 1960) with DNase I ; the reaction mixture contains in 5 ml : *E. coli* DNA 2 µmole P containing 6 µc ^{32}P ; pancreatic DNase 0.005 mg ; bovine plasma albumin to ensure DNase stability 500 mg ; Tris buffer pH 7.5 50 µmoles ; MgCl$_2$ 5 µmoles. After incubation at 37° for one hour, the mixture is cooled in ice, and 1.0 vol. cold trichloroacetic acid (70 % w/v) is added. The suspension is kept at 0° for 5 minutes, then centrifuged at 12,000 g for 5 mins. The precipitate is dissolved in 4 ml 0.02 N sodium hydroxide, then reprecipitated by the addition of 4 ml 1 N ice-cold perchloric acid, the solubilization and reprecipitation being repeated. The final precipitate is dissolved in 2 ml 0.02 N sodium hydroxide, 0.1 N HCl is added to obtain pH 7, and the volume is adjusted to 8 ml with distilled water ; this solution contains 0.2 µmole P per milliliter.

0.01, 0.02 and 0.04 ml of a crude extract of *E. coli* diluted 50 times, respectively 360, 367, 379 and 334 units enzyme per milliliter extract were obtained.

b. *Purification*

Crude extracts of *E. coli* are prepared by ultrasonic disintegration; the whole preparation is carried out at 0-4º. These extracts undergo the following series of operations : precipitation with protamine sulfate and elution, fractional precipitation of the eluate with ammonium sulfate; chromatography on DEAE-cellulose.

The specific activity of the enzyme rises from 10.6 units per mg protein in the crude extract to 1,430 units per mg protein after chromatography on DEAE-cellulose.

c. *Properties*

Exonuclease I from *E. coli* hydrolyzes polynucleotides in stepwise manner, beginning at the end carrying a free hydroxyl group in the C-3′ position, and liberating one after the other mononucleotides of the pX type (nucleoside-5′-monophosphates). This property was incontrovertably demonstrated by allowing the enzyme to act on a sample of thymus DNA which was labeled on its terminal C-3′ hydroxyl group by a ^{14}C-deoxycytidylate residue. The DNA thus labeled was in turn obtained by treating the thymus DNA with deoxycytidine-^{14}C-triphosphate in the presence of purified *E. coli* polymerase (Adler et al., 1958). When the DNA labeled with ^{14}C-cytidylate is treated with *E. coli* exonuclease, 70 % of the radioactive nucleotides are already in solution when only 3 % of the unlabeled nucleotides have been liberated, the latter being determined by following the appearance of acid-soluble nucleotides absorbing in the UV. This phenomenon can be compared with that observed using snake venom phosphodiesterase but it is, however, different from the hydrolysis of labeled DNA by DNase I, where the appearance of labeled fragments exactly follows the appearance of soluble nucleotides in general.

It can also be established that *E. coli* exonuclease hydrolyzes intact DNA at a speed that is 100 times slower than is observed with DNA previously treated with DNase; this observation is in agreement with what we have already noted in the case of venom diesterase. Furthermore, when the DNA is previously heated for ten minutes at 100º, the rate of enzymic hydrolysis is 300 times more than that observed with unheated DNA. DNA from the bacteriophage ϕ X 174 is known to possess only a single-stranded structure (Sinsheimer, 1959), and is hydrolyzed without preliminary degradation 200 times faster than intact DNA from *E. coli*, and at a rate equivalent to that of heated DNA. Lehman has also shown that if pre-heated (10 minutes at 100º) thymus DNA is treated with *E. coli* exonuclease I, the DNA is entirely converted into acid-soluble products, more than 85 % of which are in the form of mononucleotides. It can therefore be seen that this enzyme shows no specificity so far as the nature of the bases in the nucleotide sequences is concerned, but does, on the other hand, towards the nature of the pentose, since *E. coli* RNA is only slightly hydrolyzed in conditions giving optimal hydrolysis of DNA.

These experiments show that the most extensively attacked substrates by the *E. coli* exonuclease are DNAs that have undergone collapse of their secondary structure after heating, or the DNA of the bacteriophage ϕ X 174, known to contain only a single helix. In the light of these facts, Lehman has proposed a new definition of enzymes attacking polynucleotides, by which phosphodiesterases would be those able to attack only single coil DNA, and DNases those able to attack both single and double-stranded types. This definition does not take into account the numerous diesterases which are able to hydrolyze quite a number of phosphoric diesters, but which have nothing to do with the nucleic acids.

During recent work carried out by Lehman and Nussbaum (1964), exonuclease I was purified to the extent of a 1,400-fold enrichment over the starting extracts, but the enzyme obtained was still heterogeneous from the physical point of view. The specificity was characterized, in addition to the observations that have just been described, by stepwise attack beginning exclusively from the 3'-terminal end of the single-stranded chain. There is produced therefore, nucleoside-5'-monophosphates and a dinucleotide diphosphate from chains having a 5'-phosphoryl group, and deoxyribonucleoside-5'-monophosphates and a dinucleoside monophosphate from chains having a free 5'-terminal group.

2. Exonuclease II from Escherichia coli

This enzyme effect a purely exonucleolytic hydrolysis starting from the end carrying the 3'-terminal-hydroxyl group, and successively liberating mononucleotide-5'-phosphates. This exonuclease II continues its attack down to the mononucleotide stage. Attack on intact DNA is faster than on denatured DNA (contrary to exonuclease I). The enzyme has been purified, along with DNA-polymerase from which it is, in fact, inseparable, by Aposhian et al. (1962). A certain number of routine kinetic constants have been determined by using synthetic oligonu-cleotides and various polynucleotides as substrates (table XXXIX).

Table XXXIX. Kinetic constants for hydrolysis of deoxyribonucleotide substrates by *E. coli* exonuclease II (Lehman and Richardson, 1964)

Substrate*	K_m**	V_{max} (mononucleotide formed per hour per mg of enzyme protein)***
	M	μmoles
p-Nitrophenyl-d-pT****	6.0×10^{-3}	2.3
d-pTpT	3.4×10^{-4}	8.0*****
d-pTpTpT	1.0×10^{-4}	43.8
d-TpTpT	0.9×10^{-4}	41.6
d-pTpTpTpTpT	1.5×10^{-4}	82.3
Native *E. coli* DNA	1.7×10^{-10}	4.3
Denatured *E. coli* DNA	2.1×10^{-10}	1.5
d-AT polymer	1.9×10^{-10}	59.0

* Assay A was used for DNA and d-AT polymer ; Assay B was used for deoxythymidine oligonucleotides.
Assay A measures the conversion d-AT copolymers or DNA labeled with ^{32}P to perchloric acid soluble fragments and assay B the liberation of inorganic orthophosphate from deoxyribonucleotide 5'-phosphates by 5'-nucleotidase after action of exonuclease II on deoxyribo-oligonucleotides.
** These values are expressed per mole of polymer ; in the case of DNA and d-AT a molecular weight of 6×10^6 is assumed.
*** Hydroxyapatite fraction. The particular fraction used in these studies had lost some activity upon storage, and values as high as 103 have been observed for the d-AT polymer.
**** p-Nitrophenyl ester of deoxythymidine 5'-phosphate.
***** In calculating this value, a correction has been made to account for the fact that hydrolysis of a single diester bond in d-pTpT results in the formation of two 5'-nucleotidase-sensitive units. In the case of the tri-and penta-nucleotides, only a small fraction of the total substrate was utilized, so that only the terminal pT was hydrolyzed. No correction was therefore required.

Exonuclease II of *Escherichia coli* is unable to hydrolyze oligonucleotides carrying a phosphoryl group in the C-3′ position; however, the latter do not inhibit the hydrolysis of oligonucleotides that only carry a hydroxyl in the C-3′ position.

The enzyme has an optimum activity at pH 9.0; for its activity it requires the presence of Mg^{++} and Mn^{++} ions, an optimal activity being registered at 7×10^{-3} to 2×10^{-2} M in Mg^{++}, using DNA as substrate. The enzymic activity is inhibited by NaCl and KCl.

3. Exonuclease III from Escherichia coli : "phosphatase-exonuclease"

This enzyme, isolated from extracts of the β strain of *E. coli* (Richardson and Kornberg, 1964; Richardson et al., 1964) possesses the unique property of effecting, under certain conditions, two types of hydrolysis on the same substrate. Initially it hydrolyzes a phosphomonoester linkage, and then it hydrolyzes phosphodiester linkages exonucleolytically.

It has been purified by using the following six-step process :
1) extraction,
2) precipitation with streptomycin,
3) acetone fractionation,
4) fractionation on DEAE-cellulose,
5) fractionation on phosphocellulose,
6) "Pervaporation", i.e. concentration in a dialysis tube of the phosphocellulose fraction. This fraction represents a 1,300-fold purification over the starting material, and contains 15 % of the activity initially present.

Properties. This enzyme is relatively stable, and has an optimum activity from pH 6.8 to 7.4 for the purified enzyme in potassium phosphate buffer, and an optimum from pH 6.7 to 7.10 in Tris-maleate buffer.

E. coli phosphatase-exonuclease quantitatively liberates inorganic phosphate from DNA terminated by a 3′-phosphate group; it is less active on heat-denatured DNA than on intact DNA. It is devoid of action on DNA terminated by a 5′-phosphate group or on RNA terminated by a 3′-phosphate group.

Differing from *E. coli* alkaline phosphatase, this phosphatase-exonuclease will not act on short oligonucleotides ending in 3′- or 5′-phosphates. The enzyme carries out, therefore, two types of reactions : provided there is a terminal 3′-phosphoryl on a DNA chain, preferably intact, the enzyme liberates the terminal phosphoryl group, subsequently proceeding to exonucleolytic hydrolysis with liberation of the nucleoside-5′-phosphates. This two-step process can be represented schematically as figure 58.

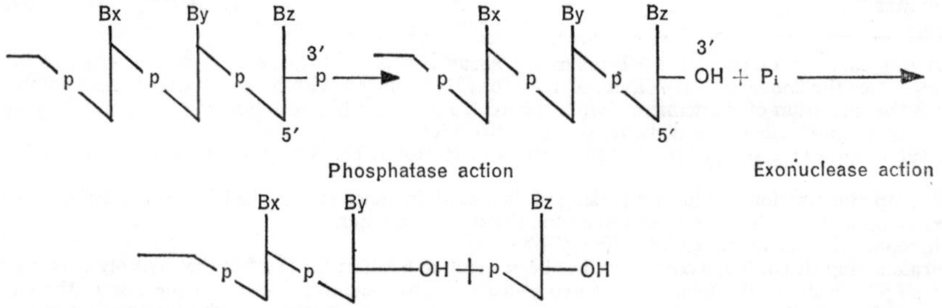

Figure 58. Mechanism of action of *E. coli* phosphatase exonuclease (Richardson et al., 1964)

The preference of the enzyme for double stranded DNA is suggested by the practically complete absence (less than 5 %) of hydrolysis of heat-denatured DNA. Support of this observation is provided by the fact that degradation of double-stranded DNA stops when 35 — 45 % of the substrate has been hydrolyzed. If it is supposed that the enzyme begins its stepwise attack from both 3'-hydroxyl ends; at about 50 % degradation, all the remaining DNA must be present in single-stranded form. A good idea of how this type of hydrolysis is effected can be obtained by looking at figure 59, taken from Richardson et al. (1964).

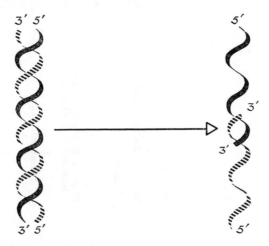

Figure 59. Postulated mechanism of action of the exonucleolytic activity of the DNA phosphatase-exonuclease. (Richardson et al., 1964)

The comparative properties of the exonucleases I, II and III from *E. coli* are listed in table XL.

4. Exonuclease IV from *Escherichia coli*

This enzyme was detected by Jorgensen and Koerner (1965), and attacks preferentially deoxyribooligonucleotides of low molecular weight, such as those produced by the controlled hydrolysis of DNA with pancreatic DNase. This exonuclease IV has been purified 100-fold; it can be clearly distinguished from the previous three *coli* exonucleases described above by its behavior during purification and by its enzymic properties.

5. Exonuclease V from *Escherichia coli*

Another exonuclease preferentially attacking oligonucleotides has also been isolated from *E. coli* by Jorgensen and Koerner (1965). This enzyme, like the preceding one, catalyzes exonucleolytic cleavage of deoxyribooligonucleotides to produce nucleoside-5'-phosphates. This enzyme has little action on intact or denatured DNA. It has been purified 50-fold from cell-free extracts of *E. coli*, and may be separated from exonuclease IV by chromatography on DEAE-cellulose.

Table XL : Comparison of *E. coli* exonucleases I, II & III   (Richardson et al., 1964)

	Exonuclease I	Exonuclease II	Exonuclease III
Required end group on DNA: [3'-OH terminus diagram]	Active	Active	Active
[3'-P terminus diagram]	Inactive	Inactive	Active; because initial attack removes P_f terminus
Required DNA structure	Single stranded	Single or double stranded	Double stranded
Extent of action	Up to terminal dinucleotide	Complete	Up to 40 % degradation; residual single stranded chains are resistant
Type of attack	Stepwise beginning at 3'-hydroxyl end of chain	Stepwise beginning at 3'-hydroxyl end of chain	Stepwise beginning at 3'-hydroxyl or phosphoryl end of chain
Products from DNA	Mono- and dinucleotides with 5'-phosphodiester group	5'-Mononucleotides	P_i, 5'-mononucleotides and large molecular weight single-stranded oligonucleotides
Action on synthetic oligonucleotides :			
pTpTpTpT	Produces 5'-mononucleotides and pTpT	Produces 5'-mononucleotides	Inactive
TpTpTp	Inactive	Inactive	Inactive

B. Exonuclease — phosphodiesterase from *Lactobacillus acidophilus*

Among the other exonuclease-phosphodiesterases of bacterial origin, mention must be made of the one isolated by Fiers and Khorana (1963a, b) from the deoxyribonucleoside-requiring organism *Lactobacillus acidophilus* R.26.

This enzyme was obtained in a highly purified state (over 100-fold enrichment) and in 32 % yield, by using the standard techniques in 9 successive stages, the last of which were chromatography on Sephadex G-25 and chromatography on DEAE-cellulose. The purest preparations obtained had a sufficiently low phosphomonoesterase concentration not to interfere with subsequent experiments concerned with the specificity of the exonuclease.

Stability tests with these preparations showed that the enzyme can be stored for more than three months at 2° without significant loss of activity. The optimal stability is situated in the neutral region between pH 6.0 and 8.5, and at pH 6.5, this phosphodiesterase is most stable thermally.

No particular action was found with the standard activators or inhibitors (bivalent cations, thioglycol, EDTA, etc.). The specificity of this exonuclease is comparable, but not identical, with that of calf spleen phosphodiesterase : TpT is hydrolyzed to Tp + T, i.e. with production of the nucleotide-3'-phosphate; Tp-nitrophenyl is also hydrolyzed, but not nitrophenyl-pT. Ribo- and deoxyribo-oligonucleotides are hydrolyzed in stepwise fashion, starting at the end carrying the free 5'-hydroxyl group following the scheme :

$$TpTpTpT... \longrightarrow Tp + TpTpT... \text{ etc.}$$

So far as the hydrolysis of t-RNA is concerned, in view of the presence of the 5'-phosphomonoester groups, it would be expected that these nucleic acids might be resistant to action by the *L. acidophilus* exonuclease, and such is indeed the case.

Table XLI, taken from Fiers and Khorana (1963a) shows the specificity of the *L. acidophilus* phosphodiesterase towards various substrates.

C. Phosphodiesterase from *Lactobacillus casei*

This enzyme was extracted from the ribosomal fraction of *Lactobacillus casei* cells; it degrades RNA to the stage of nucleoside-5'-monophosphates, this activity being stimulated by K⁺ ions. (Keir et al., 1964).

The purification was mainly effected by ammonium sulfate fractionation and chromatography on alumina Cγ. The enrichment obtained was 28-fold, with a final yield of 7.3 %. In the presence of K⁺ ions, the purified preparation exhibits two activities, endonuclease and exonuclease, and was found to be free from enzymes attacking DNA, nucleoside-3'-phosphates and glycerophosphate. The preparation described possesses a principal optimum activity at pH 8.0 — 8.2, and a minor peak of activity at pH 7.4.

D. Exonuclease from *Micrococcus lysodeikticus*

A recent publication by Tsuda and Strauss (1964) concerns a peculiar enzyme system from *Micrococcus lysodeikticus* which hydrolyzes DNA in the presence of Mg⁺⁺ ions and a single nucleo-

Table XLI : Specificity of *L. acidophilus* phosphodieterase for various compounds (Fiers & Khorana 1963 *a*)
All compounds were tested at a concentration of 0.002 M.   In several experiments the enzyme concentration
and incubation time were increased many fold to improve the sensitivity of the determination.   The results,
calculated on a molar basis, are expressed relative to the activity with Tp-nitrophenyl at pH 7.8.

| Compound | Hydrolysis at | | Assay method[5] |
	pH 7.8	pH 4.5	
Tp-nitrophenyl	100	33.5	I,II
Nitrophenyl-pT	(0.05)[1-2]	0.44[2]	I
Di-*p*-nitrophenyl phosphate	(0.2)[1]	18.2	I
TpT	52.1	27.6	II, III
TpTp	15.5	2.4	II, III
pTpT	(0.07)[1-3]	(0.08)[1-3]	II, III
Tp-methyl	(0.2)[1]	(0.2)[1]	II, III
Cyclo-pTpTpTpT[4]	(0.03)[1]	(0.04)[1]	II
UpA	65.0	28.6	II, III
pApA	(0.4)[1]	(0.04)[1]	II, III
Up-methyl	(0.6)[1]	(0.03)[1]	II
$2' \rightarrow 5'$-UpU	(0.1)[1]	(0.09)[1]	II
U-cyclic-p	0.9	1.14	II
C-cyclic-p	0.3	0.15	II
A-cyclic-p	0.9	0·40	II

1. Values in parentheses are not considered significant.
2. Also checked for hydrolysis to *p*-nitrophenyl phosphate and thymidine, and found negative.
3. Also checked for hydrolysis to pTp and thymidine, and found negative.
4. The concentration was 5×10^{-4} M.
5. Assay I   : release of *p*-nitrophenol
   Assay II : release of phosphomonoesterase-sensitive phosphate
   Assay III : paper chromatography.

side di- or triphosphate, the reaction also requiring the presence of intact DNA. The DNA
appears to be degraded from one end, since no fall in the viscosity is observed in the initial stages
of the reaction, nor is there found any alteration in the transforming activity of this same DNA.
Furthermore, since the reaction products are sensitive to the action of alkaline phosphatase,
they must be mononucleotides.   The action of the enzyme would thus be stepwise, and it would
be an *exonuclease*.   The purification, allowing the preparation of an enzyme that is enriched
about 25-fold over the crude starting material, utilizes two successive ammonium sulfate fractionations and two chromatograms on DEAE-cellulose.

An activity optimum is obtained at pH 9.5 in glycine buffer.   The optimal activity in the
presence of Mg^{++} ions is found to be at a Mg^{++} concentration of 5×10^{-3} M.   Mn^{++} can replace
Mg^{++} to a certain extent, but 0.02 M Ca^{++} totally inhibits the enzyme in the presence of Mg^{++}
and cannot replace the latter in its absence.

Phosphatases and nucleotidases

Phosphatases, classified by the Enzyme Commission as Phosphoric Monoester Hydrolases (EC.3.1.3), are defined as hydrolases capable of catalyzing the hydrolysis of phosphomonoesters with the production of free inorganic phosphate and an alcohol or phenol following the scheme

$$O = P \diagup\!\!\!\!\begin{array}{c} OR \\ \diagdown \end{array}\!\!\!\!\begin{array}{c} \\ OH \\ OH \end{array} + H_2O \xrightarrow{\text{phosphatase}} O = P \diagup\!\!\!\!\begin{array}{c} OH \\ \diagdown \end{array}\!\!\!\!\begin{array}{c} \\ OH \\ OH \end{array} + ROH$$

Specificities of varying degrees have been observed among the many phosphatases that have so far been described :

1) the so-called "non-specific" phosphatases. They are named this way because they hydrolyze all phosphomonoesters without distinguishing between the groups esterifying the phosphoryl residue. This category includes the two groups of enzymes that have been known for a long time under the name of alkaline and acid phosphatases.

2) Phosphatases that are specific as to the nature of the substituent on the phosphoryl group include at least 17 series of enzymes (cf. nomenclature in "Comprehensive Biochemistry" ed. Florkin and Stotz, 1965, volume 13, p. 130-133) and to which belong phosphoserine-phosphatase, phosphatidate phosphatase, 5'-nucleotidase, 3'-nucleotidase, phosphoadenylate-3'-nucleotidase, phytase, etc. Among all these series, the most useful for nucleic acid structural investigations are the nucleotidases, which are in turn subdivided into 5'-nucleotidases and 3'-nucleotidases, according at the position of the phosphoryl group to be hydrolyzed on the nucleotide substrate.

PHOSPHOMONOESTERASE ESTIMATION

A. Estimation of calf intestinal mucosa phosphomonoesterase, or "alkaline phosphatase" (after Heppel, 1955)

Principle : formation of inorganic phosphate from sodium β-glycerophosphate, then determination of this phosphate by a conventional method (Fiske and Subbarow, 1925).

Reagent : 0.1 M sodium β-glycerophosphate, 0.1 M ethanolamine-HCl buffer at pH 9.5, 0.005 M or 0.05 M magnesium acetate.

Experimental procedure : weak Mg acetate concentration is used for estimating crude preparations, since high concentrations are inhibiting. One ml of each of the three solutions are mixed, and the volume adjusted to 4.8 ml. A quantity of enzyme that is such as not to cause more than 5 % hydrolysis is added. The mixture is incubated for 15 minutes at 38°, and the inorganic P is estimated. The reaction is stopped by addition of 2.8 ml 25 % (w/v) trichloroacetic acid. If a precipitate forms, it is removed by filtration on Whatman no. 42 paper.

One unit of phosphatase is the amount enzyme causing the liberation of 1 γ inorganic phosphate per minute at 38°.

B. Estimation of prostate phosphomonoesterase, or "acid phosphatase"

Identical to the previous determination except that 0.1 M sodium acetate buffer at pH 5.6 is used and no magnesium acetate.

C. Estimation of snake venom 5′-nucleotidase

Principle. Liberation of inorganic phosphate from adenosine-5′-monophosphate or muscle adenylic acid, and determination of this phosphate as inorganic P by a conventional method such as that of Fiske and Subbarow (1925).

Experimental procedure. In a test-tube are mixed 0.2 ml enzyme solution, 0.1 ml 0.3 M $MgSO_4$ and 0.4 ml 0.3 M glycine — NaOH buffer at pH 9.0. The tube is then placed in a bath at 37°, and left there 5 minutes for it to attain the bath temperature. Then, 0.3 ml of a 0.01 M solution of adenosine-5′-monophosphate is added, and the solution is allowed to incubate at 37° for 15 minutes. The tube is then removed from the water-bath, and 10 ml molybdenum reagent and 1 ml of Fiske and Subbarow's reducing reagent are added immediately.

This procedure only works if the protein concentration of the preparation being examined is weak enough not to cause trouble when the molybdenum reagent is added. If this is not the case, the reaction must be stopped by the addition of trichloroacetic acid, and after filtering, the P estimation is made on an aliquot as in the case of the alkaline phosphatase determination (see above).

One phosphomonoesterase unit is the amount of enzyme capable of liberating 10^{-6} atoms P per hour (or of hydrolyzing one μmole AMP/hr).

D. Direct colorimetric estimation of the various phosphatases, automated methods

The method of Garen and Levinthal (1960) involves allowing the enzyme to react with *p*-nitrophenylphosphate in Tris buffer solution at pH 8.0. During this reaction, *p*-nitrophenol and free inorganic phsophate are produced. The progressive liberation of nitrophenol can be measured spectrophotometrically at 410 mμ.

Other reagents leading to the formation of colored derivatives measurable spectrophotometrically in the visible or ultraviolet have been described. Among the oldest of these is *o*-carboxyphenylphosphate, liberating by the action of phosphatases salicylic acid, which absorbs at 300 mμ in the UV, the starting material being transparent (Brandenberger and Hanson, 1953; Hofstee, 1954).

Pauwels (1965) suggested the use of Na-phenolphthalein diphosphate in succinate buffer solution. The optical density is measured at 553 mμ after incubation for one hour in the presence of the phosphatase. It is not necessary to make a correction for the spontaneous hydrolysis of the substrate.

Fomina (1964) proposed the use of Na-phenolphthalein phosphate for the estimation of intestinal alkaline phosphatase, red-colored phenolphthalein being formed in alkaline medium.

Tsou and Su (1965) have similarly used indoxyl phosphate as substrate for the determination of alkaline phosphatase. This method is based on the development of a blue color (indigo) when the liberated indoxyl is oxidized in air.

Marner et al. (1966), suggested a modification of the photometric method for estimation of acid phosphatases using α-naphthyl phosphate as a substrate and diazotized 5-nitro-o-anisidine as the coupling agent.

Automated methods for the determination of phosphatases mostly in human serum, were described by Sterling et al. (1964) using p-nitrophenyl phosphate as substrate, by Klein et al. (1965, 1966) using both phenyl phosphate and α-naphthyl phosphate and by Pré and Boigné (1966) using phenyl phosphate as substrate.

II. PROPERTIES OF THE PHOSPHATASES

The phosphatases are enzymes of the highest importance on account of their biological role, up to the point where phosphatase determinations in human serum and urine were extensively used for diagnostic purposes. These applications are, of course, far beyond the scope of this book and will be only briefly outlined below.

As far as the applications of phosphatases to structural studies of nucleic acids are concerned, it may be said that these applications are manifold.

So-called "specific" phosphatases like the 5′-nucleotidases and 3′-nucleotidases allow the determination of the position of a phosphoryl group on a mononucleotide. In this way adenosine-5′-monophosphate will be dephosphorylated by 5′-nucleotidase with the formation of adenosine and free inorganic phosphate, while under the same conditions adenosine-3′-monophosphate will not be hydrolyzed.

"Non-specific" phosphatases, hydrolyzing as they do all phosphomonoesters, such as glycerophosphate, phenylphosphate, various nucleotides, etc., have also a large number of applications in the structural determination of nucleotides. Initially they make it possible to know whether a nucleotide is phosphorylated at the end of its chain and whether it involves one or two terminal phosphoryl groups, and secondly they allow the size of the nucleotide to be measured by establishing the ratio of monoesterified phosphorus to the total phosphorus.

In addition, well-defined enzymes such as certain alkaline phosphatases (for instance from bovine intestinal mucosa or from *Escherichia coli*), brought some insight into the mechanism of enzymic actions as did RNase A and DNase I.

A. ANIMAL PHOSPHATASES

1. Human phosphatases

a) In *human serum*, Moss (1966), reported the separation of two different phosphatases : a 5'-nucleotidase and a non-specific alkaline phosphatase. Sera from patients with obstructive biliary diseases, in which both enzyme activities are enhanced, were used as enzyme source.

Still in serum, the activity of 5'-nucleotidase has been investigated by Schwartz and Bodanski (1965) in 15 normal individuals, 11 patients with Paget's disease and 31 patients with various types of neoplasm.   It is elevated in the serum of cancer patients with hepatobiliary disease.   There seems to be no correlation, however, between the level of this enzyme activity and other biochemical or clinical parameters of liver involvement.   Successive determinations in two patients of 5'-nucleotidase and other parameters of liver function have indicated that serum 5'-nucleotidase can be useful in following the progression of carcinoma metastatic to the liver.

The alkaline phosphatase activity of *neutrophiles* was investigated by Vakulenko and Shubich (1966), who showed that this activity was markedly increased in osteomyelofibrosis and polycythemia; in chronic myeloid leukemia, on the contrary, the activity in neutrophiles was absent or markedly dicreased.   The activity of alkaline phosphatase in neutrophiles of the peripheral blood was higher than in bone marrow.

The distribution of phosphatases in human *erythrocytes* has been the subject of a number of publications, notably by Abul-Fadl and King (1949), Tsuboi and Hudson (1955), Iio and Hashimoto (1964) and Georgatsos (1965).   The latter started from an erythrocyte extract, and was able to separate two acid phosphatases by filtration on Sephadex gel.   These two enzymes, designated E_1 and E_2 could be differentiated by their differing molecular weights, optimum pH and metal requirements.   Phosphatase E_1 had two optimal regions of activity, one at pH 5.0 and the other at pH 6.0.   This phosphatase was activated by Mg^{++} ions, this activation being optimal in the presence of 6.6×10^{-3} M Mg^{++}.   The E_2 phosphatase had a single optimum activity at pH 5.2.

b) Neale et al. (1965), studied the thermal stability of human alkaline phosphatase from the following five sources :

A — a fresh filtrate from minced placenta

B — a solution from an alcoholic fraction of placenta tissue

C — serum from an osteoporosis patient

D — normal serum

E — serum from a patient suffering from Paget's disease.

It was found that heating to 56° reduced the enzymic activity of fractions D and E to 10 % and 3 % respectively in 20 minutes, the samples A, B, and C not being affected.

Heating the solutions to 75° completely destroys the alkaline phosphatase in fractions D and E in 5 minutes, while fractions A, B and C are practically intact after $\frac{1}{2}$ hour.

These experiments show that the fractions A, B and C are thermally much more stable than fractions D and E.

c) The enzyme that can be extracted from prostate tissue (Schmidt, 1955a) (E.C.3.1.3.2) has its optimum pH on the acid side (5.3 — 5.6) and has no specificity towards the phosphomonoesters utilized as substrates — at least at first sight, but if the rate of hydrolysis of various phosphoric esters is studied, it is found, for instance, that hydrolysis of adenosine-5'-phosphate is approximately 3 times slower than the hydrolysis of adenosine-2': 3'-phosphate.

Human prostate phosphatase is partially inhibited by p-chloromercuribenzoate, but is not affected by iodoacetamide, iodoacetate or iodobenzoate. The work of Domanski et al. (1964) has demonstrated that one molecule of this phosphatase contains two unreactive -SH groups, blocking of which with p-chloromercuribenzoate or Ag^+ only causes a partial fall of the activity (30-50%). This enzyme has, furthermore, 10 disulfide bridges which probably play an essential part in the internal conformation of the enzyme molecule.

Vernon et al. (1955), succeeded in isolating human prostatic phosphatase in amounts sufficient for preliminary structural studies. The enzyme was purified thanks to the following operations : ammonium sulfate fractionation, then chromatographies on DEAE-cellulose, Sephadex G-100 and again DEAE-cellulose. The activity was resolved in two different peaks P_1 and P_2 each one having a constant activity across the peak. The Svedberg constants are 5.23 S and 5.36 S, respectively for P_1 and P_2. Preliminary measurements of the diffusion constants indicate molecular weights in the region of 110,000-130,000. Aminoacid analyses show some difference, notably in the relative amounts of valine and alanine.

Quite similar results were independently obtained by Ostrowski and Rybarska (1965), who also observed the resolution of purified prostatic phosphatase into two different active peaks, this time on CM-cellulose columns. The main fraction was shown to be homogeneous to free boundary electrophoresis; it has a sedimentation coefficient of 5,684 to 5,786 which corresponds to an approximate molecular weight of 89,000 to 102,500.

d) Vernon et al. (1965), thought that *human seminal plasma* might be, at a first glance, a convenient source of prostatic phosphatase. However the enzyme purified from this source show properties different from those isolated directly from prostate : in particular, they have much lower molecular weights indicating that they may not be of prostatic origin.

e) In *human urine*, Butterworth et al. (1965) have noted that alkaline phosphatase forms, during electrophoresis, a migrating zone corresponding to a higher mobility than the zones corresponding to phosphatases from other tissue (kidney, liver, small intestine and bladder). The phosphatase from the urine of patients with acute renal disease does not differ qualitatively from that found in the urine of normal subjects.

f) Human phosphatases have been the subject of many other investigations, among which may be mentioned those of Dubach and Padlina (1966) on urine phosphatases, those of Vecerek et al. (1965) on intestinal and kidney tissues, those of Arvy (1965a, b) on nervous tissue, those of Moss et al. (1966), on liver and intestinal tissues, those of Agus et al. (1966), on human kidney alkaline phosphatase.

2. Bovine phosphatases

a) The most extensively examined of the bovine phosphatases is the alkaline phosphatase of calf intestinal mucosa (E.C.3.1.3.1) which has been the subject of studies by a number of groups, notably Heppel (1955), Portmann (1957), Engström (1961, 1964), Lazdunski and Ouellet (1962), Behal and Center (1965), Fernley and Walkers (1966). According to Engström (1961), a high purification of the enzyme may be obtained by chromatography on triethylaminoethyl (TEAE) cellulose, without the final product being completely homogeneous. The principal component obtained after TEAE-cellulose chromatography could not be purified further, although various systems were tried, such as chromatography on ECTEOLA-cellulose or hydroxyapatite, or zone electrophoresis.

The activity of the purest product remains invariably around 400,000 Portmann units (see definition in Portmann, 1957) per milligram nitrogen.

Sedimentation gives a single well-defined limit. Determination of the molecular weight by the Archibald method results in a value of 100,000. The enzyme contains a neutral sugar and hexosamine, but no sialic acid, and 0.2 % zinc.

By chromatography of this phosphatase on DEAE-cellulose, Behal and Center (1965) also found the activity was resolved into several components having distinct electrophoretic mobilities. Nevertheless, the heat-sensitivity of these different components is the same, indicating that there is probably a great similarity between the protein molecules constituting them.

Lazdunski and Ouellet (1962) examined the action of various inhibitors on intestinal alkaline phosphatase. Inorganic phosphate and glycerophosphate (a substrate) function as competitive inhibitors, showing the microheterogeneity of the active center of the enzyme. Cysteine and imidazole are purely non-competitive inhibitors. Thiol group inhibitors like iodosobenzoate, iodoacetamide and p-chloromercuribenzoate are mixed inhibitors with a greater affinity for the enzyme-substrate complex than for the enzyme. These results can be interpreted by supposing that a zinc atom and a sulfur atom play an important part in the active center of the phosphatase.

According to Fernley and Walker (1966), this enzyme is capable of hydrolyzing, besides class-sical phosphomonoesters : inorganic pyrophosphate, adenosine triphosphate and monofluoro-phosphate.

Engström's experiments (see bibliography given in Engström, 1964) have shown that this phosphatase can be phosphorylated by inorganic phosphate or by glucose-6-phosphate. A particular serine molecule is phosphorylated during this reaction and there is every reason to believe that the latter molecule plays a fundamental part in the active center of the enzyme. Phosphatase, purified by Engström's method (1961), was labeled with ^{32}P by incubation with inorganic ^{32}P phosphate, then hydrolyzed in strongly acid medium at low temperature. Engström then showed that the labeled peptides identified in the hydrolysate had the structure Asp-Ser^{32}P and Ser^{32}P-Ala, from which he concluded that the tripeptide sequence Asp-SerP-Ala formed part of the site incorporating phosphorus into the calf intestinal mucosa alkaline phosphatase. This sequence is the same as the one identified in E. coli phosphatase (Milstein, 1963; Schwartz et al., 1963, p. 288).

b) Alkaline phosphomonoesterases have been isolated from a number of other bovine sources, namely from milk (Morton, 1955), bones (Gulland and Jackson, 1936; Volkin, 1955), bull seminal plasma (Heppel and Hilmoe, 1951, 1955), synovial fluid (Dabich and Neuhaus, 1966). The enzyme from seminal plasma is a 5'-nucleotidase. Another 5'-nucleotidase of bovine origin was characterized by Center and Behal (1966) in calf intestinal mucosa. The fundamental properties of these enzymes are described in the tables in the appendix, p. 326.

3. Rat phosphatases

As in other higher animals, phosphatases are widely distributed in the rat. Important variations of the levels of these enzymes in the various rat tissues may be observed in the course of different nutritional states as shown by the experiments of Terroine et al. (Terroine 1961a, b;

Lys and Terroine 1962). Rossier and Portmann (1965) have studied the levels of activity and the distribution of alkaline and acid phosphatases in the organism of normal and adrenalecto-mized rats. These authors noted that in the adrenalectomized animals, alkaline phosphatase was stimulated in the organism in general, though not in the small intestine or kidneys. On the other hand, no stimulation of acid phosphatases was observed after adrenalectomy.

4. Avian phosphatases

An intestinal alkaline phosphatase was partially purified from chickens and examined by Kunitz (1960), and later, systematic studies of avian alkaline phosphatases were undertaken by Motzok et al. (see full literature references in Motzok, 1963). These workers noticed in particular that the optimum pH for the alkaline phosphatase depended on various factors, notably the source of the enzyme and the concentration of substrate, buffers and activators. Moreover, working under well-defined standard conditions, the optimum pH for the activity of chicken intestinal phosphatase moves to higher values as the birds become older. Variations are also observed in the optimum pH of the enzyme at various nutritional states, the optimum pH of the alkaline phosphatase being lower in birds fed on a diet deficient in Ca^{++} than in those receiving a Ca^{++}-rich diet. Motzok has also observed that manganese or molybdenum supplements in the diet cause a rise in phosphatase activity of the avian intestinal mucosa.

5. Phosphatases from snake venom

Specific and non-specific phosphatases were shown many years ago to exist in numerous snake venoms (Uzawa, 1932; Takahashi, 1932; Gulland and Jackson, 1938; Hurst and Butler, 1951; Heppel and Hilmoe, 1955: etc...) and we have already pointed out (p. 260) the vital need there is to separate these phosphomonoesterases from the diesterases and endonucleases if one wants to obtain unequivocal results in structural studies of nucleic acids and their derivatives.

a) The venom of *Bothrops atrox* has served as the starting point in the purification of several nucleolytic enzymes; Sulkowski et al. (1963) in particular, have characterized two alkaline phos-phatases in this venom, one being specific and the other non-specific for nucleoside-5'-phosphatase.

5'-Nucleotidase was purified from *B. atrox* venom by the following steps :
1) acetone fractionations, 1 and 2,
2) ammonium sulfate fractionation,
3) Sephadex G-100,
4) DEAE-cellulose.

The specific activity rises from 2.4 in the first extract obtained from the 42 % acetone preci-pitate, to 630, an enrichment of about 260-fold from the acetone precipitate, or 1,000-fold from the crude venom.

The properties are as follows. The enzyme has an optimum pH in the region of 9; it is without action on 3'-phosphates, and among the 5'-phosphates, the most sensitive nucleotide is pA which was used as a routine substrate by Sulkowski et al. Inhibition by EDTA is observed, and slight activation by Mn^{++} and Co^{++} ions.

The non-specific phosphatase from *B. atrox* venom has been purified by the following steps :
1-2) acetone fractionation,
3) fractionation on CM-cellulose,

4) phosphate gel,

5) Sephadex G-100,

6) DEAE-cellulose.

The specific activity rises from 0.0013 in the crude venom to 0.243 in the most purified fraction, an approximately 200-fold enrichment.

This phosphatase has an optimum pH of 9.5 in glycine buffer.

It is found that this enzyme, too, is activated by Mg^{++} and Ca^{++} ions in the same way as the phosphodiesterase. Many substrates tried have shown that the enzyme has little specificity, all monophosphates except inorganic pyrophosphate being hydrolyzed.

The enzyme purified in this way no longer contains phosphodiesterase.

b) *Crotalus adamanteus* venom has also been used as a source of 5'-nucleotidase (Hurst and Butler, 1951; Heppel and Hilmoe, 1955; Björk, 1964, etc.).

c) Björk (1964) has shown that the method of purification of 5'-nucleotidase on DEAE-cellulose perfected by Sulkowski et al. (above) works not only for the venom of *B. atrox*, but also for those from *Crotalus adamanteus, Hemachatus haemachates, Vipera russellii*, etc.

The optimum pH for the activity of the 5'-nucleotidase of these venoms lies between 8 and 9.

5'-Nucleotidases purified from the venoms of several snakes have common properties. Mono-, di- and probably trinucleotides with a 2'- or 3'-phosphate group increase the activity and the thermostability of the purified enzyme. The maximum activation is about 2.6 times. The enzyme is also activated, but not stabilized, by α-aminoacids. The enzymic activity is not influenced by oxidizing or reducing agents, nor by reagents having -SH groups (Björk, 1964).

B. PLANT PHOSPHATASES

1) One of the enzymes produced by the graminaceous plant *Lolium multiflorum* is a 3'-nucleotidase (EC.3.1.3.6). This enzyme has been studied in turn by Shuster and Kaplan (1953, 1955) and by Cohen and Goodwin (1961). The specificity of the enzyme, which hydrolyzes only nucleoside-3'-phosphates, and its optimum activity at pH 7.4 distinguish it clearly from non-specific phosphatases that are also found in the Graminaae, but which have their optimum point on the acid side.

2) Another 3'-nucleotidase is produced by the plant *Phaseolus radiatus* (Green gram). According to Ahluwalia and Maller (1962), this phosphatase was purified 27-fold from *P. radiatus* seeds. Its optimum activity is at pH 7.8 and at a temperature of 70°; its thermal stability is exceptionally high. It is found that Ap is rapidly attacked by this enzyme, which does not depend for its activity on a metal, and which is not of the "hydrosulfide group-type enzymes". It is comparable to the 3'-nucleotidase from *Lolium multiflorum* previously described (Shuster and Kaplan, 1953-1955; see above). The purification mainly employs fractional precipitation with ammonium sulfate and adsorption on tricalcium phosphate gel then elution from the gel. *P. radiatus* 3'-nucleotidase is clearly more active on Ap than on the other nucleoside 3'-phosphates tried as substrates. Its activity on these substrates decreases in the order Ap>Gp>Up. It is inactive on nucleoside-5'-phosphates and on nucleoside-2'-phosphates, as it is on non-nucleotide substrates like glycerophosphate, glucose-1-phosphate, etc.

3) A phosphatase with a preference for nucleoside-5′-phosphates has been characterized from potatoes (Kornberg and Pricer, 1950 *a, b*; Heppel and Hilmoe, 1955). This enzyme is an acid phosphatase with its optimum activity at pH 5.0. So far as the specificity of this phosphatase is concerned, it has been found that pA is hydrolyzed preferentially, Ap also being hydrolyzed to a lesser extent. The ratio of the activities on the two substrates, all other conditions being the same is pA/pA = 3/1. At pH 9.4, i.e. at a pH well removed from its optimal pH, it is found that this potato phosphatase only hydrolyzes pA, but three times slower than it does at pH 5.0.

C. MICROBIAL PHOSPHATASES

1. Alkaline phosphatase from *Dictyostelium discoideum*

A recent publication by Gezelius and Wright (1965) has established the presence of intracellular alkaline phosphatase in the slime mold *Dictyostelium discoideum*. This phosphatase has an activity optimum at pH 9.0; it is a 5′-nucleotidase attacking the following substrates : adenosine-5′-phosphate and deoxyadenosine-5′-phosphate, as well as *p*-nitrophenyl phosphate.

2. Phosphatases from *Escherichia coli*

a) The extensive work carried out on the alkaline phosphatase of *E. coli* came about as a result of the observations of Horiuchi et al. (Horiuchi, Horiuchi and Mizuno, 1959; Horiuchi, 1960) and of Toriani (1960), according to whom a high alkaline phosphatase level appeared when the inorganic phosphate became limiting in cultures of *E. coli*.

According to Garen and Levinthal (1960), measurement of the enzymic activity can be effected by reacting the enzyme with *p*-nitrophenyl phosphate in Tris buffer at pH 8.0. The rise in the optical density at 410 mμ as the nitrophenol is liberated, is measured in a spectrophotometer.

The preparation of the highly purified phosphatase is effected from cells of *E. coli*, it being found that centrifugation of the culture results in all the phosphatase activity being concentrated inside the cells. The purification takes place essentially by liberating the enzyme from the cells by treatment of them at 85° for 15 minutes and chromatography of the freed enzyme on DEAE-cellulose.

The alkaline phosphatase of *Escherichia coli* K$_{12}$ is liberated almost quantitatively in the culture medium when the cells are converted into spheroblasts by the action of lysozyme and EDTA (Malamy and Horecker, 1964*a*). The same phenomenon is observed for the strain ML 308, which is unrelated to the strain K$_{12}$. This phosphatase is reported to be enclosed in a compartment between the cell wall and the cell membrane.

The supernatant obtained when the cells are converted to spheroblasts by the action of lysozyme + EDTA can serve as starting material for the purification of *E. coli* alkaline phosphatase. In this way Malamy and Horecker (1964*b*) were able to obtain a crystalline enzyme, the purest samples of which were free from neighboring enzymes — ribonuclease and phosphodiesterase — and the authors were able to show that incubation of t-RNA in the presence of the purified enzyme caused no decrease in the biological activity of this RNA, implying that not one of the phosphodiester bonds was broken. The crystallized phosphatase is stable and homogenous to analytical ultracentrifugation, although electrophoresis on agar gel reveals the presence of three bands, all of which possess phosphatase activity. The purified protein has a sedimentation constant of 6.15.   It is sensitive to inhibition by compounds of the thiol type, such as cysteine and thioglycolic acids.   This inhibition is removed by addition of Zn^{++}.

Manson et al. (1965) have shown that digitonin lysis of the E. *coli* penicillin spheroblasts furnishes a particular fraction which is still capable of synthesizing alkaline phosphatase.   Inorganic phosphate inhibits this synthesis *in vitro*, since it prevents the formation of the active dimeric form of the enzyme.

Schlesinger (1964, 1965a, b, c), demonstrated that E. *coli* alkaline phosphatase is a dimer having a molecular weight of 86,000.   The acidic treatment of this dimer denatures the enzyme : below pH 3.0 the enzyme dissociates in two enzymically inactive subunits which have a molecular weight half that of the original molecule : $s_{20,w} = 2.3$ at pH 2.0 (active enzyme $s_{20,w} = 6.1$).   Reassociation of these subunits to active enzyme is most rapid in low ionic strengh buffers containing Zn^{++} ions.

Studies carried out on the active center of *coli* alkaline phosphatase led Milstein (1962) to suppose that the polypeptide sequence in the neighborhood of the active center would contain the tripeptide Asp-SerP-Ala.   The serine group situated between aspartic acid and alanine was supposed to play a particularly important part, since it is this which can fix the inorganic phosphate.   This sequence of three aminoacids is the same as that which was found in the alkaline phosphatase of calf intestinal mucosa (p. 284).   Schwartz et al. (1965) were subsequently able to characterize a sequence of fourteen aminoacids including the active center :

Thr-Gly-Lys-Pro-Asp-Tyr-Val-│Thr-Asp-SerP-Ala│-Ala-Ser-Ala.

The encircled part of this formula exhibits analogies with the sequences found around the active centers of several esterases, all of which include an active serine group.   Phosphorylation of alkaline phosphatase shows characteritics that would be expected for a reaction at the active center of the enzyme, and indicates that the hydrolysis of phosphomonoesters involves the transient fixation of the phosphoryl group of the latter on the phosphatase (Schwartz, 1963).   The presence of a phosphoserine group in the active center is often associated with the presence of an imidazole group that is also active.   This is why Plotch and Lukton (1965) looked for possible sensitive imidazole groups by allowing the standard reagents for these groups to react on the enzyme, e.g. iodoacetamide and light.   The phosphatase showed no change in activity on being treated with iodoacetamide, and it is, furthermore, only slightly sensitive to photooxidation.   The stability of the intact enzyme towards photooxidation would appear to indicate the absence of any labile histidine residue.

Among other remarkable properties of *coli* alkaline phosphatase, its exceptional stability might be mentioned, since it is possible to heat it at 85° for at least 30 minutes without loss of activity.   The optimum activity is at pH 8.0.

Measurement of the Michaelis constant, K_m, by Garen and Levinthal on p-nitrophenylphosphate as substrate, gave a value of

$$K_m = 1.17 \times 10^{-5}.$$

Jenkins and d'Ari (1966), demonstrated the advantage of an integrated equation for the analysis of E. *coli* alkaline phosphatase kinetics and Lazdunski (1966), on the basis of the results obtained by studying the catalytic action of this enzyme, concluded that it is similar to the mechanisms observed for chymotrypsin and trypsin.

Heppel and co-workers (1962) found that by plotting the standard double reciprocal graph of Lineweaver-Burk (1934), two consecutive straight lines were obtained, the sudden change of slope corresponding to a very slight variation of the substrate concentration (figure 60).

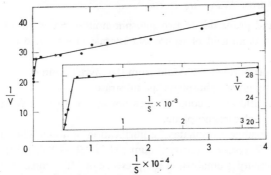

Figure 60. Graph after Lineweaver-Burk, of the values obtained by reaction of *E. coli* alkaline phosphatase on *p*-nitrophenyl phosphate. The incubation mixture contained 0.1 M Tris buffer at pH 8.2, 0.2 μg of alkaline phosphatase, sodium *p*-nitrophenyl phosphate and a sufficient amount of water to make up a total of 1.0 ml. The optical densities were measured at 1 minute intervals at 410 mμ. Temperature 24°. The insert represents an enlargement of the left hand part of the graph (reproduced from Heppel et al., 1962)

The other substrates behave in the same manner, except that the curved transition line is longer.

Heppel et al. also noted that *E. coli* phosphatase hydrolyzed many other compounds containing monoesterified phosphate, notably ribonucleoside polyphosphates, deoxyribonucleoside polyphosphates, inorganic pyrophosphate, tripolyphosphate, short-chain polymetaphosphate, etc. Most monophosphates are hydrolyzed at about the same rate, and near the speed observed with adenosine monophosphate.

E. coli phosphatase has already received many applications in the determination of the chain-length of nucleotides by measuring the total P/terminal P ratio.

Heppel et al. mention the possibility of stepwise degradation of oligonucleotides utilizing this phosphatase. In an initial step, an oligonucleotide like UpUpU, not carrying any terminal phosphoryl group, can be oxidized with periodate, making two aldehyde groups appear in the 2′ and 3′-positions; excess periodate is destroyed by ethyleneglycol, when the oxidized nucleotide can be hydrolyzed in the presence of lysine so that selectively it loses its terminal oxidized nucleoside, a 3′-terminal phosphoryl group appearing at the same time, which can be eliminated by the phosphomonoesterase with formation of the compound UpU, isolated by paper chromatography. In future, it might be possible to apply this technique to longer chains.

b) In addition to the alkaline phosphatase that has just been described, *E. coli* contains several enzymes catalyzing the hydrolysis of phosphomonoesters. One of these components, having an optimal activity at pH 4.7, has been purified by van Hofsten and Porath (1962) using in turn chromatography, zone electrophoresis and filtration on Sephadex gel. The purified product finally obtained was homogeneous.

The Michaelis constant for p-nitrophenyl phosphate as substrate is

$$K_m = 3 \times 10^{-3}.$$

The aminoacid constitution allows the molecular weight to be placed at between 13,000 and 14,000.

3. Phosphomonoesterases from *Neurospora crassa*

The purification and properties of two phosphomonoesterases have been described by Kuo and Blumenthal; one was an acid phosphomonoesterase (1961a) and one an alkaline phosphomonoesterase (1961b).

The first enzyme was purified 1,400-fold from the mycelium in 40 % yield. The pH of optimum activity is 5.6 using glycerophosphate as substrate.

The presence of a cation or a cofactor does not appear to be necessary. The most rapidly hydrolyzed substrate is α-glycerophosphate.

In the case of the alkaline phosphatase, a purification of about 40-fold was obtained starting from the mycelium of *N. crassa*. The optimum pH is 8.9 — 9.0, using β-glycerophosphate as substrate. Maximal activity is obtained in the presence of Mg^{++} ions.

4. *Saccharomyces* phosphatases

A long time ago the presence of numerous phosphatases in yeast was observed, all of them having more or less strict specificities.

In the course of a systematic investigation, Tonino and Steyn-Parvé (1963) examined the localization of some phosphatases in yeast cells that had been broken up either by shaking intact cells with glass balls, or by hypotonic or hypertonic rupture of protoplasts obtained from intact cells.

a) An acid phosphatase with an optimum activity at pH between 3 and 4 is found in the cell wall of commercial baker's yeast (*Saccharomyces cerevisiae*).

b) A single non-specific alkaline phosphatase is to be found in *S. carlbergensis* No. 74. The distribution of this enzyme depends on the age of the culture; in a 17-hour old culture, 2/3 of the enzyme is bound to the particles sedimented at 3,000 g to 100,000 g, only 1/3 being soluble. In a 24-hour old culture, 70-85 % of the enzyme occurs in the soluble fraction.

c) Finally, a highly specific α-glycerophosphatase is present in the unstructured cytoplasm of a *S. carlbergensis* No. 74 culture, 17 hours old.

These experiments demonstrate the considerable variability in the yeast non-specific phosphatases.

CHAPTER IX

Final remarks on
enzymes in nucleic acid chemistry

Despite our all too obvious deficiencies in what we know of the structure and properties of many of the nucleolytic enzymes, it is impossible not to marvel at the progress made since the time in 1930 when Levene and Bass recommended the following procedure for hydrolyzing thymonucleic acid (deoxyribonucleic acid) :

"hydrolysis of the nucleic acid is effected by passing a solution of the compound through a segment of the gastro-intestinal tract of a laboratory animal (dog), subsequently collecting it with an intestinal fistula. In order to avoid contamination with food residues, a gastric fistula is made so as to have a clean empty segment. A solution of 50 grams of nucleic acid is allowed to flow through the gastric fistula and the digestion mixture is collected from the intestinal fistula, the entire procedure lasting from one to two hours. The volume of fluid varies from 700 cc to 350 cc. Toluene is added to the solution which is then placed in a thermostat for different intervals, the shortest being four days and the longest seven. According to the most recent procedure, small portions of gastro-intestinal secretion are added daily and it has been found that hydrolysis of the nucleic acid can be accomplished by adding portions of the secretions daily to the solution of nucleic acid without passing the latter through the segment of the gastro-intestinal tract. The yields of nucleosides varies, the maximal being 1.5 grams of guanine nucleoside from 200 grams of nucleic acid, The other nucleosides are obtained in minimal quantities and many experiments yielded only the guanine derivative. The great resistance of thymonucleic acid to hydrolysis as compared with yeast nucleic acid is illustrated by the fact that 200 grams of the latter yield about 5 grams of guanosine ".

As may be seen from the above description, only nucleosides, still in a poor yield could be obtained and no nucleotides. The situation has much improved since.

Thanks to the diligence of a large number of biochemists, we now have at our disposal a whole spectrum of enzymes in a high state of purity, some of which have been crystallized, and whose specificities have been well defined. Among these enzymes, pancreatic ribonuclease, crystallized as long ago as 1940 by Kunitz, deserves pride of place, for it is this enzyme that has given rise to the largest amount of work. Since the complete structure of the RNase has been defined, we now possess important information concerning the mechanism of its action, since we also know precisely how specific it is towards natural substrates like RNA from various sources or synthetic substrates such as the cyclic phosphates.

Enzymology of nucleic acids is therefore a branch of biochemistry that has made spectacular progress these last few years, since, taking the crystallization of pancreatic RNase as starting point it can be seen that all the publications forming the background literature to the present book have been written in the last 25 years.

The applications of these enzymes are threefold :

I. They are used to obtain new nucleic derivatives (polynucleotides, mononucleotides, nucleosides) by controlled degradation of natural substrates.

II. They are used to study the mechanism of enzyme action.

III. They are useful in structural studies of nucleic acids.

I. NEW NUCLEIC DERIVATIVES

Among the first applications of RNase A, we have mentioned the total enzymic hydrolysis of RNA, compared with its alkaline hydrolysis (Markham and Smith, 1952a, b, c).

With the help of paper electrophoresis and paper chromatography, and by comparison of the products obtained with synthetic procedures, Markham and Smith were able to provide evidence for the existence of not only the four free mononucleotides terminated by 3'-phosphate groups, but also the four mononucleotide-2': 3'-cyclic phosphates, the cyclic nucleotides corresponding to the pyrimidine bases (cytosine and uracil) being present in larger amounts than the cyclic nucleotides corresponding to the purine bases (adenine and guanine). In addition to the mononucleotides, they found that the following dinucleotides were present :

ApCp!, ApUp!, UpUp!, ApCp, ApUp, ApGp, GpUp, GpCp, GpUp!,

and the following trinucleotides :

UpUpUp!, ApCpCp!, ApApCp, ApApCp, ApApUp, ApGpUp.

An interesting series of oligonucleotides was also isolated and characterized by Volkin and Cohn (1953) after the action of ribonuclease on calf liver RNA. One of the first roles of RNase was thus to supply the means of obtaining enzymically a series of mono- and oligonucleotides, all ending with 3'-phosphate groups, sometimes more easily than by synthesis. The two methods are, in fact, complementary.

Using other nucleases, such as the one from *Azotobacter agilis* which acts on RNA or biosynthetic polynucleotides, allows ribonucleotides to be obtained that are terminated by 5'-phosphates, thereby completing the series of those obtained by the action of RNase A.

The use of the DNases and various endonucleases acting on DNA results in the formation of mononucleotides and oligonucleotides terminated either by 5'-phosphate groups or by 3'-phosphate groups. The series of oligonucleotides obtained after the action of DNase I has been mentioned (p. 240), as well as the series of mono- and oligonucleotides obtained after the action of *S. pyogenes* nuclease (p. 176). Action in turn of DNase I and intestinal phosphodiesterase on natural DNA hydrolyzes the latter to the stage of the deoxyribonucleic mononucleotides;

these mononucleotides may be then fractionated by chromatography on ion exchangers, and this still constitutes the principal industrial method for the preparation of these substances.

II. MECHANISM OF ENZYME ACTION

We have noted that the properties of pancreatic ribonuclease A are sufficiently well known at present to have enabled Rabin and his co-workers to formulate an elegant theory concerning the method by which it exerts its enzymic activity.

The reaction of the RNA depolymerization is considered as the fundamental criterion of RNase activity, and several methods of estimation are based on it, although it is, in fact, only the result of transferring a phosphoryl group. According to the International Enzyme Commission, ribonuclease, or ribonuclease pyrimidine nucleotido-2'-transferase (cyclizing), E.C.2.7.7.1.6, is the enzyme which transfers the 3'-phosphate of a pyrimidine nucleotide residue of a polynucleotide from the 5'-position of the adjoining nucleotide to the 2'-position of the pyrimidine nucleotide itself, forming a cyclic nucleotide. It also catalyzes the transfer of the phosphate group from the 2'-position in the cyclic phosphate to water; the overall reaction brings about the depolymerization of RNA.

The other ribonucleases react by the same principle, but are not necessarily specific for pyrimidine nucleotides. This phenomenon explains why all the ribonucleases effect one type of hydrolysis, which of necessity leads to the formation of a nucleoside-3'-phosphate, or just possibly of a nucleoside-2': 3'-cyclic phosphate if the reaction is interrupted before completion (with the exception of *E. coli* RNase II, which leads to the formation of 5'-phosphates, cf. p. 227).

Obtaining ribonucleic oligonucleotides terminated by 5'-phosphate groups can, however, be accomplished by endonucleases that are not specific towards the nature of the pentose.

So far as the situation around the active centers of various nucleolytic enzymes is concerned, we have seen that RNase A possesses at least two particularly reactive imidazole groups, belonging to the histidine residues in position 12 and 119, and that these two groups are at 5 A distance from the active center of the enzyme. In the DNase I case, it seems to be the tryptophan which is implicated in the active center (p. 242), whilst in the alkaline phosphatase, the enzyme is one that functions by virtue of an active phosphoserine group, as do several other well-known esterases.

Considering their possible applications in structural studies, the specificity of the nucleases sets a particular problem; it turns out that in general the number of fragments obtained after their action on macromolecular nucleic acids is too great, when a "dust" of small fragments is obtained from which it is difficult — if not impossible — to reconstitute the starting polynucleotide. This observation takes into account the fact that the variety of possible linkages in the nucleic acids is restricted by the occurrence of only four different bases. It can be seen, for example, that an enzyme specific for the hydrolysis of the p-purine/p-pyrimidine bond will hydrolyze one linkage in four, if the nucleotides are randomly distributed.

This is indeed what happens in the case of pancreatic DNase or DNase I, which has been shown to attack preferentially the pyrimidine — purine linkage, and after exhaustive hydrolysis by this enzyme, there is indeed approximately one linkage in four that has been broken (table XLII).

Table XLII : Schematic diagram showing cleavages preferentially effected by DNase I.

	Pu	Py
Pu	PuPu	PuPy
Py	PyPu	PyPy

By the same reasoning, it can be seen that in the case of pancreatic RNase, preferentially hydrolyzing Py — p-R linkages, at least 50 % of the linkages must be broken.

If we consider an enzyme that is specific for attack of a single nucleotidic sequence, since there are four different nucleotides. and consequently 16 possible types of linkage, only one linkage in sixteen should be cleaved. The average size of the fragments obtained after the action of this theoretical enzyme would be that of a hexadecanucleotide. It is possible that such highly specific nucleolytic enzymes exist, but they have not yet been characterized with any certainty.

Fortunately the specificity of existing nucleases can be modified, notably under special temperature conditions : for instance, RNase T_1, in principle specific for the Gp Xp link (Ribonucleate guaninenucleotide-2'-transferase (cyclizing) EC.2.7.7.2.6) and which should theoretically hydrolyze one linkage in four, only produces two large fragments from alanyl-t-RNA when the hydrolysis is carried out at 0° (Penswick and Holley, 1965).

III. ENZYMES IN THE STRUCTURAL DETERMINATION OF NUCLEIC ACIDS

A. GENERAL ASPECTS OF NUCLEIC ACID STRUCTURE

Concerning the general aspect of the nucleic structure, the nature of the internucleotide link, the first results yielded by the nucleases were acquired as early as 1952 by the work of Markham and Smith. The series of oligonucleotides characterized by these authors enabled fundamental information to be obtained about the the RNase specificity, and led them to propose a hypothesis for the structure of yeast RNA. According to these authors, the overall structure of RNA is a series of chains of different composition, but having the general appearance of the diagram below :

ApCp : *Up* : Cp : *Up* : Cp : Cp : ApGpApGpCp : *Up* : Cp : Cp : ApApGp*Up* : *Up* : Gp*Up* : *Up* : Cp : Cp : GpCp : Cp : *Up* : ApGpCp : Ap!

in which the colon represents the point of cleavage by the RNase. The residues that can be dephosphorylated by prostate phosphomonoesterase are in italics. In addition, Markham and Smith postulated that the chain was unbranched and terminated by a cyclic nucleotide.

The use of nucleases also provides confirmation of the position of the internucleotide linkage.

Action of spleen or snake vencm phosphodiesterases on the oligonucleotides isolated after

RNA hydrolysis by RNase, yielded respectively the series of mononucleotides with their terminal phosphoryl group in the C-3' position, and the series of mononucleotides with their terminal phosphoryl group in the C-5' position; it is therefore probable that in these circumstances the internucleotide linkage in natural RNA macromolecules is situated in the 3'-5' position. This observation is also valid for the DNAs, where the fact that sometimes 3'-phosphates and sometimes 5'-phosphates are obtained from the same substrate after the action of various DNases, is evidence supporting the 3'-5' position for the initial phosphodiester linkage.

The use of two nuclease systems : first 5'-formers, then 3'-formers (e.g. the system pancreatic DNase + snake venom phosphodiesterase, then the system *S. pyogenes* nuclease + spleen phosphodiesterase) enabled Kornberg and his co-workers to demonstrate that the polynucleotides synthesized by the action of DNA-polymerase have a similar structure to that of the natural DNAs; indeed, the polynucleotides are hydrolysed by pancreatic DNase, yielding a series of nucleotides comparable to those obtained after the hydrolysis of thymus DNA; i.e. nucleotides all terminated by 5'-phosphate groups. In a second stage, treatment of these same substrates by *S. pyogenes* DNase followed by treatment with calf spleen phosphodiesterase causes the almost complete hydrolysis of the DNA to 3'-deoxyribonucleotides. The only mode of linkage possible within the chains of biosynthetic DNA is thus a 3'-5'-phosphodiester linkage.

Use of the 3'-forming nucleases has received another important application : the method of "nearest neighbor analysis" or "nearest neighbor base sequences in nucleic acids" (Kornberg, 1961; Josse et al., 1961). This method was originally developed for DNA analysis, but is also applicable to RNA on condition that the appropriate enzymes are employed, and it allows precise determination in a given nucleic acid, the relative frequency of 16 types of possible linkage corresponding to the four principal nucleotides. The principle of the method is as follows. DNA (or RNA) is synthesized using one of the standard polymerases acting on a substrate consisting of a nucleoside ^{32}P-triphosphate, e.g. pppT, and three unlabelled nucleoside triphosphates. In the case of DNA experiments, it is known that it is possible to obtain in this way indefinite reproduction of the primer by using any natural DNA as this primer, the highly polymerized product finally being identical to the natural starting product, except that the ^{32}P-attached to the hydroxyl group at C-5' of pT functions as the phosphodiester bond between pT and the nearest neighboring nucleoside. The DNA labelled in this way is then isolated and hydrolyzed to the stage of the nucleoside-3'-phosphate by successive action of *S. pyogenes* nuclease and spleen phosphodiesterase. The ^{32}P content of each of the 3'-nucleotides thus isolated (by paper electrophoresis) constitutes a measure of the relative frequency with which a particular substrate (pT, in the present case) reacts with each one of the four nucleotides in the DNA synthesis considered.

....p · C   p* · T   p · G   p · A   p* · T   p · C   p · ...

The above scheme represents a portion of the DNA sequence synthesized using pT as label; after hydrolysis by the system of the two nucleases (dotted lines), it can be seen that the labeled phosphoryl group is transferred to the nearest nucleoside to T. If this process is carried out four times, one after the other, each time using a new ^{32}P-labeled substrate, the relative frequency of the 16 possible types of internucleotide linkage can be obtained. These analyses have led Kornberg to recognize two fundamental aspects of the DNA structure :

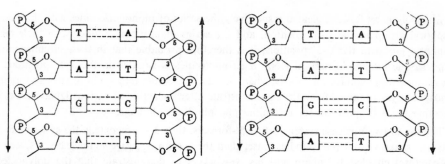

Figure 61. Contrast of a Watson and Crick DNA model with strands of opposite polarity with a model with strands of similar polarity. The predicted matching nearest-neighbor sequence frequencies are different. (Kornberg 1961)

Table XLIII. Nearest neighbor frequencies of *Mycobacterium phlei* DNA* (Kornberg. 1961)

Reaction No.	Labeled Triphosphate	Isolated 3'-Deoxyribonucleotide			
		Tp	*Ap*	*Cp*	*Gp*
1	dATP³²	*a* TpA 0.012	*b* ApA 0.024 I	*c* CpA 0.063 II	*d* GpA 0.065 III
2	dTTP³²	*b* TpT 0.026 I	*a* ApT 0.031	*d* CpT 0.045 IV	*c* GpT 0.060 V
3	dGTP³²	*e* TpG 0.063 II	*f* ApG 0.045 IV	*g* CpG 0.139	*h* GpG 0.090 VI
4	dCTP³²	*f* TpC 0.061 III	*e* ApC 0.064 V	*h* CpC 0.090 VI	*g* GpC 0.122
	Sums	0.162	0.164	0.337	0.337

Identical roman numerals designate those sequence frequencies that should be equivalent in a Watson and Crick DNA model with strands of opposite polarity; identical lowercase letters designate sequence frequencies that should be equivalent in a model with strands of similar polarity. The symbol TpA stands for deoxyadenylyl-(5'-3')-deoxythymidine.

* Chemial analysis of the base composition of the primer DNA indicated molar proportions of thymine, adenine cytosine, and guanine of 0.165, 0.162, 0.335, and 0.338, respectively.

a) the fact that the two paired complementary chains are of opposite polarity; this result is particularly apparent if table XLIII and figure 61 are examined, when it can be seen from figure 61 that of the two possible models of paired complementary chains, the left hand one has opposite polarity when the pentose plane is considered, the right hand one having similar polarity for the same reason. Comparison of the values obtained for certain dinucleotide pairs (such as, for exemple, ApG = CpT = 0.045 and GpA = TpC = 0.061) which can only correspond in the case of opposite polarity, makes this mode of representation the only one possible. The only pairs allowing the two systems to be differenciated are those consisting of two different purines or two different pyrimidines (a total of four pairs out of the sixteen possible). All the others are identical for both systems of polarity.

b) The nucleotide distribution, studied in samples as different as thymus DNA and *B. subtilis* DNA, does not occur at random, and this result is in accord with that obtained by examination of the fragments obtained after controlled chemical degradation of the DNA (cf. p. 122).

B. Sequence Analysis

The contribution made by enzymes to the determination of nucleotide sequences has also been considerable, as it was decisive in the case of polypeptide sequences. In order to judge the extent of this contribution, we shall compare it with the information supplied by the other methods of investigation. The methods of investigation are effectively of three kinds : physical and chemical methods, and enzymatic methods. These methods are not, of course, mutually exclusive, but quite the reverse, are often complementary.

1. Physical methods

We have pointed out (p. 66) that X-ray diffraction of nucleic compounds has already supplied important information, both concerning the spatial configuration of macromolecular DNA (the work of Wilkies et al., 1953), and concerning the exact configuration of a mononucleotide, adenylic acid *b* (the work of Brown et al., 1953). Recently, a new physical method of investigation has made its appearance, namely the photography of nucleic acid macromolecules in the electron microscope, and this would appear assured of a sound future. Excellent photographs of isolated DNA strands have been obtained by Kleinschmidt et al. (1962, 1963) from the phage T 2 and the phage ϕX 174, using the monolayer technique. By refining the electron microscopic photographic techniques, it ought to be possible to determine the nucleotide sequence, if one could specifically label a particular nucleotide by an appropriate reaction. The work of Moudrianakis (1962), and Moudrianakis and Beer (1964, 1965*a*, *b*), has shown that diazotized 2-amino-*p*-benzenedisulfonic acid can selectively label the guanine residues in DNA. The reaction is sufficiently mild for there not to be any excessive degradation of the chain. The DNA thus marked, and "stained" with uranyl acetate, has a particular configuration that is distinct from intact DNA in the electron microscope. This is an interesting method, since it should initially localize the guanine residues of the DNA, at the same time fixing the cytosine residues in the complementary chain in the case of double stranded DNA; in this way, half the sequence ought to be already known.

Another reaction, susceptible of applications in the determination of base sequences in DNA, with the electron microscope, was studied by Beer et al. (1966) : this reaction involves the selective oxidization of thymidylic acid residues in DNA (probably to 4,5-dihydroxythymine derivative) with osmium tetroxide, OsO_4, in neutral aqueous solutions, at 23° or 55°. It was shown that under these conditions, OsO_4 reacts predominantly with the thymine residues of denatured DNA and does not react with native double stranded DNA.

2. Chemical methods

Various methods have been proposed to characterize the ends of the nucleic acid chains. Rajbhandary et al. (1964), for instance, demonstrated that t-RNA could be labeled as its cetyl-trimethylammonium salt, by reaction with ^{14}C-methylphosphomorpholine by the following reaction, (figure 62) :

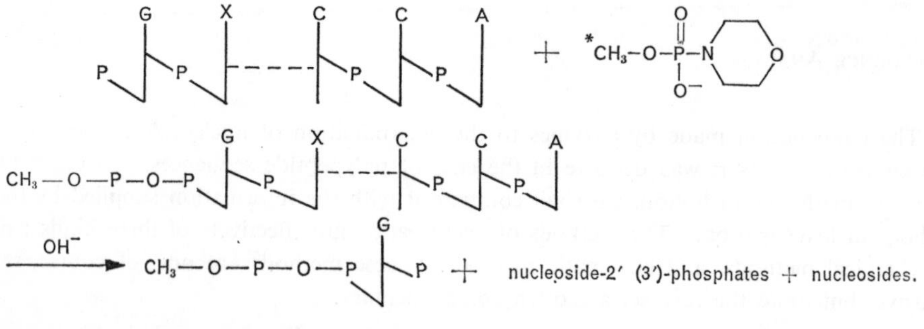

Figure 62. Reaction of t-RNA with ^{14}C methyl phosphomorpholine (Rajbhandary et al., 1964)

The conditions of the reaction are sufficiently mild for the product obtained with this phosphorylating agent and t-RNA to retain all the accepting properties of the starting RNA. By this method, it was confirmed that guanosine occurs in a predominating proportion at the phosphorylated end of t-RNA, together with lesser amounts of other constituents.

In order to label the ends of deoxyribonucleates carrying free hydroxyl groups, Stuart and Khorana (1964), have proposed a special acetylation method employing the treatment of an aqueous polynucleotide solution with an excess of acetic anhydride at pH 7 at room temperature for about 15 minutes. In the case when the oligonucleotides d-pTpApTpApTpA and d-pCpGpCpG are used as substrates and the acetic anhydride is tritiated, the specificity of the reaction for labeling the extremities of the oligonucleotide chain has been shown. The method could also find useful application in determining the ends of the chains.

Labeling of the ends of RNA chains carrying free hydroxyl groups can be carried out according to Hunt (1965) by reaction of oxidized (with periodate) RNA (or polynucleotides) with isoniazide, and formation of monohydrazones by the following scheme (figure 63) : t-RNA from *coli* fixes 36.6 moles isoniazide/10^6 g RNA, a figure which agrees with the values recorded in the literature.

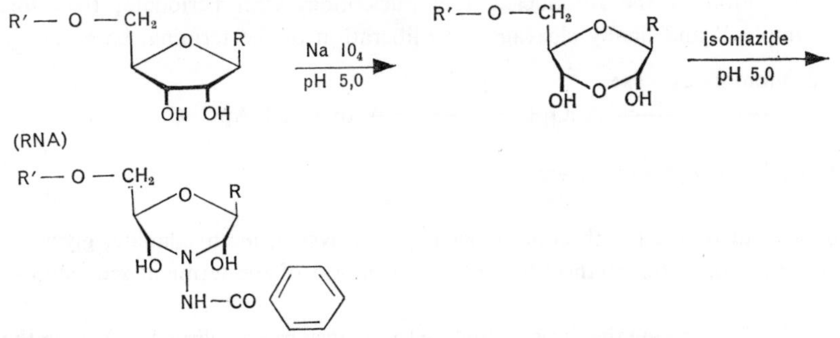

Figure 63. Oxidization of RNA followed by reaction with isoniazide (Hunt 1965)

A method for controlled RNA degradation that could serve in future applications for the structural determination of this material was proposed by Kochetkov et al. (1965). This method utilizes the reaction of RNA with hydroxylamine at high pH and 0°. Under these conditions, cleavage of uracil is observed with formation of ribosylurea residues; at higher temperature with more prolonged treatment, the ribosylurea is converted to ribosyloxime. The alkaline cleavage of deuridyl-RNA could result in β-elimination and cleavage of the 3′-phosphodiester bonds at the position of the modified residues. This method should be further examined, since it would enable the position to be located where there previously were uridyl residues (fig. 64).

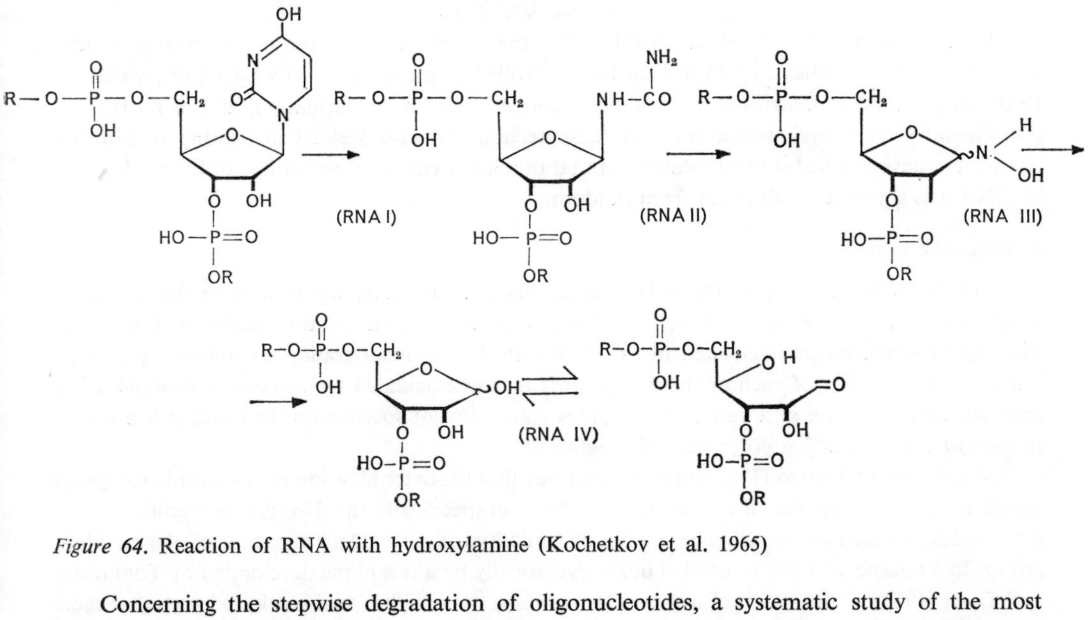

Figure 64. Reaction of RNA with hydroxylamine (Kochetkov et al. 1965)

Concerning the stepwise degradation of oligonucleotides, a systematic study of the most favorable reaction conditions was undertaken by Neu and Heppel (1960). The reaction that they recommend, which is in fact a combination of both chemical and enzymatic techniques, involves an oxidation of the ribonucleic oligonucleotides with periodate, then formation of an "amine complex" and finally cleavage with liberation of the terminal base, e.g.

$$\text{ApGpCp} \xrightarrow{\text{phosphomonoesterase}} \text{ApGpC} \xrightarrow{\text{periodate}} \text{oxidized ApGpC}$$

$$\xrightarrow[\text{pH 10.5}]{\text{glycine}} \text{ApGp} + \text{cytosine ... etc.}$$

Various amines can be used with equal efficiency, e.g. lysine, methylalanine, glycine. Neu and Heppel successfully used the method for the confirmation of the terminal sequence — pCpCpA of t-RNA.

Whitfeld (1965), applying the same technique to tobacco mosaic virus RNA, with the exception that methylamine was employed as a catalyst for the removal of the oxidized ultimate residue, confirmed that adenine was the terminal base, with cytosine as the penultimate one.

As another application of this technique Steinschneider and Fraenkel-Conrat (1966a, b) also studied the nucleotide sequence of tobacco mosaic virus RNA. They showed first that the treatment of this RNA with a 100 fold excess periodate oxidizes the terminal 2′,3′-glycol group quantitatively, for subsequent treatment with [^{14}C]-semicarbazide consumes two equivalents of this reagent per mole of oxidized RNA. The same authors demonstrated that aniline could be a convenient catalyst for the elimination of the terminal residue of periodate oxidized TMV-RNA.

By applying successively periodate oxidation, aniline catalyzed cleavage and removal of the terminal phosphate with alkaline phosphatase, Steinschneider and Fraenkel-Conrat tentatively suggested the following terminal sequence for TMV-RNA :

$$(-\text{Gp})\text{-Cp-Cp-Cp-A}.$$

Finally, amongst the chemical methods for the investigation of the polynucleotide chain, are the numerous studies carried out on the controlled degradation of DNA (p. 119), which led to the preparation of a series of pyrimidine oligonucleotides by depurination, and of purine oligonucleotides by depyrimidination. All these techniques have yielded interesting oligonucleotides, and have enabled it to be established that in many cases the distribution of the nucleotides in DNA was significantly different from random.

3. Enzymatic methods

The principle of these methods is straightforward. Initially, the idea is to fractionate a macromolecular ribonucleic or deoxyribonucleic substance into a certain number of fragments. Each of these fragments is isolated in the pure state by chromatography on ion exchangers or paper. The structure of each of these fragments is then elucidated by stepwise hydrolysis using exonucleases. The use of a variety of enzymes with different specificities then makes it possible to reconstruct the starting polynucleotide (figure 65).

Mandeles and Tinoco (1963) have pointed out that the determination of nucleotide sequences would be greatly simplified if it were possible to label specifically the 3′-and 5′-extremities of the nucleotides by particular reagents before the enzymic hydrolysis. Determination of the terminal groups in a nucleic acid can be carried out enzymatically by a technique developped by Tomlinson and Tener (1963). The action of a particular nuclease on a nucleic acid is selected such that there should be three sorts of nucleotides among the products of its action : those with no terminal phosphoryl group, those with one, and those with two. The mixture of the polynucleotides

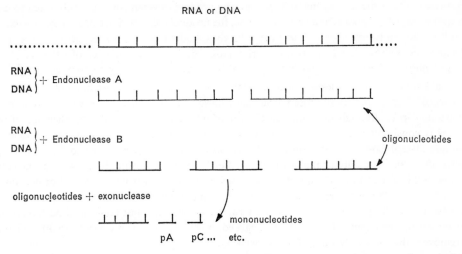

Figure 65. Schematic diagram of the determination of nucleic acid structure by enzymatic methods

obtained is fractionated by chromatography (in 7 M urea) on DEAE-cellulose, with elution in an NaCl gradient. Each fraction is isolated and treated with phosphomonoesterase. The polynucleotide derived from the extremity of the chain now differs from the other nucleotides in the same fraction by two units, and can be separated from them by chromatography in the same system as before (figure 66). Rice and Bock (1965) maintain that a hectonucleotide sequence (100 nucleotides, corresponding fairly closely to the size of transfer RNAs) can be determined by calculation, provided that after cleavage of the nucleotide with four nucleases which are specific for a single base, the longest fragments can be separated and their internal sequences determined. This method remains of purely theoretical interest for the moment, since the four necessary nucleases have not yet been discovered.

1st Stage			2nd Stage (after phosphomonoesterase)		
1) XpYp	....	Z	XpYp	....	Z
2) XpYp	....	Zp	XpYp	....	Z + Ip
3) pXpYp	....	Zp	XpYp	....	Z + 2p

Figure 66. Differentiation of chain ends after phosphomonoesterase action, (Tomlinson and Tener 1963)

Looking at the applications that have already been made of nucleases in the structural elucidation of nucleic acids, it is apparent that the results obtained are very encouraging.

The stepwise action of phosphodiesterase on ribonucleic chains has been studied by Nihei and Cantoni (1963) using yeast t-RNA as substrate. These authors have verified the concept according to which phosphodiesterase acts in a stepwise manner on t-RNA like an exonuclease, causing successive liberation of nucleoside-5'-phosphates. They brought forward five sets of arguments in favor of the concept : *a*) in the initial stages of the hydrolysis there is no formation of short oligonucleotides; *b*) a rise in the number of terminal 3'-hydroxyl groups is observed, together with a rise in the number of terminal 5′-phosphoryl groups; *c*) when t-RNA is submitted to diges-tion with RNase T_1 or alkali for a very short time, the products obtained are much more mixed than when it is allowed to react for a short time with phosphodiesterase; *d*) experiments with synthetic oligonucleotides show that there is no discrimination between the sequence of the bases; *e*) the action of phosphodiesterase on t-RNA occurs at a steady rate, right up to completion.

Snake venom phosphodiesterase has also been used in a stepwise determination of the terminal sequence of TMV-RNA (Singer and Fraenkel-Conrat, 1963). This sequence was reported to be UpApCpUpA, although the sequence UpApUpCpA was not excluded. Neither one of these schemes is consistent with the sequence more recently determined by the ʹperiodate oxidation technique : (-Gp)-Cp-Cp-A, cited on p. 300. Hydrolysis of the nucleotides 1 to 3 does not signi-ficantly affect the infectivity or the behavior of the RNA on sedimentation. As the nucleotides are removed, it is found that the infectivity slowly falls, removal of from 2 to 5 nucleotides amoun-ting to less than the lethal requirement (average residual activity 46 %). This loss of activity could be due to the progressive loss of the terminal nucleotides, but could also be the result of cleavage within the chain. It should be remarked, however, that even when 10 to 30 nucleotides are removed, the infectivity rarely falls below 1 %.

The applications of snake venom phosphodiesterase concern the 5′-linked (" right ") end of the chain; the possibility of using spleen phosphodiesterase to release in a stepwise manner mononucleotides from the 3′-linked (" left ") end of the TMV-RNA molecule, was investigated by Singer et al. (1965). All that can be said for the moment is that limited digestion of this RNA by this enzyme caused the release of a constant pattern of nucleotides : $A = U > G > C$.

For the same general purpose Singer and Fraenkel-Conrat (1965), have tried to use polynu-cleotide phosphorylase (in phosphorolysis) to carry out the stepwise hydrolysis of TMV RNA, but found that the reaction was not, in fact, as simple as might have been at first thought. The problem of the nucleotide sequence in TMV is particularly intricate in view of their very high number, 6,400.

For this reason, the molecules that would appear to be most suitable for this type of study are the t-RNA, which only involve 70 — 80 nucleotides. The application of several specific nucleases to the determination of the complete sequence of various t-RNA (Holley et al., Zachau et al., Cantoni et al., Armstrong et al., etc.), are among the most significant examples of the rational use of these enzymes. The elucidation of the complete sequence of alanyl-t-RNA by Holley and his co-workers (1965*a*, *b*) constituted an event that is as important as the determination of the complete insulin sequence by Sanger (1945-1951). These two studies exhibit considerable ana-logies, since both were carried out largely by the aid of enzymatic methods.

---

pG-G-G-C-, G-U-G-, U-MeG-G-C-, G-C-,
G-U-A-G-, DiHU-C-G-, G-DiHU-A-G-,
C-G-, C-DiMeG-, C-U-C-C-C-U-U-I-G-C-,
MeI-ψ-, G-G-G-A-G-A-G-U*-C-U-C-C-G-,
G-T-ψ-C-G-, A-U-U-C-C-G-, G-A-C-U-
C-G-, U-C-C-A-C-C-A$_{OH}$

Table XLIV. Sequences that account for all of the nucleotide residues in the alanine RNA. (Holley et al. 1965).

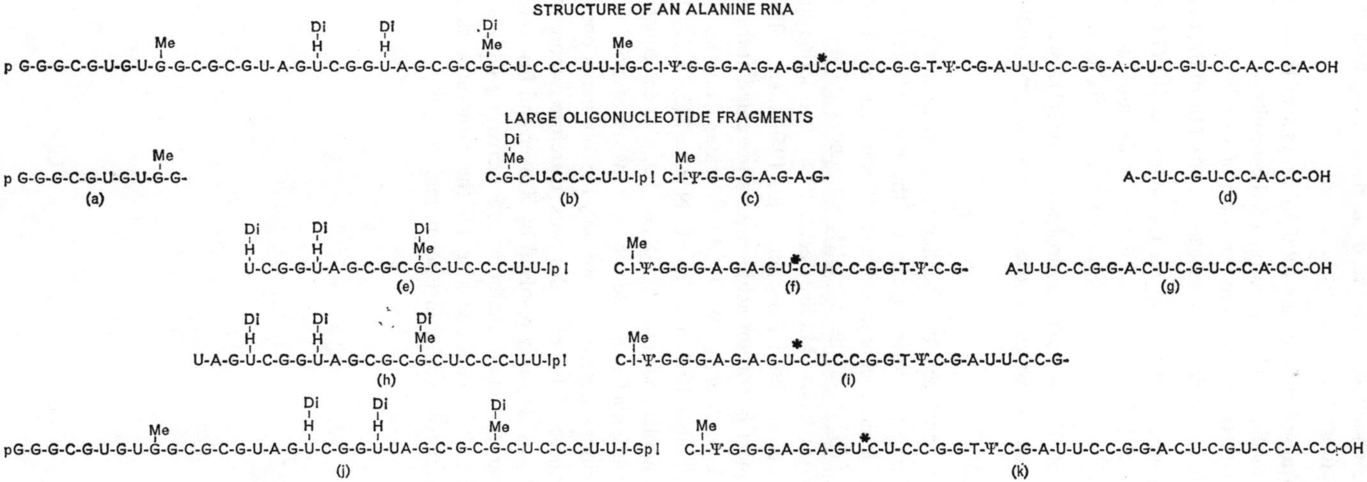

STRUCTURE OF AN ALANINE RNA

            Me   Di   Di   .Di   Di

p G-G-G-C-G-U-G-U-G-G-C-G-C-G-U-A-G-U-C-G-G-U-A-G-C-G-C-G-C-U-C-C-C-U-U-I-G-C-I-Ψ-G-G-A-G-A-G-U-C-U-C-C-G-G-T-Ψ-C-G-A-U-U-C-C-G-G-A-C-U-C-G-U-C-C-A-C-C-A-OH

(a)

LARGE OLIGONUCLEOTIDE FRAGMENTS

          Me   Di   A-C-U-C-G-U-C-C-A-C-C-OH

p G-G-G-C-G-U-G-U-G-G-   Me

(a')   C-G-C-U-C-C-C-U-U-I-p I C-I-Ψ-G-G-G-A-G-A-G-   (d)

                   (b)   (c)

            Di   Me   A-U-C-C-G-G-A-C-U-C-G-U-C-C-A-C-C-OH

       Me

U-C-G-G-U-A-G-C-G-C-G-C-U-C-C-C-U-U-I-p I   C-I-Ψ-G-G-A-G-A-G-U-C-U-C-C-G-G-T-Ψ-C-G-   (g)

         (e)   (f)

          Di   Me   Me

U-A-G-U-C-G-G-U-A-G-C-G-C-G-C-U-C-C-C-U-U-I-p I   C-I-Ψ-G-G-G-A-G-A-G-U-C-U-C-C-G-G-T-Ψ-C-G-A-U-U-C-C-G-   (i)

        (h)

         Di   Di   Me

pG-G-G-C-G-U-G-U-G-G-C-G-C-G-U-A-G-U-C-G-G-U-A-G-C-G-C-G-C-U-C-C-C-U-U-I-G-C-I-Ψ-G-G-A-G-A-G-U-C-U-C-C-G-G-T-Ψ-C-G-A-U-U-C-C-G-G-A-C-U-C-G-U-C-C-A-C-C-OH

(k)

Figure 67. The structure of an alanine transfer RNA, isolated from yeast, is shown at the top. Large oligonucleotide fragments that were crucial in the proof of structure are shown below. (Holley et al. 1965*a, b*)

20

The determination of the complete sequence of a ribonucleic acid (actually yeast alanyl-t-RNA) can be summarized as follows :

a) Initially, all the short fragments from the total hydrolysis of this RNA by RNase T_1 and RNase A were isolated and purified. Combination of the results obtained allows the provisional description of the alanyl-t-RNA structure in the form of 16 oligonucleotide sequences (table XLIV), the position of which in the chain is still unknown, apart from the two terminal sequences.

b) The presence of the 5 -phosphate group on the sequence pG-G-G-C indicates that this sequence is to be found on the "left hand side" of the molecule, and the free 3 -hydroxyl on the sequence U C C A C C A (OH) shows that this must be at the right hand end.

c) Obtaining large fragments by controlled hydrolysis of the RNA with RNase T_1 (see p. 221) yielded sufficient information for the whole of the molecule to be reconstituted (figure 67).

Similar studies have been continued on the nucleotide sequences of various RNAS. The aminoacyl oligonucleotides from TIRNase digests of the t-RNAS charged respectively with serine, glycine, threonine, and alanine, were investigated (Smith C.J. and Herbert 1966; Smith C.J. et al. 1966). Within the last two years the complete sequences of several t-RNAS have been elucidated, those of yeast tyrosine t-RNA (Madison et al. 1966), two serine specific transfer RNAS (Melchers et al. 1965; Zachan et al. 1966; Doepner et al. 1966)... etc. The final result of these investigations was among the most important achievements presented at the Seventh International Congress of Biochemistry (Tokyo, August 1967). At the same Congress it was also shown by Sanger and his coworkers (see also Brownlee et al. Nature 215, 735, 1967), that enzymatic methods could be successfully applied not only to t-RNA but also to sequence studies on RNA5S from Escherichia coli : this particular molecule which consists of no fewer than 120 subunits strunt together, contains no « minor » nucleotides but only the four major ones. The determination of the complete sequence of these 120 nucleotides was therefore a more intricate problem than that of t-RNA sequence yet it was elegantly resolved by Sanger and his coworkers.

These examples show that enzymatic methods are increasing daily in importance in the biochemistry of nucleic acids, and if we consider all the structures that still remain to be determined, we can see that their role is only just beginning.

Synoptic Tables of Nucleolytic Enzymes

Designation	Origin	Activators Inhibitors	pH optimum	Substrates investigated
ENDONUCLEASES **NUCLEASES** ("non-specific")				
Animal	Lamb brain	Activated by Mn^{++} and Mg^{++}	7.0 and 9.0	Native DNA Denatured DNA
	Rat liver	Absolute requirement for Mg^{++} & for Mn^{++} Inhibited by Ca^{++}	ForRNase 6.8 — 7.0. ForDNase 6.6 — 6.8.	DNA and RNA
	Bothrops atrox		5.0	RNA, DNA
Vegetal	*Phasoleus aureus*		5.0	RNA, DNA
	Potato	Inactivated by EDTA	6-7	DNA, RNA
Microbial	*Azotobacter agilis*	Activated by Mg^{++} ions		Poly- A, RNA, DNA
	Bacillus subtilis	Maximum of stimulation observed with Ca^{++}	9.0-9.6	Denatured DNA
	Neurospora crassa	No effect of divalent cations. Inhibited by K phosphate	6-9	Denaturated DNA, RNA
	N. crassa mitochondria	Requires divalent cations Mg^{++}, Mn^{++}, Co^{++}. Inhibited by EDTA	6.0-7.5	DNA, RNA
	Staphylococcus pyogenes	Activated by Ca^{++} ions	8.6	Natural DNA, biosynthetic DNA, TMV-RNA, poly A ... etc.

Products (terminal phosphates)	Linkages preferentially split	Authors	Observations
5'-phosphates		Healy et al. (1963)	Acts preferentially on denatured DNA; could be used to detect single stranded fragments in DNA
5'-phosphates	No clear specificity	Curtis et al. (1966) Curtis, Smellie (1966)	Enzyme distinct from pancreatic DNase; shows close similarities to the endonuclease of lamb brain and an enzyme from pig nuclei.
3'-phosphates		Georgatsos, Laskowski (1962)	At first, preferential hydrolysis of the linkage d-Gp-Gp.
3'-phosphates	d-pA-pX	Sung & Laskowski (1962)	Mode of action chiefly endonucleolytic
		Bjork (1965)	Purified 1000 times from crude extract.
5'-phosphates	Any, provided nucleotide higher than tetra	Stevens, Hilmoe (1960)	Non specific of pentose, but specific of base sequence, since poly A less resistant than other biosynthetic polymers.
		Birnboim (1966 b)	This enzyme may be located at or near the cell surface.
5'-phosphates	pX — pG	Linn, Lehman (1965 a, b)	Denatured DNA hydrolyzed 100 times faster than native DNA
Small nucleotides terminated by 5'-phosphates	d-Xp-Tp d-Xp-Ap	Linn, Lehman (1966)	Clearly distinguishable from the extra mitochondrial enzyme described above.
3'-phosphates		Cunningham et al. (1956-1958), Privat de Garilhe et al. (1958-1961), Sulkowski, Laskowski (1962) Anfinsen et al. (1963)	Fast hydrolysis of DNA with production of 30 to 40 % mononucleotides. Isolated dinucleotides are not hydrolyzed. Sedimentation constant 1.7 S. Molecular weight 11,000 to 12,000; contains 2 His and 1 Try residues and no free -SH group.

Designation	Origin	Activators Inhibitors	pH optimum	Substrates
RIBONUCLEASES *Animal* Human	Pancreas HPa	Inhibited by Hg^{++}, Zn^{++}, Cu^{++}	7.6	RNA
	Pancreas HPb	Inhibited by Hg^{++}, Zn^{++}, Cu^{++}	7.6	RNA
	Spleen		6.5	RNA
	Urine (RNase P)		8.0	RNA, Cp!
	Urine (RNase U)		6.5	RNA
Bovine	Adrenal medulla	50% inhibition with $2,5.10^{-5}$ M Cu^{++}	5.5	Yeast RNA, RNA « Core » left by RNase A
	Liver			RNA
	Milk	Inhibited by Zn^{++}, Cd^{++} & polyvinyl sulfate	7.5	RNA
	Pancreas (RNase A)	Inhibited by Cu^{++}	7.7	RNA, polynucleotides of the RNA type Cp!, Up!. etc.
	Pancreas (RNase B)			
	Sperm	Inhibited by Fe^{++} and Zn^{++}	8.0	RNA
	Spleen	Activated by Mg^{++}	6.0-6.5	RNA
	Spleen (acid RNase)			
	Thymus			RNA
	Thyroïd gland			RNA
Porcine	Liver (mitochon-drial soluble fraction)		6.7-8.5	RNA

Products (terminal phosphates)	Linkages preferentially split	Authors	Observations
Nucleoside 3'-phosphates		Ukita et al., (1964)	Properties comparable to bovine RNase A
Nucleoside-3'-phosphates		Ukita et al., (1964)	Isoelectric point pH 10.3; properties comparable to bovine pancreatic RNase A.
		Delaney (1963)	Chromatographic properties comparable to urine RNase U. Molecular weight 18,320.
		Delaney (1963)	Comparable to bovine RNase A. Molecular weight 13,370. Exhibits RNase A immunologic activity.
		Delaney (1963)	Different from RNase A. Molecular weight 18,840. Does not exhibit the RNase A immunologic activity.
		Smith A.D., Winkler (1965)	This enzyme is thermolabile and different from pancreatic RNase A.
		Kaplan Heppel (1956)	Important production of cyclic dinucleotides.
3'-nucleotides	Py-Py Py-Pu	Ibuki et al. (1965)	Properties comparable to bovine pancreatic RNase A.
3'-phosphates	Pyp-Pyp Pyp-Pup Pyp-R	Kunitz (1940), Markham, Smith (1952), Moore, Stein et al. (1950-1964), Heppel et al. (1954) Findlay et al. (1962)	The constituton of RNase A is completely elucidated. Its enzymic mechanism involves 2 His residues.
		Plummer, Hirs (1963-1964)	Glycoprotein, the protein part of which has the same composition as RNase A. Molecular weight 14,700 ± 300.
		D'Alessio (1963)	Properties comparable to other animal RNases.
3'-phosphates		Kaplan, Heppel (1956)	Comparable to RNase A. The core left by RNase A is not hydrolyzed by this RNase
		Bernardi, Bernardi (1966)	
		Bernardi (1962)	
		Dierick, Stockx (1965)	
		Beard, Razzell (1964)	

Designation	Origin	Activators Inhibitors	pH optimum	Substrates investigated
Murine	Rat adipose tissue		1° 6.2-6.3 2° 7.5-8.2	
	Rat adrenals (2 RNases)		1) pH5.6 2) pH7.8	RNA
	Rat liver	Inactivated by heat	7.8	RNA
	Rat liver parti- culates	Inhibited by most monovalent and divalent cations	9.0-9.5	RNA
	Rat pancreas		7.8	RNA
	Serum (rat and guinea pig)	RNA	7.4	
Rabbit	Rabbit reticulocytes			RNA
Snakes	Cobra venom	Activated by Mg^{++} ions	7.6-7.8	RNA
	Vipera russellii			RNA, ribonucleic polynu- cleotides
Fish	Ophidion elongatus	Inhibited by Zn^{++} and Cu^{++}, Iodoace- tate, CH_2O, NaF, etc.		RNA
Plant ribonucleases.	Acetabularia		1° 7.2 2° 5.0	RNA
	Agaricus campestris	Inhibited by divalent cations in the or- der $Cu^{++} < Zn^{++}$ $< Hg^{++} < Mg^{++}$	1° acid RNase pH 4.6 2° alkali- ne RNase pH 7.1	

Products (terminal phosphates)	Linkages preferentially split	Authors	Observations
		Eichel et al. (1961)	
		Girija, Sreenivasan (1966)	In addition to these 2 RNases, the art adrenal supernatant fraction contains a considerable amount of free RNase inhibitor.
		Gordon (1965 a, b, 1966)	The overall purification of the rat liver RNase was 6,700 fold.
		Rahman (1966)	The enzyme is localized in the sedimentable fraction of the rat liver.
		Gordon (1965 a, b, 1966) Bientema, Gruber (1965) Cozzone, Marchis-Mouren (1966)	The purification of this enzyme was less difficult than those of liver, since pancreas is richer in RNase. Molecular weight 15,000. Aminoacid composition different from that of bovine pancreatic RNase A.
		Rabinovitch, Dohi (1957)	Comparable to RNase A
		Rosenthal et al. (1964)	
5'-phosphates		Vasilenko, Babkina (1965)	This enzyme releases mainly oligonucleotides from di-to hexanucleotides.
(Np)n Py! (n=1, 2, ...etc.)		McLennan, Lane (1965)	Specificity comparable to RNase A; does not produce mononucleotides
Nucleoside-3'-phosphtase		Tomlinson (1958)	Such enzymes are present in the muscles of numerous fish species
		Schweiger (1966)	This enzyme is heat stable
3'-phosphates		Cuigniez et al. (1965)	

Synoptic Table

Designation	Origin	Activators Inhiitbors	pH optimum	Substrates investigated
	Alium (germinating garlic)		7.0	RNA
	Lolium multiflorum (germ)	Inhibited by KCN and cystein	4.5	RNA
	Nepenthes spp.		5.0	RNA
	Phaseolus aureus Robx.		1° 5.0 2° 5.2 3° 5.6	RNA
	Pisum sativum (leaf)	Inactivated by Cu^{++} and Zn^{++}	5.0	RNA
	(root)		1° 5.8 2° 7.1	yeast RNA
	Potato tuber Nuclease II		5.2-6.1	RNA
	Soya bean (germ)		5.2	RNA
	Tobacco (leaves)	Inactivated by Cu^{++} and Zn^{++}	5.1	RNA
	Zea mays RNase A	Activated by KCl Activated by $MgCl_2$ at pH 5.0 Inhibited by $MgCl_2$ at pH 5.8	5.0	RNA
	RNase B	Activated by $MgCl_2$ at pH 5.8	6.2	RNA (DNA)
Microbial	*Aspergillus oryzae* (Takadiastase) RNase T1	Inhibited by Zn^{++}	7.5	RNA, t-RNA ribonucleic polynucleotides
	(Takadiastase) RNase T2	Inhibited by Cu^{++}	4.5	RNA, t-RNA, ribonucleic polynucleotides

Products (terminal phosphates)	Linkages preferentially split	Authors	Observations
		Carlsson, Frick (1964)	Molecular weight 20,000. Sedimentation coefficient 2.45S; properties comparable to bovine RNase A.
3′-phosphates		Shuster (1957) Shuster et al. (1959)	
		Matthews (1960)	Almost complete degradation to the four 2′:3′ cyclic nucleotides.
3′-phosphates	Phosphoesters of 3′-nucleosides	Stockx, Vandendriessche (1961) Stockx et al. (1964)	The 3 fractions isolated from *P. aureus* probably derive from a single molecule
		Holden, Pirie (1955) Markham, Strominger (1956), Pierpoint (1956)	Important production of 2′, 3′-cyclic nucleotides
		Lyndon (1966)	RNase was measured in nuclear, michondrial, microsomal and soluble fractions. All activity appeared to be in the cytoplasm.
		Bjork (1965)	Purified 830 times from the crude extract in 60 % yield.
3′-phosphates		Merola, Davis (1962)	Ap! cleaved to the 3′-nucleotide. The cyclic pyrimidine nucleotides are resistant to this enzyme
3′-phosphates		Frisch-Niggemeyer, Reddi (1957)	RNA Hydrolyzed 96.8 %
Oligonucleoside 3′-P. Nucleotide 2′, 3′-cyclic		Wilson (1963)	Comparable to mung bean enzyme. Could also be isolated from corn meal.
Nucleoside-5′-P.		Wilson (1963)	Apparently a non-specific nuclease
3′-phosphates	Gp ┊ Gp or Gp ┊ Xp	Sato, Egami (1957-1960) Egami et al. (1964)	Molecular weight ca. 11,000. Isoelectric point 2.9
3′-phosphates		Egami et al. (1964)	Molecular weight 36,200. Isoelectric poii t ca. 6

Designation	Origin	Activators Inbihitors	pH optimum	Substrates
	Bacillus subtilis		8.5	RNA and ribonucleic poly-nucleotides
	Escherichia coli RNase I			RNA and ribonucleic poly-nucleotides
	E. coli RNase II	Activated by mono-valent plus diva-lent cations (Mg^{++}, Mn^{++}...)	7-8	RNA and ribonucleic poly-nucleotides
	E. coli Cellular debris RNase		8.2	RNA and ribonucleic poly-nucleotides
	E. coli acid-solu-ble ribosomal RNase	Inhibited by mer-capto ethanol and salts at high con-centrations		RNA, poly-C, poly-A, t-RNA poly-U etc
	Neurospora crassa (ribosomal nu-clease)	Activated by Mg^{++}		yeast t-RNA
	Streptomyces erythreus	Strong inhibition by NaCl and $MgCl_2$		RNA and ribonucleic poly-nucleotides
	Ustilago sphaerogena		7.0-7.5	Various RNAs, poly A-G, Gp! .. etc.

DEOXYRIBONUCLEASES

Animal

Human	Plasma Serum	Heat stable Activated by Mg^{++}	7.5	DNA DNA
Bovine	Kidney type I	Activated by Mg^{++}	7.0	DNA
	Kidney type II	Activated byMg^{++}	4.5	DNA

Products (terminal phosphates)	Linkages preferentially split	Authors	Observations
3'-phosphates	Gp ⁝ Gp Gp ⁝ Ap	Nishimura, (1960) Nishimura, Ozawa (1960), Rushizky et al. (1963), Hartley et al. (1963)	Enzyme obtained in the crystalline state. Amino acid composition differs from that of pancreatic RNase A. Sedimentation constant 1.4S. Molecular weight 10,700 ± 400.
3'-phosphates		Tal, Elson (1963) Neu, Heppel (1964)	Enzyme localized in a latent state in 30S ribosomes. Total hydrolysis of RNA to mononucleotides.
Nucleoside-5'-phosphates		Spahr (1965)	Michaelis constant for the hydrolysis of poly U : $7.5 \cdot 10^{-8}$ M.
Nucleoside-3'-phosphates		Anraku, Mizuno (1965)	
Nucleoside-2',3'-cyclic phosphates and oligonucleotides		Anderson, Carter (1965)	The molecular weight of this enzyme was estimated at 10,000-30,000 by gel filtration.
		Somberg, Davis (1965)	
Nucleoside-3'-phosphates	Gp ⁝ Gp or Gp ⁝ X Methyl Gp ⁝ X	Tanaka, Cantoni (1963)	Comparable to RNase T_1
Oligonucleotides terminated by Gp (3'-phosphates)	Gp ⁝ Xp Gp 2', 3'-phosphate→ Gp	Glitz, Dekker (1964)	Comparable to RNase T_1, in particular, sedimentation coeficient 1.6S, heat stability and absence of reaction with iodoacetate
		Doctor (1963) Wroblewski, Bodansky (1950)	Purified 600 fold by Cohn's technique for serum globulins.
		Cunningham, Laskowski (1953)	
		Cunningham, Laskowski (1953)	

Synoptic Table

Designation	Origin	Activators Inhibitors	pH optimum	Substrates
	Meduloadrenal		4.6	DNA
	Pancreas (DNase I)	Activated by Mg^{++}	7.0	DNA, deoxyribonucleic po lynucleotides
	Spleen type II DNase	Activated by KCl and $MgCl_2$ Inhibited by SO_4^-, PO_4^{--}, AsO_4^{---}	4.5	DNA
	Thymus DNase II	Divalent cations activators at low conc.; inhibitors at high conc.	4.5	DNA
Other animal sources.	Hog spleen "acid DNase"		acid region	DNA
	Guinea pig (spleen, brain)	Inhibited by Mg^{++} ions	5.2	DNA
	Cat serum compared with rabbit, rat and mouse sera, all DNase I type		7.5	DNA
	Mouse Mammary tumours of C_3H mice, (DNase I)	Activated by divalent cations	5.5	DNA
	Mammary tumours of C_3H mice (DNase II)	Activated by Mn^{++} Inhibited by Na^+	8.0	Denaturated DNA
	Rabbit leucocytes	Inhibited by phosphate and heparin	5.0	
	Chicken embryo DNase I	Optimal activity with 0,0026 м. $Mg Cl_2$	7.1	DNA

Products (terminal phosphates)	Linkages preferentially split	Authors	Observations
5'-phosphates	d-pPu-pPy	Smith, Winkler (1965) Kunitz (1950) Sinsheimer (1954-1957) Garilhe, Laskowski (1954-1957) Laskowski et al. (1957-1961)	DNA hydrolyzed with production of 1 % mononucleotides. One linkage out of 4 is broken
5'-phosphates		Maver, Greco (1949-1954), McDonald (1955) Koerner, Sinsheimer (1957), Hodes, Swenson (1962)	Apparently indefinite hydrolysis of DNA to the stage of oligonucleotides
3'-phosphates	d-Pyp-Pup	Maver, Greco (1949) Webb (1953) Garilhe, Laskowski et al. (1953-1957)	Production of a very small amount of mononucleotides terminated by 3'-phosphates. Important production of higher polynucleotides.
		Bernardi et al. (1963)	Sedimentation coefficient 3 — 4 S
		Tempel, Roessner (1965)	
		Riou et al (1966)	Cat serum was shown to be exceptionally rich in DNase I activity compared to human serum.
		Georgatsos, Symeonidis (1965)	
		Georgatsos, Symeonidis (1965)	Acts preferentially on denatured DNA
Oligonucleotides of an average chain length = 4.8		Bornstein et al. (1966)	This enzyme has some of the characteristics of a DNase II.
		Tempel, Zipf (1966)	Km for DNA hydrolysis $= 2.08 \times 10^{-7}$

Designation	Origin	Activators Inhibitors	pH optimum	Substrates
	Chicken embryo DNase II	Optimal activity with 0.165M Na OAc	4.35-4 5	DNA
	Mustelus canis	Optimum in NaCl 0.1M. Divalent cations such as Mg^{++}, Mn^{++}, Co^{++} necessary	8.0	DNA, preferentially denatu turated
	Crab testes "alkaline DNase"	Synergism Cu^{++} and Mg^{++}	8.5	DNA
	Octopus vulgaris hepatopancreas	Mg^{++} ions necessary	8.5	DNA
	Helix pomatia L. hepatopancreas	Inhibited by Mg^{++} and Mn^{++}	5,6	DNA preferentially native
Microbial	Aspergillus oryzae (Takadiastase)	Activated by Zn^{++}, Inhibited by RNA	4.4-4,6	DNA preferentially denatured
	Bacillus subtilis SB19. Phage SP_3 induced DNase			Preferentially denaturated DNA
	Clostridium septicum	Inhibited by Mn^{++} ions		
	Escherichia coli K 12 DNase I or E. coli B Endonuclease I		7-8	Native DNA
	E. coli DNase II		7-8	DNA
	E. coli DNase III		8.5-9.0	Denaturated DNA hydrolysed 10 times faster than native DNA
	E. coli DNase IV		8.5-9.0	Denaturated DNA hydrolyzed 10 times faster than native DNA

Products (terminal phosphates)	Linkages preferentially split	Authors	Observations
		Tempel, Zipf (1966)	Km for DNA hydrolysis $= 5.5 \times 10^{-7}$.
		Ashe et al. (1965)	Endonucleolytic process of hydrolysis
3'-phosphates	Xp-Tp	Georgatsos (1965)	The linkage Xp Gp is particularly resistent
5'-phosphates	d-pX-pC	Georgatsos, Antonoglou (1966)	This, enzyme was purified 400-fold.
		Laval et al. 1966	Molecular weight smaller than 100,000.
5'-phosphates		Ando (1966)	This enzyme is defined as a denatured DNA-(probably single-stranded-DNA-) specific nuclease.
		Trilling, Aposhian (1965)	This DNase was demonstrated by the rise of DNase in *B. subtilis* at the time this microorganism was infected with phage SP$_3$
		Meisel et al. (1959-1962)	This DNase is inhibited by *Cl. septicum* antitoxic serum
Oligonucleotides higher than pentanucleotides, 5'-phosphates		Lehman et al. (1962, *a*, *b*) Weissbach, Korn (1963) Lehman (1963)	These fractions I and II extracted from *E. coli* K12 are comparable to the *E. coli* DNase described by Lehman et al. (1962*a*, *b*) as *E. coli* B endonuclease
Oligonucleotides higher than pentanucleotides		Weissbach, Korn (1963)	
Mainly mononucleotides (5'-phosphates)		Weissbach, Korn (1963)	These two enzymes, *E. coli* DNases III and IV, classified as exonucleases attacking denatured DNA more rapidly than native DNA (cf. *E. coli* exonucleases, p. 270)
5'-phosphates		Weissbach, Korn (1963)	

Designation	Origin	Activators Inhibitors	pH optimum	Substrates investigated
	E. coli DNase from mitomycin C induced phage k$_{12}$		9-10	Attacks native DNA 5-€ times faster than denatured DNA
	E. coli DNase DNA exonuclease associated with the formation of phage 434	Inhibited by p-chloromercuribenzoate Inhibited by 0.1 M NaCl or 0.1 M KCl Activated by divalent cations Mg^{++}, Mn^{++}		Preferential attack of native DNA
	Saccharomyces cerevisiae	Activated by Mg^{++}	6.0	DNA
	Streptococci: "streptodornase"	Activated by Mg^{++}	7.5	DNA
	Streptococcus pyogenes DNase A	Activated by divalent cations	8-9	DNA
	Str. pyogenes DNase B	Activated by divalent cations	8-9	DNA
	Str. pyogenes DNase C	Activated by divalent cations	5-6	DNA
	Str. pyogenes DNase D	Activated by divalent cations	6-7	DNA

EXONUCLEASES
 (Phosphodiesterases)

Animal tissues

	Origin	Activators Inhibitors	pH optimum	Substrates investigated
	Bovine spleen		7.0	RNA and DNA types polynucleotides, any phosphodiester
	Bovine intestinal mucosa		7.0	RNA and DNA types polynucleotides, any phosphodiester

Products (terminal phosphates)	Linkages preferentially split	Authors	Observations
		Korn, Weissbach (1963)	
Liberation of mo-nonucleotides, 5'-phosphates		Korn, Weissbach (1964)	
		Zamenhof, Chargaff (1949)	
5'-phosphates	pPy-pPu	McCarty (1949) Potter, Laskowski (1959) Stone, Burton (1961-1962) Georgatsos et al. (1962)	Inhibition of this DNase by human and rabbit antisera. The DNA hydrolyzate contains 1.5 % mononucleotides and 90 % 5-10 residues oligonucleotides
5'-phosphates	pX-pG	Winter, Bernheimer (1964)	
5'-phosphates	pX-pG	Winter, Bernheimer (1964)	
5'-phosphates		Winter, Bernheimer (1964)	
5'-phosphates	pX-pA	Winter, Bernheimer (1964)	
3'-phosphates	Any phosphodi-ester TpTpTp...→ Tp + TpTp	Heppel et al. (1955) Razzell, Khorana (1958)	Stepwise hydrolysis starting at the 5'-OH terminal end. Catalyzes exchange and synthesis reactions as RNase does; eg. ApUp + C → ApC + U
3'-phosphates	Any phosphodi-ester	Heppel, Hilmoe (1955) Razzell (1961 b)	The four mononucleotides are rapidly hydrolyzed to the corresponding 3'-phosphates

Synoptic Table

Designation	Origin	Activators Inhibitors	pH optimum	Substrates
	Dog heart a)	Activated by imidazole inhibited by cafeine and theophylline	8.0	cyclic 3,'5'-nucleotide phosphodiesters. particularly uridine-3',5'-cyclic phosphate
	Dog heart b)	Activated by Mg^{++}, NH_4^+ and imidazole. Inhibited by caffeine	8.6	Nucleoside-3, 5'-cyclic phosphates
	Bovine milk microsomes	Activated by Mg^{++} and Ca^{++}; inhibited by EDTA and reducing reagents.	9.5	Various phosphodiesters, thymidine — 5'-p-nitrophenyl phosphate:NpT.
	Hog kidney	Activated by Mg^{++} Inhibited by EDTA		Any phosphodiester
	Mouse leukemic cells			Polynucleotides only
Snake venoms	Agkistrodon piscivorus		8-9	Any phosphodiester
	Bothrops atrox			Any phosphodiester
	Crotalus adamanteus	Activated by Mg^{++}	8.6	
	Vipera lebetina "Gurza"			
	Vipera russellii		9.3	Any phosphodiester
Plant exonucleases	Germinating barley		5-6	Oligonucleotides

Products (terminal phosphates)	Linkages preferentially split	Authors	Observations
5'-phosphates		Hardman and Sutherland (1965)	This enzyme should be specific for uridine 3',5'-phosphate
5'-phosphates		Nair (1966)	This enzyme, purified from dog ventricular myocardium, shows a preference for nucleoside-3',5'-cyclic phosphates with purine bases.
5'-phosphates		Matsushita et. al. (1965)	Km value was 7.4×10^{-4} for NpT at pH 9.5.
5'-phosphates		Razzel (1961 b)	
5'-phosphates	..pX-pY...	Anderson, Heppel (1960)	Has no action on simple phosphoric diesters such as benzyl-adenosine-5'-phosphate
5'-phosphates	pX-pY	Gulland, Jackson (1938), Butler (1955) Bjork (1963)	Properties comparable to C. adamanteus phosphodiesterase
5'-phosphates	pX-pY...	Gulland, Jackson (1938), Butler (1955) Garilhe, Laskowski (1955-1957) Razzell, Khorana (1959)	Stepwise hydrolysis commencing at the 3'-OH terminus with successive liberation of pX type mononucleotide
5'-phosphates		Nikolskaya et al. (1964, 1965)	This enzyme is specific of denatured DNA
		Gulland, Jackson (1938), Buter (1955)	
		Georgatsos (1963)	This enzyme has no action on native and denatured DNA, DNA core and yeast t-RNA.

Designation	Origin	Activators Inhibitors	pH optimum	Substrates
Microbial	*Bacillus subtilis*	Activated by Ca^{++}		DNA and RNA
	Escherichia coli B Exonuclease I	Activated by Mg^{++}	9.2	Polynucleotides of the DNA type
	E. coli B Exonuclease II	Activated by Mg^{++} and Mn^{++} ions	9.0	Deoxyribonucleic oligonucleotides
	E. coli B Exonuclease III *E. coli* "Phosphatase-exonuclease"	Inhibited by $ZnCl_2$ and *p*-chloromercuribenzoate	7	DNA terminated by 5'-phosphate
	E. coli (cf. *E. coli* RNase II)	Activated by K^+ and Mg^{++}	7-8	m-RNA
	E. coli B Exonuclease IV			Deoxyribonucleic oligonucleotides
	E. coli B Exonuclease V		7.8	Deoxyribonucleic oligonucleotides
	Lactobacillus acidophilus			Ribo- or deoxyribo-oligonucleotides
	Lactobacillus casei	Activated by K^+ ions		RNA and ribonucleic oligonucleotides
PHOSPHATASES *Animal* Human	Erythrocytes E_1 E_2 Placenta	Activated by Mg^{++}	5.0 and 6.0 5.2	
	Prostate "acid" phosphatase	Inhibited by F^-	5.3-5.6	Glycerophosphate Phenyl phosphate Yeast adenylic acid etc.
	Serum (cancerous) 5'-nucleotidase	Inhibited by Ni^{++}		5'-nucleotides

Products (terminal phosphates)	Linkages preferentially split	Authors	Observations
3'-phosphates		Kerr et al. (1965), Okazaki et al. (1966)	Denatured DNA is preferentially hydrolyzed.
5'-phosphates	d-pX-pY	Lehman (1960)	The hydrolysis begins at the end bearing a free hydroxyl in position C-3'.
5'-phosphates		Lehman, Richardson (1964)	Stepwise hydrolysis to the stage of the mononucleotides. This enzymic activity remains associated with DNA polymerase
Dephosphorylates DNA, then releases mononucleotides 5'-phosphates		Richardson, Kornberg (1964) Richarson et al. (1964)	First monoesterase activity, then exonuclease acting preferentially on double-stranded DNA.
5'-phosphates		Spahr, Schlessinger (1963), Spahr (1965)	In principle this enzyme is specific for m-RNA.
5'-monophosphates		Jorgensen, Koerner (1965)	These two exonucleases, although having closely related properties, can be nevertheless separated by DEAE-cellulose chromatography
5'-phosphates		Jorgensen, Koerner (1965)	
3'-phosphates	e.g. : TpTpT→ Tp + TpT ...etc.	Fiers, Khorana (1963)	Stepwise hydrolysis beginning at the end which bears the free 5'-hydroxyl
5'-monophosphates		Keir et al. (1964)	This enzyme has no action on DNA.
		Georgatsos (1965)	
		Neale et al. (1965)	
Alcohol or phenol and free phosphate	Any phosphodiester	Schmidt (1955)	The prostatic phosphatase posesses 10-SH groups per mole, playing a fundamental role in the molecular configuration.
Nucleoside + phosphate	Nucleoside 5'-phosphates	Schwartz, Bodansky (1965)	The 5'-nucleotidase can be useful in following the progression of carcinoma metastatic to the liver.

Designation	Origin	Activators Inhibitors	pH optimum	Substrates
	Urine alkaline phosphatase			
Bovine	Bone alkaline phosphatase		8.6-9.0	Glycerophosphate, phenyl phosphate, mononucleotides
	Intestinal mucosa. Alkaline phosphatase	Zn^{++} necessary	9.5	Glycerophosphate, phenyl phosphate, glucose-6-phosphate Phosphoramides
	Intestinal mucosa 5'-nucleotidase	Activated by Ca^{++}, Co^{++}, Mn^{++}, Mg^{++}. Inhibited by EDTA		Nucleoside-5'-phosphates.
	Milk alkaline phosphatase	Activated by Mg^{++}, Zn^{++}, Mn^{++}	9.5-10-5	Glycerophosphate
	Bovine pituitary gland 5'-nucleotidase	Inhibited by Na-dodecyl sulfate, aminoacids, nucleosides...		Nucleoside-5'-phosphates
	Sperm 5'-nucleotidase	Activated by Mg^{++}	with Mg^{++} : a) 7.5-8.0 b) 9.1-9.3	Adenosine 5'-monophosphate pA and various nucleotides
	Synovial fluid alkaline phosphatase	Activated by Sr^{++}, Ca^{++} and Mg^{++}; inhibited by cyanide, fluoride and EDTA		β-Glycerophosphate and various phosphomono-esters.
Other animal sources.	Hog kidney alkaline phosphatase		9.9	β-Glycerophosphate, p-Nitrophenyl phosphate.
	Ovine serum alkaline phosphatase	Activated by Mg^{++} inhibited by EDTA		p-Nitrophenyl phosphate.

Products (terminal phosphates)	Linkages preferentially split	Authors	Observations
		Butterworth et al. (1965)	The phosphatase observed in the urine of patients having acute renal diseases, does not differ qualitatively from that of normal urine.
Alcohol or phenol and free phosphate	Any phosphomonoester	Gulland, Jackson (1938), Volkin (1955)	This enzyme has little specificity and hydrolyzes any phosphomonoester.
Alcohol or phenol and free phosphate	Any phosphomonoester	Heppel (1955) Engstrom (1961-1964), Lazdunski, Ouellet (1962)	Molecular weight about 100,000. Fixes phosphate in an active center constituted by the peptide Asp. SerP.Ala
Nucleoside + phosphate	Nucleoside 5'-phosphate	Center, Behal (1966)	Optimun pH is 6.0-6.5 in Tris-acetate; at this pH the Km values for pA hydrolysis is in the range of $14\text{-}20 \times 10^{-5}$ M. Optimun pH is 8.0 in Na diethyl barbitate. At this pH, Km were $5.0\text{-}5.8 \times 10^{-5}$ M for pA and $5.0\text{-}8.0 \times 10^{-5}$ for pG.
Alcohol or phenol and free phosphate	Any phosphomonoester	Morton (1955)	Has little specificity; hydrolyzes any phosphomonoester.
Nucleoside + phosphates		Lisowski (1964, 1965, 1966)	The molecular weight is around 237,000 and the molecule has an elongated shape.
Nucleoside and free phosphate	Nucleotides 5'-phosphates	Heppel, Hilmoe (1951, 1955) Levin and Bodansky (1969)	Hydrolyzes 5'-nucleotides only, and exhibits a double pH optimum. The apparent Km values for deoxyribonucleotides were much larger than those for the corresponding ribonucleotides.
	Any phosphomonoester	Dabich and Neuhaus (1966)	This enzyme was purified 2,300 fold. A molecular weight of 72,300 was determined from sucrose density gradient studies.
Alcohol or phenol + phosphate	Any phosphomonoester	Alvarez et al. (1965)	
Alcohol or phenol + phosphate	Any phosphomonoester	Aalund et al. (1965)	The molecular weight of this enzyme is approximately 200,000.

Designation	Origin	Activators Inhibitors	pH optimum	Substrates
	Rat, various organs			Sodium β-glycerophosphate
	Chicken Intestinal mucosa			Sodium β-glycerophosphate
Snake venoms	*Bothrops atrox* alkaline phosphatase	Activated by Mn^{++} and Ca^{++}	9.5 (gly buffer)	Any phosphomonoester
	Bothrops atrox 5'-nucleotidase	Inhibited by EDTA; Activated by Mn^{++} and Ca^{++}	9.0	Nucleoside-5'-phosphates; optimal activity on pA
	Crotalus adamanteus 5'-nucleotidase		8.5	pA
Plant phosphatases	*Lolium multiflorum* germ, 3'-nucleotidase	Inhibited by thiols and CN$^-$	7.5	Ap
	Phaseolus radiatus 3'-nucleotidase	Does not require metallic ions	7.8	Nucleoside-3'-phosphates Ap preferentially
	Phaseolus vulgaris L. var. Pinto, acid phosphatases	Inhibited by fluoride	5.2	p-nitrophenyl phosphate
	Potato-non specific phosphatase	Inhibited by phosphate	5.5	p-nitrophenyl phosphate
	Potato 5'-nucleotidase		5.0	pA
Microbial	*Escherichia coli* 1° acid phosphatase		4.7	p-nitrophenyl phosphate and any other phosphomonoester

Products (terminal phosphates)	Linkages preferentially split	Authors	Observations
Glycerol and phosphate		Rossier, Portmann (1964)	These authors studied the distribution of phosphatases among the organs of normal and adrenalectomized rat
Glycerol and phosphate		Motzok (1963)	Study of the variation of alkaline phosphatase levels as a function of various factors (age, diet, etc.)
Alcohol or nucleoside + phosphate	Any phosphomonoester	Sulkowski et al. (1963)	
Nucleoside & inorganic phosphate	Nucleoside -5′-monophosphates	Sulkowski et al. (1963)	The preparation from *B. atrox* venom achieved with a 1000 fold enrichment
Nucleoside & free phosphate	Nucleoside 5′-monophosphates	Hurst, Butler (1951), Heppel, Hilmoe (1955)	Specific for nucleoside 5′-monophosphates.
Nucleoside and free phosphate	Nucleoside 3′-monophosphates; Ribosides only	Shuster, Kaplan (1955-1957), Cunningham (1958) Cohen, Goodwin (1961)	Hydrolyses riboside 3′-phosphates. Apparently no action on corresponding deoxyribonucleotides.
Nucleoside + phosphate		Ahluwalia, Maller (1962)	Heat-stable enzyme; optimum activity at 70°.
Alcohol or phenol + phosphate	Any phosphomonoester	Staples et al. (1965)	Two iso-enzymes could be separated by electrophoresis.
Alcohol or phenol + phosphate	Any phosphomonoester	Hsu et al. (1966)	This enzyme was purified 100-fold over the crude extract.
Nucleoside and free phosphate	Nucleoside 5′-monophosphates	Kornberg, Pricer (1950a, b,), Heppel, Hilmoe (1955)	Hydrolyzes preferentially pA, but also Ap in the proportion pA/pA = 3/1. At pH 9.4 hydrolyzes but pA (3 times slower than at pH 5.0).
Alcohol or phenol and free phosphate	Any phosphomonoester	Van Hofsten, Porath (1962)	By using *p*-nitrophenyl-phosphate as substrate Km = 3.10^{-3} M. Molecular weight 13,000 to 14,000.

Désignation	Origin	Activators Inhibitors	pH optimum	Substrates investigated
	2° alkaline phosphatase	Inhibited by thiol, carboxyl compounds	8.0	p-nitrophenyl phosphate, various phosphomonoesters, pyrophosphate, etc.
	Neurospora crassa 1° acid phosphatase		5.6	Glycerophosphate and other phophomonoesters
	2° alkaline phosphatase	Activated by Mg++	8.9-9.0	Glycerophosphate and other phosphomonoesters
	Saccharomyces cerevisiae acid phosphatase		3-4	Any phosphomonoester
	Saccharomyces carlbergensis alkaline phosphatase	Inhibited by EDTA and cyanide	9-10	Any phosphomonoester
	Saccharomyces 5′-nucleotidase			Adenosine 5′-monophosphate

Products (terminal phosphates)	Linkages preferentially split	Authors	Observations
Alcohol, phenol or phosphate + free phosphate	Any phosphomonoester, polyphosphates included	Horiuchi et al. (1959-1960), Torriani (1960), Garen, Levinthal (1960), Heppel et al. (1962), Malamy, Horecker (1965)	Heat-stable at 85° for 30 min. Molecular weight 75,000 to 80,000. By using p-nitrophenyl-phosphate as substrate, Km= 1.17. × 10⁻⁵ M.
Alcohol or phenol and phosphate	Any phosphomonoester	Kuo, Blumenthal (1962 a)	The most rapidly hydrolyzed substrate ? α-glycerophosphate.
Alcohol or phenol and phosphate	Any phosphomonoester	Kuo, Blumenthal (1962 b) Nyc et al. (1966)	Localized in cell walls
Alcohol + phosphate	Any phosphomonoester	Tonino, Steyn-Parvé, (1963)	Localized in cell walls.
Alcohol + phosphate	Any phosphomonoester	Tonino, Steyn-Parvé, (1963)	Localized in protoplast membranes.
Adenosine + phosphate		Takei (1965)	This enzyme shows a high specificity for adenosine-5'-monophosphate.

References

AALUND O., RENDEL J., FREEDLAND R.A. (1965), *Biochim. Biophys. Acta*, **110**, 113.
ABDERHALDEN E., SCHITTENHELM A. (1906), *Z. Physiol. Chem.*, **47**, 452.
ABRAMS A., McNAMARA P. (1962), *J. Biol. Chem.*, **237**, 170.
ABUL-FADL M. A. M., KING E.G., (1949), *Biochem. J.*, **45**, 51.
ADACHI K., NAGANO K., NAKA T., NAKAO M., (1964), *Biochim. Biophys. Acta*, **92**, 59.
ADLER A.J., RICH A. (1962), *J. Am. Chem. Soc.*, **84**, 3977.
ADLER J., LEHMAN I.R., BESSMAN M.J., SIMMS E.S., KORNBERG A. (1958), *Proc. Natl. Acad. Sci. U.S.*, **44**, 641.
AGUILERA A., COLOMBARA E., JIMENEZ R., TOHA J., (1965), *Biochim. Biophys. Acta*, **95**, 569.
AGUS S., COX R.P., GRIFFIN M.J. (1966), *Biochim. Biophys. Acta.*, **118**, 363.
AHLUWALIA R.K., MALLER R.K. (1962), *J. Sci. Ind Res.* (India), **21C**, 293.
ALBAUM H.G., UMBREIT W.W. (1947), *J. Biol. Chem.*, **167**, 369.
ALEXANDER M., HEPPEL L.A., HURWITZ J. (1961), *J. Biol. Chem.*, **236**, 3014.
ALLFREY V.G., MIRSKY A.E. (1957), *Proc. Natal. Acad. Sci. U.S.*, **43**, 589.
ALLFREY V.G., MIRSKY A.E. (1958), *Trans. N.Y. Acad. Sci. Ser.* II, vol. **21**, p. 3.
ALLFREY V.G., MIRSKY A.E., OSAWA S. (1955), *Nature*, **176**, 1042.
ALLFREY V.G., MIRSKY A.E., OSAWA S. (1957a), *J. Gen. Physiol.*, **40**, 451.
ALLFREY V.G., MIRSKY A.E., OSAWA S. (1957b), *in The Chemical Basis of Heredity*, p. 200, ed. McElroy W.D. and Glass B., The Johns Hopkins Press, Baltimore Md.
ALTESCU E.J. (1964), *Anal. Biochem.*, **8**, 373.
ALTUNINA V.K., ZAGREBEL'NYI S.N., KNORRE D.G. (1965), *Biokhimiya*, **30**, 189.
ALVAREZ E.F., PENALVER M.D., TAMAYO M.L. (1965), *Anales Real Soc. Espan. Fis. Quim.* (Madrid), Ser. B, 61 (9-10) — 1039.
ANDERSON E.P., HEPPEL L.A. (1960), *Biochim. Biophys. Acta*, **43**, 79.
ANDERSON J.H., CARTER C.E. (1965), *Biochemistry*, **4**, 1102.
ANDO T. (1966), *Biochim. Biophys. Acta*, **114**, 158.
ANDO T., NATORI S., DENICHI M. (1963), *Biochim. Biophys. Acta*, **76**, 477.
ANFINSEN C.B., REDFIELD R.R., CHOATE W.L., PAGE J., CARROLL W.R. (1954), *J. Biol. Chem.*, **207**, 201.
ANFINSEN C.B., RUMLEY M.K., TANIUCHI H. (1963), *Acta Chem. Scand.*, **17**, Suppl. 1, S. 270-276.
ANFINSEN C.B., SELA M., COOKE. J.P. (1962), *J. Biol. Chem.*, **237**, 1825.
ANRAKU Y., MIZUNO D. (1965), *Biochem. Biophys. Res. Communs.*, **18**, 462.
APGAR J., EVERETT G.A., HOLLEY R.W. (1965) *Proc. Natl. Acad. Sci. U.S.*, **53**, 546.
APGAR J., EVERETT G.A., HOLLEY R.W. (1966), *J. Biol. Chem.*, **241**, 1207.
APGAR J., HOLLEY R.W. (1962), *Biochem. Biophys. Res. Comm.* **8**, 391.

APGAR J., HOLLEY R.W. (1964), *Biochem. Biophys. Res. Comm.* **16**, 121.
APGAR J., HOLLEY R.W., MERRILL S.H. (1962), *J. Biol. Chem.*, **237**, 796.
APOSHIAN H.V., RICHARDSON C.C., SCHILDKRAUT C. (1962), *Fed. Proc.*, **21**, 381.
ARAKI T. (1903), *Z. Physiol. Chem.*, **38**, 84.
ARMSTRONG A., HAGOPIAN H., INGRAM V.M., SJÖQUIST I., SJÖQUIST J., (1964), *Biochemistry*, 3, 1194.
ARVY L. (1965 *a*), *Biol. Med.* (Paris), **54**, 639.
ARVY L. (1965 *b*). Les phosphatases du tissu nerveux. Hermann, Paris.
ASHE H., SEAMAN E., VAN VUNAKIS H., LEVINE L. (1965), *Biochim. Biophys. Acta*, **99**, 298.
ASKONAS B.A., SIMKIN J.L., WORK T.S. (1958), *4th Int. Congress of Biol. Chemistry*, Vienna. Symp. n° VIII.
ATEN J.B.T., COHEN J.A. (1965), *J. Mol. Biol.*, **12**, 537.
AUBEL-SADRON G., BECK G., EBEL J.P. (1961), *Biochim. Biophys. Acta*, **53**, 11.
AUBEL-SADRON G., BECK G., EBEL J.P., SADRON C. (1960), *Biochim. Biophys. Acta*, **42**, 542.
AUGUST J.T., SHAPIRO L., EOYANG L. (1965), *J. Mol. Biol.*, **11**, 257.
AVERY O.T., MCLEOD C.M., MCCARTY M. (1944), *J. Exptl. Med.*, **79**, 137.
AZAKAWA I.K. (1929), *J. Biochem.* (Japan), **11**, 143.

BABINET C., ROLLER A., DUBERT J.M., THANG M.N., GRUNBERG-MANAGO M. (1965), *Biochem. Biophys. Res. Comm.*, **19**, 95.
BABSON A.L., PHILLIPS G.E. (1966), *Clin. Chim. Acta*, **13**, 264.
BACHRACH H.L. (1961), *Proc. Soc. Exp. Biol. Med.*, **107**, 610.
BADDILEY J., CLARK V.M., MICHALSKI J.J., TODD A.R. (1949), *J. Chem. Soc.*, 815.
BADDILEY J., MICHELSON A.M., TODD A.R. (1948), *Nature* **161**, 761.
BAEV A.A., VENKSTERN T.V., MIRZABEKOW A.D., TATARSKAYA R.I. (1963), *Biokhimya*, **28**, 931.
BAGULEY B.C., BERGQUIST P.L., RALPH R.K. (1965), *Biochim. Biophys. Acta*, **95**, 510.
BAHR J.T., CATHOU R.E., HAMMES G.G. (1965), *J. Biol. Chem.* **240**, 3372.
BAILEY J.L., MOORE S., STEIN W.H. (1956), *J. Biol. Chem.* **221**, 143.
BAILEY K. (1948), *Biochem. J.*, **43**, 271.
BAILLY O., GAUMÉ J. (1935), *Bull. Soc. Chim. France*, **2**, 354.
BALLARD P., WILLIAMS-ASHMAN H.G. (1964), *Nature*, **203**, 150.
BALLIO A., DELFINI C., RUSSI S. (1966), *Gazz. Chim. Ital.*, **96**, 4, 337.
BALTIMORE D., BECKER Y., DARNELL J.E. (1964), *Science*, **143**, 1034.
BALTIMORE D., EGGERS H.J., FRANKLIN R.M., TAMM I. (1963), *Proc. Natl. Acad. Sci. U.S.*, **49**, 843.
BALTIMORE D., FRANKLIN R.M. (1962), *Biochim. Biophys. Res. Comm.* **9**, 388.
BARBER R., JONES A.S. (1964), *Nature*, **203**, 45.
BARKER G.R., PAVLIK J.G. (1966), *Biochem. J.*, **98**, 4 p.
BARMAN T.E., GUTFREUND H. (1966), *Biochem. J.*, **101**, 460.
BARONDES S.H. (1964), *J. Neurochem.*, **11**, 663.
BARTOS E.M., RUSHIZKY G.W., SOBER H.A. (1963), *Biochemistry*, **2**, 1179.
BAUTZ E.K.F., HALL B.D. (1962), *Proc. Natl. Acad. Sci. U.S.*, **48**, 400.
BAWDEN F.C., PIRIE N.W. (1938), *Brit J. Exptl. Path.*, **19**, 251.
BEARD J.R., RAZZELL W.E. (1964), *J. Biol. Chem.*, **239**, 4186.
BEAVEN G.H., HOLIDAY E.R., JOHNSON E.A. (1955), in *The Nucleic Acids*, vol. 1, p. 493. Ed. by Chargaff E., Davidson J.N., Academic Press, New York.
BECK K., GILL S.J., DOWNING M. (1965), *J. Am. Chem. Soc.* **87**, 901.
BECKING G.C., HURST R.O. (1963), *Can. J. Biochem. Physiol.*, **41**, 1433.
BEER M. (1961), *J. Mol. Biol.*, **3**, 263.
BEER M., MOUDRIANAKIS E.N. (1962), *Proc. Natl. Acad. Sci. U.S.*, **48**, 409.
BEER M., STERN S., CARMALT D., MOHLHENRICH K.H. (1966), *Biochemistry*, **5**, Nr. 7, 2283.
BEERS R.F. Jr. (1957), *Biochem. J.*, **66**, 686.
BEERS R.F. Jr (1960), *J. Biol. Chem.*, **235**, 2393.
BEINTEMA J.J., GRUBER M. (1965), *Bull. Soc. Chim. Biol.*, **47**, 2307.
BEHAL F., CENTER M. (1965), *Arch. Biochem. Biophys.*, **110**, 560.

BELLO J., NOWOSWIAT E.F. (1965), *Biochim. Biophys. Acta.* **105**, 325.
BENDICH A., FRESCO J.R., ROSENKRANZ H.S., BEISER S.M. (1955), *J. Am. Chem. Soc.*, **77**, 3671.
BENDICH A., PAHL H.B., KORNGOLD G.C., ROSENKRANZ H.S., BEISER S.M. (1955), *J. Am. Chem. Soc.* **80**, 3949.
BENZER S., WEISBLUM R. (1961), *Proc. Natl. Acad. Sci. U.S.*, **47**, 1149.
BERG T.L., FRÖHOLM L.O., LALAND S.G. (1965), *Biochem. J.*, **96**, 43.
BERGER G. (1965), *Compt. rend.*, **260**, 3499.
BERGMANN W., BURKE D.F.) (1955 a), *J. org. chem.*, **20**, 1501.
BERGMANN W., BURKE D.F. (1955 b), *Angew. Chem.*, **67**, 127.
BERGMANN W., FEENEY R.J. (1951), *J. Org. Chem.*, **16**, 981.
BERGQUIST P.L. (1965), *Biochim. Biophys. Acta*, **103**, 347.
BERGQUIST P.L., ROBERTSON J.M. (1965), *Biochim. Biophys. Acta* **95**, 357.
BERNARD J., BOIRON M., JACQUILLAT C., NAJEAN Y., SELIGMANN M., TANZER J., WEIL M. (1966), *Presse Med.*, **74**, 1241.
BERNARDI G. (1961a), *Biochim. Biophys. Acta*, **53**, 216.
BERNARDI G. (1961b), *Biochim. Biophys. Comm.* **6**, 54.
BERNARDI G. (1965 a), *J. Mol. Biol.*, **13**, 603.
BERNARDI G., (1965b), *Nature*, **206**, 779.
BERNARDI G., APPELLA E., ZITO R. (1965), *Biochem.*, **4**, 1725.
BERNARDI A., BERNARDI G. (1966), *Biochim. Biophys. Acta.*
BERNARDI G., CHAMPAGNE M., SADRON C. (1960), *Nature*, **188**, 228.
BERNARDI G., CORDONNIER C. (1965), *J. Mol. Biol.*, **11**, 141.
BERNARDI G., GRIFFÉ M. (1964), *Biochemistry*, **3**, 1419.
BERNARDI G., GRIFFÉ M., APPELA E. (1963), *Nature*, **198**, 186.
BERNARDI G., SADRON C., (1961), *Nature* **191**, 809.
BERNARDI G., SADRON C. (1964), *Biochemistry*, **3**, 1411.
BERNARDI G., TIMASHEFF S.N. (1961), *Biochem. Biophys. Res. Comm.* **6**, 58.
BERNFIELD M.R. (1965), *J. Biol. Chem.*, **240**, 4753.
BERNFIELD M.R. (1966), *J. Biol. Chem.*, **241**, 2014.
BERNFIELD M.R., NIRENBERG M.W. (1965), *Science*, **147**, 479.
BERNS K.I., THOMAS C.A. (1961), *J. Mol. Biol.* **3**, 289.
BERNS K.I., THOMAS C.A. (1965), *J. Mol. Biol.*, **11**, 476.
BESSMAN M.J., LEHMAN I.R., ADLER S.B., ZIMMERMAN S.B., S SIMMS E.S., KORNBERG A. (1958), *Proc. Natl. Acad. Sci. U.S.*, **44**, 633.
BESSMAN M.J., LEHMAN I.R., SIMMS E.S., KORNBERG A. (1958), *J. Biol. Chem.* **233**, 171.
BIEMANN K., TSUNAKAWA S., SONNENBICHLER J., FELDMANN H., DUETTING D., ZACHAU H.G. (1966), *Angew. Chem.*, **5**, 6, 590.
BIETH R., MANDEL P. (1953), *Experientia*, **9**, 185.
BINGHAM E.W., KALAN E.B. (1966), *Abstr. Papers Am. Chem. Soc.*, n° 152, 271C.
BIRNBOIM H. (1966 a), *Biochim, Biophys. Acta*, **119**, 198.
BIRNBOIM H. (1966 b), *J. Bact.*, **91**, 1004.
BISHOP D.H.L., BRADLEY D.E. (1965), *Biochem. J.*, **95**, 82.
BJÖRK W. (1961), *Biochim. Biophys. Acta* **49**, 195.
BJÖRK W. (1963), *J. Biol. Chem.*, **238**, 2487.
BJÖRK W. (1964), *Biochim. Biophys. Acta*, **89**, 483.
BJÖRK W. (1965), *Biochim. Biophys. Acta*, **95**, 652.
BLADEN H.A., BYRNE R., LEVIN J.G., NIRENBERG M.W. (1965), *J. Mol. Biol.*, **11**, 78.
BLANCHARDIÈRE P. (de la) (1913), *Z. Physiol. Chem.*, **87**, 291.
BOIRON M., LÈVY J.P., THOMAS M. (1965), *Ann. Inst. Pasteur*, **108**, 298.
BOIRON M., PAOLETTI C., THOMAS M., REBIÈRE J.P., BERNARD J. (1962), *Compt. rend.*, **254**, 2097.
BOIRON M., THOMAS M., CHENAILLE P. (1965), *Virology* **26**, 150.
BOIVIN A., VENDRELY C. (1948), *Compt. rend.*, **226**, 1061.
BOLLUM F.J. (1960), *J. Biol. Chem.*, **235**, 2399.
BOLLUM F.J. (1965), *J. Biol. Chem.*, **240**, 2599.

BOMAN H.G. (1957), *Nature*, **180**, 1181.

BOMAN H.G., KALETTA U. (1957), *Biochim. Biophys. Acta* **24**, 619.

BORNSTEIN D.L., WEINBERG A.N., SWARTZ M.N. (1966), *Proc. Soc. Exptl. Biol. Med.*, **121**, 677.

BOVÉ J.M., YOT P., MELAMED R., MOREL G. (1964), *Bull. Soc. Chim. Biol.*, **46**, 1027.

BRACHET J. (1953), *Quart. J. Microscop. Sci.*, **94**, 1.

BRACHET J. (1955), in *The Nucleic Acids*, vol. II, p. 476. Ed. by Chargaff E. and Davidson J.N., New York, Academic Press.

BRACHET J. (1958), *Bull. Soc. Chim. Biol.*, **40**, 1387.

BRACHET J. (1958), *Exposés annuels de biochimie médicale*, p. 181.

BRACHET J., CHANTRENNE H., VANDERHAEGHE F. (1855), *Biochim. Biophys. Acta*, **18**, 544.

BRACHET J., MIRSKY A.E. (1959-1964). *The Cell : Biochemistry, Physiology, Morphology*, 6. Vol., Academic Press, New York.

BRADBURY E.M., PRICE W.C., WILKINSON G.R. (1961), *J. Mol. Biol.*, **3**, 301.

BRANDENBERGER H., HANSON R. (1953), *Helv. Chim. Acta* **36**, 900.

BREEDIS C., BERWICK L., ANDERSON T.F. (1962), *Virology*, **17**, 84.

BRENNEMAN F., SINGER M.F. (1964), *J. Biol. Chem.*, **239**, 893.

BRENNER S., JACOB F., MESELSON M. (1961), *Nature*, **190**, 576.

BRETSCHER M.S., GRUNBERG-MANAGO M. (1962), *Nature*, **195**, 285.

BRINK J.J., LE PAGE G.A. (1963), *Fed. Proc.*, **22**, 184.

BRODY S. (1958), *Nature*, **182**, 1386.

BROOKES P., LAWLEY P.D. (1961), *Biochem. J.*, **80**, 496.

BROOMFIELD C.A., RIEHM J.P., SCHERAGA H.R. (1965), *Biochemistry*, **4**, 751.

BROWN D.M., FASMAN G.D., MAGRATH D.I., TODD A.R., COCHRAN W., WOOLFSON M.M. (1953), *Nature*, **172**, 1184.

BROWN D.M., HAYNES L.J., TODD A.R. (1950), *J. Chem. Soc.* 2399.

BROWN D.M., MAGRATH D.I., TODD A.R. (1952), *J. Chem. Soc.* 2708.

BROWN D.M., PARIHAR D.B., REESE C.B., TODD A.R. (1958), *J. Chem. Soc.* 3035.

BROWN D.M., TODD A.R. (1952), *J. Chem. Soc.* 44.

BROWN D.M., TODD A.R. (1953), *J. Chem. Soc.* 2040.

BROWN D.M., TODD A.R. (1955) in *The Nucleic Acids*, vol. 1, p. 409. Ed. by Chargaff E., Davidson J.N., Academic Press, New York.

BROWN D.M., TODD A.R., VARADARAJAN S. (1956), *J. Chem. Soc.* 2388.

BROWN G.L., M'EWEN M.B., PRATT M.I. (1955), *Nature*, **176**, 161.

BROWN H., SANGER F., KITAI R. (1955), *Biochem. J.*, **60**, 556.

BROWN K.D., JACOBS G., LASKOWSKI M. (1952), *J. Biol. Chem.*, **194**, 445.

BULL H.B., BREESE K. (1965), *Arch. Biochem. Biophys.*, **110**, 331.

BURNY A., MARBAIX G. (1965a), *Arch. Int. Physiol. Biochem.*, **73**. 141.

BURNY A., MARBAIX G. (1965b), *Biochim. Biophys. Acta*, **103**, 409.

BURTON K. (1960), *Biochem. J.*, **77**, 547.

BURTON K. (1962), *Biochim. Biophys. Acta*, **55**, 412.

BURTON K. (1965), *in : Assays in Biochemistry*, vol. I, p. 57, Ed. by P.M. Campbell & G.D. Greville, Acad. Press. N.Y.

BURTON K., PETERSEN G.B. (1957), *Biochim. Biophys. Acta*, **26**, 667.

BURTON K., PETERSEN G.B. (1960), *Biochem. J.*, **75**, 17.

BURTON R.L., SINSHEIMER R.L. (1963), *Science*, **142**, 962.

BUSH H. (1965), Histones and other nuclear proteins, Acad. Press, New York, London.

BUTLER G.C. (1955), in *Methods in Enzymology*, vol. 2, p. 561. Ed. by Colowick S.P., Kaplan N.O., Academic Press, New York.

BUTLER J.A.V., LAURENCE D.J.R., ROBINS A.B., SHOOTER K.V. (1957), *Nature*, **180**, 1340.

BUTLER J.A.V., PHILLIPS D.M., SHOOTER K.V. (1957), *Arch. Biochem. Biophys.*, **71**, 423.

BUTTERWORTH P.J., MOSS D.W., PITKANEN E., PRINGLE A. (1965), *Clin. Chim. Acta*, **11**, 220.

BYRNE R., LEVIN J., BLADEN H.A., NIRENBERG M. (1964), *Proc. Nartl. Acad. sci. U.S.*, **52**, 140.

CAIRNS J. (1962), *J. Mol. Biol.*, **4**, 407.

CAIRNS J. (1963), Cold Spring Harbor Symp. Quant. Biol., **28**, 43.

CANTONI G.L., ISHIKURA H., RICHARDS H.H., TANAKA K. (1963), Cold Spring Harbor Symp. Quant. Biol., **28**, 123.

CARDEILHAC P.T., COHEN S.S. (1964), *Cancer Res.*, **24**, 1595.

CARLSSON K., FRICK G. (1964), *Biochim. Biophys. Acta*, **81**, 301.

CARO L.G. (1965), *Virology*, **25**, 226.

CARTER C.E. (1950), *J. Amer. Chem. Soc.*, **72**, 1467.

CARTER C.E., ANDERSON S.H. (1965), *Fed. Proc.* **24**, 602.

CARTER C.E., COHN W.E. (1949), *Fed. Proc.*, **8**, 190.

CASPERSSON T. (1936), *Skand. Arch. Physiol.* **73**, suppl. n° 8.

CASPERSSON T. (1940), *J. Roy. Micros. Soc.*, **68**, 8.

CASPERSSON T. (1947), Symp. Soc. Exp. Biol., **1**, 127.

CASPERSSON T. (1950), *Cell Growth and Cell Function*, New York, Norton.

CAVALIERI L.F., DEUTSCH J.F., ROSENBERG B.H. (1961), *Biophys. J.*, **1**, 301.

CAVALIERI L.F., ROSENBERG B.H. (1961a), *Biophys. J.*, **1**, 317.

CAVALIERI L.F., ROSENBERG B.H. (1961b), *Biophys. J.*, **1**, 323.

CENTER M.S., BEHAL F.J. (1966), *Arch. Biochem. Biophys.*, **114**, 414.

CHA C.Y., SCHERAGA H.A. (1960), *J. Am. Chem. Soc.*, **82**, 54.

CHA C.Y., SCHERAGA H.A. (1963a), *J. Biol. Chem.*, **238**, 2958.

CHA C.Y., SCHERAGA H.A. (1963b), *J. Biol. Chem.*, **238**, 2965.

CHAMBERLIN M., BERG P. (1962), *Proc. Natl. Acad. Sci. U.S.*, **48**, 81.

CHAMBERLIN M., BERG P. (1963), Cold Spring Harbor Symp. Quant. Biol. **28**, 67.

CHAMBERS R.W., MOFFATT J.G., KHORANA H.G. (1957), *J. Am. Chem. Soc.*, **79**, 3747.

CHANG P.K., WELCH A.D. (1961a), *Biochemical Pharmacology* **6**, 50.

CHANG P.K., WELCH A.D. (1961b), *Biochemical Pharmacology* **8**, 327.

CHAPEVILLE F., CARTOUZOU G., LISSITZKY S. (1963), *Biochim. Biophys. Acta*, **68**, 496.

CHAPEVILLE F., LIPMANN F., EHRENSTEIN G. von, WEISBLUM B., RAY, W.J., BENZER S. (1962), *Proc. Nat. Acad. Sci. U.S.*, **48**, 1086.

CHARGAFF E. (1950), *Experientia*, **6**, 201.

CHARGAFF E. (1955) in *The Nucleic Acids*, vol. 1, p. 307. Ed by Chargaff E., Davidson J.N., New York Academic Press.

CHARGAFF E. (1962), *Nature*, **194**, 86.

CHARGAFF E., BUCHOWICZ J., TÜRLER H., SHAPIRO H.S. (1965), *Nature*, **206**, 145.

CHARGAFF E., LIPSHITZ R. (1953), *J. Am. Chem. Soc.*, **75**, 3658.

CHARGAFF E., LIPSHITZ R., GREEN C. (1952), *J. Biol. Chem.* **195**, 155.

CHARGAFF E., LIPSHITZ R., GREEN C., HODES M.E. (1951), *J. Biol. Chem.* **192**, 223.

CHARGAFF E., MAGASANIK B., VISCHER E., GREEN C., DONIGER R., ELSON D. (1950), *J. Biol. Chem.*, **186**, 51.

CHARGAFF E., RÜST P., TEMPERLI A., MORISAWA S., DANON A. (1963), *Biochim. Biophys. Acta*, **76**, 149.

CHARGAFF E., SEIDEL H.F. (1949), *J. Biol. Chem.*, **177**, 417.

CHARGAFF E., VISCHER E. (1948), *Ann. Rev. Biochem.*, **17**, 201.

CHARGAFF E., VISCHER E., DONIGER R., GREEN C., MISANI F. (1949), *J. Biol. Chem.*, **177**, 405.

CHARGAFF E., ZAMENHOF S. (1948), *J. Biol. Chem.*, **173**, 327.

CHENG T.Y., SUEOKA N. (1964), *Science*, **143**, 1442.

CHEN-PIN LIU, PING-CHENG H., HUI W., CHIH-CHUAN L. (1963), *Scientia Sinica*, **12**, 473.

CHERAYIL S.D., BOCK R.M. (1965), *Biochemistry*, **4**, 1174.

CHEUNG C.C.S., ABRASH H.I. (1964), *Biochemistry*, **3**, 1883.

CHU M.Y., FISHER G.A. (1962), *Biochim. Pharmacol.*, **11**, 423.

CHUNG H., MANDELES S. (1964), *Biochim. Biophys. Acta*, **92**, 403.

CLARK V.M., TODD A.R. (1950a), *J. Chem. Soc.* 2023.

CLARK V.M., TODD A.R. (1950b), *J. Chem. Soc.* 2030.

COHEN R.Z., GOODWIN T.W. (1961), *Phytochemistry*, **1**, 47.

COHEN S.S., STANLEY W.M. (1942), *J. Biol. Chem.*, **144**, 589.

COHN M. (1959), *J. Cellular Comp. Physiol.*, **54**, suppl. 1.

COHN W.E. (1950a), *J. Am. Chem. Soc.*, **72**, 1471.

Cohn W.E. (1950b), *J. Am. Chem. Soc.*, **72**, 2811.
Cohn W.E. (1951), *J. Cellular Comp. Physiol.*, 38, suppl. 1, 21.
Cohn W.E. (1955) in *The Nucleic Acids*, vol. 1, p. 211. Ed. by Chargaff E., Davidson J.N., New York, Academic Press.
Cohn W.E. (1957) in *Methods in Enzymology*, vol. III, p. 724. Ed. by Colowick S.P., Kaplan N.O., New York, Academic Press.
Cohn W.E. (1959), *Biochim. Biophys. Acta*, **32**, 569.
Cohn W.E. (1960), *J. Biol. Chem.*, **235**, 1488.
Cohn W.E., Wolkin E. (1951), *Nature*, **167**, 483.
Cohn W.E., Volkin E. (1957), *Biochim. Biophys. Acta*, **24**, 364.
Commerford S.L., Hunter M.J., Oncley S.L. (1962), *J. Biol. Chem.*, **238**, 2123.
Commission on Enzymes (1961), *Report.* Oxford and London, Pergamon Press.
Consden R., Gordon A.H., Martin A.J.P. (1944), *Biochem. J.*, **38**, 224.
Cooper E.J., Trautmann M.L., Laskowski M. (1950), *Proc. Soc. Exp. Biol. Med.*, **73**, 219.
Corby N.S., Kenner G.W., Todd A.R. (1952), *J. Chem. Soc.*, 3669.
Cordonnier C., Bernardi G. (1965), *Biochem. Biophys. Res. Commun.*, **20**, Nr. 5, 555.
Cotton F.A., Hazen E.E., Richardson D.C. (1966), *J. Biol. Chem.*, **241**, 4389.
Coutsogeorgopoulos C., Khorana H.G. (1964), *J. Am. Chem. Soc.*, **86**, 2926.
Cowgill R.W. (1966), *Biochim. Biophys. Acta*, **120**, 189.
Cozzone A., Marchis-Mouren G. (1966), *Biochim. Biophys. Acta*, **128**, 396.
Craig L.C., King T.P., Crestfield A.M. (1963), *Biopolymers*, **1**, 231.
Cramer J.W., Prusoff W.H., Welch A.D. (1961), *Biochemical Pharmacology*, **8**, 331.
Crampton C.F., Lipshitz R., Chargaff E. (1954), *J. Biol. Chem.*, **206**, 499.
Crawford L.V. (1964a), *J. Mol. Biol.*, **8**, 489.
Crawford L.V. (1964b), *Virology*, **22**, 149.
Crawford L.V. (1965), *J. Mol. Biol.*, **13**, 362.
Crestfield A.M., Smith K.C., Allen F.W. (1955), *J. Biol. Chem.*, **216**, 185.
Crestfield A.M., Stein W.H., Moore S. (1963a), *J. Biol. Chem.*, **238**, 618.
Crestfield A.M., Stein W.H., Moore S. (1963b), *J. Biol. Chem.*, **238**, 2413.
Crestfield A.M., Stein W.H., Moore S. (1963c), *J. Biol. Chem.*, **238**, 2421.
Crick F.H.C. (1963a), *Angew. Chem.*, **75**, 425.
Crick F.H.C. (1963b), *Science*, **139**, 461.
Crook E.M., Mathias A.P., Rabin B.R. (1960), *Biochem. J.* **74**, 230.
Crosbie G.W., Smellie R.M.S., Davidson J.N. (1953), *Biochem. J.*, **54**, 287.
Crothers D.M., Zimm B.H. (1965), *J. Mol. Biol.*, **12**, 525.
Cuigniez J., Dehennin L., Stockx J., Vandendriessche L. (1965), *Naturwiss.*, **52**, 187.
Cunningham L. (1958), *J. Am. Chem. Soc.*, **80**, 2546.
Cunningham L. (1959), *Ann. N. Y. Acad. Sci.*, **81**, 788.
Cunningham L., Catlin B.W., Privat de Garilhe M. (1956), *J. Am. Chem. Soc.*, **78**, 4642.
Cunningham L., Laskowski M. (1953), *Biochem. Biophys. Acta*, **11**, 590.
Curtis P.J., Burdon M.G., Smellie R.M.S. (1966), *Biochem. J.*, **98**, 813.
Curtis P.J., Smellie R.M.S. (1966), *Biochem. J.*, **98**, 818.

Dabich D., Neuhaus O.W. (1966), *J. Biol. Chem.*, **241**, 415.
Dabrowska W., Cooper E.J., Laskowski M. (1949), *J. Biol. Chem.*, **177**, 991.
D'Alessio G. (1963), *Boll. Soc. Ital. Biol. Sper.*, **39**, 1174.
Daly M.M., Allfrey V.G., Mirsky A.E. (1950), *J. Gen. Physiol.*, **33**, 497.
Danner J. (1965), *Diss. Abs.*, **25**, 4385.
Davidson J.N. (1947), Cold Spring Harbor Symp. Quant. Biol., **12**, 50.
Davidson J.N. (1949), *Ann. Rev. Biochem.*, **18**, 155.
Davidson J.N. (1953a), *The Biochemistry of the Nucleic Acids*, London, Methuen. and Co., Ltd.
Davidson J.N. (1953b), *Bull. Soc. Chim. Biol.*, **35**, 49.
Davidson J.N., Smellie R.M.S. (1952a), *Biochem. J.*, **52**, 594.
Davidson J.N., Smellie R.M.S. (1952b), *Biochem. J.*, **52**, 599.

DAVIDSON J.N., SMELLIE R.M.S., KEIR H.M., McARDALE A.H. (1958), *Nature*, **182**, 589.
DAVIDSON J.N., WAYMOUTH C. (1944), *Biochem. J.*, **38**, 379.
DAVISON P.F. (1960), *Nature*, **183**, 918.
DAVOLL J., LYTHGOE B. (1949), *J. Chem. Soc.*, 2536.
DAVOLL J., LYTHGOE B., TODD A.R. (1948a), *J. Chem. Soc.*, 967.
DAVOLL J., LYTHGOE B., TODD A.R. (1948b), *J. Chem. Soc.*, 1685.
DEAVIN A., MATHIAS A.P., RABIN B.R. (1966a), *Biochem. J.*, **101**, 14c.
DEAVIN A., MATHIAS A.P., RABIN B.R. (1966b), *Nature*, **211**, 252.
DECKEN A. von der, CAMPBELL P.N. (1962), *Biochem. J.*, **84**, 449.
DE FILIPPES F.M. (1964), *Science*, **144**, 1380.
DEKKER C.A. (1960), *Ann. Rev. Biochem.*, **29**, 453.
DEKKER C.A., TODD A.R. (1950), *Nature*, **166**, 557.
DELANEY R. (1960), *N.Y. State Dept. Health Ann. Rept. Div. Labs of Res.*, **38**.
DELANEY R. (1962), *N.Y. State Dept. Health Div. Lab. Res.*, **67**.
DELANEY R. (1963), *Biochemistry*, **2**, 438.
DE RUDDÈR J., PRIVAT DE GARILHE M. (1966), *Path. Biol. Sem.Hôp.* Paris, **14**, 369.
DIERICK W., STOCKX J. (1965), *Arch. Intern. Physiol. Biochem.*, **73**, 364.
DI MAYORCA G.A., EDDY B.E., STEWART S.E., HUNTER W.S., FRIEND C., BENDICH A. (1959), *Proc. Nat. Acad. Sci. U.S.*, **45**, 1805.
DIRKSEN M.L., DEKKER C.A. (1960), *Biochem. Biophys. Res. Commun.*, **2**, 147.
DISCHE Z. (1930), *Mikrochemie*, **8**, 4.
DOCTOR B.P., APGAR J., HOLLEY R.W. (1961), *J. Biol. Chem.*, **236**, 1117.
DOCTOR B.P., CONNELLY C.M., RUSHISZKY C.W., SOBER H.A. (1963), *J. Biol. Chem.*, **238**, 3985.
DOCTOR B.P., McCORMICK G.J. (1965), *Biochemistry*, **4**, 49.
DOCTOR B.P., MUDD J.A. (1963), *J. Biol. Chem.*, **205**, 959.
DOCTOR V.M. (1963), *Arch. Biochem. Biophys.*, **103**, 286.
DOEPNER H., SEIDEL H., CRAMER F. (1966), *Angew. Chem.*, **5**, 671.
DOLIN M.I. (1962), *J. Biol. Chem.*, **237**, 1626.
DOMÁNSKI J., KONIECZNY L., OSTROWSKI W. (1964), *Biochim. Biophys. Acta*, **92**, 405.
DONOVAN J.W. (1965), *Biochemistry*, **4**, 823.
DORNER R.W., KNIGHT C.A. (1953), *J. Biol. Chem.*, **236**, 1117.
DOSCHER M.S., RICHARDS F.M. (1963), *J. Biol. Chem.*, **238**, 2399.
DOSKOCIL J., ŠORM F. (1961), *Coll. Czech. Chem. Comm.*, **26**, 2739.
DOSKOCIL J., ŠORM F. (1962), *Coll. Czech. Chem. Comm.*, **27**, 1476.
DOTY P., BUNCE B.H. (1952), *J. Am. Chem. Soc.*, **74**, 5029.
DOTY P., MARMUR J., EIGNER J., SCHILDKRAUT C. (1960), *Proc. Nat. Acad. Sci. U.S.*, **46**, 461.
DUBACH U.C., PADLINA G. (1966), *Klin. Wschr.*, **44**, Nr. 4, 180.
DUBUISSON M. (1947), *Experientia*, **3**, 372.
DUNN D.B. (1960), *Biochim. Biophys. Acta*, **38**, 179.
DUNN D.B. (1963), *Biochem. J.*, **86**, 14 P.
DUNN D.B., SMITH J.D. (1955), *Nature*, **175**, 336.
DUNN D.B., SMITH J.D. (1958), *Biochem. J.*, **68**, 627.
DURE L., WATERS L. (1965), *Science*, **147**, 410.
DURLAW E.J. (1965), *Proc. Nat. Acad. Sci. U.S.*, **53**, 161.
DÜTTING D., KARAU W., MELCHERS F., ZACHAU H.G. (1965), *Biochim. Biophys. Acta.* **108**, 194.
DÜTTING D., ZACHAU H.G. (1964), *Biochim. Biophys. Acta* **91**, 573.
DUVE C. (de), PRESSMAN B.C., GIANETTO R., WATTIAUX R., APPELMANS F., *Biochem. J.*, **60**, 604.

EDMONDS M., ABRAMS R. (1963), *J. Biol. Chem.*, **238**, PC 1186.
EDSALL J.T. (1962), *Science*, **138**, 498.
EDSTRÖM J.E. (1964), *in : Methods in Cell Physiology*, vol. I, p. 147, Ed. by D.M. Prescott, New York Acad. Press.
EAKER D., KING T.P., CRAIG L.C. (1965 a), *Biochemistry*, **4**, 1473.

EAKER D., KING T.P., CRAIG L.C. (1965 b), *Biochemistry*, **4**, 1479.

EAKER D., KING T.P., CRAIG L.C. (1965 c), *Biochemistry*, **4**, 1486.

EGAMI F., TAKAHASHI K., UCHIDA T. (1964), in *Progress in Nucleic Acid Research*. Ed. by Davidson J.N., Cohn W.E. Vol. 3, p. 59. New York, Academic Press.

EICHEL H.J., FIGUEROA E.M., GOLDENBERG E.K. (1961), *Biochim. Biophys. Acta*, **51**, 216.

EIGNER J., DOTY P. (1965), *J. Mol. Biol.*, **12**, 549.

EIGNER J., STOUTHAMER A.H., VAN DER SLUYS I., COHEN J.A. (1963), *J. Mol. Biol.*, **6**, 61.

EIKENBERRY E.F., RICH A. (1965), *Proc. Nat. Acad. Sci. U.S.*, **53**, 668.

ELSON D., CHARGAFF E. (1954), *Nature*, **173**, 1037.

ELSON D., GUSTAFSON T., CHARGAFF E. (1954), *J. Biol. Chem.*, **209**, 285.

ENGSTRÖM L. (1961), *Biochim. Biophys. Acta*, **52**, 36.

ENGSTRÖM L. (1964), *Biochim. Biophys. Acta*, **92**, 79.

ENZYME NOMENCLATURE. (1965), vol. 13, of *Comprehensive Biochemistry*, Ed. by Florkin M., Stotz E.H., Elsevier Publishing Co.

EPSTEIN C.A., GOLDBERGER R.F., YOUND D.M., ANFINSEN C.B. (1962), *Arch. Biochem. Biophys.*, Suppl. n°. 1, 223.

ERON L.J., MC AUSLAN B.R. (1966), *Biochim. Biophys. Acta*, **114**, 633.

EULER H. von, HAHN L. (1946), *Svensk. Kem. Tidskr.*, **58**, 251.

EULER H. von, HAHN L. (1947), *Chem. Abs.*, **41**, 2108.

EVANS J.S., MUSSER E.A., MENGEL G.D., FORSBLAD K.R., HUNTER J. (1961), *Proc. Soc. Exp. Biol. Med.*, **106**, 350.

FELIX F., POTTER J.L., LASKOWSKI M. (1960), *J. Biol. Chem.*, **235**, 1150.

FELIX K. (1952), *Experientia*, **8**, 312.

FELIX K. (1953), in *The Chemical Structure of Proteins*, a Ciba Foundation Symposium, Boston, Little, Brown and Co.

FELIX K. (1958), *Bull. Soc. Chim. Biol.*, **40**, 17.

FELSENFELD G., CANTONI G.L. (1964), *Proc. Nat. Acad. Sci. U.S.*, **51**, 818.

FERNLEY H.N., WALKER P.G. (1966), *Biochem. J.*, **99**, 39P.

FESTY B., LE PECQ S.B., PAOLETTI C., TRUHAUT R. (1965), *Ann. Biol. Clin.* (Paris), **23**, 37.

FEULGEN R. (1935), *Z. physiol. Chem.*, **237**, 261.

FEULGEN R., ROSSENBECK H. (1924), *Z. physiol. Chem.*, **134**, 203.

FIERS W. (1962), *J. Chromatography*, **7**, 269.

FIERS W., KHORANA H.G. (1963a), *J. Biol. Chem.*, **238**, 2780.

FIERS W., KHORANA H.G. (1963b), *J. Biol. Chem.*, **238**, 2789.

FIERS W., VANDENDRIESSCHE L. (1961), *Arch. Int. Physiol. Biochim.*, **69**, 339.

FINDLAY D., HERRIES D.G., MATHIAS A.P., RABIN B.R., ROSS C.A. (1962), *Biochem. J.*, **85**, 152.

FINDLAY D., MATHIAS A.P., RABIN B.R. (1962a), *Biochem. J.*, **85**, 134.

FINDLAY D., MATHIAS A.P., RABIN B.R. (1962b), *Biochem. J.*, **85**, 139.

FISKE C.H., SUBBAROW Y. (1925), *J. Biol. Chem.*, **66**, 375.

FITCH W.M. (1964), *Proc. Nat. Acad. Sci. U.S.*, **52**, 298.

FLORKIN M., STOTZ E.M. (1965), *Comprehensive Biochemistry*. Elsevier, Amsterdam.

FOMINA L.S. (1964), *Sovrem. Metody v. Biokhimii* (Moscow), 292.

FOX J.J., YUNG N., BENDICH A. (1957), *J. Am. Chem. Soc.*, **79**, 2775.

FOX J.J., YUNG N., DAVOLL J., BROWN J.B. (1956), *J. Am. Chem. Soc.*, **78**, 2117.

FOX J.J., WEMPEN I. (1959), *Adv. Carbohydrate Chem.*, **14**, 283.

FRAENKEL-CONRAT H. (1956), *J. Am. Chem. Soc.*, **78**, 882.

FRAENKEL-CONRAT H. (1957), *Fed. Proc.*, **16**, 810.

FRAENKEL-CONRAT H. (1957-1958), *Harvey Lectures*, ser. LIII, p. 56. Academic Press, New York (1959).

FRAENKEL-CONRAT H., OLCOTT H.S. (1945), *J. Biol. Chem.*, **161**, 259.

FRAENKEL-CONRAT H., SINGER B. (1957), *Biochim. Biophys. Acta*, **24**, 540.

FRAENKEL-CONRAT H., SINGER B. (1959), in *Biochemistry of Viruses*, p. 9, Symp. n°. VII of the 4th Int. Congress of Biochemistry, Vienna 1958. Ed by Broda E. and Frisch-Niggemeyer W., Pergamon Press, Oxford and London.

FRAENKEL-CONRAT H., SINGER B., WILLIAMS R.C. (1957), in *The Chemical Basis of Heredity*. Ed. by McElroy W.D., Glass B. Baltimore, The Johns Hopkins Press.
FRAENKEL-CONRAT H., WILLIAMS R.C. (1955), *Proc. Nat. Acad. Sci. U.S.*, **41**, 690.
FRANKLIN R., GOSLING R.G. (1953), *Nature*, **171**, 740.
FREDERICQ E. (1959), *Arch. Int. Physiol. Biochim.*, **67**, 511.
FREDERICQ E. (1960), *Bull. Soc. Chim. Belges*, **69**, 475.
FREDERICQ E. (1961), *Arch. Int. Physiol. Biochim.*, **69**, 382.
FREDERICQ E., OTH A. (1958), *Biochim. Biophys. Acta*, **29**, 281.
FREDERICQ E., OTH A., DESREUX V. (1960), *Biochemical Pharmacology*, **4**, 3.
FRÉDÉRICQ E., OTH A., FONTAINE F. (1961), *J. Mol. Biol.*, **3**, 11.
FREIFELDER R.L. (1964), Science, **146**, 254.
FRESCO J.R., SU D.F. (1962), *J. Biol. Chem.*, **237**, PC 3305.
FRICK G. (1949), *Biochim. Biophys. Acta*, **3**, 103.
FRISCH D.M., VISSER D.W. (1959), *J. Am. Chem. Soc.*, **81**, 1757.
FRISCH-NIGGEMEYER W., REDDI K.K. (1957), *Biochim. Biophys. Acta*, **26**, 40.
FRUCHTER R.G., CRESTFIELD A.M. (1965 a), *J. Biol. Chem.*, **240**, 3868.
FRUCHTER R.G., CRESTFIELD A.M. (1965 b), *J. Biol. Chem.*, **240**, 3875.
FUJIOKA K., SCHERAGA H.A. (1965 a), *Biochemistry*, **4**, 2197.
FUJIOKA K., SCHERAGA H.A. (1965 b), *Biochemistry*, **4**, 2206.
FURTH J.J., HO P. (1965), *J. Biol. Chem.*, **240**, 2602.
FURTH J.J., LOH P. (1963), *Biochem. Biophys. Res. Comm.*, **13**, 100.

GALE E.F., FOLKES J.P. (1958a), *Biochem. J.*, **69**, 611.
GALE E.F., FOLKES J.P. (1958b), *Biochem. J.*, **69**, 620.
GANDELMAN B., ZAMENHOF S., CHARGAFF E. (1952), *Biochim. Biophys. Acta*, **9**, 399.
GARDNER R.S., WAHBA A.J., BASILIO C., MILLER R.S., LENGYEL P., SPEYER J.F. (1962), *Proc. Nat. Acad. Sci. U.S.*, **48**, 2087.
GAREN A., LEVINTHAL C. (1960), *Biochim. Biophys. Acta*, **38**, 470.
GEHRMANN G., OKADA S. (1957), *Biochim. Biophys. Acta*, **23**, 621.
GEIDUSCHEK E.P., DANIELS A. (1965), *Analyt. Biochem.*, **11**, 133.
GEORGATSOS J.G. (1963), *Arch. Int. Physiol. Biochim.*, **71**, 674.
GEORGATSOS J.G. (1965a), *Arch. Biochem. Biophys.*, **110**, 354.
GEORGATSOS J.G. (1965b), *Biochim. Biophys. Acta*, **95**, 544.
GEORGATSOS J.G., ANTONOGLOU O. (1966), *J. Biol. Chem.*, **241**, 2151.
GEORGATSOS J.G., LASKOWSKI M. (1962), *Biochemistry*, **1**, 288.
GEORGATSOS J.G., SYMEONIDIS A. (1965), *Nature*, **206**, 1362.
GEORGATSOS J.G., UNTERHOLZNER W.C., LASKOWSKI M. (1962), *J. Biol. Chem.*, **237**, 2626.
GERBER P. (1962), *Virology*, **16**, 96.
GERMANYUK Y.L., DEMCHUK M.V., GAVRILETS E.S. (1961), *Nauk. Pratsi L'vinsk Zoovet. Inst.*, **11**, 321.
GEZELIUS K., WRIGHT B.E. (1965), *J. Gen. Microbiol.*, **38**, 309.
GIERER A. (1957), *Nature*, **179**, 1297.
GIERER A. (1963), *J. Mol. Biol.*, **6**, 148.
GIERER A., SCHRAMM G. (1956), *Nature*, **177**, 702.
GILBERT W. (1963), *J. Mol. Biol.*, **6**, 374.
GILES K.W., MYERS A. (1965), *Nature*, **206**, 93.
GILHAM P.T. (1962), *J. Am. Chem. Soc.*, **84**, 1311.
GILHAM P.T. (1964), *J. Am. Chem. Soc.*, **86**, 4982.
GILHAM P.T., KHORANA H.G. (1958), *J. Am. Chem. Soc.*, **80**, 6212.
GILHAM P.T., ROBINSON W.E. (1964), *J. Am. Chem. Soc.*, **86**, 4985.
GIRIJA N.S., SREENIVASAN A. (1966), *Biochem. J.*, **98** 562.
GIVOL D., GOLDBERGER R.F., ANFINSEN C.B. (1964), *J. Biol. Chem.*, **239**, PC 3114.
GLAUDEMANS C.P.J., FLETCHER H.G. (1963), *J. Org. Chem.*, **28**, 3004.
GLITZ D.G., DEKKER C.A. (1963), *Biochemistry*, **2**, 1185.
GLITZ D.G., DEKKER C.A.(1964), *Biochemistry*, **3**, 1391.

GOLDSTEIN J., BENNETT T.P., CRAIG L.C. (1964), *Proc. Nat. Acad. Sci. U.S.*, **51**, 119.
GOODGAL S.H., POSTEL E.H. (1965), *Science*, **148**, 1095.
GORDON J. (1965 *a*), *Arch. Biochem. Biophys.*, **112**, 421.
GORDON J. (1965 *b*), *Arch. Biochem. Biophys.*, **112**, 429.
GORDON J., MYERS J. (1966), *Biochim. Biophys. Acta*, **113**, 187.
GOTTSCHLING H., ZACHAU H.G. (1965), *Biochim. Biophys. Acta.* **103**, 418.
GREEN M., PIÑA M. (1964), *Proc. Natl. Acad. Sci.*, **51**, 1251.
GREER S., ZAMENHOF S. (1962), *J. Mol. Biol.*, **4**, 123.
GRIFFITH F. (1928), *J. Hyg.*, **27**, 113.
GRINNAN E.L., MOSHER W.A. (1951), *J. Biol. Chem.*, **191**, 719.
GRIPPO P., IACCARINO M., ROSSI M., SCARANO E. (1965), *Biochim. Biophys. Acta*, **95**, 1.
GROS F., GILBERT W., HIATT H., KURLAND C.G., RISEBROUGH R.W., WATSON J.D. (1961), *Nature*, **190**, 581.
GRUNBERG-MANAGO M. (1955), *Bull. Soc. Chim. Biol.*, **38**, 589.
GRUNBERG-MANAGO M. (1963), in *Progress in Nucleic Acid Research*, vol. 1, p. 93, ed by Davidson J.N., Cohn W.E., New York, Academic Press.
GRUNBERG-MANAGO M., DONDON J. (1965), *Biochem. Biophys. Res. Comm.*, **18**, 517.
GRUNBERG-MANAGO M., MICHELSON A.M. (1964*a*), *Biochim. Biophys. Acta*, **80**, 431.
GRUNBERG-MANAGO M., MICHELSON A.M. (1964*b*), *Biochim. Biophys. Acta*, **87**, 593.
GRUNBERG-MANAGO M., OCHOA S. (1955*a*), *Fed.Proc.*, **14**, 221.
GRUNBERG-MANAGO M., OCHAO S. (1955*b*), *J. Am. Chem. Soc.*, **77**, 3165.
GRUNBERG-MANAGO M., ORTIZ J., OCHOA S. (1955), *Science*, **122**, 907.
GRUNBERG-MANAGO M., ORTIZ J., OCHOA S. (1956), *Biochim. Biophys. Acta* **20**, 269.
GRUNBERG-MANAGO M., WISNIEWSKI J. (1957), *Compt. rend.*, **245**, 750.
GUBLIN C., LAVIRON E., BARON C. (1965), *Bull. Soc. Chim. Biol.*, **47**, 723.
GULLAND J.M., JACKSON E. (1938), *Biochem. J.*, **32**, 590.
GULLAND J.M., JORDAN D.O., THRELFALL C.J. (1947), *J. Chem. Soc.* 1129.
GUPTA S., HERRIOTT R.M. (1963), *Arch. Biochem. Biophys.*, **101**, 88.
GUSCHLBAUER W., RICHARDS E.G., BEURLING K., ADAMS A., FRESCO J.R. (1965), *Biochemistry*, **4**, 964

HABERMANN V. (1963), *Biokhimiya*, **28**, 999.
HABERMANN V., MAIDLOVA E. (1963), *Coll. Czech. Chem. Comm.*, **28**, 2537.
HAKIM A.A. (1957*a*), *Arch. Biochem. Biophys.*, **70**, 591.
HAKIM A.A. (1957*b*), *J. Biol. Chem.*, **228**, 459.
HALL J.B., SEDAT J.W., ADIGA P.R., UEMURA I., WINNICK T. (1965), *J. Mol. Biol.*, **12**, 163.
HALL J.B., SINSHEIMER R.L. (1963), *J. Mol. Biol.*, **6**, 115.
HALL R.H. (1963*a*), *Biochem. Biophys. Res. Comm.*, **12**, 361.
HALL R.H. (1963*b*), *Biochem. Biophys. Res. Comm.*, **13**, 394.
HALL R.H. (1964*a*), *Biochemistry*, **3**, 769.
HALL R.H. (1964*b*), *Biochemistry* **3**, 879.
HALL R.H. (1965), *Biochemistry* **4**, 661.
HALL R.H., ROBINS M.J., FITTLER F. (1966), *Abstr. Papers Am. Chem. Soc.*, n° 152, 130 C.
HAMILTON M.G., CAVALIERI L.F., PETERMAN M.L. (1962), *J. Biol. Chem.*, **237**, 1155.
HAMMARSTEN E. (1924), *Biochem. Z.*, **144**, 383.
HAMMES G.G., SCHERAGA H.A. (1966), *Biochemistry*, **5**, 3690.
HAMOIR G. (1951), *Biochem. J.*, **48**, 146.
HAMOIR G. (1952), *Biochem. J.*, **50**, 140.
HANAWALT P.C., Ray D.S. (1964), *Proc. Natl. Acad. Sci.*, **52**, 125.
HANCOCK R.L., JURKOWITZ M.S., JURKOWITZ L. (1965), *Arch. Biochem. Biophys.*, **110**, 124.
HANDSCHUMACHER R.E., WELCH A.D. (1960) in *The Nucleic Acids*, vol. III, p. 453. Ed. by Chargaff E. and Davidson J.N., New York, Academic Press.
HARDMAN J.G., SUTHERLAND E.W. (1965), *J. Biol. Chem.*, **240**, PC 3704.
HARSHAW J.P., BROWN R.A., GRAHAM A.F. (1962), *Anal. Biochem.*, **4**, 182.

HARTLEY R.W., RUSHIZKY G.W., GRECO A.E., SOBER H.A. (1963), *Biochemistry*, **2**, 794.

HARTMANN G., COY U. (1961*a*), *Biochim. Biophys. Acta*, **47**, 612.

HARTMANN G., COY U. (1961*b*), *Biochim. Biophys. Acta*, **51**, 205.

HARTMANN G., COY U. (1961*c*), *Z. Physiol. Chem.*, **323**, 285.

HARUNA I., NOZU K., OHKATA Y., SPIEGELMAN S. (1963), *Proc. Nat. Acad. Sci. U.S.*, **50**, 905.

HARUNA I., SPIEGELMAN S. (1965), *Proc. Nat. Acad. Sci. U.S.*, **54**, 1189.

HASELKORN R. (1962), *J. Mol. Biol.*, **4**, 357.

HATHAWAY J.A., FRAJOLA W.J. (1965), *Fed. Proc.*, **24**, 227.

HASKILL J.S., HUNT J.W. (1965), *Biochim. Biophys. Acta*, **105**, 333.

HAYES D.H., MICHELSON A.M., TODD A.R. (1955), *J. Chem. Soc.* 808.

HEALY J.W., STOLLAR D., SIMON M.I., LEVINE L. (1963), *Arch. Biochem. Biophys.*, **103**, 461.

HEINRIKSON R.L. (1966), *J. Biol. Chem.*, **241**, 1393.

HEMMENS W.F. (1963), *Biochim. Biophys. Acta*, **68**, 284.

HENSTELL H.H., FREEDMAN R.I. (1952), *Science*, **115**, 357.

HENSTELL H.H., FREEDMAN R.I., GINSBURG B. (1952), *Cancer Res.*, **12**, 346.

HEPPEL L.A. (1955), in *Methods in Enzymology*, vol. 11, p. 530. Ed. by Colowick S.P., Kaplan N.O., New York, Academic Press.

HEPPEL L.A., HARKNESS D.R., HILMOE R.J. (1962), *J. Biol. Chem.*, **237**, 841.

HEPPEL L.A., HILMOE R.J. (1951), *J. Biol. Chem.*, **188**, 665.

HEPPEL L.A., HILMOE R.J. (1955*a*), in *Methods in Enzymology*, vol. II, p. 546. Ed. by Colowick S.P., Kaplan N.O., New York, Academic Press.

HEPPEL L.A., HILMOE R.J. (1955*b*) in *Methods in Enzymology*, vol. II, p. 565. Ed. by Colowick S.P., Kaplan N.O., New York, Academic Press.

HEPPEL L.A., MARKHAM R., HILMOE R.J. (1953), *Nature*, **171**, 1152.

HEPPEL L.A., ORTIZ P.J., OCHOA S. (1956), *Science*, **123**, 415.

HEPPEL L.A., ORTIZ P.J., OCHOA S. (1957*a*), *J. Biol. Chem.*, **229**, 679.

HEPPEL L.A., ORTIZ P.J., OCHOA S. (1957*b*), *J. Biol. Chem.*, **229**, 695.

HEPPEL L.A., RABINOWITZ J.C. (1958), *Ann. Rev. Biochem.*, **27**, 613.

HEPPEL L.A., WHITFELD P.R. (1955), *Biochem. J.*, **60**, 1.

HEPPEL L.A., WHITFELD P.R., MARKHAM R. (1955*a*), *Biochem. J.*, **60**, 8.

HEPPEL L.A., WHITFELD P.R., MARKHAM R. (1955*b*), *Biochem. J.*, **60**, 19.

HERMANS J. (1958), *Thesis*, Leyden, quoted by Sadron C., Pouyet, J., 4th International Congress of Biochemistry, Vienna, 1958, Symposium n°. IX, p. 52.

HERRIES D.G., MATHIAS A.P., RABIN B.R. (1962), *Biochem. J.*, **85**, 127.

HERSHEY A.D., BURGI E., INGRAHAM L. (1963), *Proc. Natl. Acad. Sci.*, **49**, 748.

HERSKOVITS T.T., SINGER S.J., GEIDUSCHEK E.P. (1961), *Arch. Biochem. Biophys.*, **94**, 99.

HERVÉ G., CHAPEVILLE F. (1963), *Biochim. Biophys. Acta*, **76**, 493.

HEYMAN H., GULICK Z.R., MAYER R.L. (1958), *Nature*, **182**, 1234.

HILMOE R.J. (1960), *J. Biol. Chem.*, **235**, 2117.

HILMOE R.J., HEPPEL L.A., SPRINGHORN S.S., KOSHLAND D.E. (1961), *Biochim. Biophys. Acta*, **53**, 214.

HIPPEL P.H. von, FELSENFELD G. (1964), *Biochemistry*, 3, 27.

HIPPEL P.H. von, WONG K.Y. (1965), *J. Biol. Chem.*, **240**, 3909.

HIRS C.H.W. (1960), *J. Biol. Chem.*, **235**, 625.

HIRS C.H.W., HALMANN M., KYCIA J.H. (1965), *Arch. Biochem. Biophys.*, **111**, 209.

HIRS C.H.W., KYCIA J.H. (1965), *Arch. Biochem. Biophys.*, **111**, 223.

HIRS C.H.W., MOORE S., STEIN W.H. (1953), *J. Biol. Chem.*, **200**. 493.

HIRS C.H.W., MOORE S., STEIN W.H. (1956), *J. Biol. Chem.*, **219**, 623.

HIRS C.H.W., MOORE S., STEIN W.H. (1960), *J. Biol. Chem.*, **235**, 633.

HIRS C.H.W., STEIN W.H., MOORE S. (1954), *J. Biol. Chem.*, **211**, 941.

HIRS C.H.W., STEIN W.H., MOORE S. (1956), *J. Biol. Chem.*, **221**, 151.

HIRSCHMAN S., FELSENFELD G. (1966), *J. Mol. Biol.*, **16**, 347.

HIRTH L., LEBEURIER G., AUBEL-SADRON G., BECK G., EBEL J.P., HORN P. (1960), *Nature*, **188**, 689.

HOAGLAND M.B. (1958), 4th International Congress of Biochemistry, Vienna, Symp. n°. VIII, p. 199,

HOAGLAND L.B. (1960), in *The Nucleic Acids*, vol. III, p. 349. Ed. by Chargaff E., Davidson J.N., New York, Academic Press.

HOAGLAND M.B., STEPHENSON M.L., SCOTT J.F., HECHT L.I., ZAMECNIK P.C. (1958), *J. Biol. Chem.* **231**, 241.

HODES M.E., SWENSON M.K. (1962), *Biochim. Biophys. Acta*, **61**, 612.

HOFMANN K., FINN F., HAAS W., SMITHERS M.J., WOLMAN Y., YANAIHARA N. (1963), *J. Am. Chem. Soc.*, **85**, 833.

HOFSTEE B.H.J. (1954), *Arch. Biochem. Biophys.*, **51**, 139.

HOFSTEN B. van, PORATH J. (1962), *Biochim. Biophys. Acta*, **64**, 1.

HOLDEN M., PIRIE N.W. (1955a), *Biochem. J.*, **60**, 39.

HOLDEN M., PIRIE N.W. (1955b), *Biochem, J.*, **60**, 46.

HOLDEN M., PIRIE N.W. (1955c), *Biochem. J.*, **60**, 53.

HOLIDAY E.R., JOHNSON E.A. (1949), *Nature*, **163**, 216.

HOLLEY R.W., (1963), *Biochem. Biophys. Res. Comm.*, **10**, 186.

HOLLEY R.W., APGAR J., DOCTOR B.P., FARROW J., MARINI M.A., MERRILL S.H. (1961), *J. Biol. Chem.*, **236**, 200.

HOLLEY R.W., APGAR S., EVERETT G.H., MADISON J.T., MARQUISEE M., MERRILL S.H., PENSWICK J.R., ZAMIR A. (1965a), *Science*, **147**, 1462.

HOLLEY R.W., APGAR J., EVERETT G.A., MADISON J.T., MERRILL S.H., PENSWICK J.R., ZAMIR A. (1965b), *Fed. Proc.*, **24**, 216.

HOLLEY R.W., EVERETT G.A., MADISON J.T., ZAMIR A. (1965c), *J. Biol. Chem.*, **240**, 2122.

HOLLEY R.W., LAZAR V.A. (1961), *J. Biol. Chem.*, **236**, 1446.

HOLLEY R.W., MADISON J.T., ZAMIR A. (1964), *Biochem. Biophys. Res. Comm.*, **17**, 389.

HORIUCHI S. (1959), *Japan J. Med. Sci., Biol.*, **12**, 429.

HORIUCHI T., HORIUCHI S., MIZUNO D. (1959), *Nature*, **183**, 1529.

HOSKINSON R.M., KHORANA H.G. (1965), *J. Biol. Chem.*, **240**, 2129.

HOTCHKISS R.D. (1948), *J. Biol. Chem.*, **175**, 315.

HOTCHKISS R.D. (1949), Colloque Int. C.N.R.S., Paris, **8**.

HOTCHKISS R.D. (1952), in *Phosphorus Metabolism*, Ed. by McElroy W.., Glass B., vol. 2, p. 426. Johns Hopkins Press, Baltimore, Md.

HOTCHKISS R.D. (1955), in *The Nucleic Acids*, vol. II, p. 435. Ed. by Chargaff E., Davidson J.N., New York, Academic Press.

HOTTA Y., BASSEL A. (1965), *Proc. Natl. Acad. Sci.*, U. S., **53**, 356.

HOUCK J.C. (1958), *Arch. Biochem. Biophys.*, **73**, 383.

HOUCK J.C. (1959), *Arch. Biochem. Biophys.*, **82**, 135.

HOWARD G.H., LYTHGOE B., TODD A.R. (1947), *J. Chem. Soc.*, 1052.

HSU R.Y., CLELAND W.W., ANDERSON L. (1966), *Biochemistry*, **5**, 799.

HUBERT-HABART M., COHEN S.S. (1962), *Biochim. Biophys. Acta*, **59**, 468.

HUMMEL J.P., ANDERSON B.S. (1965), *Arch. Biochem. Biophys.*, **112**, 443.

HUNT J.A. (1965), *Biochem. J.*, **95**, 541.

HUNTER J.H. (Upjohn Co.).(1963), *U.S. Pat.*, 3, 116, 282.

HUPPERT J., PELMONT J. (1962), *Arch. Biochem. Biophys.*, **98**, 214.

HUPPERT J., REBEYROTTE N. (1960), *Biochim. Biophys. Acta*, **45**, 189.

HUPPERT J., SEMMEL M. (1965), *Biochim. Biophys. Acta*, **108**, 501.

HURST R.O., BUTLER G.C. (1951), *J. Biol. Chem.*, **193**, 91.

HURST R.O., LITTLE J.A., BUTLER G.C. (1951), *J. Biol. Chem.*, **188**, 705.

HURST R.O., MARKO A.W., BUTLER G.C. (1953), *J. Biol. Chem.*, **204**, 847.

HURWITZ J., EVANS A., BABINET C., SKALKA A. (1963), Cold Spring Hafbor Symp. Quant. Biol., **28**, 59.

IBUKI F., MORI T., MATSUSHITA S., HATA T. (1965), *Agr. Biol. Chem.* (Tokyo), **29**, 635.

IIO M., HASHIMOTO T., YOSHIKAWA H. (1964), *J. Biochem.* (Tokyo), **55**, 321.

IMRIE R.C., HUTCHINSON W.C. (1965), *Biochim. Biophys. Acta.* **108**, 106.

INGLE J. (1963), *Biochim. Biophys. Acta*, **73**, 331.

IRIE M. (1964), *Tampakushitsu Kakusan Koso*, **9**, 257.

ITO Y. (1960), *Virology*, **12**, 596.

JACOB F., MONOD J. (1961), *J. Mol. Biol.*, **3**, 318.

JACOB T.M., KHORANA H.G. (1965), *J. Am. Chem. Soc.*, **87**, 368.

JACQUEMIN-SABLON A., LAVAL J., LE TALAER J.Y., LE PECQ J.B., PAOLETTI C. (1964), *Compt. rend.*, **259**, 2551.

JENKINS W.T., D'ARI L.M. (1966), *J. Biol. Chem.*, **241**, 295.

JOHNSON T.B., COGHILL R.D. (1965), *J. Am. Chem. Soc.*, **47**, 2338.

JONES A.S., ROSS G.W., TAKEMURA S., THOMPSON T.W., WALKER R.T. (1964), *J. Chem. Soc.*, 373.

JONES A.S., WALKER R.T. (1964a), *Nature*, **202**, 24.

JONES A.S., WALKER R.T. (1964b), *Nature*, **202**, 1108.

JONES K.W., TRUMAN D.E.S. (1964), *Nature*, **202**, 1264.

JORDAN D.O. (1955), in *The Nucleic Acids*, vol. 1., p. 447. Ed. by Chargaff E., Davidson J.N., New York, Academic Press.

JORGENSEN S.E., KOERNER J.F. (1965), *Fed. Proc.*, **24**, 349.

JOSEFSSON L., L., LAGERSTEDT S. (1962), in *Methods of Biochemical Analysis*, vol. IX, p. 39. Ed. by Glick D., New York, Interscience Pub. John Willey and Sons.

JOSSE J., EIGNER J. (1966), *Ann. Rev. Biochem.*, **35**, 789.

JOSSE J., KAISER A.D., KORNBERG J. (1961), *J. Biol. Chem.*, **236**, 864.

KALNITSKY G., HUMMEL J.P., RESNICK H., CARTER J.R., BARNETT L.B., DIERKS C. (1959), *Am. N.Y Acad. Sci.*, **81**, 542.

KAPLAN H.S., HEPPEL L.A. (1956), *J. Biol. Chem.*, **222**, 907.

KARAU W., ZACHAU H.G. (1964), *Biochim. Biophys. Acta*, **91**, 549.

KASAI K. (1963), *Compt. rend. Soc. Biol.*, **157**, 1864.

KAY E.R.M., SIMMONS N.S., DOUNCE A.L. (1952), *J. Am. Chem. Soc.*, **74**, 1724.

KAZIR Y., KAMIYAMA M. (1965), *Biochem. Biophys. Res. Comm.*, **19**, 433.

KEILIN D., HARTREE E.F. (1938), *Proc. Roy. Soc.*, B. **124**, 397.

KEIR H.M., MATHOG R.H., CARTER C.E. (1964), *Biochemistry*, **3**, 1188.

KELLER E.B. (1964), *Biochem. Biophys. Res. Comm.*, **17**, 412.

KELLER E.B., ZAMECNIK P.C. (1956), *J. Biol. Chem.*, **221**, 45.

KELLER P.J., COHEN E., NEURATH H. (1958), *J. Biol. Chem.*, **233**, 344.

KERR I.M., PRATT E.A., LEHMAN I.R. (1965), *Biochem. Biophys. Res. Comm.*, **20**, 154.

KERSTEN H., SCHNIEDERS B., LEOPOLD G., KERSTEN W. (1965), *Biochim. Biophys. Acta*, **108**, 619.

KHORANA H.G. (1959), *J. Cell. Comp. Physiol.*, suppl. 1, vol. **54**, 5.

KHORANA H.G. (1960), in *The Nucleic Acids*, vol. III, p. 105, Ed. Chargaff E., Davidson J.N., New York, Academic Press.

KHORANA H.G. (1961 a), *Enzymes*, **5**, 79.

KHORANA H.G. (1961 b). *Some Recent Developments in the Chemistry of Phosphate Esters of Biological Interest*. New York, John Wiley and Sons.

KHORANA H.G., RAZZELL W.E., GILHAM P.T., TENER G.M., POL E.H. (1957), *J. Am. Chem. Soc.*, **79**, 1002.

KHORANA H.G., TENER G.M., RAZZELL W.E., MARKHAM R. (1958), *Fed. Proc.*, **17**, 253.

KHORANA H.G., VIZSOLYI J.P. (1961), *J. Am. Chem. Soc.*, **83**, 675.

KHORANA H.G., VIZSOLYI J.P., RALPH R.K. (1962), *J. Am. Chem. Soc.*, **84**, 414.

KHOUVINE Y., ROBICHON-SZULMAJSTER H. (de) (1951), *Bull. Soc. Chim. Biol.*, **33**, 1508.

KHOUVINE Y., ROBICHON-SZULMAJSTER H. (de) (1952a), *Bull. Soc. Chim. Biol.*, **34**, 1050.

KHOUVINE Y., ROBICHON-SZULMAJSTER H. (de) (1952b), *Bull. Soc. Chim. Biol.*, **34**, 1056.

KIEPAL-KOCHANSKA Z., TAYTSCH F.Z. (1963), *Med. Doswiadczalna Mikrobiol.*, **15**, 167.

KIMBALL A.P., LE PAGE G.A., BOWMAN B. (1965), *Fed. Proc.*, **24**, 668.

KIRBY K.S. (1956), *Biochem. J.*, **64**, 405.

KIRBY K.S. (1961), *Biochim. Biophys. Acta*, **47**, 18.

KIRBY K.S. (1962a), *Biochim. Biophys. Acta*, **55**, 382.

KIRBY K.S. (1962b), *Biochim. Biophys. Acta*, **55**, 545.

KIRBY K.S. (1964), *Biochem. J.*, **93**, 5c.

KIRBY K.S. (1965), *Biochem. J.*, **96**, 266.

KLEE W.A. (1965), *J. Biol. Chem.*, **240**, 2900.

KLEIN B., AUERBACH J., MORGENSTERN S. (1965), *Clin. Chem.*, **11**, 998.

KLEIN B., OKLANDER M., MORGENSTERN S. (1966), *Clin. Chem.*, **12**, 226.

KLEINSCHMIDT A.K., BURTON A., SINSHEIMER R.L. (1963), *Science*, **142**, 961.

KLEINSCHMIDT A.K., KASS S.J., WILLIAMS R.C., KNIGHT C.A. (1965), *J. Mol. Biol.*, **13**, 749.

KLEINSCHMIDT A.K., LANG D., JACHERTS D., ZAHN R.K. (1962), *Biochim. Biophys. Acta*, **61**, 857.

KLEINSCHMIDT A.K., ZAHN B.K. (1959), *Z.* Naturforsch., **14** b, 770.

KLUG A., CASPAR D.L.D. (1960), *Adv. Virus Res.* **7**, 225-325.

KNIGHT C.A. (1952), *J. Biol. Chem.*, **197**, 241.

KNIGHT E. Jr., FITT P.S., GRUNBERG-MANAGO M. (1963), *Biochem. Biophys. Res. Comm.*, **10**, 488.

KOCH G., KUBINSKI H. (1964), *Z. Naturforsch.*, **19***b*, 683.

KOCHETKOV N.K., BUDOWSKY E.I., DOMKIN V.D., KROMOV-BORISSOV N.N. (1964), *Biochim. Biophys. Acta*, **80**, 145.

KOCHETKOV N.K., BUDOWSKY E.I., TURCHINSKY M.F., SIMUKOVA N.A. (1965), *Biochem. Biophys. Res. Comm.*, **19**, 49.

KOERNER J.F., SINSHEIMER R.L. (1957*a*), *J. Biol. Chem.*, **228**, 1039.

KOERNER J.F., SINSHEIMER R.L. (1957*b*), *J. Biol. Chem.*, **228**, 1049.

KOPYLOVA-SVIRIDOVA T.N. (1964), *Biofizika*, **9** (1), 13.

KORBECKI M. (1963), *Bull. Acad. Polon. Sci., Ser. Sci. Biol.*, **11**, *371.*

KORN D., WEISSBACH A. (1964), *J. Biol. Chem.*, **239**, 3849.

KORNBERG A. (1960), *Science*, **131**, 1503.

KORNBERG A. (1962), *Enzymatic Synthesis of DNA ;* CIBA Lectures. New York, John Wiley and Sons.

KORNBERG A., BERTSCH L., JACKSON J.F., KHORANA H.G. (1964), *Proc. Nat. Acad. Sci. U.S.*, **51**, 315.

KORNBERG A., LEHMAN I.R., BESSMAN M.J., SIMMS E.S. (1956), *Biochim. Biophys. Acta*, **21**, 197.

KORNBERG A., LEHMAN I.R., SIMMS E.S. (1956), *Fed. Proc.*, **15**, 291.

KORNBERG A., PRICER W.E. (1950 *a*), *J. Biol. Chem.*, **182**, 763.

KORNBERG A., PRICER W.E. (1950 *b*), *J. Biol. Chem.*, **186**, 557.

KORSON R. (1951), *Stain Technol.*, **26**, 265.

KRAKOW J.S. (1965), *Biochim. Biophys. Acta*, **95**, 532.

KRAKOW J.S., OCHOA S. (1963*a*), *Biochem. Z.*, **338**, 796.

KRAKOW J.S., OCHOA S. (1963*b*), *Proc. Nat. Acad. Sci. U.S.*, **49**, 88.

KREBS H.A., HEMS R. (1953), *Biochim. Biophys. Acta*, **12**, 172.

KUBINSKI H., KOCH G. (1962), *Virology*, **17**, 219.

KUEMMERLE H.P., PREZIOSI P. (1964), editors. *IIIrd International Congress of Chemotherapy,* July 22-27, 1963, Georg Thieme Verlag, Stuttgart.

KUNITZ M. (1940), *J. Gen. Physiol.*, **24**, 15.

KUNITZ M. (1946), *J. Biol. Chem.*, **164**, 563.

KUNITZ M. (1950), *J. Gen. Physiol.*, **33**, 349.

KUNITZ M. (1960), *J. Gen. Physiol.*, **43**, 1149.

KUNITZ M., SIMMS H.S. (1928), *J. Gen. Physiol.*, **11**, 641.

KUO M.H., BLUMENTHAL H.J. (1961*a*), *Biochim. Biophys. Acta*, **52**, 13.

KUO M.H., BLUMENTHAL H.J. (1961*b*), *Biochim. Biophys. Acta*, **54**, 101.

KURNICK N.B. (1952), *Stain Technol.*, **27**, 233.

KURNICK N.B. (1962), in *Methods of Biochemical Analysis*, vol. IX, p. 1. Ed. by Glick D., New York, Interscience Pub., John Willey and Sons.

LAMIRANDE G. de, ALLARD C., DACOSTA H.C., CANTERO A. (1954), *Science,* **119**, 351.

LANOT R., STEPHAN F. (1964), *Compt. rend. Soc. Biol.*, **158**, 1567.

LAPIDOT Y., KHORANA H.G. (1963*a*), *J. Am. Chem. Soc.*, **85**, 1363.

LAPIDOT Y., KHORANA H.G. (1963*b*), *J. Am. Chem. Soc.*, **85**, 3852.

LAPIDOT Y., KHORANA H.G. (1963*c*), *J. Am. Chem. Soc.*, **85**, 3857.

LASKOWSKI M. (1946), *Arch. Biochem. Biophys.*, **11**, 41.

LASKOWSKI M. (1951), in *The Enzymes*, vol. 1, part II, p. 956. Ed. by Summer J.B. and Myrbäck K., New York, Academic Press.

LASKOWSKI M. (1959), *Ann. N.Y. Acad. Sci.*, **81**, 776.

LASKOWSKI M. (1961), in *The Enzymes*, vol. V, p. 123. Ed. by Boyer P.D., Lardy H. and Myrbäck K., New York, Academic Press.

LASKOWSKI M., HAGERTY G., LAURILA U.R. (1957), *Nature*, **180**, 1181.

LASKOWSKI M., SEIDEL M. (1945), *Arch. Biochem. Biophys.*, **7**, 465.

LASKOWSKI M., STEBERL E.A., AKKA R., WATSON P. (1954), *Biochim. Biophys. Acta*, **13**, 595.

LAUFFER M.A. (1944), *J. Am. Chem. Soc.*, **66**, 1188.

LAURILA U.R., LASKOWSKI M. (1957), *J. Biol. Chem.*, **228**, 49.

LAVAL J., LAVAL F., PAOLETTI C. (1966), *Compt. Rend.*, **262**, Série D, 2093.

LAZDUNSKI C., LAZDUNSKI M. (1966), *Biochim. Biophys. Acta*, **113**, 551.

LAZDUNSKI M., OUELLET L. (1962), *Can. J. Biochem. Physiol.*, **40**, 1619.

LEDER P., CLARK B.F.C., SLY W.S., PESTKA S., NIRENBERG M.W. (1963), *Proc. Nat. Acad. Sci. U.S.*, **50**, 1135.

LEDER P., NIRENBERG M. (1964), *Proc. Nat. Acad. Sci. U.S.*, **52**, 420.

LEDOUX L. (1953), *Biochim. Biophys. Acta*, **10**, 190.

LEE W.W., BENITEZ A., GOODMAN L., BAKER B.R. (1960), *J. Am. Chem. Soc.*, **82**, 2648.

LEE W.W., MARTINEZ A.P., TONG G.L., GOODMAN L. (1963), *Chem. and. Ind.*, 2007.

LEE-HUANG S., CAVALIERI L.F. (1963), *Proc. Nat. Acad. Sci. U. S.*, **50**, 1116.

LEE-HUANG S., CAVALIERI L.F. (1964), *Proc. Nat. Acad. Sci. U.S.*, **51**, 1022.

LEGAULT-DÉMARE J., REBEYROTTE N., LEPRIEUR A., ROUSSAUX J. (1964), *Biochim. Biophys. Acta*, **87**, 165.

LEHMAN I.R. (1960), *J. Biol. Chem.*, **235**, 1479.

LEHMAN I.R. (1963), *Progress in Nucleic Acid Research*, **2**, 83.

LEHMAN I.R., BESSMAN M.J., SIMMS E.S., KORNBERG A. (1958), *J. Biol. Chem.*, **223**, 163.

LEHMAN I.R., LINN S., RICHARDSON C.C. (1965), *Federation Proc.*, **24**, 1460.

LEHMAN I.R., NUSSBAUM A.L. (1964), *J. Biol. Chem.*, **239**, 2628.

LEHMAN I.R., RICHARDSON C.C. (1964), *J. Biol. Chem.*, **239**, 233.

LEHMAN I.R., ROUSSOS G.G., PRATT E.A. (1962a), *J. Biol. Chem.*, **237**, 819.

LEHMAN I.R., ROUSSOS G.G., PRATT E.A. (1962b), *J. Biol. Chem.*, **237**, 829.

LEHMAN I.R., ZIMMERMAN S.B., ADLER J., BESSMAN M.J., SIMMS E.S., KORNBERG A. (1958), *Proc. Nat. Acad. Sci. U.S.*, **44**, 1191.

LENGYEL P., SPEYER J.F., BASILIO C., OCHOA S. (1962a), *Proc. Nat. Acad. Sci. U.S.*, **48**, 282.

LENGYEL P., SPEYER J.F., BASILIO C., WAHBA A., OCHOA S. (1962b), *Biochem. J.*, **84**, 86P.

LERMAN L.S. (1955), *Biochim. Biophys. Acta*, **18**, 132.

LERNER L. M., KOHN P. (1964), *J. Med. Chem.*, **7**, 655.

LESLIE I. (1955), in *The Nucleic Acids*, vol. 2, p. 1. Ed. by E. Chargaff and J.N. Davidson, New York, Academic Press.

LE TALAER J.Y., FESTY B., LE PECQ J.B., PAOLETTI C. (1962), *Nature*, **194**, 1176.

LE TALAER J.Y., FESTY B., TRUHAUT R. (1963), *Clin. Chim. Acta.*, **8**, 925.

LEVENE P.A., BASS L.W. (1931), *Nucleic Acids*, New York, The Chemical Catalog Company.

LEVIN S.J., BODANSKY O. (1966), *J. Biol. Chem.*, **241**, 51.

LINDBERG U. (1964), *Biochim. Biophys. Acta*, **82**, 237.

LINDERSTRÖM-LANG K. (1940), *Bull. Soc. Chim. Biol.*, **22**, 339.

LINDLEY H. (1962), *Biochim. Biophys. Acta*, **55**, 206.

LINEWEAVER H., BURK D. (1934), *J. Am. Chem. Soc.*, **56**, 658.

LINN S., LEHMAN I.R. (1965), *J. Biol. Chem.*, **240**, 1287.

LINN S., LEHMAN I.R. (1966), *J. Biol. Chem.*, **214**, 2694.

LIPMANN F. (1941), *Advances in Enzymology*, **1**, 99.

LIPSETT M.N. (1965), *Biochem. Biophys. Res. Comm.*, **20**, 224.

LIPSETT M.N., HEPPEL L.A., BRADLEY D.F. (1961), *J. Biol. Chem.*, **236**, 857.

LIPSHITZ R., CHARGAFF E. (1956), *Biochim. Biophys. Acta*, **19**, 256.

LISOWSKI J. (1964), *Arch. Immunol. Therap. Exp.*, **12**, 542.

LISOWSKI J. (1965), *Arch. Immunol. Therap. Exp.*, **14**, 195.

LISOWSKI J. (1966), *Biochim. Biophys. Acta*, **113**, 321.

LIS A.W., LIS E.W. (1962), *Biochim. Biophys. Acta*, **61**, 799.

REFERENCES   347

Lis A.W., Passarge W.E. (1966), *Arch. Biochem. Biophys.*, **114**, 593.
Littauer U.Z., Kornberg A. (1957), *J. Biol. Chem.*, **226**, 1077.
Littlefield J.W., Dunn D.B. (1958), *Biochem. J.*, **70**, 642.
Littlefield J.W., Keller E.B. (1957), *J. Biol. Chem.*, **224**, 13.
Llosa P. (de la), Tertin C., Jutisz M. (1966), *Biochim. Biophys. Acta*, **115**, 464.
Loddo B., Scarpa B., Muntoni S. (1963), *Experientia*, **19**, 246.
Loeb G.I., Saroff H.A. (1964), *Biochemistry*, **3**, 1819.
Lohrmann R.R., Khorana H.G. (1964), *J. Am. Chem. Soc.*, **86**, 4188.
Lohrmann R., Söll D., Hayatsu H., Ohtsuka E., Khorana H.G. (1966), *J. Am. Chem. Soc.*, **88**, 819.
Loring H.S. (1939a), *J. Biol. Chem.*, **128**, Sci. Proc., LXI.
Loring H.S. (1939b), *J. Biol. Chem.*, **130**, 251.
Loring H.S., Carpenter F.H., Roll P.M. (1947), *J. Biol. Chem.*, **169**, 601.
Lucas J.M., Grunberg-Manago M. (1964), *Biochem. Biophys. Res. Comm.*, **17**, 395.
Luzzati V. (1961), *J. Chim. Phys.*, **58**, 899.
Luzzati V., Luzzati D., Masson F. (1962), *J. Mol. Biol.*, **5**, 375.
Luzzati V., Nicolaieff A. (1959), *J. Mol. Biol.*, **1**, 127.
Luzzati V., Nicolaieff A., Masson F. (1961), *J. Mol. Biol.*, **3**, 185.
Luzzati V., Witz J., Timasheff S.N. (1961), Coll. Intern. CNRS, Strasbourg, 6-12 July, 1961, p. 123.
Lwoff A., Horne R.W., Tournier P. (1962), *Compt. rend.*, **254**, 4225.
Lyndon R.F., (1966), *Biochim. Biophys. Acta*, **113**, 110.
Lys G., Terroine T. (1962), *Compt. rend.*, **254**, 1514.

McAuslan B.R. (1965), *Biochem. Biophys. Res. Comm.*, **19**, 15.
McCarty M. (1946), *J. Gen. Physiol.*, **29**, 123.
McCarty M. (1949), *J. Exp. Med.*, **90**, 543.
McDonald M.R. (1948), *J. Gen. Physiol.*, **32**, 39.
McDonald M.R. (1955a), in *Methods in Enzymology*, vol. 2, p. 427. Ed. by Colowick S.P., Kaplan N.O., New York, Academic Press.
McDonald M.R. (1955b), in *Methods in Enzymology*, vol. 2, p. 437. Ed. by Colowick S.P., Kaplan N.O., New York, Academic Press.
McFadyen D.A. (1934), *J. Biol. Chem.*, **107**, 299.
McHattie L.A., Berns K.I., Thomas C.A. (1965), *J. Mol. Biol.*, **11**, 648.
McLennan B.D., Lane B.G. (1965), *Fed. Proc.*, **24**, 602.
McQuillen K., Roberts R.B., Britten R.J. (1959), *Proc. Nat. Acad. Sci. U.S.*, **45**, 1437.
Madison J.T., Everett G.A., Kung H. (1966), *Science*, **153**, 531.
Madison J.T., Holley R.W. (1965), *Biochem. Biophys. Res. Comm.*, **18**, 153.
Magasanik B. (1955), in *The Nucleic Acids*, vol. 1, p. 373. Ed. by E. Chargaff, Davidson J.N., New York Academic Press.
Main R.K., Cole L.J. (1957), *Arch. Biochem. Biophys.*, **68**, 181.
Main R.K., Cole L.J. (1964), *Nature*, **203**, 646.
Main R.K., Wilkins M.J., Cole L.J. (1959), *J. Am. Chem. Soc.*, **81**, 6490.
Malamy M.H., Horecker B.L. (1964a), *Biochemistry*, **3**, 1889.
Malamy M.H., Horecker B.L. (1964b), *Biochemistry*, **3**, 1893.
Mandell J.D., Hershey A.D. (1960), *Anal. Biochem.*, **1**, 66.
Mandel P., (1951), *Exposés annuels de Biochimie médicale*, 13th series, p. 255. Masson, Paris.
Mandel P., Borkowska I. (1964), *Biochim. Biophys. Acta*, **91**, 683.
Mandel P., Jacob M., Mandel L. (1949), *Compt. rend. Soc. Biol.*, **148**, 536.
Mandel P., Jacob M., Mandel L. (1950), *Bull. Soc. Chim. Biol.*, **32**, 80.
Mandel P., Jacob M., Mandel L. (1954), *Compt. rend.*, **238**, 288.
Mandel P., Schmidt M.L. (1957), *Compt. rend. Soc. Biol.*, **151**, 368.
Mandeles S., Tinoco I. (1963), *Biopolymers*, **1**, 183.
Manson L.A., Pelmont J., Yapo A., Roche C., Nisman B. (1965), *Biochem. J.*, **95**, 215.
Marcot-Queiroz J., Monier R. (1965), *J. Mol. Biol.*, **14**, 490.

MARFEY P.S., KING M.V. (1965), *Biochim. Biophys. Acta*, **105**, 178.
MARFEY P.S., NOWAK H., UZIEL M., YPHANTIS D.A. (1965), *J. Biol. Chem.*, **240**, 3264.
MARFEY P.S., UZIEL M., LITTLE J. (1965), *J. Biol. Chem.*, **240**, 3270.
MARKHAM R., SMITH J.D. (1949), *Biochem. J.*, **45**, 294.
MARKHAM R., SMITH J.D. (1951), *Biochem. J.*, **49**, 401.
MARKHAM R., SMITH J.D. (1952a), *Biochem. J.*, **52**, 552.
MARKHAM R., SMITH J.D. (1952b), *Biochem. J.*, **52**, 558.
MARKHAM R., SMITH J.D. (1952c), *Biochem. J.*, **52**, 565.
MARKHAM R., SMITH J.D. (1954), in *The Proteins*, vol. II, part A, p. 1. Ed. by Neurath H., Bailey K., New York, Academic Press.
MARKHAM R., STROMINGER J.L. (1956), *Biochem. J.*, **64**, 46P.
MARMUR J., DOTY P. (1959), *Nature*, **183**, 1427.
MARMUR J., DOTY P. (1961), *J. Mol. Biol.*, **3**, 585.
MARMUR J., LANE D. (1960), *Proc. Nat. Acad. Sci. U.S.*, **46**, 453.
MARMUR J., SCHILDKRAUT C.L., DOTY P. (1961), *J. Chim. Phys.*, 945.
MARSHAK A., VOGEL H.J. (1951), *J. Biol. Chem.*, **189**, 597.
MARTIN R.G., MATTHAEI J.H., JONES O.W., NIRENBERG M.W. (1962), *Biochem. Biophys. Res. Comm.* **6**, 410.
MASE K. (1962), *Seikagaku*, **34**, 339.
MATSUSHITA S., IBUTI F., MORI T., HATA T. (1965), *Agr. Biol. Chem.* (Tokyo), **29**, 436.
MATTHEWS R.E.F. (1960), *Biochim. Biophys. Acta*, **38**, 552.
MAVER M.E., GRECO A.E. (1949), *J. Biol. Chem.*, **181**, 861.
MAVER M.E., GRECO A.E. (1954), *Fed. Proc.*, **13**, 261.
MAVER M.E., GRECO A.E. (1956), *J. Nat. Cancer Inst.*, **17**, 503.
MAVER M.E., PETERSON E.A., SOBER H.A., GRECO A.E. (1959), *Ann. N.Y. Acad. Sci.*, **81**, 598.
MAXWELL R.E., NICKEL V.S., LEWANDOWSKI V. (1963), *J. Pharm. Sci.*, **52**, 796.
MAZIA D., PRESCOTT D.M. (1955), *Biochim. Biophys. Acta*, **17**, 23.
MEHROTRA B.D., KHORANA H.G. (1965), *J. Biol. Chem.*, **240**, 1750.
MEISEL H., ALBRYCHT H., RYMKIEWICZ D. (1959), *Bull. Acad. Pol. Sci., Ser. Sci. Biol.*, **7**, 139.
MEISEL H., ALBRYCHT H., RYMKIEWICZ D. (1962), *Bull. Acad. Pol. Sci., Ser. Sci. Biol.*, **10**, 239.
MEISEL H., ALBRYCHT H., RYMKIEWICZ D., KUDELSKI Z. (1961), *Bull. Acad. Pol. Sci., Ser. Sci. Biol.*, **9**, 391.
MEJBAUM W. (1939). *Z. Physiol. Chem.*, **258**, 117.
MELCHERS F., DÜTTING D., ZACHAU H.G. (1965), *Biochim. Biophys. Acta*, **108**, 182.
MELCHERS F., ZACHAU H.G (1964), *Biochim. Biophys. Acta*, **91**, 559.
MELCHERS F., ZACHAU H.G. (1965), *Biochim. Biophys. Acta*, **95**, 380.
MEROLA A.J., DAVIS F.F. (1962), *Biochim. Biophys. Acta*, **55**, 431.
MESELSON M., STAHL F. W. (1958), *Proc. Nat. Acad. Sci. U.S.*, **44**, 671.
MESELSON M., STAHL F.W., VINOGRAD J. (1957), *Proc. Nat. Acad. Sci. U.S.*, **43**, 581.
MESNARD G., VASILESCU D. (1963), *Compt. rend.*, **257**, 4177.
MEURON-LANDOLT M. de, PRIVAT DE GARILHE M. (1964), *Biochim. Biophys. Acta.*, **91**, 433.
MICHELSON A.M. (1958), *Nature*, **181**, 303.
MICHELSON A.M. (1959), *J. Chem. Soc.*, 3655.
MICHELSON A.M. (1963), *The Chemistry of Nucleosides and Nucleotides*. New York, Academic Press.
MICHELSON A.M. (1964), private communication.
MICHELSON A.M., DONDON J., GRUNBERG-MANAGO M. (1962), *Biochim. Biophys. Acta*, **55**, 529.
MICHELSON A.M., GRUNBERG-MANAGO M. (1964), *Biochim. Biophys. Acta*, **91**, 92.
MICHELSON A.M., SZABO L., TODD A.R. (1956), *J. Chem. Soc.*, 1546.
MICHELSON A.M., TODD A.R. (1949), *J. Chem. Soc.*, 2476.
MICHELSON A.M., TODD A.R. (1954), *J. Chem. Soc.*, 34.
MICHELSON A.M., TODD A.R. (1955), *J. Chem. Soc.*, 2632.
MICKLE H.J. (1948), *J. Roy. Microcop. Soc.*, **48**, 10.
MILSTEIN C. (1962), *Biochem. J.*, **92**, 419.
MILSTEIN C. (1963), *Biochim. Biophys. Acta*, **67**, 171.

Mirsky A.E., Pollister A.W. (1942), *Proc. Nat. Acad. Sci. U.S.*, **28**, 344.
Mirsky A.E., Pollister A.W. (1943a), *Biol. Symposia*, **10**, 247.
Mirsky A.E., Pollister A.W. (1943b), *Trans. N.Y. Acad. Sci.*, **5**, 190.
Mirsky A.E., Pollister A.W. (1946a), *J. Gen. Physiol.*, **30**, 101.
Mirsky A.E., Pollister A.W. (1946b), *J. Gen. Physiol.*, **30**, 117.
Mirsky A.E., Ris H. (1949), *Nature*, **163**, 666.
Mirsky A.E., Ris H. (1951), *J. Gen. Physiol.*, **34**, 451.
Miura K.I., Miura T., Hiruki C., Hidaka Z., Watanabe I. (1963), *Virology*, **19**, 140.
Monier R. (1962), *Bull. Soc. Chim. Biol.*, 44, 109.
Monier R., Naono S., Hayes D., Hayes F., Gros F. (1962), *J. Mol. Biol.*, **5**, 311.
Monier R., Stephenson M.L., Zamecnik P.C. (1960), *Biochim. Biophys. Acta*, **43**, 1.
Moore S. (1964), *Bull. Soc. Chim. Biol.*, **46**, 1739.
Moore S., Hirs C.H.W., Stein W.H. (1956), *Fed. Proc.*, **15**, 840.
Morris A.J., Dickman S.R. (1960), *J. Biol. Chem.*, **235**, 1404.
Moss D.W. (1966), *Nature*,**209**, 806.
Moss D.W., Eaton R.H., Smith J.K., Withby L.G. (1966), *Biochem. J.*, **98**, 32c.
Morton R.K. (1955), in *Methods in Enzymology*, vol. II, p. 533. Ed. by Colowick S.P., Kaplan N.O., New York, Academic Press.
Motzok I. (1963), *Biochem. J.*, **87**, 172.
Moudrianakis E.N., Beer M. (1964), *Nature*, **204**, 685.
Moudrianakis E.N., Beer M. (1965a), *Biochim. Biophys. Acta*, **95**, 23.
Moudrianakis E.N., Beer M. (1965b), *Proc. Nat. Acad. Sci. U.S.*, **53**, 564.
Mukai J.I., Ohsaka A., McEvoy C., Laskowski M. (1965), *Biochem. Biophys. Res. Comm.*, **18**, 136.
Murdock A.L., Grist K.L., Hirs C.H.W. (1966), *Arch. Biochem. Biophys.*, **114**, 375.
Myer Y.P., Schellman J.A. (1962). *Biochim. Biophys. Acta*, **55**, 361.

Naber J.E., Schepman A.M.J., Rörsch A. (1965), *Biochim. Biophys. Acta*, **99**, 307.
Nabèr J.E., Schepman A.M.J., Rorsch A. (1966), *Biochim. Biophys. Acta*, **114**, 326.
Nair K.G. (1966), *Biochemistry*, **5**, 150.
Neale F.C., Clubb J.S., Hotchkis D., Posen S. (1965), *J. Clin. Pathol.*, **18**, 359.
Nelson C.A., Hummel J.P. (1962a), *J. Biol. Chem.*, **237**, 1567.
Neu H.C., Heppel L.A. (1964a), *J. Biol. Chem.*, **239**, 2927.
Neu H.C., Heppel L.A. (1964b), *Proc. Nat. Acad. Sci. U.S.*, **51**, 1267.
Neurath H., Dixon G.H., Pechere J.F. (1960), in *Proteins*, Proc. 4th Int. Congress of Biochemistry Vienna, Symposium n°. VIII, p. 63. London, Pergamon Press.
Nichols J.L., Lane B.G. (1966), *Biochim. Biophys. Acta*, **119**, 649.
Nihei T., Cantoni G.L. (1963), *J. Biol. Chem.*, **238**, 3991.
Nikol'skaya I.I., Kislina O.S., Salina N.M., Tikhonenko T.I. (1965), *Biokhimiya*, **30**, 1236.
Nikolskaya I.I., Shalina N.M., Budovski E.I. (1963), *Biokhimiya*, **28**, 759.
Nikolskaya I.I., Shalina N.M., Tikhonenko T.I. (1964), *Biochem. Biophys. Res. Comm.*, **91**, 354.
Nilsson R., Sjunnesson M. (1961), *Acta Chem. Scand.*, **15**, 1017.
Nirenberg M.W., Jones O.W., Leder P., Clark B.F.C., Sly W.S., PestPa S.. (1963), Cold Spring Harbor Symp. Quant. Biol., **28**, 549.
Nirenberg M.W., Leder P. (1964), *Science*, **145**, 1399.
Nirenberg M.W., Leder P., Bernfield M., Brimacombe R., Trupin J., Rottman F., O'Neal C. (1965), *Proc. Nat. Acad. Sci. U.S.*, **53**, 1161.
Nirenberg M.W., Matthaei J.H. (1961), *Proc. Nat. Acad. Sci. U.S.*, **47**, 1588.
Nirenberg M.W., Matthaei J.H., Jones O.W. (1962), *Proc. Nat. Acad. Sci. U.S.*, **48**, 104.
Nishimura S. (1960), *Biochim. Biophys. Acta*, **45**, 15.
Nishimura S., Jacob T.M., Khorana H.G. (1964), *Proc. Nat. Acad. Sci. U.S.*, **52**, 1494.
Nishimura S., Novelli G.D. (1965), *Proc. Nat. Acad. Sci. U.S.*, **53**, 178.
Nishimura S., Ozawa H. (1962), *Biochim. Biophys. Acta*, **55**, 421.
Niyogi S.K., Stevens A. (1965a), *J. Biol. Chem.*, **240**, 2587.
Niyogi S.K., Stevens A. (1965b), *J. Biol. Chem.*, **240**, 2593.

NORTHROP J.H., KUNITZ M., HERRIOTT R.M. (1948), *Crystalline Enzymes*, New York, Columbia University Press.
NYC J.F., KACHER R.J., CROCKEN B.J. (1966), *J. Biol. Chem.*, **241**, 1468.

OCHOA S. (1957a), *Arch. Biochem. Biophys.*, **69**, 119.
OCHOA S. 1957b), *Special Publications*, vol. 5, N.Y., Acad. Sci., p. 191.
OCHOA S. (1964a), *Bull. N.Y. Acad. Med.*, 2nd ser., **40** [5], 387.
OCHOA S. (1964b), *Experientia*, **20**, 57.
OCHOA S., Mii S. (1961), *J. Biol. Chem.*, **236**, 3303.
OGUR M., ROSEN G. (1950), *Arch. Biochem. Biophys.*, **25**, 262.
OHSAKA A., MUKAI J.I. LASKOWSKI M., (1964), *J. Biol. Chem.*, **239**, 3498.
OKADA S. (1957 a), *Arch. Biochem. Biophys.*, **67**, 95.
OKADA S. (1957 b), *Arch. Biochem. Biophys.*, **67**, 102.
OKADA S. (1957 c), *Arch. Biochem. Biophys.*, **67**, 113.
OKADA S., FLETCHER G.L. (1959), *Radiation Res.*, **13**, 92.
OKADA S., FLETCHER G.L. (1961), *Radiation Res.*, **15**, 452.
OKADA S., GEHRMANN G. (1957), *Biochim. Biophys. Acta*, **25**, 179.
OKAZAKI R., OKAZAKI T., SAKABE K. (1966), *Biochem. Biophys. Res. Commun.*, **22**, Nr. 6, 611.   b
OLESSON A.E., KOERNER J.F. (1964), *J. Biol. Chem.*, **239**, 2935.
OLMSTED P.S. (1957), *Fed. Proc.*, **16**, 229.
OLMSTED P.S., LOWE G.L. (1959 a), *J. Biol. Chem.*, **234**, 2965.
OLMSTED P.S., LOWE G.L. (1959 b), *J. Biol. Chem.*, **234**, 2971.
OOI T., RUPLEY J.A., SCHERAGA H.A. (1963), *Biochemistty*, **2**, 432.
OOI T., SCHERAGA H.A. (1964), *Biochemistry*, **3**, 641.
OSOWIECKI H., DOBRZANSKI W.T. (1963), *Bull. Acad. Pol. Sci.*, Cl. II, **11**, [2], 85.
OSOWIECKI H., PAKULA R. (1962), *Med. Doswiadczalna Mikrobiol.*, **14**, 173.
OSOWIECKI H., PAKULA R. (1963), *Med. Doswiadczalna Mikrobiol.*, **15**, [1], L-11.
OSTER G., DOTY P.M., ZIMM B.H. (1947), *J. Am. Chem. Soc.*, **69**, 1193.
OSTROWSKI W. (1961), *Experientia*, **17**, 398.
OSTROWSKI W., RYBARSKA J. (1965), *Biochim. Biophys. Acta*, **105**, 196.
OTAKA E., MITSUI H., OSAWA S. (1962), *Proc. Nat. Acad. Sci. U.S.*, **48**, 425.
OTAKA Y., UCHIDA K., SAKAI T. (1963), *J. Biochem. (Japan)*, **54**, 322.
OTH A., FREDERICQ E., HACHA R. (1958), *Biochim. Biophys. Acta*, **29**, 287.

PAOLETTI C., ORTH G., BOIRON M., LAMONTHEZIE N., ATANASIU P. (1963), *Ann. Inst. Pasteur*, **104**, 717.
PARSONS C.H., Jr. (1953), *Arch. Biochem. Biophys.*, **47**, 76.
PARVIN R., PANDE S.V. (1964), *Experientia*, **20**, 671.
PAULING L., COREY R.B. (1953 a), *Nature*, **171**, 346.
PAULING L., COREY R.B. (1953 b), *Proc. Nat. Acad. Sci. U.S.*, **39**, 84.
PAUWELS G. (1965), *Analyt. Biochem.*, **10**, 208.
PENSWICK J.R., HOLLEY R.W. (1965), *Proc. Nat. Acad. Sci. U.S.*, **53**, 543.
PETERSEN G.B. (1963), *Biochem. J.*, **87**, 495.
PETERSEN G.B., BURTON K. (1964), *Biochem. J.*, **92**, 606.
PETERSON E.A., SOBER H.A. (1956), *J. Am. Chem. Soc.*, **78**, 751.
PFLEIDERER G., ORTANDER F. (1963), *Biochem. Z.*, **337**, 431.
PICHAT L., DUFAY P., LAMORRE Y. (1964), *Compt. rend.*, **259**, 2433.
PIERPOINT W.S. (1956), *Biochim. Biophys. Acta*, **21**, 136.
PISKALA A., CIHAK A., VESELY J. (1964), *Experientia*, **20**, 202.
PISKALA A., ŠORM F. (1964), *Coll. Czech. Chem. Comm.*, **29**, 2060.
PLOTCH S., LUKTON A. (1965), *Biochim. Biophys. Acta*, **99**, 181.
PLUMMER T.H., Jr., HIRS C.H.W. (1963), *J. Biol. Chem.*, **238**, 1396.
PLUMMER T.H., Jr., HIRS C.H.W. (1964), *J. Biol. Chem.*, **239**, 2530.
PLUS N. (1962), *Compt. Rend.*, **255**, 3247.
PLUS N. (1963), *Biochim. Biophys. Acta*, **72**, 93.

POCHON F. (1960), *Contribution à l'étude des propriétés de la désoxyribonucléase de* S. pyogenes, doct. thesis, Hermann Paris.

POCHON F., MASSOULIÉ J., MICHELSON A.M. (1965), *Compt. rend.*, **260**, 2937.

POCHON F., MICHELSON A.M. (1965), *Proc. Nat. Acad. Sci. U.S.*, **53**, 1425.

POCHON F., MICHELSON A.M., GRUNBERG-MANAGO M., COHN W.E., Dondon L. (1964), *Biochim. Biophys. Acta*, **80**, 441.

POCHON F., PRIVAT DE GARILHE M. (1959), unpublished observations.

POCHON F., PRIVAT DE GARILHE M. (1960), *Bull. Soc. Chim. Biol.*, **42**, 795.

POGGIOLINI D. (1962*a*), *Nuovi Ann. Igiene Microbiol.*, **13**, 335.

POGGIOLINI D. (1962*b*), *Nuovi Ann. Igiene Microbiol.*, **13**, 340.

POKROWSKII V.N. (1964), *Zh. Mikrobiol. Epidemol. i Immunol.*, **41**, 92.

POLLI E., CORNEO G., GINELLI E., BIANCHI P. (1965), *Biochim. Biophys. Acta*, **103**, 672.

POLLISTER A.W. (1950), *Rev. Hematol.*, **5**, 527.

POLLISTER A.W. (1952 *a*), *Lab. Investigation*, **1**, 106.

POLLISTER A.W. (1952 *b*), *Lab. Investigation*, **1**, 231.

POLLISTER A.W., HIMÈS M., ORNSTEIN L. (1951), *Fed. Proc.*, **10**, 629.

POLLISTER A.W., MIRSKY A.E. (1946), *J. Gen. Physiol.*, **30**, 101.

POLLISTER A.W., SWIFT H., ALFERT M. (1951), *J. Cell. Comp. Physiol.*, **38**, suppl. 1, 101.

PORTMANN P. (1957), *Z. Physiol. Chem.*, **309**, 87.

PORTOCALÀ R., POPA L., SAMUEL I., MORFEI A., LĂCĂTUS V. (1964), *Rev. Roum. Inframicrobiol.*, **1**, 213.

POTTER J.L., FELIX F., LASKOWSKI M. (1959), *Fed. Proc.*, **18** [1], 304.

POTTER J.L., LASKOWSKI M. (1959), *J. Biol. Chem.*, **234**, 1263.

POTTER J.L., LAURILA U.R., LASKOWSKI M. (1958), *J. Biol. Chem.*, **233**, 915.

POTTS J.T., BERGER A., COOKE J., ANFINSEN C.B. (1962), *J. Biol. Chem.*, **237**, 1851.

POTTS J.T., YOUNG D.M., ANFINSEN C.B. (1963), *J. Biol. Chem.*, **238**, PC 2593.

POTTS J.T., YOUNG D.M., ANFINSEN C.B., SANDOVAL A. (1964), *J. Biol. Chem.*, **239**, 3781.

POUYET J., HERMANS J., Jr., VENDRELY R. (1956), *Trans. Farad. Soc.*, **53**, 247 (1957) [cf. Chem. Abs., **51**, 12168 *b*].

PRE J., BOIGNE J.M. (1966), *Path. Biol.*, **14**, 386.

PREECE I.A., McCALLUM D.J. (1964), *Am. Soc. Brewing Chemists Proc.*, 103.

PRICE T.D., HINDS H.A., BROWN R.S. (1963), *J. Biol. Chem.*, **238**, 311.

PRIVAT DE GARILHE M. (1958-1962), unpublished experiments.

PRIVAT DE GARILHE M. (1961), *Path. Biol. Sem. Hôp. Paris*, **9**, 129.

PRIVAT DE GARILHE M. (1964), *Les Nucleases*, Hermann, Paris.

PRIVAT DE GARILHE M., CUNNINGHAM L., LAURILA U.R., LASKOWSKI M. (1957), *J. Biol. Chem.*, **224**, 751.

PRIVAT DE GARILHE M., FASSINA G., POCHON P., PILLET J. (1958), *Bull. Soc. Chim. Biol.*, **40**, 1905.

PRIVAT DE GARILHE M., LASKOWSKI M. (1954), *Biochim. Biophys. Acta*, **14**, 147.

PRIVAT DE GARILHE M., LASKOWSKI M. (1955 *a*), *Biochim. Biophys. Acta*, **18**, 370.

PRIVAT DE GARILHE M., LASKOWSKI M. (1955 *b*), *J. Biol. Chem.*, **215**, 269.

PRIVAT DE GARILHE M., LASKOWSKI M. (1956), *J. Biol. Chem.*, **223**, 661.

PRUSOFF W.H. (1959), *Biochim. Biophys. Acta*, **32**, 295.

PRUSOFF W.H. (1960), *Biochim. Biophys. Acta*, **39**, 327.

PRUSOFF W.H., BAKHLE Y.S., McCREA J.F. (1963), *Nature*, **199**, 1310.

PRUSOFF W.H., CRAMER J.W., CHU M.Y., WELCH A.D. (1961), *Biochem. Pharmacol.*, **8**, 324.

PRUSOFF W.H., HOLMES W.L., WELCH A.D. (1953), *Cancer Research*, **13**, 221.

PRYSTAŠ M., ŠORM F. (1965), *Coll. Czech. Chem. Comm.*, **30**, 537.

PULLMAN A., PULLMAN B. (1961), *Proc. Am. Reunion Soc. Chim. Phys.*, **11**, 28.

RABIN B.R., MATHIAS A.P. (1964), *Colloq. Ges. Physiol. Chem.*, **14**, 97.

RABINOVITCH M., DOHI S.R. (1957), *Arch. Biochem. Biophys.*, **70**, 239.

RABINOVITZ M., OLSON M.E. (1957), *Fed. Proc.*, **16**, 235.

RADDING C.M., KORNBERG A. (1962), *J. Biol. Chem.*, **237**, 2877.

RADDING C.M., JOSSE J., KORNBERG A. (1962), *J. Biol. Chem.*, **237**, 2869.

RAHMAN Y.E. (1966), *Biochim. Biophys. Acta*, **119**, 470.

RAHN R.O. (1966), *Science*, **154**, 503.

RAJBHANDARY U.L., STUART A. (1966), *Ann. Rev. Biochem.*, **35**, 758.

RAJBHANDARY U.L., YOUNG R.J., KHORANA H.G. (1964), *J. Biol. Chem.*. **239**, 3875.

RALPH R.K., SMITH R.A., KHORANA H.G. (1962), *Biochemistry*, **1**, 131.

RALPH R.K., MATTHEWS R.E.F., MATUS A.I., MANDEL H.G. (1965), *J. Mol. Biol.*, **11**, 202.

RANDERATH E., RANDERATH K. (1964), *J. Chromatog.*, **16**, 126.

RANDERATH K. (1961 *a*), *Angew. Chem.*, **73**, 436.

RANDERATH K. (1961 *b*), *Angew. Chem.*, **73**, 674.

RANDERATH K. (1962 *a*), *Biochem. Biophys. Res. Comm.*, **6**, 452.

RANDERATH K. (1962 *b*), *Nature*, **194**, 768.

RANDERATH K. (1962*c*), *Biochim. Biophys. Acta*, **61**, 852.

RANDERATH K. (1963), *Biochim. Biophys. Acta*, **76**, 622.

RANDERATH K. (1964), *Experientia*, **20**, 406.

RANDERATH K., RANDERATH E. (1964), *J. Chromatog.*, **16**, 111.

RAZZELL W.E. (1961*a*), *Biochim. Biophys. Acta*, **236**, 3209.

RAZZELL W.E. (1961 *b*), *J. Biol. Chem.*, **236**, 3031.

RAZZELL W.E. (1966), *Biochem. Biophys. Res. Commun.*, **22**, 243.

RAZZELL W.E., KHORANA H.G. (1958), *J. Am. Chem. Soc.*, **80**, 1770.

RAZZELL W.E., KHORANA H.G. (1959 *a*), *J. Biol. Chem.*, **234**, 2105.

RAZZELL W.E., KHORANA H.G. (1959 *b*), *J. Biol. Chem.*, **234**, 2114.

RAZZELL W.E., KHORANA H.G. (1961), *J. Biol. Chem.*, **236**, 1144.

REDDI K.K. (1958), *Nature*, **182**, 1308.

REDDI K.K. (1959), *Biochim. Biophys. Acta*, **36**, 132.

REDFIELD R.R., ANFINSEN C.B. (1956), *J. Biol. Chem.*, **221**, 385.

REICHARD P. (1958), *Acta. Chem. Scand.*, **12**, 2048.

REICHMANN M.E., REES M.W., SYMONS R.H., MARKHAM R. (1962), *Nature*, **195**, 999.

REICHMANN M.E., RICE S.A., THOMAS C.A., DOTY P. (1954), *J. Am. Chem. Soc.*, **76**, 3047.

REICHMANN M.E., VARIN R., DOTY P. (1952), *J. Am. Chem. Soc.*, **74**, 3203.

REID E., EL-ASER A.B.A., TURNER M.K. (1964), *Z. Physiol. Chem.*, **339**, 135.

REID E., NODES J.T. (1959), *Ann. N.Y. Acad. Sci.*, **81**, 618.

REIST E.J., BENITEZ A., GOODMAN L., BAKER B.R., LEE W.W. (1962), *J. Org. Chem.*, **27**, 3274.

REIST E.J., GOODMAN L. (1964), *Biochemistry*, **3**, 15.

RENDI R., OCHOA S. (1962), *J. Biol. Chem.*, **237**, 3707.

RENIS H.E., JOHNSON A.G. (1962), *Bact. Proc.*, p. 140.

RESSLER N., OLIVERO E., THOMPSON G.R., JOSEPH R.R. (1965), *Clin. Chem.*, **11**, Nr. 8, 796.

RICE W.E. (1963), *J. Theoret. Biol.*, **4**, 260.

RICH A., DAVIES D.R., CRICK F.H.C., WATSON J.D. (1961). (1961), *J. Mol. Biol.*, **3**, 71.

RICH A., WARNER J.R., GOODMAN H.M. (1963), Cold Spring Harbor Symp., Quant. Biol., **28**, 269.

RICHARDS F.M. (1958), *Proc. Nat. Acad. Sci. U.S.*, **44**, 162.

RICHARDS G.M., du VAIR G., LASKOWSKI M. (1965), *Biochemistry*, **4**, 501.

RICHARDS G.M., du VAIR G., LASKOWSKI M. (1965), *Fed. Proc.*, **24**, 227.

RICHARDSON C.C., KORNBERG A. (1964), *J. Biol. Chem.*, **239**, 242.

RICHARDSON C.C., LEHMAN I.R., KORNBERG A. (1964), *J. Biol. Chem.*, **239**, 251.

RICHARDSON C.C., SCHILDKRAUT C.L., KORNBERG A. (1963), Cold Spring Harbor Symp. Quant. Biol. **28**, 9.

RICHTER G., SENGER H. (1965), *Biochim. Biophys. Acta*, **95**, 362.

RIEHM J.P., BROOMFIELD C.A., SCHERAGA H.A. (1965), *Biochemistry*, **4**, 760.

RIEHM J.P., SCHERAGA H.A. (1965), *Biochemistry* **4**, 772.

RIEHM J.P., SCHERAGA H.A. (1966*a*), *Biochemistry*, **5**, 93.

RIEHM J.P., SCHERAGA H.A. (1966 *b*), *Biochemistry*, **5**, 99.

RIOU G., JACQUEMIN-SABLON A., TRUHAUT R. (1966), *Bull. Soc. Chim. Biol.*, **48**, 53.

RIS H., CHANDLER B.L. (1963), Cold Spring Harbor Symp. Quant. Biol., **28**, 1.

RIS H., CHANDLER B.L. (1963), *Symp. Quant. Biol.*, **28**, 1.
RIS H., MIRSKY A.E. (1949), *J. Gen. Physiol.*, **38**, 125.
RISEBROUGH R.W., TISSIÈRES A., WATSON J.D. (1962), *Proc. Nat. Acad. Sci. U.S.*, **48**, 430.
RITTER F.J., MEYER G.M. (1962), *Nature*, **193**, 941.
ROBERTS W.K., DEKKER C.A., RUSHIZKY G.W., KNIGHT C.A. (1962), *Biochim. Biophys. Acta*, **55**, 664.
ROBINSON W.S., PITKANEN A., RUBIN H. (1965), *Proc. Nat. Acad. Sci. U.S.*, **54**, 137.
RÖSCHENTHALER R., FROMAGEOT P. (1965), *J. Mol. Biol.*, **11**, 458.
ROSENKRANZ H.S., BENDICH A.J., BEISER S.M. (1963), *Biochim. Biophys. Acta*, **77**, 43o.
ROSENTHAL S., RAPOPORT S.M., HEINEMANN G. (1964), *Acta Biol. Med. Ges.*, **13**, 946.
ROSS C.A., MATHIAS A.P., RABIN B.R. (1962), *Biochem. J.*, **85**, 145.
ROSSIER R., PORTMANN P. (1964), *Helv. Physiol. Pharmacol. Acta.*, **22**, 285.
ROTH J.S. (1954), *J. Biol. Chem.*, **208**, 181.
ROTH J.S. (1957), *J. Biol. Chem.*, **227**, 591.
ROTH J.S. (1959), *Ann. N.Y. Acad. Sci.*, **81**, Art. 3, p. 511.
ROTH J.S. (1962), *Biochim. Biophys. Acta*, **61**, 903.
ROTHBERG N.W., SWARTZ M.N. (1965), *J. Bacteriol.*, **90**, 294.
ROWEN J.W., NORMAN A. (1954), *Arch. Biochem. Biophys.*, **51**, 524.
ROWND R., LANYI J., DOTY P. (1961), *Biochim. Biophys. Acta*, **53**, 225.
RUSHIZKY G.W., BARTOS E.M., SOBER H.A. (1964), *Biochemistry*, **3**, 629.
RUSHIZKY G.W., GRECO A.E., HARTLEY R.W., Jr., SOBER H.A. (1963), *Biochemistry*, **2** 787.
RUSHIZKY G.W., KNIGHT C.A., ROBERTS W.K., DEKKER C.A. (1960), *Biochem. Biophys. Res. Comm.*, **2**, 153.
RUSHIZKY G.W., KNIGHT C.A., ROBERTS W.K., DEKKER C.A. (1962), *Biochim. Biophys Acta*, **55**, 674.
RUSHIZKY G.W., KNIGHT C.A., SOBER H.A. (1961), *J. Biol. Chem.*, **236**, 2732.
RUSHIZKY G.W., SOBER H.A. (1962), *J. Biol. Chem.*, **237**, 834.
RUSHIZKY G.W., SOBER H.A. (1963), *J. Biol. Chem.*, **238**, 371.
RUSHIZKY G.W., SOBER H.A. (1965), *Biochem. Biophys. Res. Comm.*, **18**, 489.
RUSSELL A.P., PATT D.I., TERNER C. (1964), *J. Cell. Comp. Physiol.*, **63**, 71.
RUSSELL W.C. (1962), *Virology*, **16**, 355.
RUSSELL W.C., CRAWFORD L.V. (1963), *Virology*, **21**, 353.
RUSSELL W.C., CRAWFORD L.V. (1964), *Virology*, **22**, 288.

SADRON C. (1961), *J. Chim. Phys.*, **58**, 877.
SADRON C., POUYET J. (1958-1959), in *Physical Chemistry of High Polymers of Biological Interest*. Ed. by O. Kratky, Symp. n°. IX., p. 52, 4th Int. Congress of Biochemistry, Vienna, Sep. 1-6 1958, published 1959 by Pergamon Press, London.
SADRON C., POUYET J., VENDRELY R. (1957), *Nature*, **179**, 263.
SALMON J. (1952), *Compt. rend. Soc. Biol.*, **146**, 792.
SANGER F. (1945), *Biochem. J.*, **39**, 507.
SANGER F. (1949), *Biochem. J.*, **44**, 126.
SANGER F., TUPPY H. (1951 a), *Biochem. J.*, **49**, 463.
SANGER F., TUPPY H. (1951 b), *Biochem. J.*, **49**, 481.
SATO K., EGAMI F. (1957), *J. Biochem. (Japan)*, **44**, 753.
SATO-ASANO K., EGAMI F. (1958), *Biochim. Biophys. Acta*, **29**, 655.
SATO-ASANO K., EGAMI F. (1960), *Nature*, **185**, 462.
SCHACHMANN H.K., WILLIAMS R.C. (1959), in *The Viruses*, vol. 1, p. 223. Ed. by Burnett F.M., Stanley W.M., New York, Academic Press.
SCHÄFER W. (1959), in *The Viruses*, vol. 1, p. 485. Ed. by Burnett F.M., Stanley W.M., New York, Academic Press.
SCHALLER H., KHORANA H.G. (1963a), *J. Am. Chem. Soc.*, **85**, 3828.
SCHALLER H., KHORANA H.G. (1963b), *J. Am. Chem. Soc.*, **85**, 3841.
SCHALLER H., WEIMANN G., LERCH B., KHORANA H.G. (1963), *J. Am. Chem. Soc.*, **85**, 3821.
SCHERAGA H.A. (1960), *J. Am. Chem. Soc.*, **82**, 3847.
SCHERAGE H.A., RUPLEY J.A. (1962), *Adv. in Enzymol.*, **24**, 161.

SCHILDKRAUT C.L., MARMUR J., DOTY P. (1961), *J. Mol. Biol.*, **3**, 595.
SCHILDKRAUT C.L., MARMUR J., FRESCO J.R., DOTY P. (1961), *J. Biol. Chem.*, 236, PC3.
SCHILDKRAUT C.L., SCHERAGA H.A. (1960), *J. Am. Chem. Soc.*, **82**, 58.
SCHLENK F. (1942), *J. Biol. Chem.*, **146**, 619.
SCHLESINGER M.J. (1964), *U.S. At. Energy Comm. BNL-869* (C-40), 66.
SCHLESINGER M.J. (1965 a), *Brookhaven Symp. Biol.*, **17**, 66.
SCHLESINGER M.J. (1965 b), *J. Biol. Chem.*, **240**, 4293.
SCHLESINGER M.J., BARRETT K. (1965), *J. Biol. Chem.*, **240**, 4284.
SCHMIDT G. (1955 a), in *Methods in Enzymology*, vol. 11, p. 523. Ed. by Colowick S.P., Kaplan N.O., New York, Academic Press.
SCHMIDT G. (1955 b), in *The Nucleic Acids*, vol. 1, p. 555. Ed. by Chargaff E., Davidson J.N., New York, Academic Press.
SCHMIDT G. (1957), in *Methods in Enzymology*, vol. III, p. 671. Ed. by Colowick S.P., Kaplan N.O., New York, Academic Press.
SCHMIDT G., CUBILES R., ZOLLNER N., HECHT L., STRICKLER N., SERAIDARIAN K., SERAIDARIAN M., THANNHAUSER S.J. (1951), *J. Biol. Chem.*, **192**, 715.
SCHMIDT G., LASKOWSKI M. (1961), in *The Enzymes*, vol. V, p. 3. Ed. by Boyer P.D., Lardy H., Myrbäck K. New York, Academic Press.
SCHMIDT G., THANNHAUSER S.J. (1945), *J. Biol. Chem.*, **161**, 83.
SCHNEIDER W.C. (1945), *J. Biol. Chem.*, **161**, 293.
SCHRAMM G. (1959), in *Biochemistry of Viruses*, p. 1. Sympos. n°. VII of 4th International Congress of Biochemistry, Vienna 1958. Ed. by Brod E., Frisch-Niggemeyer W., London, Pergamon Press.
SCHRAMM G., GRÖTSCH H., POLLMANN W. (1962), *Angew. Chem.*, **74**, 53.
SCHRIER E.E., INGWALL R.T., SCHERAGA H.A. (1965), *J. Phys. Chem.*, **69**, 298.
SCHULMAN H.M., BONNER D.M. (1962), *Proc. Nat. Acad. Sci. U.S.*, **48**, 53.
SCHUSTER H. (1960), in *The Nucleic Acids*, vol. III, p. 245. Ed. by Chargaff E., Davidson J.N., New York, Academic Press.
SCHWANDER H., SIGNER R. (1950), *Helv. Chim. Acta*, **33**, 1521.
SCHWARTZ J.H. (1963), *Proc. Nat. Acad. Sci. U.S.*, **49**, 871.
SCHWARTZ J.H., CRESTIELD A.M., LIPMANN F. (1963), *Proc. Nat. Acad. Sci. U.S.*, **49**, 722.
SCHWARTZ M.K., BODANSKY O. (1965), *Proc. Am. Assoc. Cancer Res.*, **6**, 56.
SCHWEIGER H.G. (1966), *Planta*, 68, 247.
SCOTT R.A., SCHERAGA H.A. (1963), *J. Am. Chem. Soc.*, **85**, 3866.
SEDAT J.W., HALL J.B. (1965), *J. Mol. Biol.*, **12**, 174.
SEDAT J.W., SINSHEIMER R. (1964), *J. Mol. Biol.*, **9**, 489.
SELA M., ANFINSEN C.B. (1957), *Biochim. Biophys. Acta*, **24**, 229.
SELA M., ANFINSEN C.B., HARRINGTON W.F. (1957), *Biochim. Biophys. Acta*, **26**, 502.
SEMENZA G. (1957), *Arkiv. Kemi*, **11**, 89.
SEVAG M.G., LACKMAN D.B., SMOLENS J. (1938), *J. Biol. Chem.*, **124**, 425.
SHACK J., BYNUM B.S. (1964), *J. Biol. Chem.*, **239**, 3843.
SHAPIRO H.S., CHARGAFF E. (1960), *Biochim. Biophys. Acta*, **39**, 62.
SHAPIRO H.S., CHARGAFF E. (1963), *Biochim. Biophys. Acta*, **76**, 1.
SHAPIRO H.S., CHARGAFF E. (1964), *Biochim. Biophys. Acta*, **91**, 262.
SHAPIRO H.S., RUDNER R., MIURA K.I., CHARGAFF E. (1965), *Nature*, **205**, 1068.
SHAPIRO R., GORDON C.N. (1964), *Biochem. Biophys. Res. Comm.*, **17**, 160.
SHEN T.Y., LEWIS H.M., RUYLE W.V. (1965), *J. Org. Chem.*, **30**, 835.
SHERWOOD L.M., POTTS J.T. (1965 a), *J. Biol. Chem.*, 240, 3799.
SHERWOOD L.M., POTTS J.T. (1965 b), *J. Biol. Chem.*, **240**, 3806.
SHIMOMURA M., LASKOWSKI M. (1957), *Biochim. Biophys. Acta*, **26**, 198.
SHIMIDATE T. (1961a), *Nippon Kagaku Zasshi*, **82**, 1268.
SHIMIDATE T. (1961b), *Nippon Kagaku Zasshi*, **82**, 1270.
SHIMIDATE T., ISHIDO Y., SATO T. (1961), *Nippon Kagaku Zasshi*, **82**, 938, [(1962), Chem. Abs., 57, 15216.]
SHIOBARA Y., HAGAKI K. (1963), *J. Biochem. (Japan)*, **54**, 317.
SHORT E.C., KOERNER J.F. (1965), *Proc. Nat. Acad. Sci. U.S.*, **54**, 595.

SHORTMAN K. (1961), *Biochim. Biophys. Acta*, **51**, 37.

SHORTMAN K., LEHMAN I.R. (1964), *J. Biol. Chem.*, **239**, 2964.

SHUGAR D. (1952), *Biochem. J.*, **52**, 142.

SHUGAR D. (1955), *Postepy Biochemii*, **4**, 64.

SHUGAR D., WIERZCHOWSKI K.L. (1958), *Bull. Acad. Polon. Sci.*, Cl. II, **6**, [7], 283.

SHUSTER L. (1957), *J. Biol. Chem.*, **229**, 289.

SHUSTER L., KAPLAN N.O. (1953), *J. Biol. Chem.*, **201**, 535.

SHUSTER L., KAPLAN N.O. (1955), in *Methods in Enzymology*, vol. II, p. 551. Ed. by Colowick S.P., Kaplan N.O., New York, Academic Press.

SHUSTER L., KHORANA H.G., HEPPEL L.A. (1959), *Biochim. Biophys. Acta*, **33**, 452.

SIBATANI A., KLOET S.R. de, ALLFREY V.G., MIRSKY A.E. (1962), *Proc. Nat. Acad. Sci. U.S.*, **48**, 471.

SIERAKOWSKA H., SHUGAR G. (1960), *Acta Biochimica Polonica*, **7**, 476.

SIERAKOWSKA H., ZAN-KOWALCZEWSKA M., SHUGAR D. (1965), *Biochem. Biophys. Res. Comm.*, **19**, 139.

SIGNER R., SCHWANDER H. (1949), *Helv. Chim. Acta*, **32**, 853.

SIGOT M., MANDEL P. (1957), *Compt. rend. Soc. Biol.*, **151**, 1244.

SINGER B., FRAENKEL-CONRAT H. (1963), *Biochim. Biophys. Acta*, **72**, 534.

SINGER B., FRAENKEL-CONRAT H. (1965), *Fed. Proc.*, **24**, 603.

SINGER B., SHERWOOD L.M., FRAENKEL-CONRAT H. (1965), *Biochim. Biophys. Acta*, **108**, 306.

SINGER M.F. (1963), *J. Biol. Chem.*, **238**, 336.

SINGER M.F., GUSS J.K. (1962), *J. Biol. Chem.*, **237**, 182.

SINGER M.F., HEPPEL L.A., HILMOE R.J. (1957), *Biochim. Biophys. Acta*, **26**, 447.

SINGER M.F., O'BRIEN B.M. (1963), *J. Biol. Chem.*, **238**, 328.

SINGER M.F., TOLBERT G. (1965), *Biochemistry*, **4**, 1319.

SINSHEIMER R.L. (1954), *J. Biol Chem.* **208**, 445.

SINSHEIMER R.L. (1955), *J. Biol. Chem.*, **215**, 579.

SINSHEIMER R.L. (1959), *J. Mol. Biol.*, **1**, 43.

SINSHEIMER R.L. (1960), in *The Nucleic Acids* vol. III p. 187. Ed. Chargaff E. Davidson J.N. New York, Academic Press.

SINSHEIMER R.L. (1961), *J. Chim. Phys.*, **58**, 989.

SINSHEIMER R.L., KOERNER J.F. (1951), *Science*, **114** 42.

SINSHEIMER R.L., KOERNER J.F. (1952 *a*), *J. Am. Chem. Soc.*, **74**, 283.

SINSHEIMER R.L., KOERNER J.F. (1952 *b*) *J. Biol. Chem.*, **198**, 293.

SINSHEIMER R.L., STARMAN B., NAGLER C., GUTHRIE S. (1962), *J. Mol., Biol.* **4**, 142.

SLOBODIAN E., FLEISHER M., NEWMAN W., RUBENFELD S. (1965), *Abstr. Papers Am. Chem. Soc. Nr.* 150, 91 C.

SLOBODIAN E., NEWMAN W., FLEISHER M., RUBENFELD S. (1965), *Biochim. Biophys. Acta*, **111**, 181.

SLOR H., HODES M.E. (1965), *Fed. Proc.*, **24**, 227.

SMELLIE R.M.S., McARDLE A.H., KEIR H.M., DAVIDSON J.N. (1958), *Biochem. J.*, **69**, 37P.

SMITH A.D., WINKLER H. (1965), *Nature*, **207**, 634.

SMITH C.J., HERBERT E. (1966), *Biochemistry*, **5**, 1333.

SMITH C.J., SMITH P.M., HERBERT E. (1966), *Biochemistry*, **5**, 1323.

SMITH J.D. (1955), in *The Nucleic Acids*, vol. 1, p. 267. Ed. by Chargaff E., Davidson H.N., New York, Academic Press.

SMITH J.D. (1964), *J. Mol. Biol.*, **8**, 772.

SMITH J.D., DUNN D.B. (1959 *a*), *Biochem. J.*, **72**, 294.

SMITH J.D., DUNN D.B. (1959 *b*), *Biochim. Biophys. Acta*, **31**, 573.

SMITH J.D., MARKHAM R. (1952), *Nature*, **170**, 120.

SMITH J.D., WYATT G.R. (1951), *Biochem. J.*, **49**, 144.

SMITH K.C. (1965), *Fed. Proc.*, **24**, 292.

SMITH M., RAMMLER D.H., GOLDBERG I.H., KHORANA H.G. (1961), *J. Am. Chem. Soc.*, **84**, 430.

SMRT J. (1964), *Coll. Czech. Chem. Comm.*, **29**, 2049.

SMRT J., ŠORM F. (1964), *Coll. Czech. Chem. Comm.*, **29**, 2791.

SMYTH D.G., STEIN W.H., MOORE S. (1962), *J. Biol. Chem.*, **237**, 1845.

SMYTH D.G., STEIN W.H., MOORE S. (1963), *J. Biol. Chem.*, **238**, 227.

SOBER H.A., GUTTER F.J., WYCKOFF M.M., PETERSON E.A. (1956), *J. Am. Chem. Soc.*, **78**, 756.
SÖLL D., KHORANA H.G. (1965 a), *J. Am. Chem. Soc.*, **87**, 350.
SÖLL D., KHORANA H.G. (1965 b), *J. Am. Chem. Soc.*, **87**, 360.
SÖLL D., OHTSUKA E., JONES D.S. LOHRMANN R., HAYATSU H., NISHIMURA S., KHORANA H.G. (1965), *Proc. Natl. Acad. Sci.* (U.S.), **54**, 1378.
SOMBERG E.W., DAVIS F.F. (1965), *Biochim. Biophys. Acta*, **108**, 137.
SPACKMAN D.H., STEIN W.H., MOORE S. (1960), *J. Biol. Chem.*, **235**, 648.
SPAHR P.F. (1964), *J. Biol. Chem.*, **239**, 3716.
SPAHR P.F., SCHLESSINGER D. (1963), *J. Biol. Chem.*, **238**, 8.
SPENCER J.H., CHARGAFF E. (1961), *Biochim. Biophys. Acta*, **51**, 209.
SPENCER J.H., CHARGAFF E. (1963 a), *Biochim. Biophys. Acta*, **68**, 9.
SPENCER J.H., CHARGAFF E. (1963 b), *Biochim. Biophys. Acta*, **68**, 18.
SPENCER M., FULLER W., WILKINS M.H.F., BROWN G.L. (1962), *Nature* **194**, 1014.
SPENCER M., POOLE F. (1965), *J. Mol. Biol.*, **11**, 314.
SPEYER J.F., LENGYEL P., BASILIO C., OCHOA S. (1962 a), *Proc. Nat. Acad. Sci. U.S.*, **48**, 63.
SPEYER J.F., LENGYEL P., BASILIO C., OCHOA S. (1962 b), *Proc. Nat. Acad. Sci. U.S.*, **48**, 441.
SPIEGELMAN S. (1957), in *The Chemical Basis of Heredity*, p. 232. Ed. by McElroy W.D., Glass B., Baltimore. The Johns Hopkins Press.
SPIEGELMAN S., HALL B.D., STORCK R. (1961), *Proc. Nat. Acad. Sci. U.S.*, **47**, 1135.
ŠPONAR J., PIVEC L., MUNK P., ŠORMOVA Z. (1964), *Coll. Czech. Chem. Comm.*, **29**, 289.
ŠPONAR J., PIVEC L., ŠORMOVA Z. (1964), *Coll. Czech. Chem. Comm.*, **29**, 2077.
STAEHELIN M. (1961), *Helv. Physiol. Acta*, **19**, C30.
STAEHELIN M. (1964a), *Arch. Biochem. Biophys.*, **105**, 219.
STAEHELIN M. (1964b), *Biochim. Biophys. Acta*, **87**, 493.
STAEHELIN M. (1964c), *J. Mol. Biol.*, **8**, 470.
STAEHELIN M., PETERSON E.A., SOBER H.A. (1959), *Arch. Biochem. Biophys.*, **85**, 289.
STAEHELIN M., SCHWEIGER M., ZACHAU H.G. (1963), *Biochim. Biophys. Acta*, **68**, 129.
STAHL E. (1958), *Chemiker Z.*, **82**, 323.
STAPLES R.C., McCARTHY W.J., STAHLMANN (1965), *Science*, **149**, 1248.
STARK G.R., STEIN W.H. (1964), *J. Biol. Chem.*, **239**, 3755.
STAVY L., FELDMAN M., ELSON D. (1964), *Biochim. Biophys. Acta*, **91**, 606.
STEIN W.H. (1964), *Federation Proc.*, **23**, 599.
STEINSCHNEIDER A., FRAENKEL-CONRAT H. (1966 a), *Biochemistry*, **5**, 2729.
STEINSCHNEIDER A., FRAENKEL-CONRAT H. (1966 b), *Biochemistry*, **5**, 2735.
STEPHENSON M.L., ZAMÊCNIK P.C. (1961), *Proc. Nat. Acad. Sci. U.S.*, **47**, 1627.
STERLING R.E., WILCOX A.A., WARE A.G., UMEHARA M.K. (1964), *Clin. Chem.*, **10**, 1112.
STEVENS A., HILMOE R.J. (1960 a), *J. Biol. Chem.*, **235**, 3016.
STEVENS A., HILMOE R.J. (1960 b), *J. Biol. Chem.*, **235**, 3023.
STOCKX J., DIERICH W., VANDENDRIESSCHE L. (1964), *Arch. Int. Physiol. et Biochem.*, **72**, 647.
STOCKX J., VANDENDRIESSCHE L. (1961 a), *Arch. Int. Physiol. et Biochem.*, **69**, 493.
STOCKX J., VANDENDRIESSCHE L. (1961 b), *Arch. Int. Physiol. et Biochem.*, **69**, 521.
STOCKX J., VANDENDRIESSCHE L. (1961 c), *Arch. Int. Physiol. et Biochem.*, **69**, 545.
STOECKENIUS W. (1963), *Proc. Natl. Acad. Sci.*, **50**, 737.
STONE A.B., BURTON K. (1961 a), *Biochem. J.*, **81**, 2P.
STONE A.B., BURTON K. (1961 b), *Biochem. J.*, **81**, 3P.
STUART A., KHORANA H.G. (1964), *J. Biol. Chem.*, **239**, 3885.
STUY J.H. (1961), *Biochem. Biophys. Res. Comm.*, **6**, 328.
SUEOKA N., CHENG T.Y. (1962 a), *J. Mol. Biol.*, **4**, 161.
SUEOKA N., CHENG T.Y. (1962 b), *Proc. Nat. Acad. Sci. U.S.*, **48**, 1851.
SUEOKA N., YOSHIKAWA H. (1963), Cold Spring Harbor Symp. Quant. Biol., **28**, 47.
SUGIYAMA T., FRAENKEL-CONRAT H. (1961), *Proc. Nat. Acad. Sci. U.S.*, **47**, 1393.
SULKOWSKI E. (1963), personal communication.
SULKOWSKI E., BJÖRK W., LASKOWSKI M., Sr. (1963), *J. Biol. Chem.*, **238**, 2477.

SULKOWSKI E., LASKOWSKI M., Sr. (1962 a), *Fed. Proc.*, **21**, 373.
SULKOWSKI E., LASKOWSKI M., Sr. (1962 b), *J. Biol. Chem.*, **237**, 2620.
SULKOWSKI E., LASKOWSKI M. (1966), *J. Biol. Chem.*, **241**, 4386.
SUNG S.C., LASKOWSKI M., Sr. (1962), *J. Biol. Chem.*, **237**, 506.
SWIFT H. (1955), in *The Nucleic Acids*, vol. II, p. 51. Ed. by Chargaff E., Davidson J.N., New York, Academic Press.
SZAFRANSKI P., LUTOWICZ J., PUZYNSKA L. (1963), *Life Sci.*, **2**, 845.
SZAFRANSKI P., LUTOWICZ J., PUZINSKA L. (1964 a), *Abstracts of 6th International Congress of Biochemistry*, **1**, 193.
SZAFRANSKI P., LUTOWICZ J., PUZYNSKA L. (1964 b), *Acta Biochimica Polonica*, **11**, 71.
SZER W., SHUGAR D. (1961), *Acta. Biochem. Polonica.*, **8**, 235.

TAKAHASHI H. (1932), *J. Biochem. (Japan)*, **16**, 463.
TAKAHASHI K. (1965), *J. Biol. Chem.*, **240**, PC 4117.
TAKEI S. (1965), *Agr. Biol. Chem.* (Tokyo), **29**, 372.
TAKETO A., ONO M., SHIBUYA H. (1965), *J. Biochem. (Japan)*, **57**, 488.
TAL M., ELSON D. (1963), *Biochim. Biophys. Acta*, **76**, 40.
TAMM C., HODES M.E., CHARGAFF E. (1952), *J. Biol. Chem.*, **195**, 49.
TANAKA K., CANTONI G.L. (1963), *Biochim. Biophys. Acta*, **72**, 641.
TANFORD C., HAUENSTEIN J.D. (1956 a), *Biochim. Biophys. Acta*, **19**, 535.
TANFORD C., HAUENSTEIN J.D. (1956 b), *J. Am. Chem. Soc.*, **78**, 5287.
TANIUCHI H., ANFINSEN C.B. (1966), *J. Biol. Chem.*, **241**, 4366.
TANIUCHI H., ANFINSEN C.B., HEINS J., CARROLL W.R. (1965), *Fed. Proc.*, **24**, 288.
TAVERNE J., MARSHALL J.H., FULTON F. (1958), *J. Gen. Microbiol.*, **19**, 451.
TEMPEL K., ROESSNER W. (1965), *Arzneimittel-Forsch.*, **15**, 25.
TEMPEL K.H., ZIPF K. (1966), *Berlin. Muench. Tierärztl. Wochschr.*, **79**, 28.
TEMPERLI A., TÜRLER H., RÜST P., DANON A., CHARGAFF E. (1964), *Biochim. Biophys. Acta*, **91**, 462.
TENER G.M. (1961), *J. Am. Chem. Soc.*, **83**, 159.
TENER G.M., KHORANA H.G., MARKHAM R., POL E.H. (1958), *J. Am. Chem. Soc.*, **80**, 6223.
TERROINE T. (1961 a), *Arch. des Sci. Physiologiques*, **15**, 167.
TERROINE T. (1961 b), *Comp. rend.*, **252**, 3649.
THACH R.E., DOTY P. (1965a), *Science*, **147**, 1310.
THACH R.E., DOTY P. (1965b), *Science*, **148**, 632.
THANG M.N., GRAFFE M., GRUNBERG-MANAGO M. (1965), *Biochim. Biophys. Acta*, **108**, 125.
THIEBE R., ZACHAU H.G. (1965), *Biochim. Biophys. Acta*.
THOMAS C.A., Jr., BERNS K.I. (1961), *J. Mol. Biol.*, **3**, 277.
THOMAS C.A., MCHATTIE L.A. (1964), *Proc. Natl. Acad. Sci.*, **52**, 1297.
THOMSSEN R. (1965), *Arch. für die ges. Virusforschung*, **15**, 475.
TIKHONENKO T.I., ARTAMONOVA V.A., BUSHMARINA T.V. (1963), *Vopr. Med. Khim.*, **9**, 614.
TISELIUS A., HJERTEN S., LEVIN O. (1956), *Arch. Biochem. Biophys.*, **65**, 132.
TISSIÈRES A., HOPKINS J.W. (1961), *Proc. Nat. Acad. Sci. U.S.*, **47**, 2015.
TODD A.R. (1948), *Bull. Soc. Chim. France*, 933.
TODD A.R. (1951-1952), *Harvey Lectures*.
TODD A.R. (1954), *Proc. Roy. Soc. A.*, **226**, 70.
TOMLINSON N. (1958), *Can. J. Biochem. Biophys.*, **36**, 633.
TOMLINSON R.V., TENER G.M. (1963), *Biochemistry*, **2**, 703.
TONGUR V.S., VLADYCHENSKAYA N.S., ROMANOV V.V., VYSHEPAN E.D. (1964), *Byul. Eksp. Biol. i Med.*, **57**, 184.
TONINO G.J.M., STEYN-PARVÉ E.P. (1963), *Biochim. Biophys. Acta*, **67**, 453.
TORRIANI A. (1960), *Biochim. Biophys. Acta*, **36**, 460.
TRENTALANCE A., AMALDI F. (1965), *Nature*, **206**, 530.
TRILLING D.M., APOSHIAN H.V. (1965), *Proc. Nat. Acad. Sci. U.S.*, **54**, 622.
TRUPIN J.S., ROTTMAN F.M., BRIMACOMBE R.L.C., LEDER P., BERNFIELD M.R., NIRENBERG M.W. (1965), *Proc. Nat. Acad. Sci. U.S.*, **53**, 805.

Tsaney R. (1965), *Biochim. Biophys. Acta*, **103**, 374.
Tsou K.C., Su H.C.F. (1965), *Analyt. Biochem.*, **11**, 54.
Tsuboi K.K., Hudson P.B. (1955), *Arch. Biochem. Biophys.*, **55**, 206.
Tsuda V., Strauss B.P. (1964), *Biochemistry*, **3**, 1678.
Tsugita A., Fraenkel-Conrat H. (1963), in *Molecular Genetics*, Part I, p. 477, ed. by Taylor J.H., New York, Academic Press.
Tsugita A., Fraenkel-Conrat H., Nirenberg M.W., Matthaei J.H. (1962), *Proc. Nat. Acad. Sci. U.S.*, **48**, 846.

Ukita C., Tahahashi T., Waku K., Hoshino O. (1964), *J. Biochem.*, **55**, 293.
Ukita C., Terao T., Irie M. (1962), *J. Biochem.*, **52**, 455.
Underwood G.E. (1962), *Proc. Soc. Exp. Biol. Med.*, **111**, 93.
Underwood G.E. (1964), *3rd International Congress of Chemotherapy*, Stuttgart 1963, p. 858 Ed. by H.P. Kuemmerle and P. Preziosi. Stuttgart, Georg Thieme Verlag.
Uzawa S. (1932), *J. Biochem. (Japan)*, **15**, 19.

Vakulenko A.D., Shubich M.G. (1966), *Terapevt. Arkh.*, **38**, No 2, 66.
Vanecko S., Laskowski M. (1961 a), *J. Biol. Chem.*, **236**, 1135.
Vanecko S., Laskowski M. (1961 b), *J. Biol. Chem.*, **236**, 3312.
Vanecko S., Laskowski M., Sr. (1962), *Biochim. Biophys. Acta*, **61**, 547.
Vasilenko S.K., Babkina G.T. (1965), *Biokhimija*, **30**, 705.
Vecerek B., Kraml J., Pelichova H., Stepan J., Chmelar M., Stipek S. (1965), *Collection Czech.*, **30**, 3964.
Vendrely C. (1952), *Bull. Biol. France et Belge.*, **86**, 1.
Vendrely R. (1955), in *The Nucleic Acids*, vol. II, p. 155. Ed. by Chargaff E., Davidson J.N., New York, Academic Press.
Vendrely R., Vendrely C. (1956), *Int. rev. Cytology*, **5**, 171.
Venetianer P., Straub F.B. (1963), *Biochim. Biophys. Acta*, **67**, 166.
Venetianer P., Straub F.B. (1964), *Acta Biol. Med. Ges. Suppl.* **3**, 240.
Vernon C.A., Gauldie J., Hanson J.M., Humphreys J.M., Smith P.E., Lawrence A.J., Banks B.E.C. (1965), *Nature*, **208**, 382.
Vinograd, J., Lebowitz J., Radloff R., Watson R., Laipis P. (1965), *Proc. Natl. Acad. Sci.*, **53**, 1104.
Vischer E., Chargaff E. (1947), *J. Biol. Chem.*, **168**, 781.
Vischer E., Chargaff E. (1948 a), *J. Biol. Chem.*, **176**, 703.
Vischer E., Chargaff E. (1948 b), *J. Biol. Chem.*, **176**, 715.
Vischêr E., Zamenhof S., Chargaff E. (1949), *J. Biol. Chem.*, **177**, 429.
Volkin E. (1955), in *Methods in Enzymology*, vol. II, p. 539. Ed. by Colowick S.P., Kaplan N.O., New York, Academic Press.
Volkin E., Astrachan L. (1957), in *The Chemical Basis of Heredity*, p. 686. Ed. by McElroy W.D., Glass B. Baltimore, Johns Hopkins University Press.
Volkin E., Carter C.E. (1951), *J. Am. Chem. Soc.*, **73**, 1516.
Volkin E., Cohn W.E. (1953), *J. Biol. Chem.*, **205**, 767.
Volkin E., Khym J.X., Cohn W.E. (1951), *J. Am. Chem. Soc.*, **73**, 1533.

Wade H.E., Robinson H.K. (1965), *Biochem. J.*, **97**, 747.
Wahba A.J., Basilio C., Speyer J.F., Lengyel P., Miller R.S., Ochoa S. (1962), *Proc. Nat. Acad. Sci. U.S.*, **48**, 1683.
Wahba A.J., Gardner R.S., Basilio C., Miller R.S., Speyer J.F., Lengyel P. (1963), *Proc. Nat. Acad. Sci. U.S.*, **49**, 116.
Warner J.R., Knopf P.M., Rich A. (1963), *Proc. Nat. Acad. Sci. U.S.*, **49**, 122.
Warner R.C. (1957), *J. Biol. Chem.*, **229**, 711.
Watanabe I., Iso K. (1950 a), *J. Am. Chem. Soc.*, **72**, 4836.
Watanabe I., Iso K. (1950 b), *J. Chem. Soc. Japan.*, **71**, 280.
Watanabe I., Iso K. (1950 c), *Chem. Res. Inst. Tokyo Univ.*, **5**, 15.

WATSON J.D., CRICK F.H.C. (1953 a), *Nature*, **171**, 737.

WATSON J.D., CRICK F.H.C. (1953 b), *Nature*, **171**, 964.

WEBB M. (1952), *Nature*, **169**, 417.

WEBB M. (1953 a), *Exp. Cell. Res.*, **5**, 16.

WEBB M. (1953 b), *Exp. Cell. Res.*, **5**, 27.

WECKMAN B., CATLIN B.W. (1957), *J. Bact.*, **73**, 747.

WEIL R. (1961), *Virology*, **14**, 46.

WEILL J.D., MANDEL P., KAYSER C. (1957), *Bull. Soc. Chim. Biol.*, **39**, 1395.

WEIMANN G., KHORANA H.G. (1962), *J. Am. Chem. Soc.*, **84**, 419.

WEIMANN G., SCHALLER H., KHORANA H.G. (1963), *J. Am. Chem. Soc.*, **85**, 3835.

WEINSTEIN B., SCHECHTER A.N. (1962), *Proc. Nat. Acad. Sci. U.S.*, **48**, 1686.

WEISBLUM B., GONANO F., EHRENSTEIN G. von, BENZER S. (1965), *Proc. Nat. Acad. Sci. U.S.*, **53**, 328.

WEISBLUM B., BENZER S., HOLLEY R.W. (1962), *Proc. Nat. Acad. Sci. U.S.*, **48**, 1449.

WEISSBACH A., KORN D. (1963), *J. Biol. Chem.*, **238**, 3383.

WEISSMANN C., BILLETER M.A., SCHNEIDER M.C., KNIGHT C.A., OCHOA S. (1965), *Proc. Nat. Acad. Sci. U.S.*, **53**, 653.

WEILNER D., SILMAN H.I., SELA M. (1963), *J. Biol. Chem.*, **238**, 1324.

WHITE F.H., Jr., ANFINSEN C.B. (1959), *Ann. N.Y. Acad. Sci.*, **81**, 515.

WHITFELD P.R. (1954), *Biochem. J.*, **58**, 390.

WHITFELD P.R. (1962), *J. Biol. Chem.*, **237**, 2865.

WHITFELD P.R. (1965), *Biochim. Biophys. Acta*, **108**, 202.

WHITFELD P.R., HEPPEL L.A., MARKHAM R. (1955), *Biochem. J.*, **60**, 15

WHITFELD P.R., WITZEL H. (1963a), *Biochim. Biophys. Acta*, **72**, 338.

WHITFELD P.R., WITZEL H. (1963b), *Biochim. Biophys. Acta*, **72**, 362.

WILDY P., RUSSELL W.C., HORNE R.W. (1960), *Virology*, **12**, 204.

WILKINS M.H.F. (1961), *J. Chim. Phys.*, **58**, 891.

WILKINS M.H.F., RANDALL J.T. (1953), *Biochim. Biophys. Acta*, **10**, 192.

WILKINS M.H.F., STOKES A.R., WILSON H.R. (1953), *Nature*, **171**, 738.

WILLIAMS E.J., SUNG S.C., LASKOWSKI M. (1961), *J. Biol. Chem.*, **236**, 1130.

WILLIAMS F.R., GODEFROY T., MERY E., YON J., GRUNBERG-MANAGO M. (1964), *Biochim. Biophys. Acta*, **80**, 349.

WILLIAMS F.R., GRUNBERG-MANAGO M. (1964), *Biochim. Biophys. Acta*, **89**, 66.

WILLIAMS R.C., BAKUS R., STEERE R.L. (1951), *J. Am. Chem. Soc.*, **73**, 2062.

WILLIAMS R.C., STEERE R.L. (1951), *J. Am. Chem. Soc.*, **73**, 2057.

WILSON C.M. (1963a), *Biochim. Biophys. Acta* **68**, 177.

WILSON C.M. (1963b), *Biochim. Biophys. Acta*, **76**, 324.

WILSON C.M., SHANNON J.C. (1963), *Biochim. Biophys. Acta*, **68**, 311.

WINOCOUR E. (1963), *Virology*, **19**, 158.

WINSTEAD J.A., WOLD F. (1965), *J. Biol. Chem.*, **240**, PC 3694.

WINTER J.E., BERNHEIMER A.W. (1964), *J. Biol. Chem.*, **239**, 215.

WITZEL H. (1963), *Prog. in. Nucleic. Acid. Research.*, Vol. II., 221.

WITZEL H. (1964), *Colloq. Ges. Physiol. Chem.*, **14**, 123.

WITZEL H., BARNARD E.A. (1962), *Biochem. Biophys. Res. Communs.*, **7**, 289.

WOESE C.R. (1961a), *Biochem. Biophys. Res. Comm.*, **5**, 88.

WOESE C.R. (1961b), *Nature*, **190**, 697.

WOESE C.R. (1962), *General Electric Res. Lab. Repts.*, n°. 62 RL (2964 G), n°. 62RL (2989 G), n°. 62RL (2995 G). Schenectady, N.Y., U.S.A.

WOJNAR R.J. (1965), *Diss. Abs.*, **25**, 4395.

WROBLEWSKI F., BODANSKY O. (1950), *Proc. Soc. Exp. Biol. Med.*, **74**, 443.

WYATT G.R. (1951), *Biochem. J.*, **48**, 584.

WYATT G.R., COHEN S.S. (1952), *Nature*, **170**, 846.

WYATT G.R., COHEN S.S. (1953), *Biochem. J.*, **55**, 774.

YANG S.T., HUMMEL J.P. (1964), *J. Biol. Chem.*, **239**, 3775.

YASHINEH W., GRAY E.D., WANNAMAKER L.W. (1965), *Fed. Proc.*, **24**, 227.
YČAS M. (1960), *Nature*, **188**, 209.
YČAS M. (1961), *J. Theoret. Biol.*, **2**, 244.
YČAS M., VINCENT W.S. (1960), *Proc. Nat. Acad. Sci. U.S.*, **46**, 804.
YONEDA M. (1963), *Koso Kagaku Shinpojiumu*, **18**, 38.
YOSHIDA S. (1941), *J. Biochem. Japan*, **34**, 23.
YOUNG E.T.H., SHINHEIMER R.L. (1965), *J. Biol. Chem.*, **240**, 1274.
YOUNG M., POTTS J.T., Jr. (1965), *J. Biol. Chem.*, **238**, 1995.
YUNG N.C., BURCHENAL J.H., FECHER R., DUCHINSKY R., FOX J.J. (1961), *J. Am. Chem. Soc.*, **83**, 4060.

ZACHAU H.G., DÜTTING D., FELDMANN H. (1966), *Angew. Chem.*, **5**, 422.
ZAGURY D., POCHON P., PRIVAT DE GARILHE M. (1960), *Compt. rend.*, **250**, 196.
ZAHN R.K. (1959), *Nature*, **184**, 1324.
ZAHN R.K. (1960), *Biochem. J.*, **76**, 66P.
ZAMECNIK P.C., KELLER E.B. (1954), *J. Biol. Chem.*, **209**, 337.
ZAMENHOF S., BRAWERMAN G. CHARGAFF E. (1962) *Biochim. Biophys. Acta*, **9**, 402.
ZAMENHOF S., CHARGAFF E. (1948), *Science*, **108**, 628.
ZAMENHOF S., CHARGAFF E. (1949), *J. Biol. Chem.*, **180**, 727.
ZAMENHOF S., DE GIOVANNI R., RICH K. (1956), *J. Bact.*, **71**, 60.
ZAMIR A., HOLLEY R.W., MARQUISEE M. (1965), *J. Biol. Chem.*, **240**, 1267.
ZIMMÉRMAN S.B., SANDEEN G. (1966), *Analyt. Biochem.*, **14**, Nᵒ 2, 269.
ZITTLE C.A. (1946), *J. Biol. Chem.*, **163**, 111.
ZUBAY G. (1962), *J. Mol. Biol.*, **4**, 347.

Authors index

Berg P., 54, 79, 80.
Berger G., 255, 256.
Bergmann W., 25.
Bergquist P.L., 47.
Bernard J., 25.
Bernardi G., 143, 216, 242, 246, 247, 248, 249, 250, 253, 309, 317.
Bernfield M.R., 49, 61, 207.
Bernheimer A.W., 254, 321.
Berns K.I., 75, 119.
Bessman M.J., 103.
Bieth R., 156.
Birnboim H., 164, 307.
Björk W., 169, 266, 286, 307, 313, 323.
Bladen H.A., 81.
Blanchardière de la P., 229.
Blumenthal H.J., 290, 331.
Bock R.M., 45, 301.
Bodanski O., 282, 315, 325, 327.
Boigné J.M., 281.
Boiron M., 78.
Boivin A., 157.
Bollum F.J., 104, 241.
Boman H.G., 231, 263, 262.
Bonner D.M., 81.
Borkowska I., 81.
Bornstein D.L., 317.
Bové J.M., 90.
Brachet J., 41, 42, 75.
Bradbury E.M., 67, 131, 132.
Brandenberger H., 281.
Brawerman G., 63.
Breedis C., 150, 151.
Breese K., 203.
Brenner S., 51, 52, 150.
Bretscher M.S., 58.
Brink J.J., 25.
Brody S., 257.
Brookes P., 75.
Broomfield C.A., 194.
Brown D.M., 25, 39, 40, 41, 85, 86, 88, 89, 91, 203, 205, 297.
Brown G.L., 73, 74, 83.
Brown K.D., 116.
Bull H.B., 203.
Burke D.F., 25.
Burny A., 55.
Burton K., 34, 119, 120, 122, 254, 321.
Butler G.C., 27, 64, 65, 261, 285, 286, 323, 329.
Butler J.A.V., 75.
Bunce B.H., 73.
Butterworth P.J., 283, 327.
Bynum B.S., 242.
Byrne R., 81.

Cairns J., 75.
Campbell P.N., 51.
Cantoni G.L., 47, 227, 301, 302, 315.
Cardeilhac P.T., 90.
Carlsson K., 313.
Carpenter F.H., 182.
Carter C.E., 33, 37, 40, 135, 136, 226, 315.
Caspar D.L.D., 35.
Caspersson T., 41, 129, 157.
Catlin B.W., 116, 170, 171.
Cavalieri L.F., 75, 105.
Center M.S., 283, 284, 327.
Cha C.Y., 189, 194.
Chamberlin M., 79, 80.
Chambers R.W., 89.
Chandler B.L., 75.
Chang P.K., 25, 86.
Chapeville F., 50.
Chargaff E., 30, 32, 33, 35, 36, 58, 62, 63, 65, 66, 69, 70, 73, 106, 112, 115, 117, 119, 120, 122, 123, 124, 134, 139, 255, 321.
Cheng T.Y., 71, 105, 143, 144, 145, 149.
Chen-Pin Liu., 130.
Cherayil S.D., 45.
Cheung C.C.S., 208.
Chu M.Y., 25.
Chung H., 221.
Clark V.M., 88.
Coghill R.D., 33.
Cohen R.Z., 286, 329.
Cohen S.S., 21, 25, 33, 38, 65, 90.
Cohn W.E., 23, 25, 34, 40, 119, 120, 136, 137, 138, 161, 182, 204, 205, 292, 315.
Cole L.J., 104, 143.
Consden R., 134.
Cooper E.J., 255.
Corby N.S., 89.
Cordonnier C., 253.
Corey R.B., 64, 65.
Cowgill R.W., 201.
Coy U., 45, 114.
Craig L.C., 202, 213.
Cramer J.W., 25, 86.
Crampton C.G., 106.
Crawford L.V., 68.
Crestfield A.M., 112, 185, 186, 191, 193, 213.
Crick F.H.C., 34, 58, 65, 66, 67, 74, 120, 296, 297.
Crook E.M., 187, 208.
Cuigniez J., 220, 311.
Cunningham L., 116, 134, 140, 170, 171, 174, 179, 236, 307, 315, 329.
Curtis P.J., 307.

Subject index

IMPRIMÉ EN FRANCE — HÉRISSEY ÉVREUX
DÉPOT LÉGAL QUATRIÈME TRIMESTRE 1967
NUMÉRO D'IMPRESSION : 4171
NUMÉRO D'ÉDITION : 2197
HERMANN, ÉDITEURS DES SCIENCES ET DES ARTS